Navies
in the
Nuclear Age

Navies in the Nuclear Age

Navies in the

Warships since 1945

Editor: Robert Gardiner
Consultant Editor: Dr Norman Friedman

CONWAY
MARITIME PRESS

Series Consultant	DR BASIL GREENHILL CB, CMG, FSA, FRHistS
Series Editor	ROBERT GARDINER
Consultant Editor	DR NORMAN FRIEDMAN
Contributors	DAVID K BROWN, RCNC DR NORMAN FRIEDMAN ERIC GROVE STUART SLADE DAVID STEIGMAN

Frontispiece: *Since 1945 warship development has been dominated by electronics and missiles, symbolised here by the American cruiser* Yorktown *firing a Standard MR-SM2 surface-to-air missile. Equipped with the immensely powerful Aegis air defence system, the ships of this class are among the most potent surface combatants currently afloat.* (USN)

© 1993 Brassey's (UK) Ltd

First published in Great Britain 1993 by
Conway Maritime Press, an imprint of Brassey's (UK) Ltd
101 Fleet Street London EC4Y 1DE

British Library Cataloguing-in-Publication Data
Navies in the Nuclear Age: Warships Since
1945. – (History of the Ship Series)
  I. Friedman, Norman   II. Series
  623.8

ISBN 0-85177-568-3

Designed by Tony Hart
Typeset by Carnegie Publishing Ltd, Preston
Printed and bound by The Bath Press, Bath

Contents

Preface

THIS title is the seventh in an ambitious programme of twelve volumes intended to provide the first detailed and comprehensive account of a technology that has shaped human history. It has been conceived as a basic reference work, the essential first stop for anyone seeking information on any aspect of the subject, so it is more concerned to be complete than to be original. However, the series takes full account of all the latest research and in certain areas will be publishing entirely new material. In the matter of interpretation care has been taken to avoid the old myths and to present only the most widely accepted modern viewpoints.

To tell a coherent story, in a more readable form than is usual with encyclopaedias, each volume takes the form of independent chapters, all by recognised authorities in the field. Most chapters are devoted to the ships themselves, but others deal with topics such as 'propulsion' that are more generally applicable, giving added depth to the reader's understanding of developments. Some degree of generalisation is inevitable when tackling a subject of this breadth, but wherever possible the specific details of ships and their characteristics have been included (a table of typical ships for each relevant chapter includes a convenient summary of data from which the reader can chart the evolution of the ship type concerned). With a few historically unavoidable exceptions, the series is confined to seagoing vessels; to have included boats would be increased the scope of an already massive task.

The history of the ship is not a romanticised story of epic battles and heroic voyages, but equally it is not simply a matter of technological advances. Ships were built to carry out particular tasks and their design was as much influenced by the experience of that employment – the lessons of war, or the conditions of trade, for example, as purely technical innovation.

Throughout this series an attempt has been made to keep this clearly in view, to describe the *what* and *when* of developments without losing sight of the *why*.

The series is aimed at those with some knowledge of, and interest in, ships and the sea. It would have been impossible to make a contribution of any value to the subject if it had been pitched at the level of the complete novice, so while there is an extensive glossary, for example, it assumes an understanding of the most basic nautical terms. Similarly, the bibliography avoids general works and concentrates on those which will broaden and deepen the reader's understanding beyond the level of the *History of the Ship*. The intention is not to inform genuine experts in their particular area of expertise, but to provide them with the best available single-volume summaries of less familiar fields.

Each volume is chronological in approach, with the periods covered getting shorter as the march of technology quickens, but organised around a dominant theme – represented by the title of the book – that sums up the period in question. In this way each book is fully self-sufficient, although when completed the twelve titles will link up to form a coherent history, chronicling the progress of ship design from its earliest recorded forms to the present day.

The subject of this volume is the modern fighting ship, which since 1945 has undergone a technical revolution comparable with the nineteenth-century transition from wooden sailing ships to ironclad steamers. In appearance they may not have altered so radically – in truth, most still have the hull–superstructure–funnel–mast layout of their wartime predecessors – but the old generic similarity (and the retention of some old type designations) disguises the massive shift in strategy, tactics and technology brought about by the nuclear and, above all, electronics revolutions.

Nowadays ships are often referred to as merely the 'platform' for the weapons and control systems they carry, so in some ways the organisation of this book by ship type is less justified. The modes of warfare and their associated weaponry (predominantly anti-submarine and anti-aircraft) dictate ship development, as do the wider issues of electronics and nuclear weapons. Therefore, although the opening chapters are devoted to specific categories of ship, the later sections might well have come first, if it did not reverse the whole pattern of the series. Readers may well find that going to the chapters from 8 onwards is a more logical progression after the Introduction, but, that being said, it is not essential to read these chapters before tackling the ship-type sections.

This book has been particularly fortunate in its timing, since the collapse of the Soviet Union has released a flood of information on hitherto-secret Russian naval technology, and, more importantly, the rationale behind it. For decades Western analysts struggled to make sense of some developments, which are now revealed to be more rational than first thought. On a detail level, the actual Soviet designations of ship classes are now known, so throughout the book these Project numbers are quoted alongside the more familiar Nato codenames. Information continues to be released, and at some point a full Russian naval history may be possible, but the contributors to this volume were already privy to enough new data to complete what is probably the most coherent account so far published of Russian postwar naval thinking. As a result we believe *Navies in the Nuclear Age* to be far less one-sided than any previous naval history of the period since 1945.

Robert Gardiner
Series Editor

Introduction

WARSHIPS and the navies they served changed radically after 1945. The revolution was at least as basic as that imposed by the combination of armour and steam power about a century earlier. Not only were most existing warships suddenly made obsolete, but most of the very categories of warship ceased to have their earlier meanings. This process began with anti-submarine warfare during the Second World War, but it deepened with the new form of anti-aircraft warfare postwar, and with the introduction of anti-ship missiles. A virtually new kind of warship, the amphibious assault ship, emerged from the Second World War. As in the earlier revolution, only the capital ship, in this case the aircraft carrier, retained (indeed, increased) its earlier significance.

Although words like cruiser, destroyer, and frigate are still quite widely used, it is less and less possible to make firm distinctions. In the US Navy, for example, the *Kidd* class missile destroyers are larger than the *Belknap* and *Leahy* class cruisers and carry much the same weapon system as the *Virginia* class. *Perry* class frigates are about the same size as *Adams* class destroyers, and carry the same missile (albeit with a shorter-range fire control system). In the Royal Navy the distinction between anti-submarine frigates (Types 22 and 23) and area air defence destroyers (Type 42) is somewhat clearer, but it is striking that they are all about the same size, speed, and range. Both in France and in the United States, different versions of the same substantial hull were completed for anti-aircraft and anti-submarine roles, blurring any distinctions that might be drawn. Therefore, in this volume there is one chapter on surface combatants, rather than separate chapters on cruisers, destroyers, etc.

Many existing ships were rebuilt to fit the new kind of naval warfare, so for about two decades after 1945 navies combined earlier hulls with new kinds of weapons and sensors. Now virtually all of the older ships are gone, and the dimensions of the revolution are obvious when navies are compared with those of, say, 1939.

The electronics revolution

As in the revolution of a century ago, a new technology has emerged. Then it was the combination of armour and the new guns designed to penetrate it. Now it is electronic combat systems (including both sensors and combat direction) and self-guided missiles (including torpedoes). In each case, the new technology adds a new dimension to warship design, one not immediately visible.

In the earlier revolution, the key technology was metallurgy. Two battleships might have looked alike, but differences in the composition of their armour and the steel of their guns would determine which was superior. Thus the technical naval literature of a century ago is filled with descriptions of new processes for armour-making, such as those devised by Harvey and Krupp. Now the keys are often to be found in details of computers and their software, as well as in radars and sonars.

Nothing, of course, is entirely new. For years now it has been a cliché that a ship or an aircraft is a system; but that cliché has a real meaning. Those fighting a ship must do three things. They must detect a target (and realise that it is a legitimate target, not friendly or neutral), they must aim, and they must inflict damage. The history of warships is in large part the history of automating these functions. Once they were entirely manual. Men aboard ships saw the enemy coming. They decided what to do, and they jumped aboard the enemy's ships to do battle with hand weapons such as swords. Guns automated the process of inflicting damage: the gunner applied a match or pulled a lanyard and the machine, the gun, did the rest. Until the twentieth century, the detection and fire control functions were almost completely manual. Just how well two navies would do when they collided depended almost completely on how well their crews were trained, *ie* on how well those manual functions were performed.

That made it relatively easy to understand and compare the combat strength of warships. It was also obvious that the difference in combat performance between two apparently equivalent ships was generally crew training and tactics. That was the implication, for example, of numerous successful British frigate engagements during the Napoleonic Wars. Frigate de-

The silhouette of the postwar warship came to be dominated by radar, missile guidance equipment and other electronics. This trend reached its apogee in the 1960s, when the cumbersome first-generation equipment was fully deployed. An extreme example was the USS *Albany, one of three missile cruiser conversions, which had superimposed SPG-49 missile directors fore and aft and a very tall superstructure to provide a view over them. In recent decades, developments – at least in Western navies – have tended to concentrate on 'invisibles' like enhanced computer power and more sophisticated software, leading to less cluttered superstructures. (L & L van Ginderen.)*

Naval development since the war has been dominated by the Cold War. These Krivak *class frigates fly the old Soviet naval jack, with a hammer and sickle inside a star, but since 1992 the Russian navy has reverted to the pre-revolutionary Czarist flag, symbolising the collapse of the Soviet Union, and with it all Cold War certainties. For navies, as for all military forces, this means a search for new roles.* (CMP).

signs differed, but successful captains did as well commanding British-built ships as the French counterparts they captured.

Then another round of automation set in with advances in fire control. As Dr Jon Sumida has shown, soon after the turn of the century, naval gunnery came more and more to depend on the details of fire control instruments and, above all, on the computers used to deduce target course and speed from a few observations, and then to project these data ahead well enough to aim shells to hit as much as a minute after they had been fired. Similar considerations applied in Second World War submarine warfare, where the US Navy's very sophisticated torpedo data computer radically affected its submarine tactics.

Some of the technology of fire control, such as rangefinders and spotting tops and directors, was visible, but for the first time a significant element, the computer, was entirely invisible, and for the most part secret. Ships without sophisticated computers simply could not make many hits in combat. For example, in the Royal Navy, installation of computers was a major feature of battleship modernisation. Ships not modernised, such as HMS *Hood*, were at a severe disadvantage, quite aside from relatively well-known details of armour protection.

The next step was to automate the detection end of the engagement, initially using radar and sonar (and, more recently, optronics). For example, all of the major navies had some form of radar, but only the allies centralised radar data in a combat information centre (CIC) or action information centre (AIC). This element of shipboard organisation drastically improved ship combat performance; it helped enormously in exploiting the potential inherent in radars. The CIC or AIC was altogether invisible, but ship performance in battle depended crucially on its presence and even on its detailed arrangement. It provided the ship's commander with the tactical picture needed to make tactical decisions.

The great postwar development was to automate the CIC itself, to overcome the flood of information the sensors produced. Much clearly depended on the quality of the computers involved, and even on the sort of software they used. Ships of apparently identical appearance

might have very different combat information systems (some of which were not even automated). Automation made it painfully obvious that in combat the ship depended on a connected system to detect and engage targets – and that much of that system was buried inside, invisibly.

Hence the emphasis, in this volume, on the invisible side of the warship, its combat direction system and its electronic sensors. The story of the rise and fall of fast attack craft would seem to support this view of the importance of the invisible element of the warship. Fast attack craft rose largely because they could carry ship-killing weapons. They had little space for sensors or for combat direction systems, but their advocates tended to dismiss this lack: they seemed to offer the sort of anti-ship armament a frigate carried, but at a fraction of the cost. In combat, however, it became obvious that the visible firepower was only part of the story. The question was always how the ship combat *system* performed, and it was no stronger than its weakest element. It did not help, of course, that limited tonnage also meant very limited means of self-defence.

Some of the change is immediately visible: guns and conventional torpedo tubes were largely, though not completely, replaced by missiles, small anti-submarine torpedo tubes sprouted, big bow sonars and variable-depth sonars appeared, the existing forests of radars grew denser and more varied. These changes occurred across the spectrum of warship types. Hence the chapters on the main types of combat each ship fights: anti-aircraft, anti-submarine, and anti-ship. Had this volume been about navies rather than about warships, similar chapters would have been devoted to naval aircraft and

their weapons. By 1945 the major Western navies were transferring much of their firepower from surface ships to aircraft. Much of the momentum of that process dissipated, of course, as improvements to aeroplanes drove up the price of carriers.

Command and control

Another very important change, albeit outside the scope of this book, is in the relationship between warships and the shore-based portions of navies. In the sailing era, the shore establishment was quite limited, to shipbuilding and repair facilities plus a central administration, such as the British Admiralty. As technology grew more complex, shore training and research and development establishments were created. Even so, at the outbreak of war in 1939 virtually all of the fighting power of the navy was afloat. The major visible exceptions were shore-based naval aircraft, the most spectacular example being the Japanese long range bomber, 'Nell' (which had been conceived as an equaliser to balance the Treaty-imposed carrier superiority of the US Navy).

However, a much more basic change had set in as early as 1914. With the advent of radio, it became clear that shore stations could intercept naval communications. Often those signals could be decoded, but even when that was not the case they could often be exploited. For example, distant stations could take bearings on the same signal (radio direction-finding, or DF). The central administration became the obvious focus for such information. As it gained the ability actually to track an enemy fleet, it gained an operational role previously unimagined. This central operational role became extremely important during the Second World War, at least for the US and Royal Navies (the Russians developed their own extremely centralised form of naval command and control).

Postwar developments reinforced this tendency. By the early 1950s it appeared that fixed underwater arrays could detect submarines at ranges of many hundreds of miles. The outputs of chains of such arrays, mainly in the US (and then Nato) SOSUS (sound surveillance system), had to be constructed centrally to be exploited tactically. Ultimately it was much more efficient to use shore-based maritime patrol aircraft, such as P-3s, to exploit SOSUS contacts than to use moving naval formations, which might well not be in place when contact was made. Later the US and Soviet navies were able to detect ships, or at least their electronic emissions, from space. Again, the signals were generally collected and interpreted ashore.

Nuclear weapons also reinforced the trend towards highly centralised shore-based control of navies. From the Kennedy Administration on, there was a widespread perception in Washington that any relatively minor military incident might well trigger a nuclear holocaust. Since US and Soviet ships came into close proximity quite often, successive administrations tried hard to ensure very tight control of forces in times of tension; in at least one case, the White House was issuing rudder orders to the Sixth Fleet. This mode of thinking probably also explains the attempt to control bomb targeting during the Vietnam War. Control was relaxed as it became obvious that the Soviet leadership was not particularly enthusiastic to turn any incident into full-blown war, and the entire rationale for very tight control declined with the Cold War.

These ideas explain the emergence, in the postwar US Navy, of a class of special flagships fitted with particularly elaborate communications systems. They had to be able to communicate with the national command authority ashore. They also had to be able to plan and conduct sea-based nuclear strikes, particularly in the event that authority was wiped out. Now that the Cold War is over, the need for flagships (eg for strike planning, as in the Gulf War) remains; and the heavy-duty communications network is now needed to receive intelligence data originating with sensors, such as satellites, which report only to stations ashore. The broader question, whether it is time to centre the sources of information on the deployed fleet, is now being raised. After all, the central authority ashore does not really need masses of detailed information if it is not likely to make tactical decisions. If no deployed commander can literally lose the country in an afternoon (simply because no local war can possibly be that significant), then surely it is time to revert to the earlier idea that the deployed commander ought to call the shots, relying on the ashore authority only for necessary assistance.

For the US Navy, the emergence of the Tomahawk anti-ship missile also increased the significance of the shore establishment. To some extent, Tomahawk was a reaction to the emergence of Soviet surface forces in the Mediterranean and the Norwegian Sea. It was attractive because the airframe was already being developed to attack land targets. Anti-ship attack was a distinctly secondary role for the US Navy, so Tomahawk remained attractive only so long as it did not entail any major new expenditure.

The missile was usable only to the extent that it could be targeted effectively against targets well beyond the launching ship's horizon. The Soviets solved this problem by developing an elaborate network of dedicated shore-based high-frequency direction-finders (HF/DF), reconnaissance aircraft, intelligence-gathering ships (AGIs), 'tattletale' ships, and, ultimately, radar and passive ocean reconnaissance satellites (RORSATs and EORSATs).

The US approach was to meld available intelligence, most of it collected by passive satellites and shore stations (already built for other purposes), to form an over-the-horizon targeting (OTH-T) picture. These data were collated at Fleet Command Centres (FCCs) ashore and passed to Tomahawk-firing ships via a special satellite data link (OTCIXS, the officer in tactical command information exchange system). The ships in turn had special computers which they used to maintain the OTH targeting picture. For a battle group, the computer was part of the tactical flag command centre (TFCC), eg on board a carrier. Individual surface ship Tomahawk shooters were fitted with a Tomahawk Weapons Control System (TWCS), which incorporated a similar computer. In a group of Tomahawk shooters, one computer is used by the Force OTH Co-ordinator (FOTC),

Soviet strategic emphases on shore control and the widespread use of long range anti-ship missiles required an elaborate network of intelligence sources. Among the most visible at sea was the intelligence-gathering auxiliary, or AGI. Initially, these were the trawler-like ships seen here in 1979 trailing the British frigate Juno, *but they became larger, more sophisticated, and were eventually to be found tracking Western naval activity on virtually every ocean. (MoD, Crown Copyright)*

who creates a full tactical picture from FCC information plus information from sensors within the group. Submarines cannot accommodate a full targeting computer. Instead, they receive their data from a shore targeting terminal (STT) which functions like a TWCS node.

OTH-T is of course an imperfect art. It requires the formation of a picture of worldwide maritime activity, necessarily based on intermittent information. For example, most ships are detected and identified by their radio or radar emissions, and that information can be misleading. Yet the system works. It made possible the blockade of Iraq in 1990–91.

The Royal Navy faced much the same problem in using Harriers against warships. With the passing of its large carriers, it lost airborne early warning (AEW) aircraft, which were vital not merely to deal with air attack but also to provide a task force commander with a picture of surface activity around the force. The Harrier could search only a narrow area as it ran out to attack a surface target. The Royal Navy therefore built an FCC of its own, at North-

Since 1945 the active life of a warship has been less defined by the durability of the hull than by the effectiveness of its weapon systems. At one time the British, like many other navies, carried out mid-life refits that often cost more than the original cost of the ship concerned. The Batch 3 Leander *class frigate* Andromeda, *for example, had both Exocet and SSMs and Sea Wolf SAMs added, the 4.5in mounting, Seacat SAM and Limbo ASW mortar removed, electronics completely revised, triple ASW torpedo tubes added, and helicopter hangar extended. This three-year refit was intended to apply to all ten ships in the group, but in 1981 the policy of mid-life modernisations was abandoned, and the programme curtailed after five conversions. (C & S Taylor)*

wood (it is called OpCon, and receives US OTCIXS data).

In both cases, the only visible signs of a major change in the way the navy fights are increased attention to satellite communications (which are necessary to handle the sheer volume of information involved) and special computers aboard ship.

The other great change in modern warships has been in propulsion, as described both in the submarine chapter and in the final chapter of this book, which is devoted to that subject.

The future

Whatever the politics of the world, navies will surely continue to be extremely important. The laws of physics will continue to dictate that it is far easier to move large masses over water than over land or through the air. During the Cold War, that meant that any hope of reinforcement for Nato forces fighting in Europe had to entail control of the North Atlantic. In the Third World, it means that any sustained operation, like that in the Persian Gulf, requires supply by sea. Similarly, to sustain tactical air operations against a distant target will generally require sea-based air power. Conversely, any potential target wishing to preclude intervention will be driven to attacking ships at sea.

The other obvious point for the future is that, while individual ships are becoming far more expensive, sea power still depends in part on sheer numbers. To some extent, this circle can be squared by extending the lifetimes of ships. The US Navy is now retiring aircraft carriers at about the forty-year mark, and destroyers and cruisers at about the thirty-year mark. The Royal Navy discards its destroyers and frigates at

about twenty years. In each case, the size of the fleet depends on how long ships can be made to last. For example, the size of the US '600-ship navy' of the 1980s was set by the number it appeared the US economy could sustain: an average of twenty new ships each year, with an average lifetime of thirty years. The *composition* of the 600-ship fleet was, of course, set by strategy.

In the postwar period, effective ship life has only rarely been set by the durability of the hull. More usually it has been a question of obsolescence of weapon systems. For example, a few years ago the British Government decided to abandon a policy of mid-life upgrades (modernisation); the immediate consequence was that ships would have to be discarded when they were fifteen to twenty years old. In the case of nuclear submarines, ship lifetime is generally set by the need to refuel (recore). Refuellings are the occasion for major upgrades, so much of the 'ownership' cost of a submarine is spent at that time. Thus in the mid-1960s, when a US submarine reactor core was good for eight years, expected submarine lifetime was three cores (twenty-four years). A core now lasts much longer; *Los Angeles* class submarines are now being retired when their first core is used up, after about fifteen years at sea.

The new generation of digital weapon systems may admit major upgrade not by rewiring or reconstruction, but often largely by changing software, or by subtle changes (*eg* substitution of chips) within computers. For example, an Aegis cruiser can accommodate several generations of SM-2 missiles without changing any of its hardware, merely by changing its operational software. In theory, this sort of capability ought greatly to prolong the effective life of the ship,

One of the crucial experiences of the 1939–45 naval war was the Battle of the Atlantic, which came to dominate early postwar ASW thinking. Seakeeping had proved a major consideration for North Atlantic escorts, and Nato's hold on the choke points of the Greenland–Iceland–UK Gap meant that any future war with Soviet submarines would involve fighting in some of the world's least hospitable seas. The first generation of Western escorts, like the Canadian St Laurent *(DE-205), placed great emphasis on a 'sea-kindly' hull, demonstrated here as the ship, proceeding at high speed, throws off an Atlantic swell. (USN)*

and thus make it possible to maintain a larger fleet at a lower shipbuilding rate.

Shipbuilding and modernisation are not the only important costs. Manpower became very important in the 1950s, when expanding Western economies drew men who might otherwise have volunteered for navies, and also when new technology demanded increasingly sophisticated naval technicians. Not only naval pay but also amenities (such as habitability) had to rise to keep numbers up. As the cost per man rose, governments sought to reduce naval manning. These cuts translated into cuts in numbers of operational ships.

Navies in turn sought to reduce manning. For example, simply by switching to gas turbines or diesels, they could drastically cut engine room personnel. Modern solid-state electronics, which is far more reliable than its vacuum-tube or discrete-element predecessors, requires far fewer technicians. The other major manpower requirement is maintenance, which includes housekeeping, simply keeping a ship habitable. In the 1970s the US Navy sought to cut manning in its new *Perry* class frigates by shifting to shore-based maintenance. The concept failed, and ships' companies had to be expanded considerably. The Royal Navy seems to have done better with its new Type 23 ('Duke' class) frigates. They are cleaned in port by special contractors, who can be flown out to do the work when the ships deploy abroad. The US Navy would argue that too drastic a cut in a ship's company will leave her without sufficient manpower for damage control, particularly if the damage kills a substantial fraction of the ship's personnel (as in the 1987 attack on USS *Stark*).

That still leaves unanswered the question of whether robots of some sort can take over many routine crew functions. A ship might, for example, be designed so that much of the damage control could be done without manpower. In the case of the *Stark*, the ship was endangered mainly because the initial hit killed the experienced petty officers, who would probably have

contained the fire. The argument is that they would have recognised a key opportunity. When the Exocet hit, its rocket motor continued to burn (it needed no oxygen, since it carried its own oxidant). However, that did not last long. To do real damage, the motor had to ignite the contents of the compartment it hit. The first flash used up the oxygen in the space. It took a few vital seconds for oxygen from outside to flow in to reignite the fire. The petty officers would presumably have doused the compartment in those seconds. Without them, the fire reignited, and water had to be played on the walls of the compartment to keep the fire from spreading (by radiating heat into adjacent spaces). That water in turn could not easily be vented, since the ship's hull was unpierced. The water, not the fire, endangered the ship, by ruining her stability.

Aside from obvious measures, such as not concentrating the petty officers in any one place (an idea which recalls the wartime Royal Navy practice of spreading out officers' quarters in destroyers), the incident suggests the potential of a more automated approach to damage control. A computer system could certainly show those responsible the likely consequences of their actions. It can, for example, predict the spread of fire. Many ships are already rigged with fire and other internal sensors. However, damage control centres still often employ grease-pencil boards to display the ship's condition. They are analogous to pre-computer combat information centre (CIC) displays. It is probably time to push towards a damage control equivalent of the current automated/combat advice systems.

The radical shift in world politics will clearly affect navies. Matters seemed so simple in the 1980s. The maritime Western alliance faced a land-oriented Soviet bloc. The most important

fact of naval life was naval geography: Nato held the choke points, such as the Greenland–Iceland–UK Gap, behind which Soviet forces lay. The vital role of the Nato navies was to neutralise the Soviet threat to shipping, presented mainly by submarines and missile-armed bombers.

An offensive-defensive strategy was developed. A Nato Strike Fleet would head north into the Norwegian Sea. It would attract Soviet attackers, including bombers. Its carrier-based fighters would destroy the bombers, and their trained crews, in the air, eliminating their threat to shipping (whose escorts would lack the ability to destroy the bombers outside their missile range). Soviet submarines would be tied down by Western submarines operating in their home areas. Those which came out would have to deal with escorts, both around the Strike Fleet and around convoys, and with maritime patrol aircraft cued by long-range sensors such as SOSUS.

By the late 1980s it seemed that these ideas would work. The bombers were particularly threatening, because they were so mobile, and because they were so difficult to destroy before they launched their missiles. Enormous effort went into developing special sensors, such as land-based over-the-horizon radar (ROTHR), which would detect them early enough for carrier-based fighters to intercept them in time. Complementing this work was effort spent on cover and deception devices, which it was hoped would buy time by forcing the Soviets to search harder for the carrier battle groups.

At the same time, however, there was a general perception that the Soviets were improving their own means of finding Western warships, so that cover and deception (generally by emitting false signals, perhaps accompanied by clouds of warship-sized chaff) might have a limited future.

Furthermore, through the 1980s the Soviets

deployed supersonic anti-ship missiles, which would approach their targets at low altitude. Compared with a subsonic Exocet, a Mach 2.5 missile provides its target with less than half the warning time (it is more than 1/2.5, since the missile flies a bit higher, so it can be detected at slightly greater range). Many existing defensive systems were unlikely to react quickly enough to deal with such weapons.

There was one ray of hope. A supersonic missile must depend on either active or passive radar (it is too hot to use an infra-red sensor). Radar emissions can be controlled; a radar can operate over a spread spectrum so that its emissions are very difficult to detect. That leaves the missile only an active seeker. A ship is normally a very large radar target. However, measures can be taken to change that. The ship cannot be made to vanish altogether, but its radar cross-section can be reduced below that of the decoys it launches.

One way to do that is to shape the ship specially, as in the US *Arleigh Burke* or the Israeli *Eilat* (Sa'ar V). However, there is another, subtler, approach. New radar-absorbing materials (RAMs) are effective over broad frequency ranges. Their first public use was by the Royal Australian Navy (RAN), which draped sheets of RAM over the lifelines and superstructures of ships deploying to the Persian Gulf (lifelines form strong radar reflectors). In 1993 the US Navy revealed a radar cross-section reduction programme, Outlaw Bandit, which applied particularly to the *Spruance* and *Perry* classes, with their very boxy (hence large cross-section) superstructures. Since none of these ships has noticeably changed its outward appearance (and since the programme is not very expensive), Outlaw Bandit clearly involves some sort of covering. Given such materials, most existing ships can enjoy drastically reduced radar cross-sections, probably at least at missile-seeker frequencies. In some navies, such as the Royal Navy, RAM has been used more subtly, to reduce cross-section only amidships, so that missiles will tend to hit fore or aft, where they will do less damage.

Now the Cold War is over, the main Western (and, probably, Russian) naval mission is to be found in local conflicts, such as in the Persian Gulf or in the blockade of Serbia. Such missions were very important during the Cold War, but (at least in the United States) they were always considered subsidiary. Now they are primary, yet the major navies must always be prepared to go back to some sort of Cold War footing (probably with different enemies) should world politics turn in that direction.

Local conflict is radically different from the sort of hot war which might have emerged from the Cold War. It emphasises operations near or over a shore (the US term is 'Littoral Warfare'), in which sea-based aircraft, Marines, and land-attack missiles are the main offensive weapons. The main threats are shore-based aircraft and missiles, although submarines may often be a factor, and mines will generally be involved.

The rules and values also change. Fleets will often be engaged in presence missions short of war. Presence must be credible (the ships must present a real though generally unstated threat, and they must not be easy to dislodge or neutralise). Part of the point of presence is that it is well short of war; moreover, it is not intended to lead to war. Presence has always been a tricky mission, because it is intended to make a vital political point without crossing the boundary into combat. However, a local ruler faced by ships in a presence mission can always choose to cross that boundary himself, by attacking a ship offshore. Thus a ship on presence duty will generally be unable to fire at threatening aircraft or surface units, yet may well be attacked by surprise. Cover and deception will be pointless, since the entire point of presence is to be visible. Moreover, the loss of a warship will probably have enormous political effect, quite possibly emboldening other local powers faced by Western warships. In a Cold War setting, it was most unlikely that hostilities would be a complete surprise (although it was always possible that Western governments would allow themselves to be caught by surprise, due to their own unwillingness to believe what was happening). A Western battle group would generally enjoy some sort of layered defence, so individual ship self-defence was not so vital.

The very restrictive rules of engagement inherent in local war change that. Surprise attack may well become the norm, and individual ship self-defence becomes far more important. Also, the Russian supersonic anti-ship missiles are now very much on the market. In the past, the Russians probably would not have sold them in the Third World for fear of revealing their details to the West, prior to the big war. Now, with the big war most unlikely, that restraint is gone; and weapons are probably the most saleable Russian commodity. Ironically, then, Western navies are far more likely to face the best Russian-made weapons precisely because the Cold War is over (the big war, after all, was largely precluded by fear of nuclear escalation).

ASW is similarly affected. In the past, the emphasis was always on destroying the submarine. Ship self-defence was limited to towed decoys, which were ineffective against either unguided torpedoes fired in salvo, or against wake-followers. Now it must be admitted that there is a very good chance that a submarine will slip in (as was the case with the Argentine *San Luis* in the Falklands, although her six torpedoes failed to sink anything). There is, then, increasing interest in anti-torpedo weapons. For example, the US Navy is deploying modified Mk 46 lightweight torpedoes (Mod 7) and an associated torpedo-detection/fire control system aboard high-value units.

No active defensive system can be perfect. Ideally a ship should be able to survive one or more missile hits. The larger the ship, the better the chance that the area of damage caused by a missile will not extend into anything vital. Greater size may also mean greater durability and hence longer lifetime, which is surely more important as unit cost (dominated by electronics and weapons, not sheer ship size) increases.

It would seem, then, that interest in armour, at least around magazines, should be increasing.

Small conventional submarines like this German Type 209 have been supplied to many navies, even in the Third World, and pose one of the greatest potential threats to big power navies who may find intervention in 'brush fire' wars more common in the post Cold War environment. These boats are quieter and therefore more difficult to detect than the nuclear submarines most major navies trained against in earlier decades. (CMP)

In the immediate future, exotic hull technologies are unlikely to find much naval employment. Advanced concepts, like this 3000-ton Surface Effect Ship, once so confidently predicted, have proved less practical in service, too costly, or simply lacking a specific mission in which they could offer a distinct advantage.

Similarly, we will probably see increased interest in cruiser/destroyer ship designs which can withstand torpedo hits, including hits by weapons exploding under a ship's keel. The other important future element of passive protection is surely to distribute elements of the combat direction system so that it cannot be knocked out by a single hit. The Taiwanese navy has already specified a unified combat direction/damage control system for its next series of frigates. If the main CIC is knocked out, the general-purpose computer consoles of the damage control centre can be switched to combat direction, so the ship can fight on.

Further in the future are a new generation of self-defence weapons, probably ultimately missile-killing lasers. The US Sea Lite (MIRACL) chemical laser has already shot down a supersonic missile (a Vandal, a converted Talos) at White Sands, and for some years a US defence contractor, TRW, has promoted a sea-based version. Such weapons will probably appear at sea some time after the turn of the century. They may be electrically rather than chemically powered, in which case it may be worthwhile to shift from the current geared turbine drive to an all-electric powerplant in which ship power could be shifted to the weapon.

One other point is important. The current alliance structure is unlikely to survive for very long; the most important common interest of the members was survival against the threat posed by the Soviet Union. The forces operating in any given local conflict will be *ad hoc* assemblages. This was much the situation during the nineteenth century, when the combination in any particular situation depended on the interests at stake. At that time, naval co-operation was relatively simple. A senior admiral was chosen, there was a conference on his flagship, and simple signals were arranged.

Now the situation is far more complex. Operations will undoubtedly involve both friendly and enemy aircraft. Ships will have to be able to unscramble the air picture. Within Nato, that was relatively easy: ships all had the standard data link, Link 11. But Link 11 is not universal; it was, in effect, one of the physical reflections of the Nato alliance. The Russians retain a powerful fleet. They may well be co-operating with their former enemies in some future operations. Surely that will entail some kind of exchange of tactical data links. Otherwise, ships will shoot down friendly aircraft, and they may well fail to shoot down attackers. There was a very real fear of such 'Blue-on-Blue' errors in the Gulf War, and only the inactivity of the Iraqi air force prevented them. Future enemies will probably be less accommodating.

Much has been made of various forms of non co-operative target recognition (NCTR) to solve the identification problem and thus to avoid 'Blue-on-Blue' engagements. Existing forms of identification (IFF) are unlikely to suffice, not least because of the pick-up nature of future formations. Unfortunately, NCTR usually entails some means of recognising which type of aircraft is approaching. That was fine as long as the friendlies all flew Western-made jets and the enemies all bought from the Soviets. But now that is unlikely to be the case. Not only may the Russians be on the side of the West, but they are likely to sell their aircraft everywhere. Moreover, buyers of Western aircraft (like Iran and Iraq) may well be on the other side. Hence the vital need for co-ordination, most likely by sharing a common data linked tactical picture.

The discerning reader will notice the absence of new hull forms from this discussion: where are SWATHs, big surface effect ships, WIGs, and hydrofoils? In many cases it seems that the futuristic hull forms have proven rather specialised. SWATHs offer excellent seakeeping at low speeds, as in strategic towed-array ships (as used by the United States and Japan). It seems less likely that this configuration will be used, as has so often been suggested, for the aircraft carrier of the future. One problem is that the SWATH is very sensitive to changes in ship load. A conventional hull sinks a few inches deeper in the water when a few tons are added (one measure of ship form is tons per inch, the number of tons to sink the ship an inch). The larger the waterplane at the waterline, the more tons it takes to add an inch of draught. A SWATH is a small-waterplane twin-hull ship: it can sink almost to its upper deck when a few tons are added.

Other high-performance ships, the hydrofoils and the air cushion vehicles, suffer from similar limitations. They do offer very high speeds, sometimes even in rough water. However, to date very few applications have been found. The only hydrofoils in service are missile craft and Russian ASW craft (using sprint-and-drift tactics). Because none is very large, all are coastal types. Attempts to build naval air cushion vehicles have generally failed, although the Russians did build a large missile ship, *Sivuch* (Project 1239).

Then there is the WIG (wing in ground-effect), a quasi-aircraft/quasi-ship which flies very low to benefit from the surface effect to move loads more efficiently than an aeroplane, but at relatively high speed – well over 150kts. The Russians developed a missile-firing WIG, but never put it into service. Reportedly their transport version suffered from poor fuel economy and from corrosion. This sort of vehicle may yet enter service, but it is unlikely to replace conventional warships altogether.

Among other problems, a WIG does not offer the sort of loitering capability a conventional hull provides. A WIG is enough like a seaplane to be unable to float in anything approaching rough weather, yet that is likely to be its only loiter mode. Loiter will become, if anything, more important in the post Cold War world, since the major contribution of navies will probably be sustained presence in areas of tension. Anything which inherently limits endurance encourages a local ruler to imagine that presence will be short-lived, and thus that it can be waited out.

Norman Friedman

Aircraft Carriers

1

EW changes in naval warfare since the Second World War have been as all-embracing as the roles played by the aircraft carrier. Sea battles, instead of encompassing tens of miles, took place across hundreds. The aircraft carrier and her aircraft, when combined with the submarine, for the first time forced naval strategists and tacticians to think in three, rather than two dimensions. This ability has forced nations defending their territory to make their first line of defence hundreds of miles offshore, instead of tens of miles. Even the Soviet navy, which disdained the acquisition of carriers for many years, found its acquisition policies and strategies dictated by the Western carrier task forces, and the need to guard against them.

Carrier design, air-wings, and naval air warfare have all changed dramatically in the half-century since the American carrier task forces roamed across the Pacific Ocean. But carriers have continued to dominate discussions of naval strategy since 1945. From the simple aircraft carrier (CV in US Navy nomenclature) at the outbreak of the Second World War had come giant battle aircraft carriers (CVB) – a designation only used for the US Navy's *Midway* class – light fleet carriers (CVL) built without the extensive compartmentation and size of CVs, and escort carriers (CVE), the 'jeep carriers' or 'baby flat-tops', most often used for convoy escort.

Since the War a nation's strength has been measured usually by how many aircraft carriers it has in its fleet, and most navies have centred their naval formations around aircraft carrier task forces. Because of this, aircraft carriers have often served as determinants of cruiser, de-

stroyer, frigate, oiler, and supply ship strength, because of the requirements carrier task forces have for surface escorts and supply ships.

A good example of the aircraft carrier's influence is the apocryphal story that, whenever the United States gets involved in a foreign crisis, one of the first questions the White House asks the Pentagon is 'Where are the carriers?'. Similarly, the British government's 1966 decision not to build CVA-01 and to abandon fixed-wing naval aviation required the Royal Navy to restructure its force requirements and move from a global strategy with its focus on operations East of Suez to a North Atlantic strategy emphasising Nato. The French navy believes that having aircraft carriers and a fixed-wing naval aviation capability is vital for maintaining its strength and capability. Even the former So-

viet navy, which long professed a certain disdain towards aircraft carriers, began planning and building aircraft carriers as its strength grew during the 1980s.

The history of the aircraft carrier since the Second World War has also been a history of jet aircraft at sea. Because of the enormous changes wrought by jet aircraft, three major innovations were required to make aircraft carriers jet-capable. These three, all of which played major roles in carrier design and development during the post-Second World War era, were the angled deck, the mirror landing aid, and the steam catapult. All three were invented in Great Britain by the Royal Navy, but the US Navy developed each invention to its fullest capability. Together the three developments allowed aircraft carriers to operate jet aircraft efficiently.

A Sea Vampire jet aboard the British light fleet carrier Theseus *in 1950. The era of the naval jet began on 3 December 1945 when a prototype Vampire landed on the* Theseus's *sister,* Ocean. *The Sea Vampire was an interim design, built in small numbers and never in frontline service: the aircraft in this view belong to a Royal Naval Volunteer Reserve squadron.* (CMP)

Jet aircraft were both heavier and required higher take-off speeds than their propeller-driven predecessors, which made catapult launching essential. The old hydraulic system was not powerful enough and from 1950 the British experimented with a steam catapult aboard the light fleet carrier Perseus, *shown here. A Sea Hornet twin-engined fighter is prepared for launching at the end of the long raised catapult housing.* (Crown Copyright)

The entry of jet aircraft

The jet age dawned as the Second World War entered its last stages. By the beginning of 1945, both the US Army Air Force and the Royal Air Force had flown jet fighters; both the US Navy and the Royal Navy had begun initial studies into using jet aircraft aboard aircraft carriers. The first attempts at jet operations took place aboard the US escort carrier *Wake Island* in November 1945, when an FA-1 Fireball composite piston and jet aircraft made an experimental landing. The Royal Navy's first formal jet trials took place in December 1945 when an experimental Vampire took off and landed aboard the *Ocean*. In July 1946 the US Navy's first planned jet trials took place using an FD Phantom aboard the *Franklin D Roosevelt*. These experiments showed that jet aircraft could operate from carrier decks.

However, jet aircraft initially brought many new problems to carrier designers and operators. They required far more fuel than propeller-driven aircraft, and aviation gasoline fuel tanks had to be located behind the limited space of the carrier's protective armour belt. Jet aircraft took off and landed at higher speeds than did propeller-driven aircraft, requiring longer take-off and landing runs. But because their engines were inefficient at take-off speeds, and carrier decks lacked the length required for long take-off runs, catapult-assisted take-offs became a necessity, not a luxury.

Landing held some of the same problems. Because of their high speeds, jet aircraft required much longer landing areas than did propeller-driven aircraft. Current arresting gear was not always capable of stopping a jet in the required short distance, and if a jet missed the arresting wire, it ran into the wire barricade, which also presented a new problem. For while propeller aircraft that ran into a wire barricade only damaged their propellers, a jet aircraft's sleek design meant the barricade wires might ride over the aircraft's nose and slice through the cockpit, possibly decapitating the pilot. High landing speeds also posed a problem for pilot and landing signal officer interaction. The high speeds of jet aircraft drastically shortened the reaction time a pilot had to respond to the signals from the landing signals officer/batsman.

However, in one way, jet aircraft were a benefit to aircraft carrier operation. Propeller-driven aircraft relied on aviation gasoline, which had a low flash point, and consequently had to be kept in armoured tanks behind the carrier's armoured belt. Although the earliest jet aircraft used a slightly modified fuel mixture, most later jet aircraft could use safer fuels, such as kerosene, which had a much higher flash point. The benefits of this change were not noticed during the initial postwar era because of the shortage of such fuels.

The earliest solution was a wide-cut gasoline, AVTAG, which also had to be stored in armoured tanks. The US Navy adopted an interim solution of using AVTAG mixed with kerosene, but this required pump rooms behind the armour belt, and any unused mixed fuel had to be stored in its own separate armoured tanks.

By the 1960s, the expanding use of jets led to greatly increased production of jet fuel. Gradually, many navies converted their ships to burn distillate fuel, which is akin to kerosene. Because jets and ships now used the same fuel, ship captains could balance off the requirements for their ship's fuel against those of the air wing, greatly simplifying considerations of fuel usage.

Changing technologies: catapults, angled decks, and mirrors

The first new technology developed for post-war carriers was the steam catapult. Wartime carriers used hydraulic catapults, where pressure built up in an accumulator was transferred to the catapult shuttle through a system of wires and sheaves. The British H3 catapult in service in 1945 could launch a 20,000lb (9000kg) aircraft at 66kts. A modified BH5 hydro-pneumatic catapult, developed for the carrier *Eagle* in 1951, could do better, launching a 30,000lb (13,600kg) aircraft at 75kts. The US Navy had similar H4 and H8 catapults. But future aircraft were expected to be much heavier, with the US Navy calling for a 100,000lb (45,400kg) bomber.

The Royal Navy had considered a more powerful steam catapult as early as 1936, but no funding had been available. The steam catapult consisted of two parallel slotted cylinders, each with a steam piston. The pistons would be joined by a connector, which carried a bridle car that was attached to the aircraft; the bridle would drop clear after the launch. Steam from the ship's boilers would power the pistons. The Germans had used steam catapults to launch their V-1 flying bombs from France, and British forces captured some German systems. Using captured parts, Commander Colin C Mitchell built a prototype, and persuaded the Admiralty to conduct experiments. A single trial steam catapult was installed aboard *Perseus* in August 1950. After conducting tests in British waters, she sailed to the United States in December 1951 to hold further demonstrations.

The US Navy was considering an alternative catapult system, using a single slotted tube with an explosive charge connected to the bridle car at one end. The system promised great power, but the charges would have to be stored in the magazines, taking room from aircraft ordnance, while bringing the charges to the catapult also presented problems. The US Navy had shied away from steam catapults, fearing they would drain steam and power from the ship during launch operations. The *Perseus* trials showed the power loss only occurred with a large number of sustained launchings, and in April 1952 the US Navy received the rights to produce its own steam catapults. The first US carrier to receive steam catapults was the *Hancock*, which emerged from an overhaul with two in June 1954. The Royal Navy did not receive its first operational steam catapults until 1955, when the *Ark Royal* was commissioned. The US Navy considered using an internal combustion catapult, with aviation fuel burned in compressed air, for the nuclear carrier *Enterprise*, but these plans were cancelled, and she was completed with the conventional steam catapults.

Shortly after the steam catapult trials took place, the Royal Navy began testing a second improvement in carrier technology, the angled deck. The angled deck resulted from an August 1951 conference at the Royal Aircraft Establishment, convened to discuss ways of handling heavier carrier aircraft expected to enter service during the 1950s. Conference chairman Captain Dennis Campbell proposed angling the landing deck 10 degrees off the centreline, so that any aircraft not stopped by the arresting wires could merely increase speed and fly off for another try.

To test the idea, an angled deck layout was painted on the flight deck of the *Triumph* in February 1952 and some obstructions were re-

Since the first angled decks were applied to existing designs, they could not be steeply canted: HMS Eagle's *initial version was only 5½ degrees, and even then required the blanking-off of the port forward 4.5in gun sponson. This 1959 view shows the aircraft types of the period: Sea Hawk fighters forward (including one on the starboard catapult); twin-boom Sea Venom night fighters with wings folded amidships; dark blue US-supplied Skyraider AEW aircraft, and Gannet ASW aircraft aft.* (CMP)

moved from the port side. The arresting gear and crash barricade were not realigned. Aircraft performed touch-and-go landings to test the feasibility of the concept. While the *Triumph* tests were taking place, the US Navy held a similar series of touch-and-go landing trials aboard the carrier *Midway*. Following these trials, the US Navy overhauled the fleet carrier *Antietam* between September and December 1952, adding a complete 8-degree angled deck and realigning the arresting gear and crash barriers. The *Antietam* tests provided final confirmation of the angled deck's value. The US Navy modified the *Forrestal* design to include the new deck, and the Royal Navy completed the *Ark Royal*, *Albion* and *Bulwark* with 5½-degree angled decks.

The angled deck solved many problems for jet landings, but not all. Jet landing speeds allowed little time for the interaction between the pilot and landing signal officer to rectify faulty aircraft attitude. Jet response time was sluggish, and corrections could not be made while an aircraft was descending. During the early 1950s, Commander H Goodhart, a British exchange officer at the US Naval Air Test Center, conceived the idea of giving an approaching pilot a mirror image of his aeroplane as it

landed, so the pilot could make the necessary corrections himself. Goodhart's system called for installing a mirror along the edge of the angled deck. A light near the end of the flight deck shone into the centre of the mirror, and a row of green lights on either side of the mirror provided a reference plane. If the main light, or 'meatball' was above or below the reference plane, the pilot knew he was coming in too high or too low, and could correct his approach accordingly. The mirror landing system was first installed aboard the British carrier *Albion* in 1954. The following year, a similar system was installed aboard the US carrier *Bennington*.

During the 1960s the system was upgraded. A series of five Fresnel lenses were installed, each having three lights behind it, one lens above the other, replacing the light and mirror. A pilot landing at the correct attitude will see a single horizontal bar. The bar, which is high if the pilot is high and low if he is low, continuously moves. The new system does not blind flight deck crews at night, increasing flight deck safety. It also shines a greater distance, allowing the pilot to see it from further away.

Whilst most of the post-Second World War inventions went on to be incorporated in future carrier design, one, the flexible deck, did not.

Third of the important British contributions to postwar naval aviation was the mirror landing aid. This is the prototype aboard the Albion *in 1954, the mirror reflecting the light source further aft and a distorted image of the Skyraider touching down.* (CMP)

British naval designers realized that much of the weight of naval aircraft was in the undercarriage, which had to be strong to withstand carrier landings. If the undercarriage and arresting wires could be done away with, the result would be considerable cost and weight savings. Tests were conducted aboard the *Warrior* in 1948, using a jet aircraft with its landing gear retracted.

The concept proved feasible, but several problems became apparent. Aircraft would have to be moved to a separate flying-off deck, and new take-off arrangements would be required for aircraft that lacked an undercarriage and wheels. Naval aircraft would also have been restricted to using land bases that had flexible decks. It was also difficult to develop an under-carriageless design for an anti-submarine warfare (ASW) aircraft. ASW aircraft were expected to remain propeller-driven, and the propeller might be lower than the fuselage of an under-carriageless aircraft. With so many problems becoming apparent, the idea was abandoned shortly after the tests aboard *Warrior*.

The beginnings of the V/STOL era: the Hawker P.1127 prototype aboard the British carrier Ark Royal *in February 1963. Developed into the Harrier, this aircraft is now used by the Royal Navy, the US Marine Corps, and the navies of Spain and India; Italy is expecting to acquire some in the near future.* (CMP)

Changing technologies: V/STOL aircraft

Despite their new propulsion, most jet aircraft shared a major design factor with propeller-driven aircraft – conventional take-offs and landings. During the late 1940s, the US and Royal Navies became interested in the potential for vertical/short take-off and landing (V/STOL)

aircraft. The Royal Navy had no funds to promote such ventures, but the US Navy awarded Grumman a contract in 1947 to design a small jet that could take off from a zero-length launcher. The aircraft was never built, and though Lockheed and Convair built prototype tail-sitters, nothing came of the ventures.

The British firm Hawker Siddeley developed a V/STOL aircraft in the late 1960s. The P.1127 made its maiden flight in November 1960 and an advanced development was offered to the Royal Navy and the Royal Air Force as the P.1154. A prototype, designated the Kestrel, conducted flight trials from the *Ark Royal* in February 1963, but the Royal Navy was not interested. Proponents of big-deck carriers feared that buying V/STOL jets would lead to calls to build smaller carriers that a V/STOL aircraft could use.

Other forces reacted differently. The RAF ordered a service version, the Harrier, in 1967. The US Navy conducted flight tests from the CVA *Independence* in 1966, and the Italian Air Force held flight trials off the helicopter cruiser *Andrea Doria* in 1967. By 1972 the Spanish and Indian navies had conducted Harrier flight tests from the CVLs *Dédalo* and *Vikrant*. The US Marine Corps received its first service version AV-8A Harriers in 1971. The amphibious assault ship *Guam* conducted a series of Harrier trials in 1972 and 1973, and in 1977 a squadron

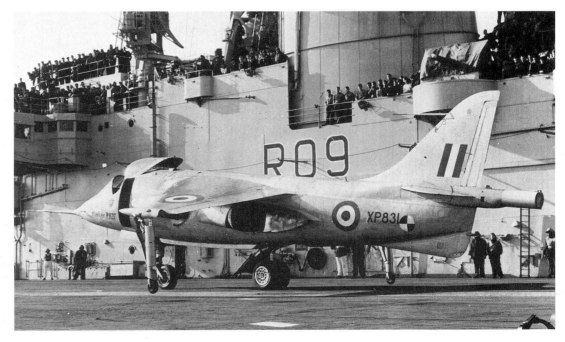

of AV-8A Harriers embarked aboard the CV *Franklin D Roosevelt* for a six-month deployment. This trial proved the ability of the Harrier to integrate with conventional jets during air operations. The ability of the Harrier to operate off small flight decks made it possible for small nations that lacked the funds for large-deck carriers to have a naval aviation capability.

Changing roles: strategic strike, land attack and anti-submarine warfare

The changing postwar strategic picture had a major effect on aircraft carrier operational roles and missions as well. Before the war, the Western powers faced a major naval power, Japan, and US and British carrier operating doctrine was aimed at conducting air strikes against both land and sea targets; but while the major postwar threat, the Soviet Union, had no surface fleet to speak of, it posed a major threat to allied interests in Western Europe and Asia. Because the possibility that the Soviet Union could overrun forward land bases was real, aircraft carriers were seen, at least by the US Navy, as a major means of striking back at Soviet forces. This forced naval planners to regard the carrier as a major forward deterrent system, with the concurrent need to base operational doctrine on long-range strikes against land-based targets. This was recognized by the decision to include the Navy's attack carriers as part of the Single Integrated Operational Plan (SIOP), which delineated strategic nuclear targets, from about 1954 through 1966. The carriers were removed from the SIOP role as ballistic missile submarines became available to perform the role, and aircraft carriers were increasingly required for Vietnam operations. The Royal Navy faced a similar land-strike requirement, although, in its case, the requirement was more to support ground troops performing colonial police missions.

Even with the new land-strike emphasis, one naval role remained vital, ASW. The Soviet Union retained the world's largest submarine force in 1946, and it had captured some of the latest German submarine technology. Any efforts to support Western Europe across the Atlantic divide would require facing the Soviet submarine fleet, and Second World War convoy operations had proved carrier aircraft to be excellent ASW weapons.

The largest carriers afloat in 1945 were the three US Midway *class ships. They were criticised for their lack of freeboard, a point emphasised by this 1980 view of* Coral Sea. *The ship's SCB-110A modernisation could do little to address this problem.* (L & L van Ginderen)

The requirement for ASW aircraft played a major part in the development of the small aircraft carrier. During the 1950s, large dipping-sonar-equipped helicopters began to play an increasing role in naval warfare. A helicopter carrier did not require the large angled deck, steam catapults, or arresting gear of a conventional carrier. The helicopter carrier offered an excellent platform for a navy interested in conducting ASW.

The United States Navy

Earliest postwar carrier designs

As the pre-eminent superpower in September 1945, the United States was the first nation to give consideration to the changing roles and missions of the aircraft carrier. September 1945 found the US Navy in possession of a vast carrier armada. Three giant *Midway* class battle carriers, twenty-four *Essex* class fleet carriers, eleven *Independence* and *Wright* class light fleet carriers, and more than eighty escort carriers were in service or under construction.

Despite the numbers and capabilities of these ships, US naval planners felt there was room for major improvements. The core of the carrier fleet, the *Essex* class, were very cramped and seen as being too small for satisfactory operations. Designed to accommodate about 2700 men, they frequently held 3500 sailors (although many of these excess crew had been added for wartime weaponry requirements). Their unarmoured flight decks had been found wanting against the destructive force of kami-

kaze aircraft. The *Midway* class battle carriers solved the problems of inadequate space and lack of an armoured deck, but the *Midways* sat low in the water and were 'wet' ships in any seaway.

To avoid these shortcomings, designs for a new fleet carrier, smaller than the *Midway* but larger than the *Essex*, were prepared in late 1945 and early 1946. The final C-2 design was slightly smaller than the *Midway*, with an overall length of 960ft, an 870ft by 111ft flight deck and a fully loaded displacement of 54,500 tons.

Wartime experience had shown deck-edge elevators to have several advantages over centreline types. Deck-edge lifts avoided the need for elevator pits and drainage systems, were less vulnerable to hangar deck explosion blast effects, and were less susceptible to mechanical misalignment. Because of this experience, the four elevators were to be deck-edge types, with two on each side of the flight deck.

The C-2 design had three catapults, two in the customary bow position and a third sponsoned out to port from a position just forward of the after port elevator. The island was split into two, with each section having its own funnel, to avoid the potential loss of all uptakes in one hit. One of the two starboard elevators was located between the islands, and the other just where the catapults began. The C-2 design had a smaller air group than either of its predecessors, carrying only 35 fighters and 18 bombers. But by late 1946 plans for the C-2 were discarded as the Navy began preparing a new war-fighting strategy and designing a new, ultra-large attack carrier to go with it.

US national strategy in the late 1940s was focused on the threat from the Soviet Union. Most plans called for any conflict to be settled with atomic weapons, and carrier aircraft were the ideal delivery platform. In 1948 the US

Crewmen clearing snow from the flight deck of USS Essex, operating off Korea in January 1952. Propeller-driven Skyraiders dominate the foreground but F2H-2 Banshees are also present in numbers; along with the less capable, but cheaper, F9F-5 Panther, these latter were the first US Navy jets to see combat. (US Navy)

Navy asked the aircraft industry to design a large twin-engined aircraft capable of flying more than 1000 miles to a target and dropping an atomic bomb.

Plans were also prepared for a giant supercarrier, the *United States*. Initial discussions surrounding the *United States* found that a tension existed between two schools of thought. One held that the new ship's mission would be nuclear attack against Soviet submarine shipyards and naval bases using heavy bombers. A carrier designed for this mission required only a small hangar deck for a limited fighter escort, the bombers being parked on deck. It also required a small magazine, because the ship would carry only a small number of very heavy atomic weapons. The second school took the view that the carrier might be needed for conventional attack missions, necessitating a large hangar deck for a larger air wing, and a large magazine to go along with the larger air group.

The nuclear attack school won out, and in January 1946 Admiral Marc Mitscher, Deputy Chief of Naval Operations for Air, called for an air wing of 16 to 24 bombers capable of mounting 100 sorties before the ship required rearming or refuelling. Because of their size, the bombers would be permanently carried on the carrier's flight deck, with no hangar deck in the design. There were to be two catapults, both

slightly off the centreline. While some aviators called for eliminating the island, to create more room, the Bureau of Ships retained one, to allow for better ship control and clearance of stack gases.

The 125ft beam meant that the new design would be unable to transit the Panama Canal. Although ability to transit the canal had been a requirement for previous US warships, the carrier's basic anti-Soviet mission meant it would have little need to transit between the Atlantic and Pacific Oceans.

Mitscher's preliminary requirements underwent a change when the Ship Characteristics Board (SCB) produced the draft characteristics for SCB-6A in February 1947. The SCB-6A design had a hangar capable of carrying the largest carrier aircraft then planned. The revised air wing was to consist of 12 to 18 turboprop attack bombers and 54 jet fighters. The drastic increase in the number of fighters was required to protect the ship against the large number of Soviet bombers it would face during strike operations.

The design called for four catapults, two in conventional bow positions and two sponsoned out to port and starboard. Behind each catapult was an elevator, positioned to allow fast, simultaneous launches 'without mutual interference and without disturbing landing arrangements'

according to the Navy's design plans. The revised design did not have an island, to ease aircraft handling. Low-power antennas around the deck edge would allow the ship to communicate with accompanying cruisers, which would carry the massive air search radars and long-range communications antennas normally festooned on the island.

Opposition to the Navy's plans was not long in coming. The newly created US Air Force saw the plans as a direct threat to its survival and independence, and it immediately began a major campaign to sink the project. The nascent Air Force said that, although air power would win the next war, it would be air power in the form of giant intercontinental B-36 bombers, which were then entering service. According to the claims of Air Force supporters, carriers would not be able to approach close enough to the Soviet Union to fly their aeroplanes off and recover them safely. Air Force proponents also claimed that a B-36 could carry more tonnage than the 12 to 18 bombers the *United States* would carry.

Agreeing with the Air Force's arguments, Secretary of Defense Louis Johnson ordered construction of the *United States* cancelled one week after the keel was laid down on 18 April 1949 at the Newport News Shipbuilding and Drydock yard.

Cancellation of the *United States* was only one manifestation of the downgrading of the US Navy's carrier forces. By the beginning of June 1950, just before the Korean War broke out, US active carrier strength was down to the three *Midway* class CVBs (*Midway, Franklin D Roosevelt,* and *Coral Sea*) and five *Essex* class CVs (*Boxer, Leyte, Antietam, Valley Forge,* and *Philippine Sea*). Even this force faced the possibility of shrinking to as few as six carriers in

1951. But Johnson's plans to cut the US Navy's carrier forces were dealt a death blow by the Korean War.

The US Navy and the Korean War

When South Korea was invaded by the North, the only US air power in a position to respond rapidly was carrier based. On 3 July the *Valley*

ABORTIVE POSTWAR CARRIER DESIGNS
Date is cancellation; tonnage is full load; scale is 1/1750

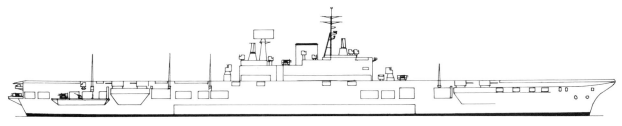

British Malta *class (four ships), 1945–46, 56,800t, 81 aircraft.*

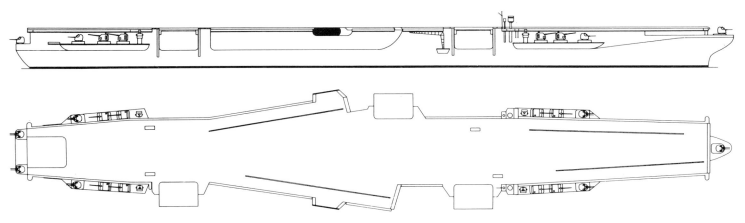

American United States *class (four ships), 1949, 83,249t, 72 aircraft.*

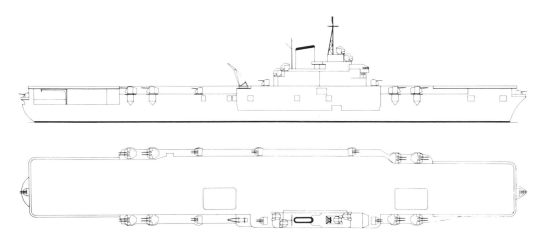

French PA 28 *design (one ship), 1950, 20,000t, 45 aircraft.*

Forge, in company with the British carrier *Triumph*, launched the first air strikes against North Korean forces. By the war's end ten other US CVs, *Boxer*, *Philippine Sea*, *Leyte*, *Princeton*, *Bon Homme Richard*, *Antietam*, *Essex*, *Oriskany*, *Lake Champlain* and *Kearsarge*, along with the CVEs *Sicily*, *Badoeng Strait*, and *Bataan*, all served with the Seventh Fleet off the Korean peninsula. Four British CVLs, *Triumph*, *Theseus*, *Glory* and *Ocean*, and the Australian CVL *Sydney*, also served during the Korean War.

Naval aircraft conducted both tactical strikes against fixed targets such as railway yards, factories and roads, and close air support in support of United Nations forces. The Korean war marked the introduction of jet aircraft into naval combat, with US Navy F2H-2 Banshees and F9F-5 Panthers seeing combat service.

The Korean war had two major effects on naval aviation. It settled most remaining questions about the value of aircraft carriers and their utility in the post-Second World War era. The war showed that future conflicts might be brushfire wars that would not involve the Soviet Union, but only its proxy states. The onset of the Cold War meant funding would become available for both Air Force bombers and air-

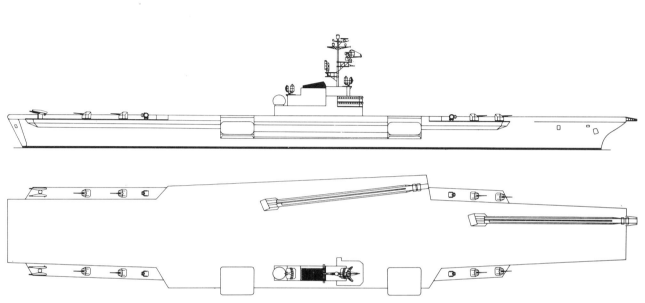

French PA 58 design (one ship), 1961, 45,000t, aircraft numbers unknown.

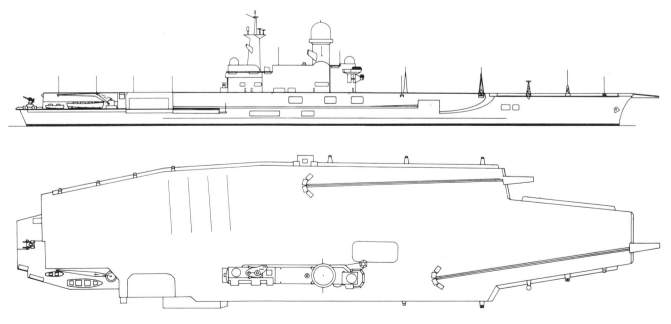

British CVA-01 design (?two ships), 63,000t, 45 aircraft.

craft carriers. It was no longer a question of which service would get the lion's share of the money - there were plenty of missions for all. This was recognized during the war by Secretary Johnson, who, by 1951, gave the Navy approval to build a new carrier, which became the *Forrestal*.

The post-Korean war carriers: *Forrestal* class

The demise of the CVA *United States* had not ended US carrier planning. While no characteristics for a new ship were drawn up, the Bureau of Shipbuilding continued design studies for a new flush-decker. These studies were encouraged by some members of Congress, particularly Representative Carl Vinson of the House Armed Services Committee, who indicated that Congress would probably back construction of a 60,000-ton CV. The *United States* formed the basis for the new carrier's design, but some modifications were made to CVA-58's plans.

One major difference was the emphasis of the two ships. Whereas the *United States* was designed for nuclear strikes against the Soviet Union, the *Forrestal* was designed for both nuclear strikes and the conventional tactical strikes that dominated the Korean War.

Both CVA-58 and CVA-59 had flush decks, but while CVA-58 had an open bow, CVA-59 was given a closed bow, which strengthened the forward end of the flight deck. Because the new carrier might spend much time operating in the stormy North Atlantic, it was important to avoid the storm damage US carriers suffered during Second World War typhoons, when high seas twisted the forward ends of carrier flight decks. The hangar deck was enclosed, again to reduce the amount of water and storm damage it might suffer.

The new carrier would have four deck-edge elevators and four catapults, with two catapults at the bow and two sponsored out from amidships. She was also to have explosive-charge catapults. Designers also considered giving the new carrier a small island that could be lowered below flight deck level on guide rails during air operations.

USS Forrestal, *first of the new generation of postwar supercarriers, as completed in 1955. Originally to have been flush-decked, the island superstructure was an afterthought, as was the fully angled deck. The ship's outfit of boats on deck emphasises the great breadth of the flight deck, the overhang being necessary to accommodate the deck-edge elevators.* (L & L van Ginderen)

An order for the new carrier, *Forrestal*, was placed with the Newport News Shipbuilding and Drydock yard on 12 July 1951, and the keel was laid down one year later, on 14 July 1952. While *Forrestal* was under construction, US and Royal Navy tests validated the concept of the angled deck. With the angled deck a proven concept, the Bureau of Ships ordered all carriers from the Fiscal Year 1955 ship to be so equipped. Faced with the possibility of having the three most recent carriers obsolescent before they entered service, Chief of Naval Operations Admiral Frank Fechteler ordered all carriers under construction changed. The estimated $2 million cost of changing *Forrestal* was justified on the grounds that building and operating the elevating island (which the angled deck had rendered unnecessary) would have cost just as much, if not more. Allied tests also proved the steam catapult's capabilities, and *Forrestal* was redesigned with the new catapult.

While *Forrestal* was being built, the Bureau of Ships continued design work on a variety of new carrier projects. These included a *Midway*-sized design capable of handling 100,000lb aircraft, and a 44,500-ton design. The basic result of the design studies was to show that any smaller carrier would rapidly become obsolescent because of the growth in carrier aircraft. Interestingly, this growth never took place, and the 70,000lb A3D Skywarrior remains the largest aircraft normally operated by an aircraft carrier, second only to the F-14 Tomcat in maximum permitted take-off weight.

One of the design studies, CV 3/54, proposed a slightly larger variant of the *Forrestal*, with a different elevator and catapult arrangement. The new arrangement called for moving the port elevator from the forward to the after end of the angled deck, and rearranging the starboard elevators, positioning two in front and one behind the island, rather than the *Forrestal* arrangement of one before and two abaft the island.

The new arrangement was a major improvement. Because of their elevator/catapult positions, the *Forrestal* class could not use their portside elevator and midships catapults simultaneously. Having only one elevator in front of the island also limited the ability to strike aircraft down after a recovery, if necessary. The revised flight deck arrangement was used for design CV 5/54, which became the *Kitty Hawk* (CVA-63) class. The new layout was also used for the nuclear-powered *Enterprise* (CVAN-65) and *Nimitz* (CVAN-68) class carriers.

Along with the new flight deck layout, the *Kitty Hawk* class also received a pair of Terrier missile launchers for self-defence. Two carriers, *Kitty Hawk* and *Constellation*, were built to the same design immediately following construction of the four *Forrestal*s. When the US Navy built a conventional carrier, *America*, after building the nuclear *Enterprise*, the *Kitty Hawk* design was chosen. A modified *Kitty Hawk* design was employed in 1964 for the US Navy's most recent conventional carrier, *John F Kennedy*.

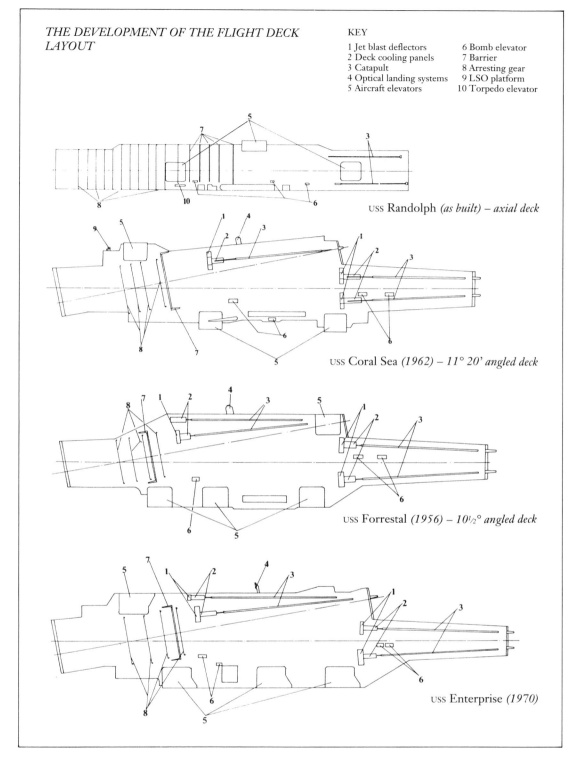

THE DEVELOPMENT OF THE FLIGHT DECK LAYOUT

KEY
1 Jet blast deflectors
2 Deck cooling panels
3 Catapult
4 Optical landing systems
5 Aircraft elevators
6 Bomb elevator
7 Barrier
8 Arresting gear
9 LSO platform
10 Torpedo elevator

USS Randolph *(as built) – axial deck*

USS Coral Sea *(1962) – 11° 20' angled deck*

USS Forrestal *(1956) – 10½° angled deck*

USS Enterprise *(1970)*

Nuclear-powered US carriers

The US Navy did not seriously consider the construction of nuclear-powered aircraft carriers until the 1950s, after design studies had already been started for nuclear submarines, cruisers, and destroyers. (The US Navy had briefly considered using nuclear power for the *United States*, but no serious design work had been undertaken for this programme.) Carriers required large fuel tanks, which were used to shield their magazines and engineering spaces. The large tanks provided fuel for the carrier, its aircraft, and escort ships. Because of the requirement for large fuel quantities, little benefit was seen from having a nuclear propulsion system, particularly since it would probably require a large amount of space.

Nonetheless, in August 1950 the Chief of Naval Operations initially asked the Bureau of Ships to conduct a study for a nuclear-powered attack carrier (CVAN). In November 1951 the Joint Chiefs of Staff followed this with a formal request for a CVAN. The Bureau of Ships issued the tentative characteristics for CVAN-65 in February 1954. These called for the ship to be capable of launching a 100,000lb aircraft, to have four elevators and catapults, and to have the same level of protection as the *Forrestal*, then under construction.

Preliminary plans called for the *Enterprise*, as the new ship was named, to have two twin Terrier surface-to-air missile launchers, but these were omitted to save cost. *Enterprise* was give a new SCANFAR radar system, comprising the large AN/SPS-32 and AN/SPS-33 phased-array air search radars. These radars had a tendency to malfunction, and they were removed during a 1979–82 overhaul. *Enterprise*'s vast size allowed her to carry 8500 tons of aviation fuel, compared with the 5880 carried by the *Forrestal* class, giving her 100-aircraft air wing the ability to carry out 12 days of intensive air operations, more than twice the operational tempo the *Forrestal* class could maintain.

Enterprise was funded in the Fiscal Year 1958 programme, and her keel was laid down on 4 February 1958. Less than four years later, on 25 November 1961, the *Enterprise* was commissioned. *Enterprise*'s construction cost aroused some controversy in the Navy and Congress. At a time when the *Kitty Hawk* class cost about $220 million each, some officials saw little value in the $330 million it cost to build a nuclear carrier.

Some of the opposition was aided by proponents of a strong Air Force, who said large bombers could find and destroy carriers at sea, while the new intercontinental ballistic missiles entering service would guarantee the peace. Navy officials were challenged in Congress by opponents of further carrier construction, who questioned the ability of the ships to operate in high-threat environments.

This opposition helped kill Navy efforts in 1963–4 to have the *John F Kennedy* built as a nuclear-powered carrier. But in February 1966 Secretary of Defense McNamara called for a fifteen-carrier fleet, with four nuclear-powered carriers. Support from McNamara, who had opposed earlier Navy efforts to build a second nuclear carrier, helped lead to a decision to order one nuclear carrier per year in 1967, 1969, and 1971, with planned commissioning dates four years after the orders were placed. Design and funding difficulties meant orders were pushed back to 1967, 1970, and 1974, and the commissionings to 1975, 1977, and 1982.

The ships designed under this programme

USS Enterprise, *the first nuclear-powered carrier, had a unique square island structure, whose shape was largely dictated by the fixed panels of the SCANFAR SPS-32/33 electronically scanned long range radar. The same system was used in the contemporary nuclear cruiser* Long Beach. *(L & L van Ginderen)*

were the first three *Nimitz* class CVANs, *Nimitz, Dwight D Eisenhower*, and *Carol Vinson*. The *Nimitz* design used a two-reactor power-plant that was more efficient than *Enterprise*'s eight-reactor plant. The flight deck layout was basically the same as that used since the *Kitty Hawk*. The *Nimitz* class has become one of the longest-lived naval designs in recent history. The basic design is being used twenty-five years after the first keel was laid down, with four ships being built to the basic design and four to a slightly modified design. The last ship built to a slightly modified *Nimitz* design, CVN-76, will not enter service until 2002/2003.

Postwar carrier modernisation

Because it ended the Second World War with so many carriers, the US Navy knew it would never receive funding for many new carriers to operate the jet aircraft of the 1950s, so modernisation of existing ships would be necessary. The earliest carrier modernisation plans were advanced in 1946, with the uncompleted *Essex* class CV *Oriskany* chosen as the first ship for modification. Construction was suspended in August 1946, while plans for the Ship Characteristics Board (SCB) 27A upgrade were completed.

The prototype modernised carrier, Oriskany *in 1953, showing the rebuilt island of the SCB-27A upgrade. Most features of the original hull remained unchanged, including the sponsons and open bow. The odd collection of aircraft on deck are presumably being returned from Korean War duty. (L & L van Ginderen)*

SCB-27A improvements included rebuilding the uptakes, more powerful hydraulic catapults, removing the 5in gun mounts from the flight deck, installing a new mast, and modifying the elevators to carry 40,000lb aircraft. *Oriskany*'s upgrade was funded in Fiscal Year 1948, and eight ships were upgraded to the SCB-27A standard between 1948 and 1952. (*Oriskany* was completed to the new standard in 1950.)

In 1950 the US Navy decided to conduct an enhanced SCB-27C modernisation programme, including the installation of steam cata-

pults, a starboard deck-edge elevator, and stronger arresting gear. Six ships received SCB-27C upgrades between 1951 and 1955. A third modernisation programme, SCB-125, was conducted between 1952 and 1957. During SCB-125 overhauls, an angled deck, an enclosed hurricane bow, and an improved primary flight control system were installed. All the *Essex* class carriers that received either the SCB-27A or SCB-27C upgrades subsequently received the SCB-125 modernisation. *Oriskany* received a separate SCB-125A overhaul, providing her with the SCB-27C improvements as well.

The US Navy did not upgrade the *Midway* class carriers during the early 1950s, because they did not want to lose the services of the only ships capable of carrying the AJ-1 Savage long range bomber. By the mid 1950s, however, the *Forrestal* class were beginning to enter service, and the modernised *Essex* class were also capable of handling the AJ-1. Therefore a SCB-110 upgrade was performed on *Midway* and *Franklin D Roosevelt* between 1954 and 1957. Each ship received a starboard deck-edge lift, an angled deck, a hurricane bow, stronger arresting gear, and three steam catapults, including a third on the angled deck. *Coral Sea* received a different SCB-110A upgrade, during which a third deck-edge elevator was installed on the starboard side

Seen towards the end of her career, in 1969, Wasp *is operating as a CVS, with ASW Sea King helicopters and fixed-wing Trackers on deck. The ship was not given the SCB-27C modernisation and along with similarly deprived sisters was reduced to CVS status (in 1957 in the case of* Wasp*). Some SCB-27C ships also ended their lives in the CVS role.* (L & L van Ginderen)

just forward of the island and the port side elevator was moved to the after edge of the angle sponson.

Midway received an additional modernisation between 1966 and 1970, when her forward centreline elevator was removed and replaced by a system similar to that of *Coral Sea*. Because the cost skyrocketed from a planned $84 million to an actual $200 million, a similar overhaul for *Franklin D Roosevelt* was cancelled.

By the late 1970s the *Forrestal* class carriers were showing the effects of twenty years' hard service. Because their thirty-year planned service life meant they would start leaving the fleet in the mid 1980s, the US Navy came up with a Service Life Extension Programme (SLEP) upgrade to add fifteen years of service life. During the thirty-month SLEP modernisation, catapults, arresting gear, and fire fighting systems were replaced, boilers and engines were thoroughly overhauled, electronics were upgraded, and crew compartments improved. Five carriers, *Saratoga, Forrestal, Independence, Kitty Hawk*, and *Constellation* received SLEP upgrades before the Navy cancelled the programme as a cost-saving measure in 1991.

Anti-submarine warfare carriers

The growing threat from Soviet submarines led the US Navy to develop a specialised anti-submarine warfare support carrier (CVS) after the Second World War. The first ASW carriers were *Commencement Bay* class escort carriers, which were modified to include a larger island with direction-finding equipment and radar homing systems. The CVEs were used as ASW carriers during the late 1940s and very early 1950s. The earliest ASW aircraft, the S-2 Tracker, was designed to fit aboard the small flight decks of the war-built CVEs, but the CVEs had difficulty operating more than a small number of S-2s. The *Independence* class CVLs were also used in the ASW role during

the late 1940s, receiving some of the same modifications as the CVEs did. During the mid 1950s, as the *Forrestal* class CVAs began entering service, the Navy took those *Essex* class carriers that had only received the SCB-27A and SCB-125 upgrades and converted them into CVS carriers. The *Essex* class were able to carry sufficient numbers of Trackers and helicopters to perform efficiently in the ASW role. Some thought was given to modernising the CVSs during the late 1960s, because of the lack of any new construction, but this had to be cancelled because of a shortage of funds. The last CVS was decommissioned in 1974.

The Vietnam War

The US Navy was not the first fleet to use aircraft carriers off Vietnam, but the South China Sea was the primary operating ground for US carriers between 1964 and 1973, and operations off Vietnam played a major role in US carrier policy during the Cold War era. The costs of the war effort also played a part in delaying planned carrier construction during the 1960s and '70s. Every US carrier based in the Pacific Fleet made multiple deployments to Vietnam, and because of the requirement for carriers, every Atlantic Fleet carrier made at least one deployment to Task Force 77, the Vietnam carrier task force.

The first carriers to conduct air strikes off Vietnam were the 27C *Essex* class CVA *Ticonderoga* and the new CVA *Constellation*, which launched the first strikes on 5 August 1964 in retaliation for North Vietnamese attacks on the US destroyers *Maddox* and *C Turner Joy*. These two ships were joined after that month by the *Ranger* and the ASW carrier *Kearsarge*, sent to search for Soviet and Chinese submarines.

During the eight years of war, the US Navy customarily kept three carriers stationed in the South China Sea, a force made up of two CVAs and one CVS. During the first years of the war,

carriers just entering the war zone normally spent a few weeks operating off South Vietnam on Dixie Station, before moving north to Yankee Station, about 100–140 miles off the coast of North Vietnam. By 1967–68, carriers routinely spent their entire deployment on Yankee Station, as Air Force and Marine Corps aircraft performed most missions over South Vietnam.

Navy aircraft conducted several types of missions over Vietnam. Preplanned Alpha strikes against fixed targets sometimes required as many as thirty-five or forty aircraft, including Intruder and A-4 Skyhawk or A-7 attack aircraft, F-8 Crusader and F-4 Phantom fighters, E-1B Tracer or E-2C Hawkeye airborne early warning aircraft, and EA-6A Intruder electronic warfare aircraft. During an Alpha strike launch, other flight operations normally came to a stop, as the aircraft being launched took up the after portion of the flight deck. A similar situation took place during a landing, as the forward portion of the flight deck was given over to aircraft being recovered or struck down to the hangar for repairs and servicing.

Flex deck operations required launching only three to six aircraft, allowing other flight deck operations to continue, but A-6 Intruders often operated singly or in pairs at night, relying on their sophisticated navigational and attack radars to get them to the target. The A-6 was designed to meet a particular shortcoming of Korean War carrier aircraft, the inability to perform ground support and air strikes at night or in foul weather. The Intruder flew during the monsoon rainstorms that kept all other aircraft on the carrier decks, marking a new stage in carrier warfare, the ability to conduct operations around the clock in any weather.

For the most part, carrier operations remained at the three-ship level, sometimes dropping to two ships, but during the 1972 Easter Offensive carrier strength shot up to five ships, with *Hancock, Midway, Saratoga, Kitty Hawk*, and *Constellation* all conducting air strikes over North and South Vietnam. Carrier strength grew to six carriers during the summer of 1972, with *Hancock, Oriskany, Midway, Saratoga, Kitty Hawk*, and *America* all conducting strike operations.

In all, seventeen attack carriers conducted

Vietnam deployments, including two anti-submarine carriers configured as attack carriers for the duration of their deployments. Four ASW carriers also operated off the Vietnam coast. The requirements of the Vietnam war threw US carrier operating patterns out of balance. Five Atlantic Fleet attack carriers had to make Vietnam deployments. For most Pacific Fleet carriers, the normal pace of operations during the late 1960s and early 1970s meant an eight- to nine-month deployment, followed by only five to seven months in homeport to conduct necessary repairs, train the air group, and provide rest for the crew. During operations off Vietnam, fresh water requirements for the boilers and catapults often meant that water for other purposes, including laundry and showers, was restricted for days at a time, with adverse effects on the temper of the crews affected. Interestingly, when the US Navy was having its racial problems during the early 1970s, the most serious outbreaks occurred aboard two carriers conducting Vietnam deployments.

Vietnam operations also showed, in three instances, that a carrier could suffer major damage and survive. On 26 October 1966 a flare accidentally ignited aboard the *Oriskany*. Although forty-four men were killed, and the hangar and the forward elevator were damaged, she could have continued flight operations if necessary. A devastating fire took place aboard the *Forrestal* on 25 July 1967, when a Zuni rocket from an F-4 Phantom on the flight line was accidentally

fired into the fuel tank of an A-4 Skyhawk just forward of it. The resulting explosions and fire engulfed the after part of the flight deck, the hangar and below decks. Although the flight deck fire was brought under control in less than an hour, secondary fires raged for 12 hours; 21 aircraft were destroyed, 43 damaged, and 134 sailors lost their lives. But helicopters from adjacent carriers were able to land on the forward end of the flight deck to bring assistance. A similar fire, from an accidental Zuni launch, struck the carrier *Enterprise* on 14 January 1969. Although twenty-eight men died and fifteen aircraft were destroyed, the navy estimated that *Enterprise* could have resumed flight operations four hours later if necessary.

The accidents re-emphasised basic lessons of carrier damage control originally developed during the Second World War. Most carrier hangar decks are divided into two or three bays by large steel fire- and explosion-proof doors that can be closed remotely or locally in a matter of seconds. Hangar deck roofs have sprinkler systems to douse any flames, and a typical Western carrier has a variety of damage control systems, including Halon extinguishers, aqueous film forming foam (AFFF) systems to smother fuel, and standard water systems.

US Navy carrier operating doctrine

Because of the lack of a major surface naval threat in 1946, the US Navy saw the primary requirement for its carriers as one of preventing the Soviet submarine fleet from getting loose on the oceans and wreaking havoc on convoys. Plans developed in 1947 called for four carrier task forces, each comprising one flush-deck CVA, one *Midway* class CVB, and two modernised *Essex* class SCB-27As. (One task force would have had three *Essex*es.) Three fast logistics task forces, to support the strike forces, would each have had one CV and two CVEs.

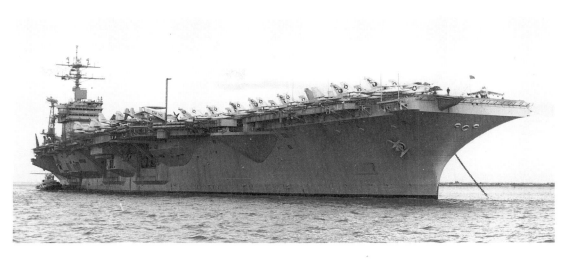

The current US carrier design, the Nimitz *class, will continue into the twenty-first century. This is the second ship,* Dwight D Eisenhower *(CVN-69) in 1981, but ships up to CVN-76 are building or projected.* (L & L van Ginderen)

The CVA would have supplied the long range punch with its 100,000lb bombers. Cancellation of the CVA *United States* and limited funds forced a revision to a planned 1951 force level of eight carriers, with four each in the Atlantic and Pacific Fleets.

Following the Korean War and the report of the the Navy's Long Range Objectives Group in December 1955, the proposed carrier force structure changed to a wartime requirement for the Atlantic and Pacific Fleets to each have one task group with three CVAs and one CVS, one reduced task group with two CVAs, and the ability to form a second three-CVA task group within seven days. By the mid 1950s, the normal air wing aboard a *Forrestal* class CVA included two fighter, one heavy attack, two attack, and one light attack squadrons, and detachments of photographic and airborne early warning (AEW) aircraft. Squadrons normally included twelve aircraft, while detachments had four to six.

By 1958 the Navy had settled on plans for a force of fifteen CVAs. This allowed for a constant peacetime forward deployment of five carriers. For each forward deployed carrier, a second would be undergoing repairs and post-deployment stand-down, and a third would be preparing for its deployment. The requirement for a fifteen-carrier force was restated by Secretary of Defense McNamara in 1966, when he called for eight *Forrestal/Kitty Hawk* class CVAs, three *Midway* class CVAs, and four CVANs.

The standard air wing had also changed during the 1960s. The end of the nuclear strategic mission meant that carriers no longer had to carry a squadron or detachment of heavy attack aircraft. The standard carrier air wing now included two squadrons of light attack A-7s and one squadron of medium attack A-6s. Dropping the heavy attack squadron was greeted with approval by many carrier captains, who had not liked having to work hangar and flight deck arrangements around the large space required by the A-3s.

Starting in 1975, the Navy also reverted to the practice of having only CV aircraft carriers. The decommissioning of the last CVS support carriers in 1974, and the lack of a new CVS or SCS, meant that each carrier had to embark a six-plane detachment of S-3 Viking ASW aircraft and ten SH-3 Sea King ASW helicopters. To make room for the new aircraft, the five-

aeroplane reconnaissance detachment of RA-5 Vigilantes was dropped from the air wing.

By the late 1970s the carrier force was in danger of dropping to twelve ships, as plans called for withdrawing all the *Midway*s by the early 1980s and new construction did not make up for force level cuts. This changed in 1980 when the new Secretary of the Navy, John Lehman, called for a force of fifteen deployable carriers, plus one in SLEP.

But the Navy's ability to maintain five forward deployed carriers was called into question in 1986, when the Navy established new operating tempos, requiring a ship to be in homeport for twelve months out of every eighteen. Cold war deployments were frequently seven to eight months in duration, even excluding the long deployments of the Vietnam War and the Iranian hostage crisis of 1979–80. During 1992 testimony before the Congress, Navy officials admitted it took seven carriers to keep one forward deployed to the Indian Ocean, because of the limits set on deployment time.

Carrier force levels were cut in 1991, when the Defense Department announced plans for a 1995 Base Force with twelve carriers. At the time of writing, the Navy will reach this number by mid 1994, because of expedited decommissionings of *Forrestal* class carriers.

The return of the small carrier in the US Navy

Since the mid 1950s, US carrier building practice had called for building large attack carriers of the *Forrestal*, then *Kitty Hawk* designs. Small carrier studies had been carried out during the 1950s, but no action was taken on any of these plans through the 1960s. By the early 1970s small carrier proponents were making their voices heard once more. The impending decommissioning of the *Midway* class, and the cutback in ship orders because of the costs of the

Vietnam War, caused naval planners to look at ways to reduce individual ship costs and boost quantities.

During his tenure as Chief of Naval Operations from 1970 to 1974, Admiral Elmo Zumwalt called for the development of two small carrier designs. The first was a 50,000- to 60,000-ton ship. This tentative conceptual base line (T-CBL) design formed the basis of most small carrier designs through the medium-sized carrier (CVV) designs of President Jimmy Carter's administration. T-CBL had two deck-edge elevators and two catapults, one at the bow and one on the angle. Using half the eight-boiler powerplant of the *Kennedy*, it had a maximum speed of 28kts. It could carry fifty-two to fifty-nine aircraft, depending on whether it had a mixed air wing or an ASW wing.

T-CBL underwent some modifications during the mid 1970s, emerging as a six-boiler, two-catapult, two-elevator ship carrying the same number of aircraft. President Carter attempted to put a CVV into the 1980 budget request, but the request was denied by Congress, which instead voted to fund a fourth *Nimitz* class nuclear carrier. The CVV's major problem was its cost. Although a CVV cost less than a *Nimitz*, the decline in operating capability was far greater than the costs saved.

The second small carrier was the Sea Control Ship (SCS). Conceived as a replacement for the CVS carriers leaving the fleet, the SCS was not intended to be a fixed-wing carrier. The SCS was to be a 16,000-ton ship with no angled deck or catapults, the air wing to consist of about twelve to sixteen Sea King ASW helicopters. The ship could carry around six AV-8A Harrier VSTOL jets for self-defence. SCS's mission would have been similar to that of the Second World War era CVEs, using her aircraft (helicopters) to provide ASW coverage. The SCS concept was tested using the amphibious assault ship *Guam* between 1972 and 1974. Although

Victorious's reconstruction showed the difficulty of rebuilding a carrier. The reconstruction took eight years, not being finished until early 1958. During the overhaul, the hangar's depth was increased from 16ft to 17ft 6in. This required raising the flight deck, the strength deck of the ship, and building a new gallery deck beneath it.

The high cost of carrier conversions also affected the *Albion/Hermes* class. When the Royal Navy decided to proceed with construction of the newest light fleet carriers, it decided to give the first three *Albion*s an interim 5½-degree angled deck and hydraulic catapults, with a 9-degree angled deck and steam catapults to be added during future refits. *Hermes*, the fourth ship, would receive steam catapults and a 6½-degree angled deck during construction.

The first three ships were completed in 1953–4, just as the British government was performing a Radical Review of its defence capabilities. The review decided that the first three ships would not receive a major upgrade, and that *Ark Royal* would be completed with steam catapults but only an interim angled deck. Because of their small size, the older *Albion*s could operate only twenty-six aircraft. Faced with having three ships that could operate only a small wing of obsolescent aircraft, the Royal Navy decided in 1958 to convert *Albion* and *Bulwark* to amphibious assault helicopter carriers between 1959 and 1961. During the conversion, the catapults and arresting gear were removed and facilities to house eight Wessex helicopters and more than 750 Royal Marines were installed.

Ark Royal received a 9-degree angled deck in 1960, and underwent a further upgrade in 1969 to operate the American F-4 Phantom fighter. *Hermes* was completed in 1959, but because of her small size she was converted in 1971 to an amphibious assault ship, losing her catapults and arresting gear. She underwent a second conversion in 1977 to become an ASW carrier, with Sea King helicopters in place of the earlier Wessex.

Efforts to build new carriers

The Royal Navy made only two efforts to build new large-deck aircraft carriers after the Second World War. The first came in early 1952, when

---

the tests were successful, Congress's General Accounting Office doubted whether the Navy would receive the advanced ASW helicopter and V/STOL aircraft the SCS would require. The SCS was also opposed by supporters of the large fixed-wing carrier, who saw the ship as an attempt by a surface line CNO to do away with large-deck carriers. The large carrier supporters were afraid that Congress and the surface Navy would not see the SCS as an adjunct to large-deck carriers, but rather as a cheap replacement.

Royal Navy carrier development

The Royal Navy faced a substantially different situation from that of the US Navy during the postwar years. It ended the war with *Illustrious/ Implacable* class fleet carriers and *Colossus* class light fleet carriers, and thirty-eight escort carriers in service, and two *Ark Royal* class fleet carriers, six *Majestic* class and four *Hermes* class light fleet carriers under construction. It also had a large building programme, with orders for three *Malta* class large fleet carriers and two *Ark Royal* class fleet carriers. But the pressing requirement to rebuild the merchant fleet meant that any carriers not nearing completion were postponed, and any carriers on order were cancelled. Most of the escort carriers were US Lend-Lease and had to be returned.

A similar situation existed with regards to the Royal Navy's aircraft. Most of the Fleet Air Arm's aeroplanes were US machines acquired through Lend-Lease. The end of the war meant

they had to be paid for or returned, but the US Navy had thousands of excess aircraft, so the Royal Navy disposed of most of the aircraft by pushing them over the sides of its carriers.

Britain also faced a different set of priorities for its carrier fleet. Because of its worldwide empire, it required a fleet capable of enforcing peace throughout the realm. Carriers, with their attack aircraft, could perform this role just as flexibly as cruisers, the traditional colonial station ships. But Britain depended heavily on international trade, and also needed anti-submarine carriers to defend convoys against a Soviet submarine offensive during any future war.

Another problem was the state of its carrier fleet. The six *Illustrious* type vessels were relatively small, and would require reconstruction to handle aircraft expected to enter service during the 1950s. The first decision made by the Royal Navy, in 1946, was not to complete any new carriers except the two fleet carriers (*Ark Royal* and *Eagle*) and the four newest light fleet carriers (*Albion*, *Bulwark*, *Centaur*, and *Hermes*).

Plans also were developed to modernise some, if not all, of the six fleet carriers commissioned during the Second World War. The first three *Illustrious* class carriers had only a single hangar deck, and would be easier to modernise than the newer ships of the *Implacable* class, which had a double-level hangar deck. *Victorious* entered the shipyard in 1950 for what was planned as a four-year overhaul to enable her to operate newer aircraft. Plans to upgrade the *Implacable*s were cancelled in 1952 because of cost.

The reconstructed British carrier Victorious *in 1959. The refit was very protracted and expensive, but the ship could operate the latest aircraft. The 1950 design complement was 33 fighters, 12 strike and 10 ASW, but the growth in aircraft size reduced this figure. On deck are Scimitar strike fighters, Sea Venom night fighters and an AEW Skyraider aft; these were later replaced by Buccaneer, Sea Vixen and Gannet aircraft. One of the ship's greatest assets – when it worked – was the massive Type 984 3-D radar seen above the rebuilt island. (CMP)*

ship, capable of handling any American attack aircraft. Such a carrier would have been 1000ft long, limiting it to only two private drydocks in the United Kingdom. Even the *Ark Royal* and *Eagle*, which were shorter than 840ft, could only enter one naval drydock.

By late 1952 a shortage of funds led to the cancellation of plans for the new CVA. Proposals were made in 1954 for 35,000-ton and 28,000-ton CVAs. The larger carrier would have had a 47-aeroplane air wing, with 12 Scimitar and 12 Sea Vixen fighters, 8 Gannet AEW/ASW aircraft, 9 Buccaneer attack jets, 4 AEW aircraft, and 2 helicopters. The smaller carrier could have accommodated 38 aircraft, including 12 Scimitars, 12 Sea Vixens, 8 Buccaneers, 4 AEW aircraft, and 2 helicopters. With design studies showing the 35,000-ton carrier to be too expensive, and the 28,000-ton ship inadequate for strike missions, planning for a new carrier was put on hold in the late 1950s.

The Royal Navy, under the leadership of First Sea Lords Admirals Louis Mountbatten and Casper John, kept pressing for new carrier construction, emphasising that *Victorious* would have to leave service in the late 1960s, followed by *Eagle* and *Hermes* in the 1970s.

By late 1965 the designs for the first of five new carriers, CVA-01, had been prepared. CVA-01 was to be a 54,650-ton ship, with an overall length of 963ft (her flight deck was to be 928ft long and 231ft wide). CVA-01 had a unique design. Her two elevators were located just forward and inboard of the island and just aft of the island on the starboard deck edge. Both elevators used a scissors leg design, rather than the conventional cables, to raise them. There was one catapult at the bow and one on the angle deck. To simplify the problem of

the Ship Design Policy Committee asked for characteristics so that a carrier could be laid down in 1954 and commissioned in 1958. By July 1952 design work had progressed sufficiently for engines to be ordered. Provisional characteristics called for a 52,000-ton fully loaded ship with a length of 870ft and a beam of 115ft. The new ship could launch 60,000lb jets and recover 40,000lb aircraft. There would be three catapults and an air wing of about sixty-five aircraft.

The Director of Air Warfare wanted a larger

The British Mediterranean Fleet's carrier force in 1956, the Eagle *(foreground),* Bulwark *and* Albion. *All were completed with interim angled decks, but only* Eagle *was large enough to cope with the next generation of aircraft and the other two ships were converted to 'commando carriers' – amphibious assault helicopter carriers – in 1959–61. (CMP)*

bringing aircraft up from the hangar, the island was set well in to port, with a 45ft taxiway between the island and the starboard deck edge. This would allow aircraft to be brought up from the hangar by the after elevator and moved to the forward catapult, outboard of the island, without disturbing operations on the flight deck. CVA-01 had only a 3-degree angled deck, rather than the 10 degrees common to most carriers. The entire flight deck was offset to port, in effect creating two separate flight decks. The arresting wires were also offset to port.

The interim air wing called for 18 Buccaneers, 18 Sea Vixens, 4 AEW aircraft and about 5 helicopters. The Buccaneers and Sea Vixens would eventually be replaced by 30 strike fighters, probably F-4 Phantoms from the United States.

While design work was going on, the British government was conducting a study to determine the best form of future air power. The Royal Navy argued for a force of five CVAs. The Royal Air Force countered with an argument in favour of buying American F-111s. During the debate, the Royal Air Force was accused of 'moving' Australia 500 miles, to claim that aircraft based on the subcontinent could cover all of the British government's commitments in the South Pacific. The debate ended in February 1966, when the British government accepted the RAF's arguments. CVA-01 was cancelled when plans were ready to go to the shipbuilders for bidding.

In the aftermath of CVA-01's cancellation, the US Department of Defense offered the Royal Navy three *Essex* class carriers. The offer was declined because a Royal Navy team felt it would be too difficult to support two different types of aircraft carriers and their equipment.

The decision to cancel CVA-01 was followed by a decision to decommission all aircraft carriers by the end of the 1970s and rely on the Royal Air Force for power projection. The Royal Navy was to be reoriented for North Atlantic ASW operations, which helped provide the genesis of the next carrier class, the *Invincible* class helicopter carriers.

The need to carry fixed-wing ASW aircraft constrained the Royal Navy's carriers from carrying as many strike aircraft and fighters as the fleet desired. To get around this requirement for ASW assets, fighters, and attack aircraft, the Royal Navy decided in 1953 to abandon fixed-wing ASW aircraft in favour of ASW helicopters. The change, to have taken place in 1958, did not actually occur until about 1968.

Helicopter carriers

The decision to concentrate on ASW did not end the need for new aircraft carriers. Even before the cancellation of CVA-01, the Royal Navy was considering the construction of a guided missile armed cruiser capable of carrying six Wessex ASW helicopters. The cruiser would have accompanied the carrier, providing the ASW coverage previously performed by the carrier's aircraft. Following CVA-01's demise, design efforts focused on a conventional cruiser design, with an alternative design having a through deck, with the superstructure off to one side. By 1968 design efforts were changing towards the 'through deck' cruiser, which could carry nine helicopters with more workshop space. Calling the ship a cruiser was important. It helped to prevent the build-up of opposition in parliament and the RAF, to what might be seen as a new carrier. But while there was opposition from the RAF, the Royal Navy's case was strengthened by the RAF's poor performance during the High Wood joint-service exercises in December 1971.

In April 1973 the new ship, now designated a Helicopter Carrying Heavy Cruiser (CAH), was ordered from Vickers, which had been in-volved in design efforts since 1971. Financial difficulties delayed the programme, but by May 1977 a second ship had been ordered and plans were under way for a third ship. The programme for helicopter-carrying cruisers gained added support because of Nato complaints during the late 1980s that Britain was not living up to its pledges to provide support for the Strike Fleet. The *Invincible* class were not limited to carrying helicopters. While the concept of a 'through-deck' cruiser was being discussed, the British government considered operating RAF ground-attack Harriers from the ship, but Hawker Siddeley had conducted studies in 1972 for a dedicated strike fighter, the Sea Harrier. Budgetary problems delayed the decision, but in 1975 the British government authorised the purchase of Sea Harriers for the three *Invincible* class carriers.

Royal Navy carrier doctrine and use

The Royal Navy traditionally had different plans for using its carriers than the US Navy. Postwar Royal Navy plans focused on policing the Empire and providing sea control during a limited war. Cruisers had traditionally performed these roles, but the carrier, with her air wing, could perform them just as well. The 1948 Nine-year Plan called for a force of six CVs and six CVLs, but this was reduced within a year to four CVs and four CVLs. These plans did not square with reality, which saw two CVs and five CVLs operational in 1947 and two CVs and four CVLs active in 1952, with three CVs in reduced operating capacity serving as training carriers.

One recent British contribution to carrier aviation is the 'ski-jump', an angled ramp that allows a more fuel-efficient rolling take-off for V/STOL jets, which consequently have come to be designated STOVL (short take-off, vertical landing). This is the first ever shipboard ski-jump launch, on 30 October 1980, from HMS Invincible. The ramp angle was 6½ degrees, but this has been increased in later ships. These 'through-deck cruisers' are now designated as CVS. (MoD, Crown Copyright)

HMS Hermes *in July 1982, newly returned from duty as Task Force flagship during the Falklands campaign. The Sea Harriers and Sea King helicopters of the ship's own air wing share the flight deck with a few 'guests'. Although a small carrier by most standards, she carried nearly twice as many aircraft during Operation Corporate as the* Invincible. *(C & S Taylor)*

By 1955 the situation had changed for the worse, with two CVs and two CVLs operational and three CVLs in reduced status. By 1959 the Royal Navy had stabilised at a force level of three CVs and two CVLs, although the CV *Victorious* was barely more capable than the newest CVL, *Hermes*. The Royal Navy apparently aimed to keep a five-carrier force level right up through the decision to cancel CVA-01. Five carriers provided the ability to keep one CV and one CVL both in the North Atlantic and in the Far East.

Despite its shortage of ships during the 1950s and 1960s, the Royal Navy has made extensive use of its carrier assets; in fact the Royal Navy's carriers have been involved in as many actions as the US Navy's, albeit on a lesser scale. The light fleet carriers *Triumph*, *Theseus*, *Glory* and *Ocean* all served in the Korean War, and *Triumph* was one of the first two United Nations carriers to arrive on the scene in late June 1950.

Because of the Royal Navy's shortage of warships, the four carriers seldom operated off Korea at the same time, although by 1952 two British carriers were often in the area at the same time.

Three years after the Korean War, British carriers were again in action, during the Suez Crisis. When the British government decided to counter Nasser's takeover of the Suez Canal, it had very few carriers ready for service. Between the July 1956 takeover and the October 1956 invasion, *Albion* had a post-refit work-up expedited, and *Bulwark* was upgraded from training carrier to full operational status. These two ships joined *Eagle* in the Mediterranean to conduct air strikes against the Egyptian forces. Two light fleet carriers, *Ocean* and *Theseus*, were converted to amphibious assault ships before the operation and landed Royal Marine commandos.

The next major action for British carriers was in July 1961, when Iraq threatened to invade Kuwait. *Bulwark*, by then a helicopter carrier, was diverted from a voyage to Pakistan, and steamed into the Persian Gulf to fly ashore her commandos. The Royal Marines secured Kuwait airfield so that additional troops could fly in. Ten days later, *Victorious* arrived from Hong Kong. She conducted air surveillance and power projection operations, serving as the linch-pin of British efforts to support the Kuwaitis. Although Iraq spoke loudly, no action was taken, possibly because of fear of *Victorious*'s Buccaneer attack aircraft.

Ark Royal and *Eagle* were also used to enforce United Nations' sanctions against Rhodesia in 1965 and 1966. In the Mozambique Channel, aircraft from the two ships tracked more than 770 ships, to ensure that none were carrying oil to the breakaway Rhodesian regime. *Eagle*'s 71 continuous days at sea in 1966 set what was then a postwar record for British carriers remaining at sea.

Probably the most famous action by British carriers in the post-Second World War era was the Falklands conflict in 1982. *Hermes* embarked 21 Sea Harriers and 6 Sea Kings, and *Invincible* carried 10 Sea Harriers and 9 Sea Kings during Operation Corporate. The Sea Harriers performed combat air patrol and anti-ground strike missions throughout the campaign. The primary hindrance to the British forces was the lack of an airborne early warning aircraft to provide long range warning of Argentine attacks. Following the Falklands campaign, the Royal Navy modified some Sea King helicopters by adding Searchwater radars, turning the ASW helicopter into a limited AEW platform.

Other carrier navies

French carrier development

The French navy's carrier forces were in a very poor shape after the Second World War. The keels for two new carriers, *Joffre* and *Painlevé*, had been laid down in 1938 and 1939, but both ships were destroyed on the stocks to stop the Germans getting the hulls. As a result, France's only aircraft-capable ship in 1946 was the obsolescent *Béarn*, which had been downgraded from a carrier to an aircraft transport during the war because of her limited capabilities. But, as one of the winning powers, France was able to receive help from her richer allies.

France was loaned the escort carrier HMS *Biter* in 1945. Renamed *Dixmude*, it sailed to Indochina in 1946, where its SBD Dauntless dive bombers, purchased from the United States, began conducting air strikes against the Vietminh guerrillas. The first carrier France received after the war was the former British light fleet carrier *Colossus*, which was handed over on five-year loan in 1946 and renamed *Arromanches*. France received SBD Dauntless and SB2C Helldiver dive bombers and F6F Hellcat fighters from the United States, and Seafire Mk XV fighters from Britain, for the air wing. *Arromanches* entered combat almost immediately, deploying to Indochina to support French troops fighting the Vietminh. By early 1951 *Arromanches* had made two deployments.

While the French navy was conducting air warfare in Southeast Asia, it was fighting government budgeteers in Paris for funds to build a new carrier. The designs for the *Joffre* class had never been discarded, and in 1947 these were updated and brought out as the PA (*Porte Avions*) 28 design. PA 28, given the provisional name *Clemenceau*, was to displace 20,000 tons fully loaded and would be 755ft long and 118ft wide. The flight deck was to be the strength deck, but the ends of the hangar deck were to be open. Two elevators were arranged just forward and aft of the island, to starboard of the centreline. This arrangement allowed aircraft to be moved to port of the after elevator, allowing a larger hangar than would have been possible with normal centreline elevators.

Clemenceau would have accommodated 49 aircraft, including 22 twin-engine dive bombers and 27 fighters. The defensive armament would have included sixteen 100mm guns, arranged in eight gun mounts, with two per quadrant. Support for the new carrier was not strong, because of the poor state of the French economy, and in 1950 the project was cancelled.

Cancellation of the *Clemenceau* did not solve the problem of maintaining a presence off Vietnam, which was difficult with one light carrier and one escort carrier. Following the cancellation of the *Clemenceau*, France asked for and received a carrier from the United States. The former *Independence* class light fleet carrier *Langley* was received in October 1950 and renamed *Lafayette*. She sailed to Indochina in June 1951, where she joined *Arromanches*. A second *Independence* class carrier, *Belleau Wood*, was received from the United States in 1953 and renamed *Bois Belleau*. She replaced *Lafayette* on the Indochina station in April 1954. The *Lafayette* also allowed the *Dixmude* to be relegated to aircraft transport duties. *Bois Belleau* and *Lafayette* were returned to the United States in 1960 and 1963, upon completion of the *Clemenceau* and *Foch*. *Arromanches* and *Lafayette* also conducted air strikes against Egyptian positions during the October 1956 Suez Crisis.

Cancellation of the *Clemenceau* had not ended the French navy's plans for building their own carriers, however, and the experience of the three loaned carriers off Indochina convinced the French navy of the value of aircraft carriers, particularly for a nation that wanted to maintain an active foreign policy. Design efforts for a new class, incorporating the new developments of an angled deck, mirrored landing system, and steam catapults, continued through the mid 1950s, by which time the French economic situation had improved.

The first of a new aircraft carrier class was ordered in 1953. The first new carrier, named *Clemenceau*, was laid down in November 1955, and was followed by her sister-ship, *Foch*, in February 1957. The new design had a flight deck angled 8 degrees to port, and a completely enclosed hangar deck. Two 174ft catapults were provided, one forward on the port side and the other on the angled deck. The two elevators comprised a forward centreline unit at the end of the catapult and a starboard deck-edge unit just aft of the island. Both catapults were to have been forward, but one was moved to the angle to create additional deck park space forward and avoid interference with the forward elevator.

The planned capacity was for 60 aircraft, but the growth in aircraft size had reduced this to about 40 aircraft per ship by the time the ships were completed in November 1961 and July 1963 respectively. Aircraft capacity has since shrunk to 16 Super Étendard IV strike aircraft, 10 F-8E Crusader fighters, 3 Étendard IV-P photo-reconnaissance aircraft and 7 Alizé ASW aircraft. The *Clemenceau* class have never carried airborne early warning aircraft, relying on the three-dimensional radars of their escort ships. The lack of AEW aircraft also reflects French carrier operating practice, which has called for using the ships in support of French policy, often in the former French colonies. The two carriers have spent most of their careers with the Mediterranean Fleet, although both were attached to the Atlantic Fleet between 1966 and 1975. Each has made deployments to the Pacific, serving as the flagship at the French nuclear test facilities in Polynesia.

While *Clemenceau* and *Foch* were under construction, the French government approved construction of a third new carrier, PA 58. She was to be a 45,000-ton ship fully loaded, capable of carrying the Mirage IV heavy strike aircraft. As happened with PA 28, French finances were not up to the task, and PA 58 was cancelled in 1961, before construction began.

While construction of PA 58 was being debated, the French navy ordered a smaller helicopter carrier, *La Resolue*, to replace the obsolescent training cruiser *Jeanne D'Arc*. Or-

After a number of false starts, France eventually completed a purpose-built carrier class in the early 1960s with the Clemenceau *and* Foch *(seen here). They are the bare minimum size for operating jet aircraft and their F-8E Crusader fighters are now long overdue for replacement, but a new nuclear-powered ship,* Charles de Gaulle, *is under construction. (ECP Armées)*

French naval aviation assets are increased by the helicopter carrier Jeanne D'Arc. *The ship is used for training in peacetime, but can adopt an ASW or amphibious assault role in war.* (French Navy)

dered in 1957, *La Resolue* was commissioned in 1964 and renamed *Jeanne D'Arc* to commemorate her predecessor. During peacetime operations she carries four Super Frélon helicopters. These can be augmented in wartime, when she would carry eight helicopters and perform either amphibious assault ship or ASW carrier duties.

By the late 1960s *Arromanches* was quite obsolescent, and the French navy was considering several replacement options. Most studies concentrated on an 18,000-ton nuclear-powered helicopter carrier, designated PH (*Porte Helicoptères*) 75. No action was taken on these plans, but in the mid 1980s, when France had to consider replacing *Clemenceau*, the PH 75 plans became the basis for a new PAN (*Porte Avions Nucleaire*) design. Construction of the PAN, named *Charles de Gaulle*, began in 1988, with a planned service date of 1996. Funding difficulties have pushed this date back about two years. *Charles de Gaulle* is to have a 40-aircraft air wing, similar to that of the *Foch* and *Clemenceau*, with a mixture of attack, fighter, and ASW aircraft. French plans had called for a sister-ship, to replace *Foch*, during the twenty-first century, but these have been put on hold because of funding difficulties.

The smaller western navies

Major power interest in the aircraft carrier was mirrored by interest in the smaller powers, particularly the smaller European navies and the

larger Commonwealth and South American navies. Some of these had ordered battleships and large cruisers during the heyday of the dreadnought, and it was almost natural that, as the aircraft carrier became the new capital ship, their gaze would turn in that direction. The wish to acquire aircraft carriers came at a fortuitous time, because the two major Western naval powers had excess carrier tonnage, particularly in the light fleet carrier classes that were the minimum size to provide some capabilities.

The first smaller navies to receive carriers were those of Australia, Canada and the Netherlands, each of which obtained a former British light fleet carrier in 1948. Canada received the *Magnificent*, Australia was given the *Terrible*, renamed *Sydney*, and the Netherlands was given the *Venerable*, renamed *Karel Doorman*. Australia received a second carrier, the *Majestic*, in 1949 and renamed her *Melbourne*. The *Vengeance* was also lent to Australia from 1953 to 1955. Canada received a second carrier, *Powerful*, renamed *Bonaventure*, in January 1957, and *Magnificent* was then returned to the Royal Navy. During the early and mid 1950s these

ships served as the major units in their respective fleets, carrying attack and fighter aircraft. All of the ships frequently took part in Nato or bilateral exercises with the larger navies.

The increasing size of high-performance jets during the late 1950s, however, left many small naval air arms in a quandary. Keeping their carriers in an attack role meant either having a carrier that could operate only a tiny, barely capable modern air wing, or having a moderate-sized air wing using obsolescent aircraft. The costs of such a decision would have been prohibitive, either in purchasing a small number of high-performance jets and the necessary logistics system, or in buying ever increasing amounts of spare parts for increasingly antiquated aircraft.

For the Western navies, the solution was to abandon carrier-based strike warfare. Canada, the Netherlands, and Australia were close allies of the United States and Great Britain, and any major conflict would find the superpowers supplying the large-deck carriers and high-performance strike aircraft. At the same time, the growing Soviet submarine threat meant that anti-submarine carriers would be required for convoy protection during a war. Allied naval doctrine also called for the smaller powers to provide convoy protection and anti-submarine warfare assets to the Nato alliance.

With the change in carrier roles and missions, Australia, Canada, and the Netherlands all converted their carriers from attack to anti-submarine CVs. Wildcat fighters and Avenger attack aircraft were replaced by S-2 Trackers, ASW Sea King and Wessex helicopters, and a

Many navies of the world were introduced to carrier aviation through the medium of surplus British light fleet carriers. As jet aircraft increased in size most were deemed too small for strike warfare, but Australia's Melbourne *retained limited capacity in that area until the 1980s by courtesy of the diminutive A-4 Skyhawk, two of which are seen forward in this view.* (Australian DoD)

limited number of small A-4 Skyhawk jets for combat air patrol and protection. Canada and the Netherlands decommissioned their carriers during the late 1960s, seeing them as expensive relics during the new age of naval warfare (and an era of expanding domestic social programmes, which took funds away from defence). Australia continued to operate its carrier until 1982. A plan to buy *Invincible* from Britain as a replacement collapsed after the Falklands War.

While most of the smaller Western powers were getting rid of their carriers, two nations were continuing to operate air-capable ships, and even building new ones. Spain received its first aircraft carrier in August 1967, when the US Navy transferred the *Independence* class light fleet carrier *Cabot*. Renamed *Dédalo*, she originally carried an air wing of Sea King ASW helicopters. The air wing configuration changed in September 1976 when *Dédalo* embarked five AV-8A Harriers and became the world's first carrier regularly to carry the V/STOL jets.

During the 1970s *Dédalo* became increasingly obsolescent, and Spain began considering different designs for a new carrier. A contract was signed in June 1977 with the naval architect firm Gibbs and Cox to modify the US Navy's Sea Control Ship design for Spanish service. A 12-degree ski-jump was added at the bow, and some Spanish electronics and weapon systems were added and construction began in 1979. Commissioned in May 1988 after a year's sea trials, the *Principe de Asturias* carries about the same sized air wing as the *Invincible* class on a smaller displacement.

Italy also began building a small carrier in the 1980s. The *Andrea Doria* class cruisers required replacement during the late 1980s. Although they carried ASW helicopters, they had a limited capacity, and a helicopter carrier would provide more capability. The keel for the new carrier, *Giuseppe Garibaldi*, was laid down in 1981, and she was commissioned in August 1987. Although *Garibaldi* was built as a helicopter carrier, the Italian navy recognized her potential as a Harrier carrier, and lobbied to change Italian law, which confined fixed-wing aviation to the air force. In 1988 the Italian Parliament voted to change the law and allow Harrier operations to be conducted from the *Garibaldi*.

Although the Italian navy was legally prevented from operating fixed-wing aircraft, the Giuseppe Garibaldi *was built with a gently sloping ski-jump forward which could only have been intended for V/STOL aircraft. Parliamentary approval has since been obtained for Harrier operations from this ship.* (Fincantieri)

Aircraft carriers in the Third World

The larger South American navies also entered the aircraft carrier market after the Second World War. Because their military procurement programmes were all based on the plans of their neighbours, they configured their aircraft carriers as attack carriers long after most other smaller navies converted theirs to anti-submarine warfare carriers.

By the late 1950s three of the largest Third World navies had entered the carrier field, all buying former Royal Navy light fleet carriers. Brazil bought the *Vengeance* in December 1956. After a four-year refit, she was recommissioned as *Minas Gerais* in December 1960. Argentina received the *Warrior* in June 1958 and renamed her *Independencia*. Argentina sold the *Independencia* for scrap in 1968. In its place, the Argentine navy bought the *Karel Doorman* from the Netherlands and renamed her *Veinticinco de Mayo*. *Karel Doorman* had suffered a bad boiler fire during her last Dutch refit in 1968, before the sale. Because of the sale, the ship received another upgrade, to repair the engineering systems and modernise the sensors. *Veinticinco de Mayo* was configured as a light attack carrier during most of her service, carrying a mixed air wing of Étendard attack aircraft, Skyhawk fighters and Tracker ASW aircraft. Despite the potent air wing, the ship had little to show for its capability during the 1982 Falklands War.

The carrier led the Argentine task force that invaded the Falkland Islands on 1 April 1982, and, following the landings, conducted some patrols off the Argentine coast, but it never closed with the British task force. After the cruiser *General Belgrano* was sunk on 4 May 1982, the remainder of the Argentine Navy withdrew to port. The aircraft from *Veinticinco de Mayo*'s air wing flew anti-surface air strikes from shore bases.

In contrast to the relative inactivity of most small carrier forces, India has had almost a Mahanian sense of how to use its fleet, and its first carrier, *Vikrant*, has had almost as active a career as those of larger carriers in the major navies. India bought the uncompleted *Majestic* class carrier *Hercules* in January 1957. Renamed *Vikrant*, it was completed in Britain and sailed to India in mid 1961. During the Indo-Pakistani war of 1971, *Vikrant* led a battle group of seven destroyers and frigates against East Pakistan. *Vikrant*'s air wing, comprising 18 British Sea Hawks and 4 French Alizé turboprop anti-submarine aircraft, conducted bombing and rocket attacks against Pakistani ships and coastal targets, including the port of Chittagong. They also mined shipping channels and harbours.

Vikrant is a small carrier, and by the late 1970s India was looking at expanding its carrier force. India obtained its second carrier in April 1986, when it bought *Hermes* from Britain and renamed the ship *Viraat*. India's use of *Vikrant* during the 1971 war shows how even a medium-sized navy with a very small naval air force can dominate its neighbours, if they lack a means of countering the carrier and its air wing.

Just as the principal South American countries acquired dreadnoughts before the First World War, so they desired aircraft carriers after the Second. Only Argentina and Brazil succeeded, in both cases ex-British light fleets being supplied. The Brazilian Minas Gerais, *shown here with Tracker aircraft on deck, is dedicated to ASW, but the Argentines bought French Étendard strike aircraft to operate from the* Veinticinco de Mayo. (Brazilian Navy)

Soviet carrier developments

Little is known about the Soviet Union's earliest attempts at postwar carrier construction. Joseph Stalin reportedly ordered the construction of at least one aircraft carrier during the first postwar build-up of the Soviet fleet, the 1945–50 Five Year Plan. This programme, designated P-71, did not proceed beyond the design stage. A second attempt, Project 72, was begun during the 1950–55 Five Year Plan. P-72 probably would have been about the size of the US Navy's *Essex* class, given the Soviet tendency to better the West at its own game. Design work on P-72 was stopped in 1953 because of a lack of suitable aircraft in the design stage. The Soviet Navy made one more attempt to get a carrier in 1955, with plans reportedly calling for simultaneous design and construction of aircraft for the ship. This design was halted in 1956 by premier Khrushchev, a noted opponent of large surface ships. Because of the poor state of Soviet shipbuilding and competition from other naval programmes, most of these efforts never progressed far enough for Western naval intelligence agencies to find out much about them.

In the late 1950s the Soviet navy began making plans for a large helicopter cruiser, the *Moskva*. From the midships forward, *Moskva* had anti-submarine rocket launchers and two surface-to-air missile launchers. The after half

Soviet carriers of the Kiev *class – this is* Minsk *– retained considerable cruiser-type firepower forward. This confined rolling take-offs for the V/STOL Forger fighters to the short angled deck, which was probably acceptable given their subordination to the ship's main role of ASW/command cruiser. (RAF)*

of the ship consisted of a large flight deck with six landing spots for anti-submarine helicopters; 14 Hormone A/B/C helicopters can be carried on the flight deck or in the two hangars, which are located between the funnel uptakes and beneath the flight deck. *Moskva* and her sister-ship *Leningrad* were designed as ASW cruisers, with large bow-mounted and variable depth sonars. Several explanations have been offered for the specific requirement for this class. Design work

started shortly after the US Navy began modifying the submarines *Grayback* and *Growler* to carry Regulus cruise missiles and announced plans to build the *George Washington* class Polaris ballistic missile submarines.

The anti-Polaris explanation is unlikely, because an anti-Polaris ship would have a wide area of ocean to cover, too large for a ship with just 14 helicopters. As an anti-Regulus submarine, the design makes more sense. Regulus I's approximate 500-mile range would have required her to operate near the Soviet coast. *Moskva*, with her 14 helicopters, would have been adequate for the anti-Regulus role. Another explanation for the *Moskva*s is that they were to have been the ASW companions to a cancelled large anti-submarine cruiser class. The Soviets planned to build at least one more *Moskva* class carrier, but this was cancelled because of problems building the first two ships.

Moskva and *Leningrad* entered service in July

1967 and late 1968. Both served primarily in the Black Sea and Mediterranean, with occasional voyages to the eastern Atlantic. They are poor sea-boats, partly because the large Moose Jaw sonar causes them to trim about three feet down by the bow.

Khrushchev's overthrow led to a change in Soviet naval planning. Freed from the criticism that large ships were merely targets, Soviet planners began to design a new carrier class in 1965–66, the *Kiev*. Simultaneously, in 1967, the Soviets flew their V/STOL aircraft, the Yakovlev Freehand. While the new class was being built, the Soviets held their first major open-ocean naval exercise, Okean '70, in 1970.

Okean '70 was hailed in the Soviet press as a major success, and cited in the Western press as an example of the fearsome new Soviet navy. But the exercise showed that the Soviets had major command and control problems with their fleet, because of poor communications both within the fleet and with fleet headquarters. With the lessons from Okean '70 fresh in mind, the new ships were designed to include a comprehensive communications suite as well as aircraft spaces.

The *Kiev* had a more conventional carrier-like appearance, with a large island on the starboard side and an angled flight deck, but only the angled deck area was for flight operations. The deck space aft of the island was for aircraft parking, and the entire deck forward of the island was given over to one twin SA-N-3 surface-to-air, four twin SS-N-12 surface-to-surface, and one twin SUW-N-1 anti-submarine missile launchers, one twin 76mm gun mount, and two RBU-6000 anti-submarine rocket launchers.

Although there were seven landing spots on the flight deck, there were no catapults or arresting wires. The aircraft complement included 13 Forger A/B V/STOL aircraft and 19 Hormone A/B or Helix A helicopters.

The *Kiev*s were built for submarine protection and naval command and control. Soviet strategy called for the four vessels to serve as command ships for task forces blocking the choke points of the Greenland–Iceland–United Kingdom (GIUK) gap and the La Perouse Straits in the Pacific. These task forces would prevent allied submarines from entering the Arctic Sea and Sea of Okhotsk bastions where *Delta* and *Typhoon* class ballistic missile submarines would hide.

The *Kiev*s carried a mixed air group. The Hormones and Helixes provided an airborne ASW capability against Western submarines and over-the-horizon targeting capabilities for Soviet cruise submarines and the *Kiev*'s own SS-N-12s. The Forgers were for close-range air strikes against hostile ships. They could also provide combat air patrol against the slow maritime patrol aircraft that would normally track the *Kiev*s.

During the late 1970s the US Navy began placing more emphasis on a policy of forward operations during any major war. The massive naval air strike thrusts implicit in the US strategy would have required more sea-based defences than the *Kiev*s could provide. In 1979–80 the Soviets began design work on a successor to the *Kiev* class. The new carriers would be optimized for conventional fixed-wing aircraft, rather than the helicopters and V/STOL jets the *Kiev*s were designed to accommodate.

The first Soviet large-deck carrier was completed in 1990. Despite being intended for conventional aircraft, she has no catapults, instead launching them up a 10½-degree ski-jump forward. The ship has fallen foul of the cataclysmic political changes that destroyed the Soviet Union, a fate symbolised by the four different names attributed to her in her short life. This photograph was taken in December 1991 when she had become the Admiral Kuznetsov. *(MoD, Crown Copyright)*

Protection of the northern bastions was only part of the reason for the construction of the *Kuznetsov* class. At the same time as the US Navy was beginning to emphasise forward strikes during a war, it was shrinking. The previous standard of fifteen attack carriers was reduced to twelve, and it looked for a time during the late 1970s as though the number of active carriers might shrink further because of overhauls and service life modernisations.

The Soviet Union had already seen the impact US carriers had on overseas political events, and Soviet planners began considering the influence they could wield overseas if they had their own aircraft carriers for power projection. The keel for the first carrier was laid down in January 1983. By the time the ship was commissioned, in 1990, she had gone through four name changes, from *Leonid Brezhnev* to *Tbilisi* to *Admiral Gorshkov* to *Admiral Kuznetsov*.

The future of aircraft carriers

The aircraft carrier has a definite place in the future of naval warfare. No other warship has shown the versatility of the carrier to perform in a variety of scenarios ranging from mere offshore presence to long range power projection. Every time critics have written the obituary of the carrier, some crisis, such as the Korean War, the Vietnam War, the Rhodesian sanctions, the Falklands conflict, or the Persian Gulf war has taken place, where carriers formed the most immediate, and sometimes the only, form of power available.

But the heyday of the carrier may have passed, simply because of the extremely high cost of new construction. Only the US Navy appears committed to building large-deck carriers, and there has been some opposition to building the ninth *Nimitz* class hull, which is to be ordered in Fiscal Year 1995. France is committed to a smaller version of the large-deck carrier, but funds for a second *Charles de Gaulle* might not be forthcoming. The same case holds true in Britain, where plans to build a small carrier could be scrapped.

The issue is different with regards to small 'Harrier Carriers'. Italy and Spain appear committed to building a second V/STOL carrier each, and there has been intense speculation since 1986 that Japan will build several such vessels.

David Steigman

Aircraft Carriers: Typical Vessels, since 1945

Class	Nationality	Displacement normal/ full load (tons)	Dimensions overall (breadth is flight deck) (feet-inches) (metres)	Armament	Machinery/ Speed (kts)	Launch/ Conversion dates	Numbers built
ARK ROYAL	British	43,340/53,060	803-8 × 164-5 × 36-0 245.0 × 50.0 × 11.0	12-4.5in, 46-40mm, 50 aircraft	ST/31	1946–50	2
ESSEX (SCB-125)	American	30,580/43,060	894-5 × 166-9 × 30-3 272.7 × 50.9 × 9.2	4-5in, approx 60 aircraft	ST/29	(modernised 1954–55)	7
FORRESTAL	American	61,163/78,509	1039-0 × 250-0 × 33-9 316.8 × 76.2 × 10.3	8-5in, approx 90 aircraft	ST/33	1954–58	4
VICTORIOUS (rebuilt)	British	30,530/35,500	781-0 × 157-0 × 31-0 238.0 × 47.8 × 9.5	12-3in, 6-40mm, 36 aircraft	ST/31	(rebuilt 1950–57)	1
FOCH	French	22,000/32,780	870-0 × 168-0 × 28-0 265.0 × 51.2 × 8.6	8-100mm, 40 aircraft	ST/32	1957–60	2
MOSKVA (Project 1123)	Soviet	14,590/17,500	620-1 × 85-3 × 27-9 189.0 × 23.0 × 8.5	2 SA-N-3 launchers, 4-57mm, 1 SUW-N-1, 2 RBU-6000, 10 TT, 14 helicopters	ST/31	1964–66	2
NIMITZ	American	73,973/91,440	1088-0 × 257-5 × 36-7 331.7 × 78.5 × 11.2	3 Sea Sparrow SAM, approx 90 aircraft	N/30	1968–	8 (more projected)
KIEV (Project 1143)	Soviet	36,000/42,000	902-0 × 154-0 × 26-9 275.0 × 47.2 × 8.2	8 SS-N-12, 2 SA-N-3, 2 SA-N-4, 4-76mm, 8-30mm, 10 TT, 1 SUW-N-1, 2 RBU-6000, 31 aircraft	ST/32	1972–82	4
INVINCIBLE	British	16,860/20,600	677-0 × 115-0 × 24-0 206.6 × 35.0 × 7.3	1 Sea Dart SAM, 3 Goalkeeper CIWS, 18–20 aircraft	COGOG/28	1977–81	3
PRINCIPE DE ASTURIAS	Spanish	—/16,700	640-0 × 98-4 × 21-8 195.1 × 30.0 × 6.7	4 Meroka CIWS, 20 aircraft	GT/26.3	1982	1
GUISEPPE GARIBALDI	Italian	9369/13,240	591-1 × 99-9 × 22-0 180.2 × 30.4 × 6.7	8 Otomat SSM, 2 Albatross SAM, 6-40mm, 6 TT, 16 aircraft	COGAG/30	1983	1
ADMIRAL KUZNETZOV (Project 1143.5)	Soviet	60,000/67,000	984-0 × 124-7 (extreme 239-4) × 36-0 300.0 × 38.0 (73.0) × 11.0	16 SS-N-19 missiles, 18 SA-N-9 launchers, 8 CADS-N-1, 6-30mm Gatling, 2 RBU-12000, 18 fighters and 12 helicopters	ST/30	1985–88	2

Machinery abbreviations:
ST = steam turbine; COGAG = combined gas and gas (turbines); GT = gas turbines; COGOG = combined gas or gas (turbines); N= nuclear.

2

Major Surface Combatants

THE POSTWAR naval revolution broke down the fixed warship categories of the dreadnought era. The advent of truly three-dimensional naval warfare with the maturing of the aircraft and submarine into the equals of the surface ship in operational importance forced surface warships to develop a much broader range of capabilities than traditional anti-surface unit warfare (ASuW). Indeed, in the major Western navies the surface ship ceased to be the primary anti-surface unit platform, becoming instead a means of deploying anti-submarine warfare (ASW) and anti-air warfare (AAW) sensors, command and control capability and weapons in and around both carrier battle groups (the successors to the traditional battle squadrons of the past) and convoys of various types. This 'escort' role seemed to subordinate the role of the surface ship, but in reality it remained a major fighting platform as much at the centre of naval operations as it had ever been, both in the fight to gain command of the sea and to exercise that command once it was obtained.

In 1945 fleets were still made up of clearly identifiable categories of surface warships: cruisers of 6000 to 17,000 tons standard displacement armed with 6in or 8in guns which defined them as 'light' or 'heavy'; destroyers in the 1500- to 2400-ton range with maximum speeds of over 30kts; and slower vessels of around 1000 tons built for mercantile escort duties and called variously 'frigates', 'escort destroyers', 'destroyer escorts', 'sloops' or 'corvettes'. The Royal Navy adopted the term frigate as a generic category to cover all these latter escort types in 1948. Already in 1945 the destroyer armaments were beginning to em-phasise AAW and ASW, but destroyers proper still retained powerful armaments of guns in the 5in range and traditional torpedoes. The escort vessels had AAW and ASW armaments as they were not intended for fleet action.

The faster submarine, first diesel-electric and then nuclear-powered, mandated higher speeds for vessels designed to cope with it. The frigate thus had to acquire the speed of the destroyer, breaking down a major distinction between the two types. The threat of the jet aircraft meant that anti-air warfare systems and C³I (command, control, communications and intelligence; C⁴I with the important addition of computers) increased in bulk and sophistication. Frigates and destroyers thus also began to acquire the same kinds of weapons, sensors and command spaces. These pressures forced the frigate to overlap with the destroyer in size, speed and performance. Similarly, the challenge of the air and subsurface threats combined with the speed and range requirements of fast carrier operations forced the fleet destroyer to take on the size of the previous light cruiser, although its AAW/ASW weapons fit united it with the smaller 'frigate'/'destroyer'. As the large destroyer came to rival it in size, the cruiser became less necessary for presence roles, while the aircraft took over its anti-surface unit and shore bombardment tasks. The cruiser still proved useful as a flagship for senior commanders, but even here the requirements of modern command and control eroded its directly combatant capability. It also began to devote its space to be an operating platform for the large ASW helicopter, but this meant it was soon merging with the aircraft carrier and being designated as such. Eventually the largest and most capable destroyers were simply redesignated cruisers as a mark of their new size and status. Thus, by the 1990s, a new common type of modern surface combatant had appeared in the size range 1000 to 10,000 tons called 'cruiser', 'destroyer' or 'frigate' according to national tradition but all exhibiting a similar mix of capabilities and characteristics to a greater or lesser degree.

Considered a major surface threat by Western navies in the 1950s, the big Soviet cruisers of the Sverdlov class *were the largest manifestations of Stalin's over-ambitious naval programme – even larger ships were laid down, but none was actually completed. The name ship of the class, seen here, visited Spithead for the Coronation Review of 1953, allowing Western observers their first close inspection of the class. (CMP)*

Gun-armed cruisers of the traditional kind were completed by some Western navies after 1945, but they mostly employed hulls laid down during, or even before the war, like the Dutch De Zeven Provincien, *seen in the foreground of this 1957 photograph. The way forward is represented by the* USS Canberra *(CAG-2) beyond, one of the US Navy's prototype missile cruisers, which were converted from wartime* Baltimore *class ships. The Dutch ship was herself later converted to fire the Terrier SAM system proven aboard* Canberra *and her sister* Boston. *(USN)*

The eclipse of the traditional cruiser

In the two decades after 1945 the traditional cruiser had something of an 'Indian Summer'. In some ways it had merged with and supplanted the battleship as the main surface unit for flagship, presence and carrier screening duties, as well as providing a potent means of short range surface bombardment if strike aircraft were not available.

The battleship did not disappear immediately. Argentina, Brazil, Chile and Turkey retained for a time pre-First World War capital ships, but these were at best semi-operational historical relics rather than combatant warships. Italy kept two much-rebuilt battleships of similar vintage into the 1950s for use as training ships, but the only truly modern battleships were in the fleets of the United States, Britain and France. They were expensive in manpower terms and even their use was limited largely to training. The Americans, however, also used battleships for shore bombardment in both Korea and Vietnam and retained in reserve the four fast *Iowas* built for operations with fast carriers, and thus latter-day battlecruisers rather than battleships. They thus proved suitable for recommissioning in the 1980s, when surface-to-surface missiles allowed a new longer reach capability to be added to that of their big guns, but they were decommissioned again when financial pressures struck once more in the 1990s. Plans to modernise them were always abandoned as not cost-effective; indeed part of their attraction was the robustness of their old fashioned armoured design, at least part of which would have been lost with the addition of large unprotected spaces on the upperworks. British plans to build new battleships hardly outlasted the war. Only the Soviet Union, which retained two old dreadnoughts in the Baltic and an Italian war trophy in the Black Sea, began a programme of new construction, laying down at least two new 40,000-ton gun- and

missile-armed battlecruisers in 1951–55, but these were cancelled later in the decade as official policy turned against large surface ships.

This left the cruiser as the most powerful traditional surface ship. Ships of prewar or wartime construction remained in commission in the major navies and were sold to smaller powers. Those cruisers that were building in Western European yards were completed, although their armaments now reflected the fact that the threat from the air was as serious as that from the surface. The two Dutch *De Ruyters* completed in 1953 had eight dual-purpose 6in guns of new design while the French *De Grasse* and *Colbert* were armed with a heavy battery of eight twin 5in rapid firing guns, a calibre adopted to utilise American ammunition. The British could not afford to proceed with postwar plans for new gun-armed cruisers but, after some soul searching, the last three wartime *Tigers* were completed in the 1950s with the latest fully automatic 6in and 3in guns. Plans to rearm other cruisers on similar lines fell through both on grounds of cost and the revised strategic emphasis on shore bombardment in areas of limited threat.

The USA did not cancel all its wartime programmes in 1945, and four new classes of traditional cruiser were commissioned between 1946 and 1949. The three huge 17,200-ton *Des Moines* class were in many ways small battleships, of the same displacement as the original *Dreadnought* of half a century earlier. Their nine fully automatic 8in guns gave enormous surface firepower, while a heavy battery of 5in and 3in guns gave equally formidable AA protection. Like their smaller cousins they served as fleet flagships, training ships and shore bombardment platforms. The *Oregon City* and *Fargo* classes were versions of the *Baltimore* and *Cleveland* classes of standard wartime heavy and light cruiser respectively, with better AA arrange-

ments, while the two *Worcesters* were large AA cruisers with automatic 6in and 3in weapons. None of these ships outlived the 1950s in commission in original form. Indeed, by the end of 1963 only two old-style gun-armed cruisers remained in service with the USN.

One reason for Western navies retaining some traditional ASuW capability was the impressive Soviet cruiser programme. The Soviet navy also completed cruisers still on the stocks after the war, and acquired a cruiser from both defeated Italy and Germany. Then in 1949 the Soviet navy began the first of no fewer than twenty-four *Sverdlov* class ships, large 16,000-ton vessels armed with twelve 6in guns and a powerful AA battery of 3.9in and 37mm weapons. The capacity of contemporary aircraft to sink these ships was a matter of some dispute, especially in the Royal Navy, which used the *Sverdlov* threat to justify the retention of heavy guns in the 1950s as well as the maintenance of its fleet carriers and the development of a dedicated strike capability for them. The NA39 Buccaneer was developed specifically as a 'Sverdlov killer'. Soviet assessments of the *Sverdlovs*' utility were less sanguine and Khrushchev cancelled the programme with only fourteen ships completed, the last one in 1955. These survived into the 1980s, although, like their Western counterparts, several were modified into guided missile or command ships.

The West was virtually unaware of an even more impressive, though more abortive, Soviet surface warship programme. Details have only recently emerged, so they are given here more fully than for other postwar surface combatants. Stalin ordered work on the prewar battleship design, Project 23, continued as Project 23NU. His 1944 ten-year naval plan (1946–55) envisaged building eight battleships, as well as battlecruisers and lesser cruisers. The battleship was abandoned in 1952. Stalin was far more inter-

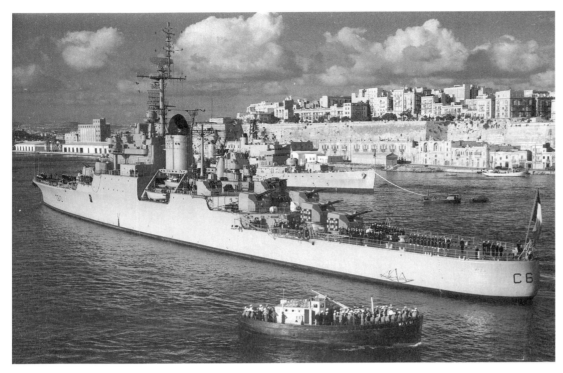

The French De Grasse *with the British* Tiger, *moored in Grand Harbour, Malta, in November 1961. They present different approaches to the last generation of gun-armed cruisers: the French ship carries a large number of guns (sixteen 5in) and is optimised for anti-aircraft duties, while the British ship – with only four 6in and six 3in – relies on the very high rate of fire (theoretically) from the advanced mountings; the 6in guns were designed with shore bombardment and ASuW in mind. (CMP)*

The project was cancelled 23 April 1953 (Stalin having died on 5 March). All three hulls were scrapped, except for a hull section retained to test the planned protective arrangements, including underwater protection. They apparently proved adequate.

Meanwhile a parallel Project 82R was developed: land-attack surface-to-surface missiles, forerunners of the later SS-N-3 Shaddock, were added to the earlier design. One ship, *Kronstadt*, was laid down in 1950 and launched in May 1955, but it was cancelled in October. This, rather than the *Sverdlov*s, is almost certainly the class of very expensive cruisers Khrushchev was so proud of having killed off. He wrote that he had allowed the navy to build four smaller ones, the *Kynda*s, and the reference is understandable because the *Kynda*s were armed with the weapon planned for Project 82R. The launched hull was broken up in 1957–59, probably after parts had been used for weapon tests, including attacks by the first Soviet anti-ship missile, SS-N-1.

In effect, quadruple SS-N-3 launchers were inserted between 'B' turret and the forward superstructure, and between 'X' turret and the after superstructure. Hangars for reloads (eight per launcher) were worked into the superstructure; missiles were transferred by monorail from hangar to launch tube. Otherwise, armament matched that of Project 82, although the 45mm guns may have been replaced by 57s. The masts were replaced by towers similar to those later placed on board the *Kynda*s, carrying Scoop Pair radars for SS-N-3 guidance.

ested in large cruisers. Wartime experience may well have convinced him that a few German capital ships devoted to commerce raiding concentrated vast Allied naval forces on relatively useless duties. Similar ships in Soviet hands would presumably make it much less likely that the Western navies would conduct the sort of amphibious operations he feared.

The prewar 12in gun heavy cruiser, Project 69, was substantially revised as Project 82. Compared with the prewar design, it had thicker side armour (330mm rather than 260mm, in each case with a 90mm deck and a 30mm splinter deck). The most striking new feature was a 12in gun designed to fire nine rounds per minute, with an ammunition capacity (more than 400 rounds per gun, twice that in Project 69) to match. It elevated to 50 degrees and required a substantially larger turret. The secondary battery, which in the prewar version was a mixture of single-purpose 5.1in guns and heavy 3.9in anti-aircraft, was twelve dual-purpose 5.1in in twin turrets of the type later adopted for *Kotlin* class (Project 56) destroyers (all on the main deck: one abeam the bridge, one forward of amidships, one abeam the after superstructure on each side). There were also twenty-four 3in

anti-aircraft guns in twin enclosed mounts (as later installed on board many Soviet warships: one alongside the bridge, three amidships, and two aft on each side); and sixteen quadruple 45mm guns (two forward of the bridge, one on each side alongside the bridge, one alongside each of the two funnels, two on each side alongside the after superstructure, one on each side abaft the aft superstructure, and two on the stern, US-style). The design could be described as a *Sverdlov* class cruiser crossed with the German *Scharnhorst*, using the new sharply raked stem introduced in the *Riga* and *Kotlin* classes. Three ships were ordered in 1951: *Stalingrad* at Nikolayev, *Moskva* in Leningrad, and a third at Molotovsk, using components from Leningrad. By the spring of 1953 the hull, main machinery, and basic armour of the lead ship (*Stalingrad*) were complete; launch was scheduled for 7 November 1953 (Revolution Day). Work on such subcomponents as the guns was well along.

One of the few visible by-products of Stalin's naval plans, cancelled by Khrushchev, was the Kynda *class, which was built as a sop to the navy instead of a class of very large Project 82R ships. The design is dominated by the two quadruple tubular launchers of the SS-N-3 Shaddock SSM originally intended as land-attack weapons for the larger ship. (CMP)*

Latin American navies, with their needs for status symbols and simple bombardment tasks, provided a ready market for redundant cruisers. The United States, United Kingdom, Netherlands and Sweden all exploited it between the early 1950s and the 1970s, to the benefit of Argentina (which retained older ships also), Brazil, Chile and Peru. The Swedish ships were the two 8200-ton *Tre Kronor*s built in the mid 1940s and armed with a triple 6in mount forward and two twins aft. These were automatic weapons with full dual AAW/ASuW capability. One of these cruisers was scrapped in the 1960s and the other sold to Chile in 1971. An older and smaller Swedish cruiser, *Gotland*, was used for training until 1960.

Cruisers had also traditionally been the largest individual units of the British Commonwealth navies and this continued after the war, with Australia, Canada and New Zealand all retaining British type cruisers as command, presence, anti-surface unit warfare, shore bombardment and – most important of all – as training assets. For the training role the large manpower demands of the old cruiser were a positive advantage. Australia laid up two of her three old and expensive-to-maintain ships in 1947–48. She kept HMAS *Australia* running until 1954, the last of her line of British heavy cruisers, and scrapped her, together with her sister *Shropshire*, the following year. The smaller mid-1930s vintage *Hobart* was to be kept as a more economical training ship, but the refit was suspended in 1956 and she spent the rest of her life in reserve before being scrapped in the early 1960s. Canada kept one wartime-built 6in cruiser on each coast, primarily as training ships, until 1960–61. In 1946 New Zealand replaced her wartime *Leander* class ships with two 6000-ton modified *Dido*s with their dual-purpose armament. One was replaced in 1954 by a ship with modernised fire control of the same class, *Royalist*, that had become superfluous to Britain's reduced requirements. She was kept in service until 1966, five years after her remaining unmodernised sister, *Black Prince*, was scrapped.

The larger New Commonwealth navies followed a similar pattern. Indeed, India took over one of the prewar New Zealand cruisers, the famous *Achilles*, and ran her on (periodically) as the *Delhi* until as late as 1977. She was replaced as fleet flagship in 1957 by a more modern *Colony* class ship obtained from Britain, the *Mysore*, that replaced *Delhi* as training ship in 1978 before paying off finally in 1981. Pakistan operated the other modernised modified *Dido* as the *Babur* from 1957 to 1982 when she was reduced to a harbour training hulk.

The Soviet Union only supplied one cruiser to a client, the *Sverdlov* class *Ordzhonikidze* to Indonesia in 1962 as the *Irian*. This was part of the abortive Soviet attempt to build up Sukarno's Indonesia as a major regional power, but a large cruiser was beyond Indonesia's capacity to maintain or operate, especially after the fall of Sukarno and the break with the USSR. She was usually non-operational and was finally disposed of in 1972. A projected second ship mercifully never appeared.

In the Mediterranean, Italy kept three prewar light cruisers throughout the 1950s, one as a training ship, the other two as operational units in the command, ASuW and limited AAW roles. The latter received improved AAW weapons and sensors at a cost in speed, an interesting comment on changing operational requirements. One was taken in hand in 1957 for modernisation as a guided-missile ship (see below) and the other two were scrapped in the

POSTWAR CRUISER CONVERSIONS

First date is original completion; tonnage is full load; scale is 1/1500.

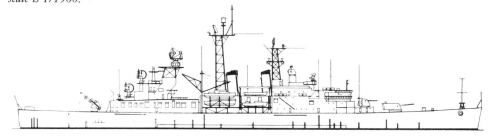

Little Rock, *USA, 1945, 15,150t, missile/command cruiser conversion 1960.*

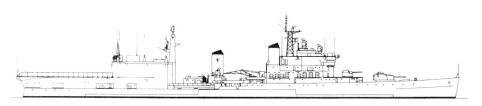

Blake, *Great Britain, 1961, 11,700t, helicopter cruiser conversion 1969.*

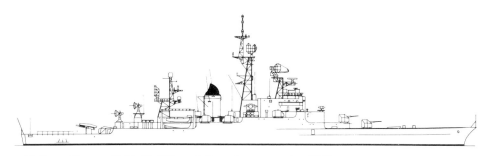

Colbert, *France, 1959, 11,300t, missile cruiser conversion 1972.*

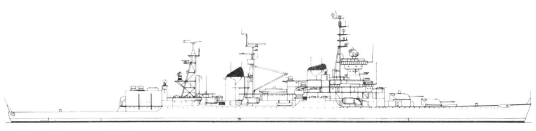

Admiral Seniavin, *USSR, 1953, 17,200t, command cruiser conversion 1972.*

1960s. Greece obtained an Italian light cruiser as reparations and operated her as the fleet flagship *Helle* from 1951 to 1964. She replaced the ancient armoured cruiser *Averoff* but proved difficult to man, given her requirement for large numbers of technicians, and was more a status symbol than anything else. Spain, cut off from the modern naval world, also retained traditional cruisers until as late as 1975 when the old heavy cruiser *Canarias* was deemed to be of no further use, even as a roomy status symbol. She had been modernised with modern command spaces, but her main armament of eight 8in guns, backed up by very limited AAW capability, was of only marginal fighting value; US funded modernisation with missiles had been considered but was deemed not to be cost-effective.

The first guided-missile cruisers

Guided missiles were required for the engagement at long range and high altitude of fast, large jet aircraft equipped with long range weapons. These early surface-to-air missiles (SAMs) were bulky in themselves and required volume and topweight-intensive electronics suites. A stable platform was also required for missile guidance and fighter direction. Cruiser hulls seemed the readiest source of both volume and stability and had enough space to be good flagships as well as screening assets. The United States led the way in 1952 with the conversion of the two *Baltimore* class heavy cruisers *Boston* and *Canberra*. Commissioned in 1955–56, these retained two-thirds of their gun armament but were heavily modified amidships and aft to carry 144 Terrier 1 surface-to-air missiles and two twin launchers. The operational capability of Terrier 1 was always highly dubious, and these ships ended their days as fire support vessels off Vietnam in 1968–69.

In order to provide more fleet escort vessels as rapidly as possible, light cruisers of the *Cleveland* class were next taken in hand for missile conversions with either the long range Talos or improved medium range Terrier 2. Two *Galveston*s retained two 6in turrets, but the four *Little Rock*s were modified as fleet flagships with an enlarged bridge structure and only one re-

maining 6in mount. These latter were more useful vessels and lasted until the 1970s. The light cruiser conversions were also later fitted with sonar to provide ASW capability in conjunction with accompanying destroyers.

So far, missile cruisers had retained some guns to provide shore bombardment and ASuW capability. By the end of the 1950s, however, confidence in the missiles had improved and the perceived requirement was for the maximum rate of missile fire. It was planned, therefore, to give the heavy cruisers of the *Baltimore* and *Oregon City* classes complete rebuilds into missile-only 'double-ended' fleet escorts/flagships. Three were completed in 1962–64 with a Talos launcher at each end, Tartar short range launchers on each beam, and an ASROC ASW missile system amidships. When it became clear that missile performance was still equivocal, two single 5in gun mounts were added as afterthoughts. The *Albany* class programme was curtailed on grounds of economy, as smaller destroyer-based ships could give an adequate if not equivalent capability at less cost. The last, *Albany* herself, decommissioned in 1980.

The Royal Navy considered missile conversions of existing ships but settled on a new cruiser design to carry the bulky Seaslug surface-to-air missile. Both single- and double-ended concepts were considered, but neither a surface-to-surface version of the missile nor a nuclear-armed version of the SAM offered sufficient certainty of countering the *Sverdlov*. The design was therefore finalised with two automatic 6in twins forward and a twin Seaslug launcher aft. A large three-dimensional 984 radar and automated CDS (Comprehensive Display System) provided a fully automated aircraft direction capability for the huge 18,400-ton monsters. It was hoped to build at least three of these ships in the early 1960s, but the programme was too expensive and was cancelled in 1957. Like the Americans, the British decided

to rely on smaller destroyer-based ships to provide fleet escort and presence assets at a fraction of the cost. It must be said, however, that the capability of these smaller ships as fully automated AAW vessels did not approach that of the larger cruisers for some time. After the abandonment of the large guided-missile ship, British cruiser design then turned to helicopter carrying ASW escorts for carriers.

The French, Dutch and Italian navies carried out missile conversions on one of their postwar cruisers to enhance their role as task force escorts. As noted above, the Italians modernised the prewar light cruiser *Giuseppe Garibaldi* in 1957–62 with Terrier and even tubes for Polaris intermediate-range ballistic missiles (presumably with a possible multilateral Nato force in mind; US missile cruisers of the time were designed for similar provision although tubes were never actually fitted). The Dutch programme was originally to equip both of their *De Ruyter*s with Terrier as escort squadron leaders in areas of high air threat, but only one conversion could be afforded. *De Zeven Provincien* was fitted with a twin launcher aft at the beginning of the 1960s. Ten years later *Colbert* received the French Masurca system in a similar single-ended configuration and served for two decades subsequently as Mediterranean Fleet flagship.

In the late 1950s, in order to improve the air defence capability of the *Sverdlov* and to test SAMs at sea, the Soviet navy carried out a conversion on one ship, *Dzerzhinski*. she was fitted with a version of the SA-2 Guideline system developed for land-based use. This suffered serious problems when fired at sea and no other ships were converted.

Command cruisers

War experience proved to the US Navy that there was a requirement for a fast ship of cruiser performance given over wholly to higher com-

uss Albany *in 1977. The ultimate in missile cruiser conversions were the three ships of this class. They were 'double-ended', with a long range twin Talos SAM system fore and aft and twin launchers for the short range Tartar each side of the bridge; ASROC ASW missiles were fitted amidships, and as completed they carried no guns whatever, although two 5in were added later, reputedly after the personal intervention of President Kennedy.* (L & L van Ginderen)

The command cruiser USS Northampton as completed in 1953. The cruiser origin of the hull is evident, but the defensive armament is reduced to that of a destroyer, the real capabilities of the ship being expressed in the large radar and electronics masts, aerials and antennas. (L & L van Ginderen)

mand functions. The original intention was to provide an amphibious flagship of greater survivability, but the priority shifted to carrier flag duties as it was considered that even the new super carriers would not have space for adequate flag and AAW task force control arrangements. The incomplete heavy cruiser *Northampton* of the *Oregon City* class was therefore completed in 1953 as a Task Force Command Ship (CLC) with a comprehensive radar fit (including the large SPS-2) and a huge combat information centre. The ship was an excellent if extreme illustration of the role of the modern surface warship as a control station for other weapons platforms, rather than as a weapons platform in her own right. Armament was limited to destroyer type 5in and 3in guns for self-defence.

Her AAW role proved less important, as the angled deck allowed more command spaces to be fitted into the carriers themselves. It was also found that adequate fleet command facilities could be fitted into the guided-missile cruisers. A new role beckoned for *Northampton*, however, as a mobile national command post in case of nuclear attack. She was redesignated command ship (CC) in 1961 and two light carriers were also converted as CCs -2 and -3. This was part of the increasing overlap between the 'cruiser' and 'light carrier' that would be reflected in the evolution of the helicopter-carrying command cruiser later in the decade. *Northampton* decommissioned in 1970, by which time two new LPH-based command ships were under con-

struction as fleet and amphibious force flagships. A 1950s plan to build a larger fast command ship based on the incomplete hull of the 12in gun 'large cruiser' *Hawaii* was abandoned in 1954 on grounds of cost.

The Soviets had by then acquired a requirement for mobile back-up command posts for their operationally dispersed but centrally controlled fleet operations, and in 1972 two *Sverdlov*s emerged from extensive conversions into command cruisers with one or both after turrets removed. Other *Sverdlov*s were also given upgraded command arrangements that involved less ship impact.

DLs and DLGs – the postwar Western fleet escort

The problem with all these missile cruisers was their size and uneconomically large crews. The best long-term solution to the problem of the battle group escort (and indeed to the Soviet anti-battle group surface combatant) was to enlarge the destroyer into a new form of light cruiser. This process marked perhaps the most important new departure in postwar surface warship development.

In 1951 the US Navy invented a new cate-

gory 'DL' to cover its large destroyer type ships that were being built for the task force escort role. DL stood for Destroyer Leader but, as the ships did not actually act as flotilla leaders, 'DLs' were re-rated as 'frigates' in 1955. This was even more confusing, however, given the British coining of the term 'frigate' for the sub-destroyer category. The latter use was the one more generally accepted and it eventually won the day, even in the USN, but the Americans were, in fact, using the term more aptly. The old sailing frigates had evolved into the cruisers of the age of steam and the new ships were the cruisers of the next generation.

The first DL, USS *Norfolk*, was not really part of the series. She was a 'Hunter Killer Light Cruiser' (CLK), laid down as the perfect answer to the newly developed fast battery drive submarine. High speed submarine hunting in heavy seas required a vessel of light cruiser dimensions and *Norfolk* displaced 5000 tons. She carried an advanced sonar fit and was equipped with homing torpedoes and Weapon Alfa ASW rocket launchers. Gun armament comprised four twin 3in guns for AA protection. She was far too expensive for a future Battle of the Atlantic, although she could have been used as a task force escort if required. In fact she spent her time as a trials ship, and plans for conversion to a missile equipped DLG came to nothing. A sister-ship was cancelled.

The first DLs proper were the four 3642-ton *Mitscher*-class vessels completed in 1953–54. Built specially for carrier battle group work, with sufficient size to sustain high speeds in rough weather, they looked under-armed with only two dual-purpose 5in single automatic mountings and two twin 3in, but their main 'armament' comprised a comprehensive radar fit and a large Combat Information Centre (CIC) that made them efficient fighter control platforms. In effect, their main armament was the aircraft of the carrier they screened. To protect their charges from submarines they had powerful sonar, torpedoes and Weapon Alfa. The next class of DLs, commissioned in 1959–61, were larger, missile-armed DLGs of the *Farragut* class which carried a Terrier installation aft and a 5in gun and ASROC ASW missile system forward. Originally conceived as gun-armed vessels with twice the firepower of a *Mitscher* and reduced ASW capability, their final

The first purpose-designed missile-armed escorts for anti-aircraft screening of fast task forces were the ten ships of the Farragut class (this is Dewey in 1983 after the class had been downgraded from DLG to DDG in 1975). ASW was given greater priority during the design stage and the ships were completed with an ASROC box launcher forward. (L & L van Ginderen)

cruiser, classified as such. USS *Long Beach*, armed with a mixed battery of Talos and Terrier SAMs on a displacement of over 15,000 tons, was commissioned in 1961, the first nuclear-powered surface warship in the world. Her size had been accepted to get a nuclear surface ship to sea as soon as possible, but a smaller DLGN proper was already under construction using specially designed D2G destroyer reactors. Two of these in a hull designed as the smallest capable of maintaining destroyer speed produced what was in effect a nuclear-powered *Leahy*. The 7250-ton USS *Bainbridge* commissioned in October 1962, to be followed by a nuclear-powered rearranged *Belknap*, the USS *Truxtun*, in 1967.

The same pressures that created the DL/DLG type in the world's largest navy worked on the other side of the Atlantic also. In 1949 the British Naval Staff drew up plans for a 5000-ton 'cruiser/destroyer' armed with new rapid-fire dual-purpose 5in guns that could both fight cruisers and act as a task force screen. The plan eventually died, as much as anything else because of problems developing the main armament, but there remained a requirement for a fast fleet escort that combined an AAW/ASW weapons fit with carrier speed and endurance. The demise of the missile cruiser was hastened by the discovery that Seaslug was compatible with such a vessel of moderate dimensions, and the final element in the mix was provision for an ASW helicopter to lessen pressure on the

AAW and ASW armament reflected the expected threat of the 1960s, both the fast strike aircraft and the nuclear-powered submarine that was a much greater problem for the carrier group than the fast battery submarine had been. A projected armament of traditional ASuW torpedoes was also abandoned.

The next step was the double-ended DLG which entered service as the *Leahy* class in 1962–64. With their two twin Terrier launchers they were meant to complement the heavy cruiser Talos conversions, but with only 25 per cent of the ship's company and over 5000 tons of presence they seemed a more cost-effective package in themselves. However, they had one major defect. A double-ended missile ship lacked flexibility against surface targets and was not an adequate general purpose substitute for the fleet destroyer. A new fleet destroyer was in fact under development, but it grew into a ship the same size as the DLG. It was decided therefore to modify the *Leahy* to give it destroyer flexibility, a 5in gun replacing the after Terrier launcher and the forward missile launcher doubling as an ASROC mounting. After nine

original *Leahy*s therefore, DLGs-26 to -34 were built to the modified *Belknap* design. The improved operational flexibility was achieved by increasing light displacement by less than 200 tons over that of the *Leahy*, although the number of Terriers was inevitably reduced: the *Leahy*s carried 40 Terriers for each launcher, the *Belknap*s only 60 missiles in all, up to a third of them ASROCs.

The DLG seemed the obvious candidate for nuclear power to complement nuclear-powered carriers, as it had been found that escort endurance was the key limiting factor in carrier battle group operations. A DLGN was first suggested in 1955 to go with the first nuclear carrier. At first the concept was an 8900-ton nuclear *Dewey*, but the ship soon grew into a fully fledged

The USS Long Beach *was the world's first nuclear-powered surface warship, and, like the* Albany *class conversions, was originally all-missile armed. The superstructure resembled no other ship afloat, except the contemporary nuclear carrier* Enterprise, *both being designed to carry the futuristic fixed-array SPS-32/33 radar system. In this 1979 view the Talos SAM system aft and its associated radars have been removed. (L & L van Ginderen)*

HMS Devonshire, *the first of eight 'DLG's, missile-armed fleet escorts with provision for operating an ASW helicopter. She is seen in May 1963 exercising with the carrier* Ark Royal, *in the screening role for which they were originally designed. The second batch of four ships were fitted with the ADAWS computerised action information system, for its day an advanced method of automating the compiling and co-ordinating of tactical data.* (CMP)

smaller British carriers' air groups. The result was the 'County' class of 6200-ton 'guided missile destroyers', the first of which, HMS *Devonshire*, commissioned at the end of 1962. The 'destroyer' name was chosen both to keep the size down and to lessen bureaucratic opposition to new 'cruisers'. The ships were generally known as 'DLGs' in the fleet. Eight were built in two batches, the last two commissioning in 1970. The option of fitting some of these ships with the 984/CDS package was considered, but this would have meant dispensing with the gun armament (two twin 4.5in mountings) which would have diminished the flexibility of the ships in limited war situations. The second batch of four ships, built between 1962 and 1970, were fitted with a computerised action information system (ADAWS) which, in combination with an improved version of the 965 long range radar, in part made up for the lack of 984/CDS (see below).

In mainland Europe the Franco-Italian naval rivalry in large destroyers had caused the evolution in Italy of a ship rather like the postwar DL, a 3700-ton cruiser/destroyer of the *Capitani Romani* class. Two were retained by Italy after the war as 'scouts' and later 'destroyer leaders', and two passed to France as '*escorteurs d'escadre*'. They were rearmed as modern DLs with new

AAW and ASW systems. During the 1960s the French navy built two fully fledged DLGs, rated '*frégates*' like their American counterparts. Over 5000 tons in displacement, the *Suffrens* were striking in appearance, with SAMs aft, ASW missile amidships, a prominent air search radar and light guns forward. Three ships were originally projected, with more to follow, but only two could be afforded given France's diversion of scarce defence funds into her nuclear programme.

The advent of computerised Action Information Organisations

Mechanical analogue computers had long been in warships as aids to solving complex fire control problems both in ASuW and AAW. They were introduced in ASW fire control systems also as the solutions became more difficult and time-sensitive. The coming of the high-speed aircraft greatly complicated the AAW control problem and the British led the way in developing a mechanised, electronic solution, the combination of 984 radar and Comprehensive Display System (CDS) in combination with threat evaluation and weapon assignment analogue electronic computers. This system was considered for both the cruiser/destroyer and the large missile cruiser, but in the end was only deployed in carriers.

The Americans were kept fully informed of British ideas – they were even passed a prototype – and began development of their own Naval Tactical Data System (NTDS). This began in 1955 and from the start it was intended to produce a means not only of compiling a single ship picture, but of distributing this

throughout a force using the British idea of digital plot transmission using data links. In order to limit space requirements and to allow maximum development potential it was decided to use standard programmable solid-state computers. A Link II joint development of the original British Link I was adopted, soon corrupted to 'Link Eleven'. Although the system was intended to deal with a comprehensive tactical picture, AAW ships got priority and the system was tested in the DLGs *King* and *Mahan* in 1961–62. The cruiser *Long Beach* was completed with NTDS, and from 1966 new DLGs were commissioned with the system that was retrofitted into earlier DLGs. The last of the converted *Albany* class cruisers, *Chicago*, received an early variant on commissioning in 1964 and she and her sister *Albany* later received the full system.

The British developed their own digital computer-based AIO system, ADAWS (Action Data Automated Weapon System), for their second batch of DLGs. This was a development of the ADA system first deployed in the carrier *Eagle* but extended to cover ASW and EW inputs. The same year as ADAWS came into service, 1966, development began of a simpler Computer Assisted Action Information System (CAAIS) for primarily ASW escorts. France also developed computerised AIO for her pair of DLGs and the cruiser *Colbert*, SENIT (*Systeme d'Exploitation Naval des Informations Tactiques*). As these and similar systems were deployed over the following decades, naval warfare became increasing interactive and extensive, with each unit part of an electronically connected network. This was a trend as crucially significant as it was invisible and subtle.

From destroyer to DDG

By the end of their careers some of the ships built as DLs and DLGs were being redesignated 'destroyer', a reflection of the growth in size of the classical destroyer as it responded to the increased requirements of air defence and ASW and converted itself into a fast fleet escort, smaller and cheaper than the first rate DL/DLG. The destroyer emerged from the Second World War as a large +2500-ton vessel armed with about six dual-purpose medium guns, a light AA battery, ten 21in torpedo tubes and depth charges. An important additional role had become that of radar picket and aircraft control, a distant early warning and aircraft direction platform directing aircraft, primarily fighters. The latter were effectively the ships' main armament, and putting in the extra radar meant reduced or deleted torpedo armament. At first radar pickets in the USN retained the DD classification, but in 1949 they became DDRs. Further conversions of American wartime destroyers to the DDR role took place in the early 1950s.

The trend in size was upward. Britain had ended the war with two types of fleet destroyer, a 1700-ton 'C' class and a large 2500-ton 'Battle' with heavier armament and longer range, designed with Pacific operations in mind. The difference in size was a reflection of building yard capacity as well as cost, and during the war both the large and small designs had been recast to reflect wartime lessons on ship layout. Engineering spaces were split to minimise damage and appearance made more gaunt to minimise visual signature and optimise gun arcs. Three types of destroyer were planned to the new layout, a fleet ASW escort, a small fleet destroyer and a large 'super Battle'. The first and last of these survived the 1945 cuts in the building programmes as the 'Weapon' and Daring classes respectively.

The eight 2830-ton Darings appeared to the resource-hungry postwar Royal Navy as eco-nomical surface combatants that could stand in for light cruisers if required. Equipped with the Squid ahead-throwing ASW weapon, but otherwise armed with three twin 4.5in mountings, Bofors AA guns and ten 21in torpedo tubes, they were classified as 'Daring type ships' and run like cruisers. The ships were cramped and extra space was soon required to provide adequate accommodation to postwar standards for the large ships' companies of about 300 men. First the after torpedo tubes were deleted and then the other set in the last four (fitted with AC electrical systems rather than DC in the older group) in order to provide a weight margin for the Seacat point-defence missile – although in the end only one ship was so fitted. The Darings proved too small to be worth fully modernising, however, and had all been decommissioned by the end of 1969.

Three more Darings were completed in the 1950s for the Royal Australian Navy with more advanced Mk 10 ASW mortars; one British ship was passed on to the RAN to replace an accidental loss and two were eventually sold to Peru. The Australians had also built two 'Battles', again to a slightly modified design. Three British 'Battles' were exported, two in 1957 to Pakistan and one as late as 1967 to Iran. The latter's three-year modernisation included Seacat point-defence SAMs, improved sensors and command spaces and deletion of the torpedo tubes. She acquired surface-to-surface missiles in the late 1970s.

Older classes of British destroyer were also given significant modernisation postwar. From 1956 all but one of the eight ships of the 'Ca' flotilla of the 'C' class, which had spent the first postwar decade in reserve, exchanged torpedo tubes for more modern Squid ASW systems and improved fire control in order to improve their capacity as three-dimensional escorts. The eighth ship became a training vessel. At the same time unmodernised 'C's were sold to Pakistan. Four had also been supplied to Norway at the end of the war as the Bergen class. Four of the surviving 'M' class fleet destroyers were transferred from British reserve (where they had been earmarked for radar picket conversion) to Turkey in 1958–59. They were fitted with Squid but still carried a set of 21in torpedo tubes in addition to three twin 4.7in dual-purpose mountings.

The 'Weapon' class destroyers with their 4in guns, Squid ASW mortars and good sonar fit (in Scorpion the prototype postwar sonar, 160X) were for a time the only effective ASW fast escorts in the Royal Navy. The advent of fast frigates (see below) released them from this role and all four were converted in 1958–9 instead of the 'M's as fast radar pickets but with a good additional ASW capability also. Unfortunately the hull proved too small for adequate air control and plotting facilities, and four 'Battles' were converted to supplement and eventually replace them in the early 1960s. The extra 500 tons of the larger ships provided a crucial additional margin.

The French also learned that a fast hull in the classical destroyer class was just too small for a full general-purpose capability. No fewer than eighteen 'escorteurs d'escadre' were built from 1951 to 1962 to what was effectively the same 2750-ton design. The original T 47 Surcouf class were designed primarily as AAW escorts for carriers with some ASW and ASuW capability. Main ar-

The French T 47 type 'escorteur d'escadre' Chevalier Paul, as completed, in June 1957. The armament demonstrates an anti-aircraft bias, but they carried twelve torpedo tubes, half for ASW torpedoes and half which could fire either ASW or ASuW torpedoes. (USN)

mament comprised three twin 5in dual-purpose mountings backed up by three twin 57mm automatic AA mounts. A set of three 21in dual-purpose ASW/ASuW long torpedo tubes was carried on each beam aft and three short 21in ASW torpedo tubes on each beam amidships. In the early 1960s three were provided with enlarged command spaces to replace the old former Italian '*escorteurs d'escadre*'. Shortly after, four were converted into guided-missile AAW ships with the American Tartar destroyer system. The remaining five were equally heavily rebuilt as specialist ASW vessels with a completely new armament including the Malafon ASW missile system, new bow sonar and VDS. The follow-on T 53 *Duperré* class were effectively radar pickets with improved aircraft control arrangements, and the last ship, designated T 56, was a specialised ASW trials platform. From 1967 the AAW ships, both the T 47 missile conversions and most of the T 53 pickets, were equipped with a version of the SENIT AIO system. The *Surcouf* hull was just too small for an effective fleet escort in *both* ASW and AAW, and if these roles were to be combined there was no alternative but to go for the fully fledged DLG.

Although the DL represented the desirable task force escort, it could not be afforded in large enough quantities even by the United States. In order to provide enough fleet escorts in peace and provide a basis for mobilisation in war a 2700-ton modernised extrapolation of the Second World War destroyer concept was developed. These *Forrest Shermans* emphasised AAW in their 5in and 3in gun batteries and carried torpedoes for ASW rather than for surface attack. Eighteen were commissioned between 1955 and 1959. Some were later modified rather

like the French *escorteurs*, some as ASW assets (with ASROC) and some as AAW ships with Tartar.

Tartar had been designed specifically for fitting into ships of traditional destroyer size, and an enlarged *Forrest Sherman* hull was designed to combine it with ASROC and high speed into a 3300-ton 'guided-missile destroyer' (DDG) to complement the still larger DLGs with their longer range missiles. The resulting *Charles F Adams* was a successful and cost-effective design, twenty-three joining the US fleet in the early 1960s and other examples being built for the Australians and West Germans. The Germans fitted their ships with a compact SATIR combat information system, based on US and French practice, which inspired the Australians to fit a variant of NTDS to their ships in the mid 1970s. The Americans also laid plans to fit their ships with NTDS but, because of budgetary constraints (each conversion cost as much as a new frigate), only three ships received the system as part of general modernisations in the early 1980s (four additional ships received a simplified combat data system). Sales of the *Adams*' class began in 1990.

Italy ordered its first postwar destroyers in 1950, a pair of 2800-ton *Impetuoso* class gun AAW/mortar ASW ships. Significantly, rather than being developments of old established Italian destroyer design, these were diminutives of the larger *Capitani Romani* class scout cruisers equipped with largely American equipment. They were not completed until 1958, at about which time two enlarged DDG derivatives were laid down to be completed as the *Impavido* class in 1963–64.

The destroyer provided the combination of

speed and endurance as well as the mix of military capabilities that made it attractive as a major unit in those navies primarily concerned with the defence of their own local sea areas. The Swedes built two 2000-ton destroyers of the Italian conception in the mid 1940s and followed them with six destroyers of their own design in the following decade. The original intention was to build four ships of over 2600 tons displacement, but this programme was cancelled after the first two, and four 2150-ton ships were substituted. Armament comprised two twin automatic 4.7in guns, 21in torpedo tubes, 57mm and 40mm AA guns and either ASW rocket launchers or the British Squid system. The larger pair, *Halland* and *Smaland*, proved by far the most flexible, were fitted with Swedish designed SSMs and outlasted their younger half-sisters, being the last large surface combatants in Swedish service before that navy became an entirely submarine and small craft fleet in 1984–85. Two modified *Halland*s with an extra twin 4.7in mount forward were sold to Colombia.

The West Germans in the early 1960s built their first postwar destroyers with rather similar work in mind, backing up lighter craft in offshore operations. Light 3.9in DP guns were combined with fixed tubes for guided ASuW torpedo tubes, and a short range ASW capability was provided by both torpedoes and rocket launchers. Exocet missiles replaced the ASuW torpedoes in 1975–77. ASW weapons comprised both rocket launchers and torpedo tubes.

Besides Colombia, other South American navies persevered with the traditional destroyer in the 1950s, using some of the last vessels of the type built. Brazil completed six traditional destroyers to a British design armed with American weapons in 1949–51 and retained four into the 1970s. In 1953–56 Venezuela purchased from Vickers three new ships based on the British 'Battles' but with a revised armament that substituted guns for some torpedo tubes, which they soon dispensed with completely to acquire Squid. In 1960 Chile received delivery of two 2730-ton *Almirante* class ships from Vickers that combined four single automatic 4in mountings with five 21in torpedo tubes, double Squid and six 40mm Bofors. Secondhand destroyers proved a cost-effective alternative to new construction here and elsewhere, but the market was limited by the main Western navies wishing

the above types carried ten traditional 21in torpedo tubes.

Soviet practice was at least five years behind Western, but this also reflected the very different role of the Soviet navy as a force attempting, together with shore-based aircraft, to deny superior Western forces the use of the sea. Neither task force nor convoy escort was a priority, and the path taken by Soviet development was therefore to modernise ASuW capability with ship-to-ship missiles, the jet propelled weapon code named SS-N-1 by the West. The last four *Kotlins* laid down were completed as ASuW missile ships with a mounting for this system instead of the after 5.1in guns, which were replaced by 57mm quick-firing AA guns forward. Thus was produced the *Kildin* of the early 1960s. In parallel to these four ships, eight larger *Krupnys* (originally conceived as larger *Kotlins*) were completed as double-ended SS-N-1 missile ships. All these were at best stopgap vessels as the missiles were unreliable and difficult to handle. At least one *Krupny* was broken up before completion. In the late 1960s conversion of the class into ASW ships began, with new sonar, a SAM launcher aft, light AA

to hang on to old high-speed hulls just in case they might prove useful in war. The Dominican Republic purchased an old British 'H' class ship of 1936 in 1948 but, apart from a few *Gleaves* class ships, it was only about 1960 that even wartime American *Fletchers* began to be available for acquisition by Latin American and other navies friendly to the West.

The same kind of imperative as drove Latin American requirements – high-speed limited general-purpose capability in the offshore zone – also drove policy in the most important outpost of the traditional destroyer in the 1950s, the USSR. There the conservative *Sverdlov* class

cruisers were complemented by equally, if not more, old fashioned destroyers. The first seventy-two 2240-ton Project 30-bis *Skorys* were basically a prewar programme reinstated, with low-angle 5.1in guns and fire control only effective for clear weather surface fire. These were followed by more flexible designs, the *Neustrashimy* and the 2850-ton Project 56 *Kotlin*. Between four and twelve of the former and thirty-six of the latter were planned, but only one and twenty-seven respectively were built. The design of these ships was still basically Second World War, but at least they had dual-purpose main guns and fire control. All three of

guns, a 660yd-range RBU-6000 ASW rocket launcher forward and enhanced torpedo armament. The result was designated *Kanin* by the West. The *Kildin*s were also rebuilt in the early 1970s with the latest variant of the SS-N-2 SSM and extra light guns (76mm) replacing the SS-N-1. The main role of these ships seems to have been acting as specialist trailing and 'tattle-tale' ships for ASuW with long range missiles.

The Soviet concept of operations of offshore defence, individual ships or small groups of ships operating under shore control, meant that there was a demand for better AAW as well as ASuW capability to deal with carrier-based aircraft after launch, long range shore-based aircraft, and to cover – rather than escort – ships with weapons optimised to other roles. This was especially true after the Soviet navy lost its dedicated fighter cover in the 1950s. Starting in 1960, nine Project 56s were rebuilt aft as 'Kotlin SAMs' to carry the SA-N-1 surface-to-air missile instead of torpedo tubes and light AA guns. One of these ships was transferred to Poland. This paralleled the appearance of the gas turbine-powered Project 61 *Kashin* class, a double-ended general-purpose vessel that combined twin 3in guns and SA-N-1 launchers fore and aft with the RBU-6000 multiple ASW rocket launchers (also fitted to the *Kotlin* SAMs) and 21in torpedo tubes capable of being used both for ASuW and ASW.

A changing emphasis in Soviet doctrine towards anti-SSBN operations saw the later examples of these impressive vessels appear in the 1960s as 'large anti-submarine ships', but they were in effect the last traditional Soviet destroyers. Both their 'tattletale' and ASW roles were enhanced in the early 1970s by the addition of rearward facing SS-N-2 missiles and variable depth sonar. Six ships were rebuilt to this Project 61M configuration and five more (with forward facing missiles) were built new for India, the last not being delivered until 1988.

The transformation of the frigate

It is hard to overestimate the impact of the Type XXI fast battery drive U-boat on the evolution of the surface warship. At a stroke it made all ASW escorts obsolete in all but a simple barrier role. The new threat mandated an increase in speed in convoy escort and support vessels to a point comparable with the speed required by fleet operations. It thus did more than anything

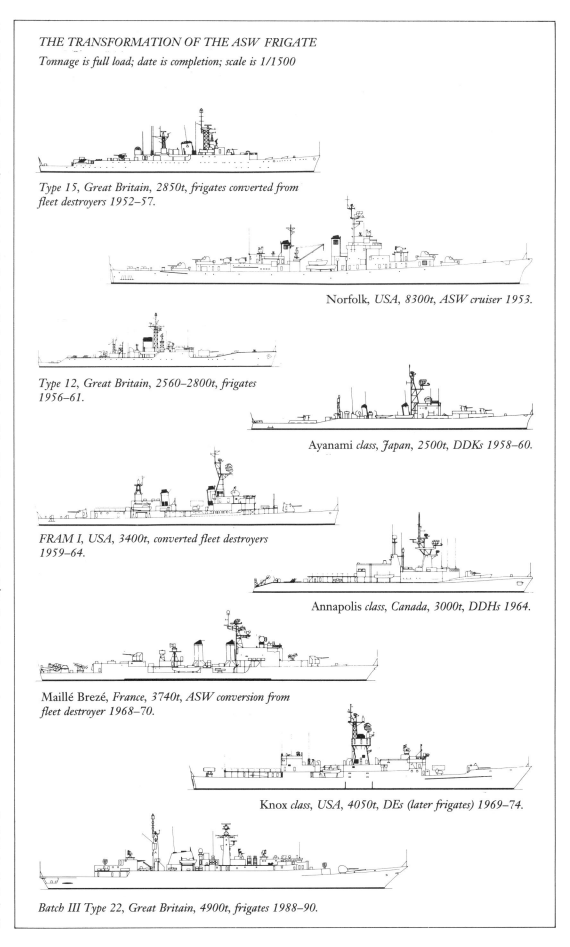

THE TRANSFORMATION OF THE ASW FRIGATE
Tonnage is full load; date is completion; scale is 1/1500

Type 15, Great Britain, 2850t, frigates converted from fleet destroyers 1952–57.

Norfolk, USA, 8300t, ASW cruiser 1953.

Type 12, Great Britain, 2560–2800t, frigates 1956–61.

Ayanami class, Japan, 2500t, DDKs 1958–60.

FRAM I, USA, 3400t, converted fleet destroyers 1959–64.

Annapolis class, Canada, 3000t, DDHs 1964.

Maillé Brezé, France, 3740t, ASW conversion from fleet destroyer 1968–70.

Knox class, USA, 4050t, DEs (later frigates) 1969–74.

Batch III Type 22, Great Britain, 4900t, frigates 1988–90.

else to break down the distinction between 'frigate' and 'destroyer'.

This can be seen most clearly in Britain. In the immediate postwar years convoy escort was viewed as the Royal Navy's overriding role. Yet the mass of existing escorts was very largely obsolete, with little if any development potential. Second World War sloops and frigates might be of use as colonial and Cold War gunboats. They saw much service as such under the White Ensign in the postwar years, and in addition British type frigates (including American- and Canadian-built versions) were widely distributed as gunboats around the world's navies. Yet for higher level operations their moderate speed made them of little utility against the modern submarine, and their AAW potential was very limited against the projected 1950s threat. New construction was planned and a '1945 frigate' design evolved, but as a stopgap the mass of wartime destroyer hulls was a ready source of high-speed ASW frigate hulls. Two conversion plans were prepared, the Type 15 being more extensive than the other, the Type 16.

The Type 15 was a dramatic demonstration of the effects of modern operational requirements on warship appearance. Swept away were the guns and torpedo tubes that gave a warship her traditional 'sex appeal'. Instead there was an extended superstructure to allow a proper operations room to be built from which the ship's Type 170 and 174 sonar suite could be fully exploited in heavy weather. There was no point in putting a gun on the forecastle as it would be useless in Atlantic conditions. Instead, a twin Bofors was mounted above the bridge and a twin 4in was positioned aft to give limited AAW and ASuW capability. The main armament was two of the new Mk 10 Limbo ASW mortars which could project depth bombs to a range of 1000yds. Supply shortages of Limbo meant that some Type 15s only received the older Squid. The supplementary armament of homing torpedoes proved a failure, but in general the class was a great success in its designed specialist role. They could also double as gunboats on peacetime duties. The less extensive conversion was abandoned as not capable enough after ten units

had been completed. An intermediate Type 18 was replaced by the full conversion before any ships were so modified. Variants on Type 15 and 16 conversions were also carried out for or by Commonwealth navies. As late as 1962–66 the increasingly isolated South Africans (who had considered buying three Type 15s but in the event purchased only one) carried out a Type 16 style conversion on their two 'W' class fleet destroyers. Provision was made for two Wasp helicopters and the ships retained destroyer designation.

For new construction the original plan was to utilise three variants of the same basic 2100-ton high-forecastle hull, developed in the light of the experience of the hard years of the Atlantic campaign. Diesel propulsion was originally intended, to provide maximum range, but this gave a maximum speed of 25kts that was deemed inadequate to counter the new submarine. There was no alternative, therefore, to steam turbines for the ASW frigate, even though mass production of this machinery was more problematical. The diesel hull, however, remained sufficient for the anti-aircraft (Type 41) and aircraft direction (Type 61) roles with different balances of radar, action information space and 4.5in guns. The steam ASW frigate (Type 12) would have a maximum speed of 29kts. Main sensors were the Type 170 and 174 sonars and the main armament was two Limbos and homing torpedoes, although the latter were soon removed. Twin 4.5in guns were mounted for-

ward and twin 40mm Bofors aft, as the ship was intended to contribute to convoy air defence; 3in rapid-fire guns had been intended for all ships, but the mountings could not be produced in time. Heavier guns also gave enhanced shore bombardment capability, a vital consideration as cold- and limited-war priorities came to predominate, so they were retained.

The Type 12 was produced in greater quantity and soon proved the most flexible. It was therefore decided to modify the design with revised internal arrangements, improved radar and air control facilities – and better appearance – to become the standard first rate general-purpose frigate (there was already a 'second rate' GP design, see below). Thus was born the *Leander*, a major landmark in postwar warship design. One Limbo was replaced by a shipborne weapons delivery helicopter to exploit the greater detection range of the 177 sonar and the follow-on 184. Seacat missiles eventually replaced the Bofors guns. The last of the specialist frigate orders were converted to *Leander*s and the first appeared in 1963, the prototype of twenty-six for the Royal Navy alone. The last ten were of slightly broader beam than the rest and displaced 2500 tons rather than 2300.

The Type 12/*Leander* design was widely adopted by the Commonwealth. Australia produced its own 'River' class derivative equipped with the Ikara ASW missile rather than the helicopter. India, which also purchased Type 41 AAW frigates, found the Type 12 to be an ex-

The highly successful Type 12 hull form culminated in the Leander *class general purpose frigates. This aerial view of* Danae *reveals the basic layout of the original group: a twin 4.5in gun forward, Type 965 air search radar on the main mast, hangar and flight deck for the Wasp helicopter aft, with Seacat short range SAM (to port) and its director on the hangar roof, and Limbo ASW mortar in a well. The design was flexible enough to allow a myriad of variations, modifications and developments.* (C & S Taylor)

The Canadian interpretation of the Type 12 specification produced a ship of very different appearance that was categorised as an escort destroyer (DDE) rather than a frigate. Saguenay, *the second of this* St Laurent *class, is shown in 1962, but apart from the gunhouse added to the forward 3in mounting, she is virtually as completed. (USN)*

cellent basis for domestic development with largely Soviet type weapons and radar. The Dutch adopted the *Leander* for a time as their standard escort and the type was also exported to Chile. It provided all its customers with a flexible and cost-effective escort, capable of operations in all contexts from the carrier group to gunboat diplomacy.

Most of the older RN Type 12s were modified to approach *Leander* standard, and the *Leanders* themselves were later heavily modified in a number of different ways, with Exocet or Ikara missiles instead of the 4.5s, Sea Wolf SAMs instead of Seacat and Lynx instead of Wasp helicopters. The Ikara *Leanders* were highly specialised task force ASW ships with ADAWS AIO and data links to provide an immediate ASW reaction capability to an entire force. Sadly, they were too specialised to be used for general-purpose duties. After trials in the Type 12 HMS *Torquay* in the early 1970s, CAAIS AIO was fitted to the non-Ikara *Leanders*, beginning with HMS *Cleopatra* in 1975; at the same time Exocet was added instead of the 4.5in guns and a Lynx ASuW/ASW helicopter substituted for both the Wasp and the Mk 10 mortar. Four of these 'Batch 2' *Leanders* very successfully pioneered the use of towed array sonar in the early 1980s. The Type 12 design in its various incarnations provided the backbone of the Royal Navy from about 1965 to 1985. Its direct descendant, the Indian *Godavari*, was still in production in the 1990s.

Frigates or destroyers?

In Canada a national variant of the Type 12 concept was developed as the basis of the post-war Royal Canadian Navy. To indulge national susceptibilities it combined Type 12 machinery with a high-forecastle hull of deliberately different appearance from the British original. Canadian and American electronics were fitted and twin American 3in guns were carried fore and aft; the main armament, however, was a pair of Mk 10 mortars. Eighteen were built in three variants, entering service between 1955 and 1963. Later ships carried the more powerful British Mk 6 3in/70 guns on the forecastle mounting. In the 1960s the RCN began to fit the original seven with large Sea King ASW

search and strike helicopters, a major leap in capability. Two more were built to carry Sea Kings as new, and four were modified less extensively with ASROC aft. The RCN decided to class all these frigates (and its Type 15s) officially as 'escort destroyers' (DDE); the Sea King ships became DDHs.

The Canadian decision on nomenclature reflected what had happened further south in the United States, where destroyer conversion had produced a series of DDE designs to cope with the high-speed submarine threat. The DDE (escort destroyer) differed from the existing and now obsolete 'destroyer escort' (DE) by being 10–14kts faster. At the end of the war four incomplete *Gearing* fleet destroyer hulls had provided opportunities to build prototype ASW destroyers, two as interim *Norfolk* (see above) type 'submarine killers' (DDKs) for hunter-killer operations, and two as convoy escorts. The DDK was to be individually capable of destroying a fast submarine, while the DDE would be expected to act with other units. The first to be completed were the two DDEs *Basilone* and *Epperson*. These had Weapon Alfa instead of 'B' gun position, trainable Hedgehog instead of two 40mm AA guns and fixed tubes for ASW torpedoes. Extra action information spaces were also provided. The two DDKs, *Carpenter* and *Robert A Owens*, had totally new bridge structures, 3in guns and heavier ASW batteries of Weapon Alfa, Hedgehog and depth charges in various

combinations. In addition, a more austere conversion was chosen for the destroyer components of two experimental operational ASW task groups. One gun mounting was suppressed to fit trainable Hedgehog, and improved sonar was fitted. The DDE designation was chosen to cover all the above ships in 1950, including the DDKs, given the general American emphasis on hunter-killer rather than escort operations which meant that DDEs were hunter-killer assets as well as – if not more than – escorts.

Alongside these developments, eighteen Second World War *Fletcher* class fleet destroyers received new sonar, associated control equipment and spaces and improved ASW armament of Weapon Alfa, Hedgehog and homing torpedoes. The intention was to build up a reserve of DDEs for war, but the programme was curtailed in 1950 on the grounds that it was premature. Given revised intelligence assessments, it was felt that less extensive conversions could cope with the existing threat and that the future submarine would probably be beyond its capabilities.

The DDE concept died in the US Navy when it was decided effectively to make all older destroyers fast ASW escorts, albeit retaining the destroyer DD rating. This was done under the FRAM (Fleet Rehabilitation and Modernisation Program) of 1958 that converted *Gearing* class destroyers into something approaching modern ASW escorts. New long range sonar

was fitted, with a DASH drone and ASROC missile launcher to exploit it. One gun mount was deleted, as were the torpedo tubes and light AA guns. Other old destroyers received less extensive FRAM modernisation and the *Gearing* DDEs were reclassified DD and given appropriate FRAM updatings to serve side by side with their sisters into the 1970s. FRAM destroyers of all types were widely distributed to Allied navies in the 1970s.

Another navy that adopted the DDE concept was the Dutch, which built destroyers in the 1950s as '*Onderzeebootjagers*' to form Atlantic escort/hunter-killer groups. These combined traditional destroyer hulls with twin dual-purpose 4.7in mountings fore and aft and 375mm (14.8in) ASW rocket launchers in 'B' position. The sonar fit was domestically produced, with two sonars in a single dome, one for search and one for attack. Traditional torpedo tubes were not carried. Guns were relied upon to cope with a light ASuW threat, and topweight concentrated on a good radar fit and control spaces for both ASW and AAW. The first four were only 2200 tons, but the remaining eight were enlarged to 2500 tons with American type propulsion machinery and heavier 40mm AA armament. British homing torpedoes were fitted in two of the later ships, but these proved unsuccessful and were removed. The Dutch later adopted the British *Leander* class as a better

The Japanese 'destroyers' of the Takatsuki *class were primarily ASW ships. In this 1983 view of Kikuzuki the ship is carrying (from forward): a 375mm ASW rocket launcher on the forecastle, ASROC between the forward 5in gun and the bridge, two triple 12.75in ASW torpedo tubes amidships, and the hangar and flight deck for three DASH drones aft. The Japanese persevered with DASH and made it more reliable, but they eventually turned to manned helicopters like most major navies. (MG Photographic)*

equipped and more modern design for the ASW role, and these frigates served side by side with the older destroyer lookalikes.

The neighbouring Nato state of Denmark, that had borrowed British 'Hunt' class frigates (built as 'escort destroyers'), retained the destroyer lines of these ships with its replacement 2200-ton *Peder Skram* class frigates, built with American funds in 1964–67. The two twin 5in guns forward made them reminiscent of American Second World War destroyers, as did the two funnels, and the intention seems to have been to achieve something approaching a new-build FRAM *Gearing*. Torpedoes and depth charges were the ASW weapons, and the intended Norwegian Terne mortar was never fitted. Maximum speed with combined diesel and gas turbine propulsion was, however, a frigate-like 28kts rather than a destroyer's 32kts or so.

Spain was another country that went for DDEs. She possessed large numbers of destroyers of domestic construction and, using American funds, began a major programme to rearm (and

USS Robert A Owens, one of the prototype DDK hunter-killer destroyer conversions, is shown here in 1978 after a further FRAM I modernisation. She has the ASROC launcher amidships and the DASH helicopter facilities aft of the usual FRAM I conversions, but most ships retained a second twin 5in mount, either in 'B' position or aft. (L & L van Ginderen)

complete the last ones) as fast ASW ships. Their 21in torpedoes were removed and replaced by ASW weapons, Hedgehog and homing torpedoes; 3in guns replaced heavier weapons in the smaller ships. They were progressively classified as 'fast frigates', 'ASW frigates' and finally from 1961 as '*destructores caza submarinas*' (ASW destroyers). Spain was also one of the first countries to receive American *Fletcher* class destroyers, in 1957.

When Japan began to move towards more combatant warships in the mid 1950s, destroyer type escorts were introduced in the shape of two former American *Gleaves* class destroyers of the minesweeping variant which carried no torpedoes but instead had guns and ASW weapons. These fitted well with both the operational and political contexts and the first Japanese-built warships commissioned two years later were new-build versions of the same concept, called at first 'high-speed escort vessels'. These 1700-ton ships had a maximum speed of 30kts and carried three American 5in guns, light AA guns and depth charges. ASW torpedo launchers were later added, and they were included from the start in the armament of hunter-killer destroyers (DDKs) of the *Ayanami* type commissioned in 1958–60 with 3in main armament and 21in torpedoes also. At the same time, in order to provide a better balanced main force of escort groups, the *Ayanami*s were paralleled by three

Although the British 'Tribal' class frigates were originally designed with the Persian Gulf in mind, they were considered general purpose ships, and originally designated 'sloops' (to differentiate them from single-purpose frigates). As if to demonstrate their versatility, HMS Tartar *is pictured here off Bear Island, about as far from Middle Eastern conditions as could be imagined. A major innovation in the class was a gas turbine for boost, which necessitated the second funnel, the first serving the steam turbine boiler room.* (RN, Crown Copyright)

Murasame class air defence (DDA) variants with heavier gun armament, and the *Akizuki*s, flotilla leaders that were fully fledged destroyers. Comparable with the US *Forrest Sherman*s, the latter's characteristics as ASW vessels were later enhanced with, in one case, a Weapon Alfa in 'B' position and in both cases improved CIC, bridges and sensors.

Despite attempts by the Finance Ministry to limit defence expenditure, the Japanese navy made a significant step forward in AAW in 1965 by commissioning its first DDG, the 3000-ton *Amatsukaze*, followed by three slightly larger *Takatsuki*s with a comprehensive ASW armament. The main technology in both cases was American. These were supplemented by nine economical 27kt diesel-powered 2100-ton DDKs devoted to ASW, some fitted with ASROC, some with DASH. In most other navies the latter would have been 'frigates', despite their rakish looks. With the larger ships serving as leaders (one or two per flotilla) the smaller DDKs and older destroyers formed the Escort Divisions, two or three of which made up each of the four Escort Flotillas of the main Fleet Escort Force. This by the 1970s was the main operational capability of the Maritime Self Defence Force.

Coastal combatants and austere frigates

The new fast frigates were as expensive as they were capable, and they would not be available in sufficient numbers either for wartime mobilisation or even to provide sufficient platforms for presence missions in peace. Attempts were therefore made to provide cheaper platforms that could be afforded in sufficient quantity. Britain planned to build 'second rate' and even 'third rate' ASW frigates to flesh out ocean escort groups and an 'East Coast Gunboat' to protect coastal convoys from attack by air and surface forces. Only the 1180-ton Type 14 'Second Rate Utility' ASW ships saw the light of day, twelve being commissioned between 1956 and 1957 as the *Blackwood* class. They carried

the ASW equipment of a Type 12 with half the power. A light slender hull gave a top speed of 27kts, but a price had to be paid in hull strength. This and the almost non-existent AAW and ASuW capability of the ships gave them a bad name and the type was known, rather ungenerously, as 'Second Rate Futility'. The only peacetime roles for such specialised ships were ASW training and fishery protection. India also obtained ships of this class, which eventually ended up in the Coast Guard.

Britain could not afford such specialised luxuries, especially when the role of navies in global war was reassessed in the mid 1950s. Peacetime presence and power projection was the priority, and the East Coast Gunboat was replaced by a 2300-ton, 27kt combined steam and gas turbine 'sloop' built as the Type 81 'Tribal' class 'Second Rate General Purpose Frigate' in the early 1960s. The prime purpose of these ships was to replace the wartime frigates used to patrol the Persian Gulf. With destroyer-type 4.5in singles at each end, compact helicopter arrangements and most of the ASW potential of a Type 12, they were useful adjuncts to the *Leander*s.

The United States transferred large numbers of its wartime DEs to friendly foreign countries (the fast transport variant proved an excellent and roomy patrol vessel). It did, however, retain some as mobilisation reserves, and in the context of the Korean war modified a few as mobilisation prototypes. Only the USS *Tweedy* received the full conversion, with four Hedgehog projectors on top of a new bridge structure that contained a combat information centre and associated control spaces for the new sonar. The

other three ships were converted to a rather more austere standard with twin Hedgehog only and a combined conning-operational bridge, but all sacrificed light AA guns for a very heavy depth charge battery. The programme was terminated in part because a new use had been found for DEs. Their ASW utility, even in a modified state, was clearly a marginal asset depending on old wartime type submarines continuing to form part of the threat, fast battery drive submarines being limited in performance by operational factors, and slow convoys requiring to be escorted. A new threat was, however, already rapidly emerging: that of Soviet air attack on the USA. The DE provided a seaworthy and high-endurance radar platform for extending the Continental air defence zone out to sea, and indeed radar picket DEs had been experimented with during the war. The first two DERs for the Continental defence role were converted by 1951, and thirty-two more ships were converted over the rest of the decade. The barrier force was stood down in 1965, but some DERs had a final lease of operational life off Vietnam as surface surveillance assets. The DERs retained ASW capability for use as escorts if required and for strategic ASW surveillance.

A new-construction DE programme began with coastal escort in mind. It was clear that the existing coastal escorts (PCs) were too slow and badly equipped to cope with the new submarine threat. If the carnage of 1942 was not to re-occur, a coastal escort affordable in quantity was required. The result was the 1314-ton *Dealey* class DE, whose single-screw steam turbine propulsion gave a creditable 27kts. The Weapon Alfa rocket torpedo was the main ar-

Beginning life as a cheap coastal escort, the US Dealey class achieved a lot on a small displacement, with a good sonar outfit and reasonable speed. Nato navies with long oceanic coastlines, like Norway and Portugal, found the design attractive, and both built modified versions. In the case of Portugal, three ships were constructed with Mutual Defence Aid Pact funding, but tropicalised for service in Portugal's African colonies. Nevertheless, as Almirante Pereira da Silva shows, the ASW function of the ships remained paramount, with Bofors 375mm rocket launchers forward, 12.75in torpedoes amidships, and a VDS aft. (L & L van Ginderen)

mament (*Dealey* herself carried a British Squid), with twin 3in guns at bow and stern. The sonar fit was a good one, the same SQS-4 as was fitted in the later FRAM II destroyer, and within their limitations they were adequate ships. Lightweight ASW torpedo tubes later complemented/replaced the original Weapon Alfa. Three received improved SQS-23 sonar in the early 1960s and DASH drone helicopter facilities to attack contacts. The rest acquired VDS. Modified versions of the class were built as coastal escorts for both Norway and Portugal, but only thirteen were built for the USN, which kept them until the early 1970s. Two were sold, one to Uruguay and the other to Colombia.

The *Dealey* was still too expensive for mass production, and in 1954 the USN decided to try to build an even cheaper DE. This appeared in the late 1950s as the *Claud Jones*, similar in size but slow (21.2kts), diesel-powered ships armed with nothing better than the Second World War Hedgehog spigot mortar. Only the first four prototypes appeared, and after use as ELINT platforms all were sold to Indonesia in 1973–74. Export versions were built in Turkey.

A last attempt at a mobilisation ocean convoy escort for the USN was made in 1958, and the new SQS-26 sonar was put into a *Dealey* type hull to produce the 1882-ton *Bronstein* class, two prototypes of which were commissioned in 1963. These were quite capable ships with DASH and the ASROC missile systems, but their speed of 26kts was too slow for the ASW hunter-killer group tactics gaining favour in the USN. If speed could be increased a little, not only would hunter-killer operations with DDs and ASW carriers be easier, but the resulting ships would be able to act as task force escorts to supplement the more capable – and expensive – DLGs and DDGs. So were born the 30kt 2400-ton *Garcia* (ASW orientated DE) and *Brooke* (AAW orientated DEG) classes, built in limited quantities in the 1960s. These were

comparable with the *Leander* paradigm except for their single screws. Destroyer type 5in main guns were fitted, although the main armament was respectively DASH and the Tartar SAM with a single channel of fire. The ships were basically enlarged *Bronstein*s fitted with lightweight pressure-fired boilers that gave 35,000hp compared with 20,000hp in the older pair. In effect they were 'third rate' fleet escorts (DLG 'first rate'; DD/DDG 'second rate').

The French navy built its equivalent of third rate frigates, the E 50 and 52 classes, to a 1250-ton design, with a hull related to the contemporary American *Dealey* design. Armament comprised three twin 57mm AA guns, a 375mm ASW rocket launcher and four triple ASW torpedo tubes. Unlike the *Dealey*s these were twin-screw ships, but were only slightly faster at a maximum of 28kts. They had similar range and speed to a British Type 12 but a price nevertheless had to be paid in seaworthiness, operational flexibility and growth potential. Even so, sufficient numbers could not be afforded and a more austere E 54 was therefore projected. Before any could be built, however, plans changed and a new class of '*escorteur d'Union Français*' was designed for colonial policing duties. This became the 1750-ton *Commandant Rivière* class of '*aviso escorteur*' (escort sloop) ordered in 1956–57 and finally commissioned in the 1960s. These carried a useful shore bombardment capacity in three 100mm (3.9in) singles, plus an ASW mortar that could double in the shore bombardment role. A limited sonar and ASW torpedo fit gave residual convoy escort capacity, but the twin diesels fitted in most of the nine-strong class gave a maximum speed of only 25kts. Four *Rivière*s were built new for Portugal, and others were sold out of French service to Uruguay.

The Portuguese in particular required a new generation of colonial sloops to replace their quite large fleet of older vessels. A Portuguese officer, Commodore Oliveira, together with

Blohm & Voss, designed in the 1960s a suitable 1250-ton diesel-powered design with simple gun and close-in ASW weapon armament together with provision for thirty-four troops. Six of these *Joao Coutinho* class were built, three in Germany and three in Spain, and four more in the mid 1970s in Spain to a slightly modified *De Andrada* design just as the colonial role was coming to an end. Attempts were made to sell the latter to Colombia but these failed. The design was taken up by the Spanish navy, which tried to give it heavier armament as the 1350-ton *Descubierta* class – 3in gun, two 40mm, Sea Sparrow point-defence SAM, 375mm ASW rocket launcher and two triple ASW torpedo tubes. Despite SEWACO AIO they still lacked vital attributes necessary for modern escort work, notably a helicopter. The Spanish navy moved on to larger types as it integrated more with Nato. Two were sold to Egypt while still under construction in 1982, and another was built for Morocco.

Mainland European navies had a tradition of small 'torpedo boats' (*ie* small destroyers) for general-purpose coastal operations, interception and patrol as well as convoy escort. This concept was retained in the postwar era, although as with ocean escorts the armament changed from an ASuW emphasis to ASW and AAW. Sweden rearmed its 1000-ton prewar torpedo boats as 'frigates' with enhanced AA armament and improved ASW equipment instead of traditional torpedo tubes. The Italians did the same with the *Spica* and *Pegaso* classes and built new small ships in the same 800-ton 'corvette' bracket, both for domestic use and export. In the 1950s American MDAP (Mutual Defence Aid Pact) money paid for three *Albatros* class ships for the Italians themselves, four for Denmark and one for the Netherlands. The armament comprised two 3in guns, two 40mm AA guns and two Hedgehog ASW weapons with a simple sonar and radar fit. The speed of these good looking diesel-powered vessels was only 19kts, and they were not a great success except for patrol and presence duties. Four more of an

The Italians attempted to produce a class of small helicopter-carrying 'corvettes', but the resulting Bergamini *class were too small to be practical, and they were succeeded by two* Alpino *class frigates (this is* Carabiniere). *Operating in the Mediterranean, always in the shadow of land-based air power, the Italian navy has given its ships a heavy AA armament, persisting with serried ranks of guns where other Western navies depended solely on SAMs – this ship carries six individual 3in guns, and the contemporary destroyers had 5in and 3in batteries, as well as Tartar SAMs.* (CMP)

improved 24kt *De Cristofaro* version were built for the Italian navy in the mid 1960s, with a raised forecastle for better seakeeping and the Menon long-range ASW mortar as well as lightweight torpedo launchers. The latter were also added to the Italian *Albatros* class.

During the 1950s the Italians had built modernised variants of the traditional torpedo boat for the export market, where ASuW was still a priority. These had sold quite well, to Venezuela (who classified them 'destroyers'), and to Portugal and Indonesia (who called them 'frigates'). These 1300-ton Ansaldo-built ships were armed with two twin 4in gun mountings (Portuguese ships carried two 3in), three 21in torpedo tubes, light AA guns, Hedgehog and conventional depth charges. Twin-shaft geared turbines gave 34kts when new, but their speed deteriorated to 29kts over time and they suffered from various mechanical and structural difficulties because of their lightweight construction. Two of the Venezuelan ships were rearmed with new 76mm guns and ASW torpedo tubes between 1968 and 1975 and lasted into the 1990s as coast guard vessels. The rest were scrapped in the 1970s.

For their own frigate purposes the Italians produced a small escort destroyer, building four 1800-ton *Canopo*s, armed with 3in dual-purpose guns, the Menon mortar and ASW torpedoes. These were followed in the early 1960s by two 1400-ton *Bergamini*s, the smallest hulls compatible with a helicopter. These were unsuccessful ships even in the Mediterranean and the follow-on design, the *Alpino*, was 2000 tons. Only two could be afforded of the four originally projected, however.

The new West German navy acquired old British frigates of the 'Hunt' and *Black Swan* type for initial training, but these were followed for

One of the old Soviet Union's best customers for warships, outside the Warsaw Pact, was India. This is Andaman, *a* Petya II *corvette, one of twelve modified Project 159 ships transferred between 1969 and 1974.* (L & L van Ginderen)

operational duties by six *Köln*s delivered in the early 1960s. Designed as '*Geleitboot 55*' (Escort 55) ships and delivered as Type 120 frigates, they were in fact rakish sea-going escort destroyers of just over 2000 tons armed with two French 100mm guns, six 40mm AA guns, ASW rocket launchers and ASW torpedo tubes. Combined diesel and gas turbine propulsion gave a high destroyer-like top speed of 32kts. When two were eventually sold off to Turkey their new owner rated them as destroyers. The West Germans also gave most of their large fleet of 2400-ton support ships, necessitated by the need to evacuate Germany's own bases in time of war, a heavy armament of guns so that they could not only defend themselves but supplement the frigates if required.

From 1953 Japan maintained security in her coastal waters with District Forces, each of which contained an Escort Squadron. The mainstay of these was at first a large fleet of old American-built British-designed wartime *Tacoma* class frigates that had been lent to the USSR during the Second World War. In addition to the pair of American DEs lent in 1955, the Japanese built three experimental 1100-ton 'B type escorts' armed with 3in and 40mm guns, Hedgehog and depth charges. Not until the early 1960s were more ships built in this category – the 1490-ton diesel-powered *Isuzu*s armed with 3in guns, both heavyweight and lightweight torpedoes and Weapon Alfa or the 375mm rocket launcher. To replace the *Tacoma*s at the beginning of the 1970s eleven *Chikugo* class frigates were built These were the smallest vessels ever to mount ASROC, having a 1500-ton diesel-powered hull also armed with 3in and 40mm guns and ASW torpedo tubes.

The Soviet navy built large numbers of coastal patrol ships (*Storozhevoy Korabl* – SKRs) to maintain a presence in their extensive coastal waters. These were similar to the wartime

German 'torpedo boat'; indeed Kaliningrad, former Königsberg, was the lead yard. The first eight were 1900-ton *Kola*s but these were unnecessarily destroyer-like and the 1260-ton production version, the *Riga*, was smaller. These were still primarily traditional ASuW assets with three single 100mm (3.9in) gun mounts and a twin or triple 21in torpedo mounting. Light AA guns were carried, plus short range ASW rocket launchers. In 1961 a new SKR appeared, the 950-ton Project 159 (*Petya*) with combined diesel and gas turbine propulsion. These were more specialised ASW ships with 406mm (16in) ASW torpedo tubes and RBU-2500 rocket launchers. Rapid-fire 76mm guns gave greater AAW protection. In 1964–66 Kaliningrad built a similar design but with different machinery arrangements and RBU-6000 rocket launchers as the Project 35 (*Mirka*). This was replaced on the production line by a modified Type 159A also with RBU-6000 rocket launchers, production of which continued both there and at Kharbarovsk until 1969. An export Project 159AE was also produced, with triple 21in torpedo tubes, and supplied to Ethiopia, India, Syria and Vietnam. Adding the Soviet navy's forty-five Project 159s and eighteen Project 35s as 'frigates' to Soviet navy strength, in comparison with ocean-going Western types, gave a very misleading impression of Soviet naval might.

Gas turbine propulsion

Although gas turbine experiments with small craft were carried out in the postwar years, the British programme to test a marine gas turbine in a frigate was abandoned in 1952. The idea of gas turbines did not die completely, however, and in the mid 1950s it was decided to give the new Type 81 sloops and 'County' class DLGs specially designed gas turbine auxiliary engines for emergency movement and as boosters for the steam turbines. These proved themselves in service in the early 1960s and the greater use of gas turbines in aircraft provided a ready source of reliable engines. The gas turbine gave high

power at immediate readiness, coupled with reduced manpower and maintenance demands. This made them very attractive either as partial or complete powerplants for major surface combatants. The main forms of installation were: CODOG (Combined Diesel Or Gas Turbine – *ie* alternative plants, a gas turbine main engine and diesel cruise engines); CODAG (Combined Diesel *And* Gas Turbine, as in the *Köln*s mentioned above); COSAG (Combined Steam and Gas, as in the British ships just mentioned); and, once trust in gas turbines grew, COGOG (Combined Gas Or Gas – alternative high power turbines or low power turbines); or COGAG (Combined Gas And Gas, with sets of similar turbines usable in whatever numbers required).

All-gas-turbine ships entered service from the 1960s onwards, with the Soviets taking the lead. The British converted a Type 14, HMS *Exmouth*, to all-gas-turbine propulsion in 1968, but even before she was in service decided in 1967 to make all future major surface ships COGOG. The disadvantages of gas turbines were a large space requirement for intakes and filters and associated problems with containing battle damage. However, these could not counterbalance their other advantages, especially in reduced manpower, and by the 1970s all the major navies abandoned steam for all but the biggest warships. Its century or so of supremacy as a source of high power at sea was at an end.

The export market

The advent of gas turbines made building simply-operated new ships for the export market attractive. New navies were coming into being as the 'Wind of Change' gave freedom to large numbers of former colonial countries. Attractive new ships that did not require too many trained men were doubly attractive compared with the manpower-intensive cast-offs of the major navies. Vosper Thornycroft climbed on this bandwagon in the 1960s with a series of combatants ranging from the 380-ton Mk 1 diesel-powered corvette sold to Ghana and Libya, through the 500-ton Mk 2 sold to Nigeria, the 1100-ton Mk 5 sold (as 'destroyers') to Iran, and the 1325-ton Mk 7 sold to Libya. Both larger ships were CODOG. Even the smallest corvettes could carry Squid and associated 164 sonar as well as a 4in gun. The larger ships carried a fully automatic 4.5in gun, point-defence SAMs and were fitted on building or later with SSMs. They were good ships for offshore patrol and presence duties, as well as ASuW and inshore ASW combat if required. Their main limitations were the skills of their owners, which were strained by sophisticated warships. Although Nigeria bought further 700-ton Mk 9 corvettes, all of its ships were in a very poor state by the 1980s.

One of Vosper's most successful coups was to sign a deal with Brazil in 1970 to build six large

Builder's trials for the Brazilian frigates Defensora *and* Niteroi, *one-third of a major export success for Vosper Thornycroft in the 1970s. Four were completed in this ASW version, with Ikara aft, and two in a general-purpose mode, with a second 4.5in gun. In an arrangement that was increasingly popular in developing countries, the British originators gave technical assistance to build two of the ships in the customer country, helping to establish a warship building infrastructure in Brazil, which has since developed a training frigate from the design. (Vosper Thornycroft)*

Even the US Navy could afford only limited numbers of the most capable ships, and this certainly applied to nuclear-powered fleet escorts – redesignated cruisers from DLGNs in 1975. The two hard-won California *class were eventually succeeded by four* Virginia *class, of which* Texas *(shown here in 1983) was the second. Improvements included the Mk 26 launcher which could fire both Standard SAM and ASROC ASW missiles, eliminating the separate box launcher for the latter. The earlier ships, designed before the advent of LAMPS, did not have a helicopter hangar, but in the new class one was contrived beneath the quarterdeck. However, its elevator was unsatisfactory and helicopters were not usually embarked.* (L & L van Ginderen)

3200-ton Mk 10 frigates – four to an ASW design with both Lynx helicopter and Ikara, ASW rocket launchers, 4.5in and 40mm guns and Seacat SAMs; and two to a general-purpose design with two guns, Exocet in place of Ikara and no VDS. CAAIS AIO was fitted, and the ships entered service between 1977 and 1980, four being built in Britain and two (together with a later associated training ship) in Brazil. The complement was only 209, a small number for such large ships.

Vosper's major British rival was Yarrow, which built a 1250-ton CODOG frigate armed with a 4.5in gun and Mk 10 mortar for Malaysia in 1971, and a rather larger 1650-ton variant with two main guns and ASW torpedo tubes and conventional depth charges for Thailand in 1973. The same yard also built a 2300-ton combined presidential yacht/frigate ordered in 1965 for Nkhruma's Ghana. The successor Government did not want her, and after standing forlornly in the Clyde she was taken over as HMS *Mermaid* by a rather reluctant Royal Navy as a simple patrol and presence asset. She was sold off to Malaysia to replace an old Second World War British frigate in 1977. Armament comprised guns and a Mk 10 mortar.

Competition to Vosper also came from the Dutch firm of Wilton Fijenoord. This yard built the 1725-ton diesel-powered training frigate *Nigeria*, armed with two 4in guns and Squid, that proved extremely useful as a blockade asset in that country's civil war.

The USA had many former US Navy ships to dispose of to friendly nations, but in order to provide a small patrol frigate (PF) of similar concept to the above ships to be provided as aid, a new 900-ton export diesel-powered PF was designed; it was armed with 3in and 40mm guns, Hedgehog and depth charges. The concept was based on the Italian ships exported in the 1950s. Four were supplied to Iran, two in 1964 and two in 1969, and two to Thailand in 1971–74.

The modern surface combatant

The pressure of cost

American naval policy during the 1960s was dominated by Secretary of Defense Macnamara and his new concept of 'cost-effectiveness'. Indeed the spiralling expense of the postwar three-dimensional navies could not go on. The US Navy had under development a long- and medium-range missile system called Typhon. This weapon and its associated radar was so power-hungry that it could only be effectively carried by nuclear-powered ships. An impressive 10,825-ton DLGN was designed for the new missile, but the project was cancelled in 1963. The existing types of missile did not work, so why invest in a new one? The funds that would have gone to Typhon were therefore redirected into investment in obtaining reliable performance from the existing systems. Macnamara wanted DDGs of new design to replace the cancelled ships, but Congress insisted on nuclear power which inflated size and costs and delayed their laying down as Executive fought Legislature. The first – and only – pair, *California* and *South Carolina*, were not begun until 1970. They were completed as 10,150-ton DLGNs in 1974–75, armed with the new Standard SAM, a modified digital electronics Tartar that worked. In general, however, their weapons fit was limited for such expensive and large ships and they had no helicopter hangar.

Another type that seemed over-large was the British follow-on DLG that began life – ironically enough – as an attempt to produce a small and cheaper carrier escort than the 'County'. A new long range (40 miles) SAM of much more compact dimensions, Sea Dart, was under development. This, it was hoped, would fit into an enlarged *Leander*, and a frigate designation, Type 82, was optimistically chosen. A helicopter could not be fitted in, but the Australian Ikara ASW missile provided stand-off capability. Despite such measures, the volume requirements of command and control spaces (an improved ADAWS 2 was fitted), the fitting of more powerful 44,000shp Olympus gas turbines in addition to a complete 30,000shp *Leander*-type steam installation and the provision of easier access to machinery spaces, all added up to a ship 500 tons larger than the previous class (albeit with a complement about seventy fewer). The cancellation of the British carrier programme led to only the first ship being built in order to get Sea Dart and Ikara to sea as soon as possible. Laid down in 1967, the 'destroyer' *Bristol* was commissioned in 1973. She was used as a trials and command ship and eventually became a training vessel.

With full-scale destroyers becoming so large and expensive, the major Western navies maintained their concentration on the frigate as the most cost-effective fleet and general-purpose escort. The British maintained *Leander* production but looked at alternatives. In the late 1960s pressure grew for Britain to acquire vessels like the Vosper export frigates, which were built to lower standards of shock resistance and quietness compared with Admiralty standards. Vosper Thornycroft were therefore asked to produce an enlarged version of the Mk 7 for the Royal Navy that might also be even more attractive on the export market because of its use by the home navy.

The French navy's surface fleet has always suffered from concentration of resources on prestige units, particularly the SSBNs and carriers that support France's independent foreign policy stance. As a result, highly capable fleet escorts like the Cassard *are few in number.* (French Navy)

The problem was that applying top-league navy standards of capability and construction meant increased size and cost. The ships, eight of which were built in the 1970s as Type 21s to replace the earlier diesel-powered Type 41s and 61s, proved more expensive than expected. They combined most of the capabilities of a *Leander* – 184 sonar, weapons delivery helicopter, 4.5in gun, Seacat point-defence co-ordinated by CAAIS – with an all-gas-turbine hull of high manoeuvrability and striking appearance. They proved popular with their crews despite being very vulnerable to action and accident damage, prone to cracking and in need of extra ballast to improve stability. Apart from the addition of Exocet missiles, it proved impossible to fit the Type 21s with improved weapons and sensors, but despite the design's self-imposed limitations it failed to obtain export orders, even from Australia, which had contributed to the design. No class better displays the problems of making a modern warship comply with the twin demands of 'naval sex appeal' and real naval capability.

Another class that suffered from superficial criticism by its operators was the US Navy's mass-production design of the late 1960s, the *Knox* class DE. In order to provide adequate performance with conventional lower pressure boilers, displacement had to be increased to just over 3000 tons. The DEGs were not considered to be good value for money, so all forty-six *Knox* class were commissioned as ASW ships. The designed main armament was DASH, but the increased size allowed easy conversion to the LAMPS manned helicopter. Once they acquired this equipment the ships were powerful ASW assets, although they tended to be unpopular both for poor seakeeping and lack of general-purpose capability. The single 5in/54 had an unfortunate tendency to jam and the point-defence AAW missile system was late in arriving. Nevertheless, the class did provide some welcome new construction in a difficult decade for the USN. Five DEG versions of the *Knox* class were built locally for Spain in the early 1970s.

In the mid 1960s France diminished the size of her DLG type '*frégates*' to produce a 3500-ton ASW fleet escort, logically – but confusingly – termed a 'corvette'. Five of this C 65 *Aconit* class were planned. Like the *Knox* class, it was a single-screw design, but this proved un-

popular and the follow-on ships were enlarged twin-screw vessels of the C 67 *Tourville* class, capable of 31kts rather than 27kts. *Aconit* relied on the Malafon missile for long range ASW, but the *Tourville*s had two helicopters as well. Both types were equipped with SENIT data systems. These *Tourville*s were large and capable fleet escorts which displaced 4850 tons and before completion had been redesignated '*frégates*'. Only three were built, commissioning between 1974 and 1977. There was no question of replacing the postwar escorts with this design, and in order to maintain fleet numbers a colonial gunboat was required, even smaller than the *Commandant Rivière*. The result was the 950-ton A 69 *aviso* (sloop), the first of which, *D'Estienne D'Orves*, was laid down in 1972. Diesel-powered for endurance, and with a speed of 24kts, the ships were fitted for coastal ASW as an important alternative role, given the need to keep clear the paths of the French SSBNs before they reached the open sea. Main armament was a 100mm gun on the forecastle, with the new Exocet surface-to-surface missiles added for sloops deployed abroad. Seventeen were laid down over the next decade. Two were built for South Africa, but a belated change of policy saw them sold instead to Argentina, together with a third built new.

The Royal Netherlands Navy decided that the modernised cruiser was not the most cost-effective answer to the problem of providing flagships and AAW protection for its escort groups. A new 4300-ton DLG design was therefore prepared with gas turbine propulsion to economise on crew. Attempts were made to obtain commonality with the British Type 82s, but eventually only the gas turbines and the Type 162 bottom profiling sonar were British. The main weapons were the American Standard and a helicopter, with two former destroyer 4.7in guns on the forecastle. Two ships only could be afforded, *Tromp* and *De Ruyter*, completed in 1975–76 and rated as 'frigates'. They were fitted with a newly developed Signaal 'Sensor Weapon

and Command System' (SEWACO), a version of which was later retro-fitted into the Dutch *Leander*s.

The Royal Canadian Navy had its own financial problems in the 1960s. Eight large 3500-ton 'Tribal' class general-purpose frigates were projected, to be armed with Tartar missiles, a single 5in gun and ASW torpedo tubes. These would have provided useful air cover to the DE force, but the project was abandoned in 1963. When the project was revived in 1968 it was changed to be a larger squadron flagship variant of the existing DDH type, with heavier calibre 5in Italian gun and provision for two ASW Sea Kings. A Dutch radar fit was carried, but most important was the provision of a computerised native Canadian CCS 280 AIO system that allowed the ships to operate as fully integrated members of Nato task forces. The system was later added to the two earlier *Annapolis* class DDHs.

Air-capable cruisers and destroyers

The advent of the ASW helicopter gave a new impetus to adding a substantial air capability to the cruiser-type ship, something that had gone out of fashion during the war because of the vulnerability of observation seaplanes and their limited utility. The British developed the concept of a large guided-missile helicopter cruiser in the 1960s, to supplement their medium-sized carriers, which were to concentrate on strike aircraft and fighters. After the abandonment of the carriers in 1966 these eventually acquired through decks and evolved into the *Invincible* class ASW support carriers. As interims the last two conventional cruisers of the *Tiger* class were rebuilt to carry Sea King ASW helicopters aft.

In the Soviet Union, where large-deck carriers were politically unacceptable, the helicopter-carrying cruiser was a means of getting into the carrier business. There is continuity from the two 15,500-ton Project 1123s (*Moskva*s) of 1967–68 through the 1143 and 1143Ms with

Leningrad, *one of two Project 1123 ships, represented the Soviet Union's first air-capable ship. The cruiser-type battery of guns and missiles forward has been perpetuated in later more carrier-like shapes, and even the* Admiral Kuznetsov *carries a SSM battery buried in the flight deck. The Project 1123s were fitted with a bow sonar, VDS in the stern, and a complement of about fifteen Hormone ASW helicopters. The rectangular markings on the flight deck indicate the elevators to the hangar below. (CMP)*

their canted 'through' decks to the 1143.4 (*Admiral Kuznetsov*) of the 1990s, whose SSM battery buried in the flight deck acts as a kind of evolutionary throwback to show the ship's cruiser ancestry.

The Italians faced not dissimilar problems to the Soviets, with legal barriers to a carrier force. The first steps toward air-capable ships were the two 5000-ton *Andrea Dorias*, enlargements of the *Impavido* class DDGs with broader beam and a hangar and flight deck aft. Commissioned in 1964, these proved too small and were followed in 1969 by the *Vittorio Veneto*, almost the archetypal helicopter cruiser and a good example of how the British 'Through Deck Cruiser' originated at the same time. This 7500-ton design had a larger flight deck above the after hangar and, like its predecessors, it carried a Terrier SAM launcher forward. Even *Vittorio Veneto*'s helicopter capacity was inadequate, however, and the Italians adopted a 'through deck' solution with the *Giuseppe Garibaldi*, laid down in 1981. This emerged as a small 10,000-ton carrier in 1987, and the Italian navy was authorised to operate STOVL aircraft from her in 1989.

In the West the most developed manifestation of the helicopter cruiser concept was the Italian Vittorio Veneto, *developed from the extremely cramped ships of the* Doria *class. Even the* Veneto *proved too small for optimum helicopter operations, and the following ship, the* Giuseppe Garibaldi, *was given a 'through deck' and an island superstructure, becoming in effect a small aircaft carrier. (Italian official)*

The other navy to produce innovative air-capable surface combatants was that of Japan. The original intention in 1969 was to procure two 8000-ton cruisers to provide Sea King and command support for two Escort Flotillas, but the original Nakasone plan was amended in 1972 to build instead a pair of 5000-ton helicopter destroyers (DDH). These combined a DD front end mounting guns and ASROC with a central hangar and provision for three large Sea King helicopters. Two were completed with old battlecruiser names, *Hiei* and *Haruna*. Two modified and slightly enlarged variants appeared at the end of the same decade.

At the end of the 1970s the US Congress tried to encourage the use of a *Spruance* destroyer hull to provide a small aviation platform for helicopters and even for Harriers. The designs included 'through deck' options, but the US Navy was never happy about the project and the ship was completed as a standard *Spruance*, the USS *Hayler*.

Admiral Isakov, a Project 1134A (Nato Kresta II) 'large anti-submarine ship' in December 1977. The most visible difference from the Kresta I is the angled box launcher for four SS-N-14 ASW missiles under each bridge wing. Since these ships were expected to be involved in a three-dimensional offensive battle, they were also heavily armed with SAMs, heavyweight torpedo tubes, and Gatling-type point-defence weapons. (MoD, Crown Copyright)

Strike cruisers and large anti-submarine ships

Having been forced by Khrushchev to abandon its cruiser programme and to embrace new technology, the Soviet navy designed a new type of 'missile cruiser' (RKR) in the late 1950s that marked a departure in warship design. This was the 4400-ton Project 58 (*Kynda*) class, armed with two quadruple SS-N-3 surface-to-surface missile launchers. These ships were designed to carry out nuclear strikes on carriers and they also carried a medium range SAM launcher forward and 76mm guns aft, as well as six tubes for large 21in torpedoes. After four were completed in the early sixties the requirement for longer range operations and greater 'combat stability' led to the SAM armament being doubled and the SSM armament halved. The resulting 5400-ton Project 1134 (*Kresta*) had enhanced ASW potential with more rocket launchers and torpedo tubes. This more three-dimensional armament allowed them to be later reclassified 'large anti-submarine ships' (BPK) along with the *Kashin* class destroyers. This reflected a greater

emphasis on countering the submarine, both the SSBN and the SSN attacking the USSR's own SSBNs. After four ships the *Kresta* was modified into a real BPK, the Project 1134A, with SS-N-14 ASW missiles replacing the SS-N-3s and improved sonar. Ten of these real BPKs were built in the 1970s. An enlarged 8200-ton gas turbine variant appeared with the Project 1134B (*Kara* class) in 1973, built on the Black Sea at Nikolayev. Seven of these were built in the 1970s simultaneously with the Leningrad-built 1134As.

An alternative approach to the BPK was provided by the enlarged SKR. A new class of such gas turbine-powered vessels, the 3000-ton Project 1135 (*Krivak*) appeared from the Kaliningrad yard in 1970. Despite much Western hype

at the time, these were hardly very capable vessels, with only four ASW missiles on the forecastle (which had replaced the originally intended SSM fit), ASW torpedoes, a point-defence AAW system and four 76mm guns. They

Apart from aircraft carriers, the largest and most impressive surface combatants built since the war are the 24,000-ton Russian Project 1144 cruisers of the Kirov class. In an attempt to convey a notion of their power and size, they are often referred to in Western literature as 'battlecruisers', but were designed as the centrepieces of forces defending the safe bastions for strategic missile submarines. In contrast to earlier Soviet warships, which seemed festooned with weapons, much of this ship's firepower is hidden beneath the foredeck hatches of the vertical launch missile systems. (MoD, Crown Copyright)

reflected Soviet concepts of short sharp engagements. The lack of the helicopter was a particular drawback. No fewer than twenty-one of these ships were commissioned between 1970 and 1982, along with eleven more to a slightly modified 1135M design with heavier guns. As the limitations of the type became clear they were reclassified SKR in 1977–8. A much more 'Western' variant, based on the same hull but with a helicopter and forward mounted gun, was built as the Project 1135P for the KGB border guards.

Soviet missile cruisers and BPKs were not primarily escort vessels, like the Western DLGs, destroyers and frigates. They were designed for co-ordinated offensive operations in co-operation with land-based air and sub-surface assets in 'fleet versus fleet' actions. They thus challenged the self esteem of the Western surface sailors, who had never been entirely happy with the escort role and the subordination to the airmen and submariners that modern technology implied. The US Navy was provoked into a major reclassification of its surface combatants in 1975 into 'cruisers' (most DLGs and DLGNs), 'destroyers' (smaller DLGs, DDGs and DDs) and 'frigates' (DEs, DEGs); corresponding letters were respectively CGs/CGNs, DDs/DDGs, and FFs/FFGs.

ASuW had not been a priority for Western warships. Although they could always use their SAMs in a surface-to-surface role, this was an expensive solution that created dilemmas for warfare officers having to measure the relative importance of the surface and air threats. The surface-to-surface capability of Western ships was therefore significantly improved with the addition of small SSMs like Exocet, Otomat and Harpoon that could be added with minimal ship impact and which gave long ranges (from 23 to over 75 miles). The provision of surface combatants that could stand alone was therefore reconsidered.

By the early 1970s the new Aegis AAW system designed as a successor to Typhon was offering levels of AAW protection that might well allow ships so equipped to dispense with fighter combat air patrols. A new DLGN designed to carry Aegis had its ASuW and power projection capabilities enhanced with Harpoon anti-ship missiles and the Tomahawk long range land-attack cruise missile, some armour protection and an 8in lightweight gun. Eight of these strike cruisers (CSGNs) were planned, but they proved too expensive and were never begun. No more nuclear-powered cruisers were built and the USN found it to be cheaper and quicker to reactivate its four old fast battleships of the *Iowa* class and fit them with Harpoon and Tomahawk to act as the centrepieces of its surface action groups (SAGs) of the 1980s. Also, existing CGNs were given cruise missiles, even at the expense of helicopter capability, to improve their power projection utility.

The Soviets were, however, impressed by American interest in the CSGN concept as it fitted in well with their doctrinal developments. The new idea of bastion SSBN defence (see chapter 9), then being developed called for large seaworthy strike platforms to keep Western fleets at bay. Soviet thinking hence swung back to an enhanced ASuW role for surface platforms. The most impressive aspect of this was the massive Project 1144 *Kirov* laid down in 1973 and completed in 1980. This 24,300-ton monster had a comprehensive fit of long range SSMs, advanced SAMs, medium guns and even ASW missiles. She was intended to command and fight a three-dimensional battle in the bastions. A modified and improved sister was built in 1978–84 and two more were laid down in 1983 and 1986.

The final Soviet 'large anti-submarine ship' design, the Udaloy, *photographed when new in 1981. The ship's main ASW weapons are the SS-N-14 below the bridge (as in the* Kresta II*s), and two helicopters hangared aft.* (MoD, Crown Copyright)

These latter-day battlecruisers were built at the Baltic yard, Leningrad. In the same city at the Zhdanov yard (the home of the *Kresta*) the steam-powered Project 1134 was developed into a 6300-ton ASuW Project 956 'destroyer'. This new class, armed with new SSMs and 130mm guns and with secondary SAM and ASW capability, entered mass production in 1976 when the first of the class, *Sovremennyy*, was laid down. At Nikolayev the 1134B was enlarged into an impressive strike cruiser, the Project 1164 or *Slava* type, a 10,000-ton gas turbine ship with serried ranks of SS-N-12 anti-carrier missiles. Aft was the same highly advanced long range SA-N-6 SAM system as in the *Kirov*, next to Aegis the most capable in the world.

In order to balance this flood of ASuW assets Kaliningrad expanded the 1135 into a real BPK of double the displacement. This Project 1155 or *Udaloy* type was built at Zhdanov as well as at Kaliningrad and was an impressive ASW hunter-killer with an excellent sonar fit, SS-N-14 ASW missiles, heavyweight torpedoes and two ASW helicopters. Four 76mm guns on the forecastle and point-defence SAMs provided supplementary capability. The first two were laid down in 1978, and between one and two per year were commissioned in the 1980s.

Most recent developments

During the 1970s and 1980s both major Western navies carried out large-scale programmes of surface combatant replacement, with new types of AAW and ASW ships being designed and procured. These assets remained primarily task force escorts, although their ASuW capability was steadily improved. In the USA Macnamara's Office of the Secretary of Defense had called in 1966–67 for a more capable mass production task force (and fast merchant ship) escort than the relatively slow and lightly armed DE. The requirement was a new DX more directly comparable with the old Second World War DDs they would replace, to be built at a single yard on a 'total package' basis to obtain economies of scale. The hull would be large enough to take SAMs in the DXG variant and expansion capacity for modernisation would be built in. With ship steel being a relatively cheap part of warship costs compared with sensors, computers and weapons, an over-size ship was not necessarily an over-costly ship, and large size gave improved speed and seakeeping.

As the concept of the DX/DXG was refined it was decided to build a nuclear version as a follow-on economy DLGN. This eventually emerged as the *Virginia* class CGN, four of which were commissioned between 1976 and 1980. This had double-ended Standard SAM launchers with combined SAM and ASROC magazines, two 5in guns and a helicopter hangar. The ships turned out more expensive than the previous *California* class, and the fact that so few could be afforded only made it more important that the basic DX be kept as cheap as possible. In fact, despite plans for new CGNs these were the last such vessels built for the US Navy.

Litton was chosen to build the new destroyers, all of which it was eventually decided would be of the cheaper ASW type. An advanced computerised yard was specially built and work began on the first ship in November 1972. USS *Spruance* was commissioned in 1975, the first of thirty. The ships had a powerful low frequency SQS-53 sonar at the bow, ASROC missiles and provision for a large helicopter. NTDS was fitted and the propulsion system was all-gas-turbine. Apparently 'underarmed', these 6000-ton ships were capable of operating their sensors and weapons in a wide range of sea states. Iran ordered four DXGs with double-ended Stand-

ard mountings and Kevlar armour protection. These were taken over by the USN as the *Kidd* class and a thirty-first *Spruance*, intended to be an air-capable ship (see above), was completed as a standard ship of the class in 1983. The *Spruance*s form the backbone of the current USN fleet escort force and have been upgraded with towed array sonar and Harpoon and Tomahawk missiles. The addition of a multipurpose vertical launch system in place of the ASROC launcher greatly increases their operational flexibility. In the Gulf War and subsequent crises they proved very useful as land-attack cruise missile launching platforms.

The *Spruance* concept was a first step to the philosophy of procurement adopted by Admiral Zumwalt, who as newly appointed CNO in 1970 thought he had a solution for maintaining the correct combination of quantity and quality. Zumwalt produced his own concept of the 'high/low' mix with not all vessels built to the same level of capability. He thought there might be cheaper ways of providing ASW capacity, but the *Spruance* hull was an excellent platform for a vessel that could take the long-awaited Aegis system to sea. Zumwalt felt that nuclear power was a luxury even at the 'high' end of the spectrum and supported an Aegis destroyer instead. This idea proved an attractive alternative to the strike cruiser and contributed to the latter's cancellation. Instead, Litton laid down the first 7000-ton Aegis version of the *Spruance* in 1980. Given its cost and capability, the designation 'cruiser' seemed appropriate and the USS *Ticonderoga* was commissioned as CG-47 in 1983. Twenty-six sisters were built, far more than if a CGN concept had been adopted. Later vessels carry the versatile VLS system and have been deployed carrying large numbers of Tomahawk SSMs.

The low end of the Zumwalt mix was provided by a new FFG (guided-missile frigate), a 2650-ton single-screw ship. The original inten-

tion was to have specialist ASW, AAW and ASuW variants, but in the event a single general-purpose type combined all capabilities. A common launcher for SAMs/SSMs was mounted forward, with provision for two ASW helicopters aft. A 3in gun amidships provided supplementary low-level firepower and a towed array compensated for a less capable hull sonar than the *Spruance*'s. A reduced version of NTDS was originally fitted without data links, but some ships were later fitted with the latter to allow full tactical interaction with other fleet units. Fifty-one FFG-7s were built from 1975 to 1989 and the design, controversial at home, proved popular in the export market as a flexible and cost-effective type. It was adopted by Australia, Spain and Taiwan.

In an attempt to provide Aegis in a less expensive form the USN in the 1980s designed a slightly smaller 'destroyer' to carry the system. Experience in the Falklands War led to more weight being used for protection (steel construction and Kevlar armour) than in earlier types, and displacement was almost the same as that of the *Ticonderoga*s at 6625 tons. The main drawback with these *Arleigh Burke*s is the lack of a helicopter hangar, but this is expected to be fitted in the 'Flight II' version. This ship, which still costs over a billion dollars per unit, will, it is hoped, replace the postwar DDGs. The Japanese have enlarged and improved the design as the *Kongo* class, the first of which was launched in 1991.

The Royal Navy eschewed the high/low concept as its smaller numbers seemed to dictate all vessels being given the highest possible level of capability. Low mix vessels were considered at various times but they either grew into high end ships or were abandoned. In 1967 the Future Fleet Working Party called for a lower cost AAW ship to replace the Type 82 DLG. The result was the 3500-ton gas-turbine-powered Type 42, numbered as a frigate design but even-

The prototype Aegis cruiser Ticonderoga *in 1989. These ships, based on the standard* Spruance *destroyer hull, were designated cruisers to reflect the much enhanced capabilities of Aegis, undoubtedly the most sophisticated air defence system currently in service. They symbolise a move away from concern with ship characteristics – in effect they have replaced the ultra-expensive nuclear cruiser – towards an emphasis on the electronics and weapons systems carried. The advantages bestowed by the CGN's machinery are lost, but far more ships can be built for the same funds.* (L & L van Ginderen)

Admiral Zumwalt's concept of a 'high/low' mix of capabilities produced the FFG-7 Oliver Hazard Perry class at the low end. To some in the USA they were too austere, while contrary critics thought them too expensive, but they were built in large numbers, doing much to replace the ageing FRAM destroyers in the US fleet. For navies without missile cruisers they appeared very capable ships, with a good general-purpose mix of SAM, medium gun and two helicopters. Versions were built for Spain, Taiwan and – here represented by HMAS Adelaide – *Australia.* (RAN)

tually classified 'destroyer' once the British decided to call all their air defence vessels by this name. The 42 was a controversial design with a confused design process: decisions on length, etc were taken on an arbitrary basis; the ships proved too short and were less than optimally laid out; the last four were lengthened, but this in turn caused hull cracking. Nevertheless they provided a useful combination of 40-mile range SAM launcher, long range aircraft direction platform and mid grade ASW ship. The AIO system was ADAWS 4, a close relative of the system in HMS *Bristol* but with Ikara deleted. Unlike the Type 82s, a helicopter was carried for weapons delivery and surface search and strike. The main weakness of the 42s was lack of a point-defence AAW system, since Sea Dart could not cope with heavy attacks, having only two channels of fire. After two were lost in the Falklands conflict the Vulcan/Phalanx close-in weapons system was fitted, which did much to close this gap. Eighteen in all were built from 1970 to 1985 and two – ironically as it turned out – were ordered by Argentina.

A two-pronged approach was taken in the 1970s to ASW frigates. It was planned to build a new generation of frigates to replace the earlier *Leander*s. The new ships would carry the latest long range 2016 sonar and have a capacity to carry two helicopters. Exocet missiles would provide ASuW capacity and Sea Wolf a fully automated AAW (including anti-missile) capability. In addition, the broad-beam *Leander*s would be brought up to the same standard. Both had the CAAIS AIO system. The new all-gas-turbine ships designated Type 22 were as large as the Type 42s and their future was in doubt for some time. The programme might have stopped at four ships had not the Royal Navy become aware of the Outboard ELINT equipment that the USA was willing to make available. This concept, developed for cruise missile targeting, was considered to be a valuable means of intelligence gathering and integration. The

Type 22 design was enlarged into a 'Batch 2' to take the equipment and its additional personnel, a dramatic example of the modern surface ship as primarily an integrated sensor platform.

The relatively noisy Type 22s were designed just too early to exploit fully another sensor breakthrough, the towed array sonar. Longer arrays than those fitted to submarines gave surface ships for the first time the same or better passive detection ranges compared with SSNs. The 2031(I) towed array was first fitted to four specially modified *Leander*s in the early 1980s, and these ships soon showed remarkable detection abilities. The relatively quiet steam-powered platforms proved much more capable long range detectors than the Batch 2 Type 22s that entered service with the production 2031 (Z) from 1984. This was not a reflection of the sensor but of the platform. To prosecute towed array contacts, most Batch 2s were fitted to carry a large search-strike ASW helicopter rather than one or two weapons delivery and surface surveillance Lynx. They were also fitted with improved AIO, CACS (Computer Assisted Command System), although the system, intended to handle both the air and towed array picture simultaneously, proved something of a disappointment.

Just as towed array was coming into service the Thatcher Government carried out a major defence review. During this process the role of the surface ship came under great scrutiny, with the Royal Navy unable to explain fully the roles of its surface combatants or the reasoning behind the appearance of relatively few 'weapons' on expensive 'platforms'. Left in ignorance, John Nott, the Secretary of State, was persuaded that submarines and maritime patrol aircraft should bear the brunt of the future Atlantic battle. Type 22 construction was to be cut back and the *Leander* rebuild programme curtailed. A new towed array ship was to be built that would be little more than a tug with self-defence capacity to allow it to operate in the isolated manner

required by the need to find quiet water. Plans for follow-on air defence ships, impressive Type 43/44 destroyers with double-ended Sea Dart installations and Sea Wolf point-defence SAMs, were abandoned.

The latter ships would have been useful in the Falklands War which caused some reversal of policy on surface combatants. The Type 22 was vindicated in the rather unusual role of 'goalkeeper' – *ie* the provider of point-defence AAW to ships not equipped with suitable systems (notable carriers and Type 42 destroyers). More ships were ordered, some as direct replacements for lost Type 42s. The last four Type 22s were built to an enlarged Batch 3 design with improved point-defence (the Dutch Goalkeeper as well as Sea Wolf), Harpoon SSMs and, most significantly, a 4.5in gun, the utility of which as a shore bombardment system had been proved by the war. These 4200-ton 'frigates' were some of the most impressive surface combatants in the world. A version of the CACS AIO was fitted that took time to get operating properly.

The war also had the effect of transforming the design of the towed array tug into a fully fledged 3000-ton Type 23 frigate. Its ancestry is clear in the ultra-quiet gas turbine/diesel-electric (CODLAG) propulsion system, but the ship itself has grown into a genuine fleet ASW destroyer like the Type 22 with the same mix of capabilities, better towed array performance and considerably greater radar and acoustic stealth. The only problem with the design was the overloading of the ship's action information organisation as its capabilities proliferated. The original system, a version of the troublesome CACS, had to be abandoned and the first ships went to sea without a fully integrated combat system. Given the distributed nature of modern electronics this had less effect than expected on the capabilities of the ship as an individual unit. It did, however make its full electronic integration into a force impossible. The first Type 23, HMS *Norfolk*, commissioned in 1990. The new SSCS (Surface Ship Command System) AIO was not expected to come into service until the

The British Type 22 frigate Brilliant lived up to her name during the Falklands War, in a point-defence role for which the ships were not primarily designed. The ASW capability of the Type 22s was barely tested during the conflict, where the ability of Argentina's German-built conventional submarines to elude a navy trained to hunt Soviet nuclear boats suggests lessons for post Cold War ASW. (MoD, Crown Copyright)

eighth ship in 1994. The British considered trying to boost hull numbers by building an austere large corvette-type offshore patrol vessel (the OPV3), but this died with the squeeze on defence expenditure that followed the post-Falklands bonanza and a reaffirmation of the decision to concentrate on high-grade vessels.

Although a formidable ASW ship, the Type 23 has only point-defence capability with vertically launched Sea Wolf. The next generation British frigate will be a Type 42 replacement. With Aegis ruled out for industrial reasons the Royal Navy decided on a European option, an AAW missile system based on the French ASTER. At first the British considered a 15-mile range 'Local Area Missile System' (LAMS) the most cost-effective, but by 1993 a longer 40-mile maximum range system was being preferred as a true Sea Dart replacement. A new 6000-ton ship to carry this is under development as a joint venture by Britain, France and Italy, with an expected in-service date of 2002. It may also carry land-attack cruise missiles.

France was in more need of joint procurement than Britain, given the travails of her surface combatant programme. Unlike Britain she pursued the high/low mix route which, given her restricted budget for conventional forces, meant very few capable ships and some very incapable low-end vessels. The chosen design of task force escort for destroyer replacement in the 1980s was the C 70 'corvette', re-rated 'frégate' in 1988. The 'corvette' category reflected reduced dimensions compared with the F 67, a standard displacement of 3830 tons. The first seven were combined diesel and gas turbine (CODOG) powered ASW ships, rather like French Type 22s but with less capable AA defences only partly compensated for by a forecastle gun. Variable depth sonar, very useful in Mediterranean conditions, was fitted and later ships carried towed array.

The problems arose with the AAW variant, inherently a more expensive vessel. The best France could afford was to refit old Standard SAM systems from the destroyers being replaced into a diesel variant of the C 70 hull. Even this stopped after two ships, Cassard and Jean Bart, had been built, because the French belatedly discovered that the SM-1 Standard was being abandoned by the USA and the SM-2 was too expensive. Two more were cancelled. With only nine new first rate surface ships France has been forced to the rather desperate expedient of building offshore patrol vessels under the guise of 'frégates'. Six Floreal class 'frégates de surveillance' appeared in the early 1990s, followed by a rather more warship-like

Lafayette class 'frégate legère'. None of these OPVs had sonar and hence an ASW capacity, although an export version of the Lafayette was available with a sonar to add to the gun, SSMs, point-defence SAM and small helicopter.

The other major mainland European countries developed more classic frigates, some of which made a considerable impact on the export market. The Dutch replaced their DDEs in the late 1970s and early '80s with an impressive 3000-ton Kortenaer type. Attempts were made to make common cause with Nato allies and eventually a deal was struck with West Germany to produce a 'standard' frigate. The Dutch ships were all-gas-turbine vessels, while the German Bremens had diesel cruise engines. The other major difference was totally different AIO, the Dutch ships having the SEWACO system and the Germans an improved version of their own SATIR. This was an expensive decision by the Germans, equivalent to the cost of two more ships. The weapons fit was roughly the same for both classes, gun and point-defence SAM (Nato Sea Sparrow) forward, two Lynx helicopters aft (equipped, unlike British Lynx, with dipping sonar). The Dutch built ten Kortenaers for themselves and two for Greece, while the Germans built eight Bremens. Two more additional ships of the type were constructed in the Netherlands as cheaper air defence ships than the Tromps. They sacrificed the ASW version's hangar and gun for an American Standard SM-1MR installation, an interesting example of the trade-offs necessary in modern warship design.

The Dutch, like the British, attempted a cheaper follow-on frigate design but operational realities pushed size and capability back upwards again. Rather than being little more than OPVs as originally suggested, the Karel Doorman class frigates turned out in the early

The latest British frigate design, the Type 23 'Duke' class, started life as a very cheap 'tug' for a towed array sonar, but gradually grew into a fleet frigate of medium size. The most novel feature of the design is the ultra-quiet electric propulsion to maximise the benefit of the sonar. The design also incorporates some radar 'stealth' measures. The fifth vessel of the class, HMS Iron Duke commissioned in May 1992. (Yarrow)

The most successful export frigate of recent years has been the German MEKO concept, which is not a single design but a variety based on modular options applied to a few basic hull sizes. This is the Turkish Turgut Reis, *a MEKO 200, armed with a 5in gun forward, three 25mm close-in weapon systems, eight Harpoon SSMs amidships, Sea Sparrow short range SAM launcher above the hangar, which, with the flight deck aft, permits the operation of an ASW helicopter.* (L & L van Ginderen)

1990s as slightly smaller but fully capable towed array frigates with helicopter, gun, self-defence AAW missiles and CIWS and Harpoon SSMs.

The Dutch produced smaller ships for export. Indonesia purchased three 1160-ton corvettes from Wilton Fijenoord in 1979–80, with a powerful general-purpose armament and a computerised AIO system. One actually carried a small helicopter. Significantly, however, the Indonesians found it more cost-effective to buy larger secondhand vessels later in the 1980s to provide more seaworthy general-purpose platforms. No fewer than six Dutch *Leander*s and three British 'Tribals' were purchased.

Italy also had exports in mind. Between building pairs of traditional DDGs in the 4000-ton class at the beginning of the 1970s and the 1990s, Italy produced a small 2200-ton *Lupo* design that tried to cram a standard frigate weapons fit into too small a space. This proved popular with some customers, Peru, Venezuela and Iraq buying examples. The Italians themselves found the *Lupo* too small and it was expanded into the much better balanced 2500-ton *Maestrale*.

France managed to obtain the Saudi Arabian order for four 2000-ton general-purpose frigates in the 1980s, but the most popular export warship of the 1980s and '90s was the West German MEKO family. This utilises modular construction which allows customers' needs to be fulfilled at minimum costs. The basic architecture of the larger options (MEKO 200 is

about 2710 tons and MEKO 360 is 2900 tons) is 'modern frigate standard' – medium gun forward, point-defence missiles and/or guns, SSMs and, most importantly, an ASW helicopter to exploit medium frequency hull sonar. Propulsion is straight diesel or CODOG with a maximum speed of 27–30kts. Variants of the design have been sold to Argentina (which rates them 'destroyers'), Greece, Nigeria, Portugal and Turkey. An enlarged variant has been adopted to replace Germany's older destroyers, and there is a related 1560-ton MEKO 140 corvette based on the Portuguese *Coutinho* concept, six of which were built by Argentina. Armament of the corvettes comprises guns, Exocet SSMs and short range ASW weapons.

The Soviet answer to the export requirement was a simple 1440-ton Project 1159 SKR developed in the late 1970s. These *Koni*s were supplied in the 1980s to Algeria, Cuba, East Germany, Libya and Yugoslavia (which developed the design in later domestic construction). Other corvette/small frigate types were the Belgian *Wielingen*s commissioned in 1978 as 1900-ton coastal escorts, and the smaller and less

capable Danish *Niels Juels*, intended for ASW but fitted out primarily for ASuW with 3in gun and Harpoon missiles. These 1100-ton vessels are the Danish navy's main fully combatant surface warships in the 1990s. The larger 'frigates' in her fleet were all offshore patrol vessels primarily for fishery protection in the extensive Danish waters around the Faeroes. A 1345-ton *Hvidbjornen* class was built in the 1960s, with an enlarged development in the following decade. They combined a 3in gun with a helicopter and simple radar and sonar fit. In 1991 the Danes began replacing the older ships with 2600-ton 'Stanflex 2000' vessels. These are being built as OPVs, although the highly flexible design allows their relatively easy conversion into fully combatant warships with SAMs, SSMs and ASW torpedoes, given the money and political will.

In Asia, Japan transformed her Escort Flotillas in the 1980s with a very impressive new generation of 'destroyers'. The twelve 30kt 3000-ton *Hayatsuki*s built in the 1980s combined British COGOG powerplants with a Sea King helicopter capacity, ASROC point-defence missiles, Harpoon SSMs and gun. This was a little tight even for the Japanese, and the following eight *Asagiri*s were expanded to 3500 tons with four full-power gas turbines in a COGAG

If the outstanding European frigate of the 1960s was the British Leander, *then the Dutch* Kortenaer *was the late 1970s equivalent. On a normal displacement of 3000 tons – relatively small for a first class ASW escort of the time – the Dutch contrived a frigate which not only satisfied their own requirements, but was also adopted by Germany (albeit with modified machinery and electronics), and exported to Greece. Furthermore, a modified air-defence version, represented here by* Witte de With, *was developed from the standard design.* (L & L van Ginderen)

Halifax, the first of a new class of twelve towed array frigates for the Canadian navy. The project has been dogged by technical problems and delays, but once the teething troubles have been sorted out the ships will be a potent addition to Nato's surface forces. (L & L van Ginderen)

arrangement to give still higher speed. The design looks as if it will be expanded yet again for future construction. These ships are all being fitted with towed array.

Three 3850-ton Standard SM-1MR equipped DDGs of classic layout had been laid down in the 1970s, while two more DDGs based generally on the *Hatsuyuki*s appeared in the 1980s. Their SM-1 launchers were bow mounted but there was still no room for anything more than a helicopter platform. The Japanese then moved to Aegis (see above). The new ships meant that each Escort Flotilla had eight modern ocean-going units and eight Sea King helicopters. The older DDKs were relegated to supplement the smaller escort vessels in the District Forces. Given the availability of these assets, only three new gas turbine-powered 1200–1500-ton DEs were built in the 1980s, armed with Harpoon missiles, guns and ASW rocket launchers and torpedoes. The small 1200-ton ship had to be enlarged, but even the bigger DE was a much less capable ASW asset than a DDK.

Canada also modernised its destroyer forces. Not only was the *Iroquois* class reconstructed with Standard AAW missiles in a VLS system, thus plugging a long-standing gap in Canadian escort group capability, but the older DDEs were replaced by an impressive new 4400-ton *Halifax* class towed array ship with CODOG propulsion and a comprehensive range of capabilities, ASW helicopter and torpedoes, point-defence SAM, harpoon SSM and light gun. Both ships carry the fully distributed SHIN-PADS combat data system. The Canadians had done much to maintain the combat capability of their earlier DDEs, including fitting them with the Automatic Data Link Plotting System (AD-

LIPS) to allow full electronic integration with Nato task forces. Some ships were also fitted with towed arrays for ASW Striking Force operations.

China only entered the world of modern ship construction in the 1990s. She built lots of warships in the preceding years, but these were of old-fashioned design, basically Soviet style hulls of the 1950s with surface-to-surface missiles instead of torpedoes. These had some export success but were not a sign of major naval capability. The 1600-ton *Siping* commissioned in 1986 carried a helicopter in addition to a French type 100mm gun, Italian lightweight ASW torpedoes and traditional Chinese SSMs and ASW rocket launchers. Not until the 1990s did the improved 1700-ton EF30 introduce China's first computerised AIO system. An export order from Thailand for a 2500-ton variant was to be fitted out with Western systems after delivery. Asia was indeed emerging in the 1990s as a major new area of naval activity, with both purchases and new construction. For some years India had been combining British hulls with Soviet weapons technology in domestic con-

struction procured side by side with Soviet destroyers/ BPKs. Taiwan, with its essentially short reach requirements, transformed old FRAM destroyers into SAM equipped general-purpose combatants bristling with light guns. North Korea copied the Chinese approach with old 1950s style ships (plus SSMs), but South Korea moved through 1500-ton corvette type light frigates armed only with guns, SSMs, torpedoes and depth charges to a new 4000-ton real frigate.

Navies with only short range force projection ambitions still find the corvette type useful. In the 1500–1700-ton class these combine guns, ASW torpedo tubes, point-defence SAMs, radar and sonar, and sometimes even a helicopter (although it is impossible to put more than the most basic operating facilities on such small ships that are not intended in any case for long patrols far from the shore). Computerised AIO is now normally fitted. Examples of this type are corvettes bought by Malaysia from Howald-swerke in the 1980s and Yarrow in the 1990s. Other examples included the less heavily equipped *Inhauma*s built in Brazil. Other coun-

Warship design and construction is no longer confined to the traditional industrial powers, but increasingly the developing countries in South America and Asia are entering the arena. For decades India was determined not to become a client of either of the Cold War power blocs, and this political stance was reflected in warships which combined Western and Soviet technology. The Ganga, for example, is based on a stretched version of the British Leander *hull, but with Soviet guns and missiles, a British helicopter, and a combination of Russian and Western electronics. (L & L van Ginderen)*

tries find it cheaper to procure less sophisticated ships in the same size bracket, like Chinese *Jianghu*s. Others still develop their own ships based on Soviet-type practice, like the Indian *Khukri*s, locally-built *Petya* replacements. The weaknesses of the fast attack craft both in combat capability and seakeeping are making seagoing corvettes ever more popular. South Africa is going in this direction because of the inadequacy of its Israeli type FACs and even Israel, which went to missile-armed FACs after its old former British destroyer was sunk by missile attack in 1967, has got highly capable 1000-ton missile corvettes on order from Ingalls in the United States with a highly comprehensive weapon and sensor fit. During the 1980s another American yard, Tacoma, had built for Saudi Arabia 900-ton general-purpose SSM armed corvettes, CODOG developments of the old export PF design.

If ocean-going endurance is required there is no alternative but to go bigger, to the frigate category, especially if size is required for a comprehensive weapons fit and associated command and control spaces. The evolution of the Western escort into an SSM armed general-purpose combatant, coupled with the parallel evolution of the Russian style offshore guard ship into an ocean-going combatant, has led to a growing uniformity in concepts of ship design. The combination is that of radar and sonar with an operations room, computerised AIO, data links, a helicopter, some shipborne ASW (usually lightweight torpedoes), point-defence AAW with missiles and/or a gun, CIWS, and a medium gun. Just as the Soviet navy was giving way to the Russian in 1992, the Kaliningrad yard produced a classic frigate that might have emerged from a Western builder any time over the previous thirty years. The Project 1154 *Neustrashimy* was a sign of the convergence of Russian and 'Western' thinking in basic frigate layout. Navies unable to afford new ships, such as those of Brazil and Pakistan, are now receiving modern computerised ocean combatants of this type on the secondhand market. This trend is being furthered by the end of the Cold War.

A proper area defence AAW capability requires something larger still, 6000 tons or more, designated 'destroyer' or 'cruiser' (or perhaps even 'frigate'), depending on one's national traditions, or perhaps more on political considerations such as making the ship seem to be something less than it is to ease it past difficult budget holders. All these ships have a capacity to exert force in a three-dimensional environment that is without parallel in naval history. Moreover, they have a capacity to interact as a unified force with other platforms on, below and over the sea that is equally unprecedented.

Eric Grove

Major Surface Combatants: Typical Cruisers, Frigates, Destroyers since 1945

Class	Nationality	Displacement normal/full load (tons)	Dimensions overall (feet-inches) (metres)	Armament	Machinery/ Speed (kts)	Launch/ * Conversion dates	Numbers built
Cruisers/DLGs							
SVERDLOV	Soviet	16,000/17,200	689-0 × 72-2 × 24-7 *210.0 × 22.0 × 7.5*	12-6in, 12-100mm, 16-37mm, 10-21in TT	ST/35	1950–56	15
FARRAGUT	American	4167/5648	512-6 × 52-4 × 17-9 *156.3 × 15.9 × 5.3*	2 Terrier SAM, 1-5in, 1 ASROC, 6-12in TT	ST/32	1958–60	10
COUNTY	British	6200/6800	521-6 × 54-0 × 20-6 *158.9 × 16.4 × 6.3*	2 Seaslug SAM, 8 Seacat SAM, 4-4.5in, 1 Wessex helicopter	COSAG/30	1960–67	8
ALBANY	American	14,394/18,777	674-11 × 69-9 × 25-9 *205.8 × 21.3 × 7.9*	4 Talos SAM, 4 Tartar SAM, 2-5in, 8 ASROC, 6-12in TT	ST/32	1962–64*	3
KYNDA (project 58)	Soviet	4400/5600	464-9 × 51-10 × 17-5 *141.7 × 15.8 × 9.3*	8 SS-N-3 SSM, 2 SA-N-1 SAM, 4-76mm, 2 RBU-6000 ASW rocket launchers, 6-21in TT	ST/34	1962–64	4
SUFFREN	French	5090/6090	517-0 × 51-0 × 20-0 *157.6 × 15.5 × 6.1*	2 Masurca SAM, 2-100mm, 2-30mm, 1 Malafon ASW missile, 4 ASW torpedo launchers	ST/34	1965–66	2
VITTORIO VENETO	Italian	7500/8850	589-3 × 63-7 × 19-9 *179.6 × 19.4 × 6.0*	2 Terrier/ASROC SAM/ASW, 8-3in, 6-12.75in TT, 9 AB-204/212 or 6 SH-3 helicopters	ST/30	1967	1
KARA (Project 1134B)	Soviet	8200/10,000	570-0 × 60-0 × 20-4 *173.8 × 18.3 × 6.2*	8 SS-N-14 ASW missiles, 4 SA-N-3 SAM, 4 SA-N-4, 4-76mm, 4-30mm, 10-21in TT, 2 RBU-6000 and 2 RBU-2000 ASW rocket launchers, 1 Ka-25 helicopter	COGAG/34	1971–77	7
UDALOY (Project 1155)	Soviet	6700/8100	531-6 × 63-4 × 20-4 *162.0 × 19.3 × 6.2*	8 SS-N-14 ASW missiles, 2-100mm, 4-30mm, 2 RBU-6000 ASW rocket launchers, 8-21in TT, 2 Ka-27 helicopters	COGAG/35	1979–89	11

Class	Nationality	Displacement normal/full load (tons)	Dimensions overall (feet-inches) (metres)	Armament	Machinery/ Speed (kts)	Launch/ * Conversion dates	Numbers built
KIROV (Project 1144)	Soviet	25,300/28,300	754-7 × 93-6 × 29-6 252.2 × 28.5 × 9.1	20 SS-N-19 SSM, 12 SA-N-6 SAM, 4 SA-N-4 SAM, 2-100mm, 8-30mm, 2 SS-N-14 ASW, 10-21in TT, 1 RBU-6000 ASW rocket launcher, 1 RBU-1000 ASW rocket launcher, 3 Ka-25/27 helicopters	CONAS/33	1977–89	4
TICONDEROGA	American	6560/8910	563-0 × 55-0 × 31-0 171.6 × 16.8 × 9.5	4 Standard SAM/ASROC, 8 Harpoon SSM, 2-5in, 6-12in TT, 2 LAMPS III helicopters	GT/30	1981–92	27
Destroyers							
SURCOUF	French	2750/3740	422-0 × 42-0 × 18-0 128.6 × 121.7 × 5.4	6-5in, 6-57mm, 4-20mm, 12-550mm TT	ST/34	1953–54	12
FRIESLAND	Dutch	2497/3070	381-0 × 38-0 × 17-0 116.0 × 11.7 × 5.2	4-120mm, 6-40mm, 2-375mm ASW rocket launchers, 2 DC racks	ST/36	1953–56	8
KOTLIN (Project 56)	Soviet	2850/3500	415-1 × 42-8 × 15-1 126.5 × 13.0 × 4.6	4-130mm, 16-45mm, 4-25mm, 6 DC throwers, 2 DC racks, 10-21in TT	ST/38	1954–57	27
CHARLES F ADAMS	American	3277/4526	437-0 × 47-0 × 15-0 133.2 × 14.3 × 4.6	2/1 Tartar SAM, 1-5in, 1 ASROC, 6-12.75in TT	ST/33	1959–63	23 (plus 3 each for Australia and Germany)
GEARING 'FRAM I'	American	2406/3493	390-2 × 40-11 × 14-4 119.0 × 12.5 × 4.4	4-5in, 8 ASROC, DASH, 6-12.75in TT	ST/32	1960–65*	77
KASHIN (Project 61)	Soviet	3750/4500	472-5 × 51-10 × 15-5 144.0 × 15.8 × 4.7	4 SA-N-1 SAM, 4-76mm, 2 RBU-6000 and 2 RBU-1000 ASW rocket launchers, 5-21in TT	COGAG/38	1962–71	18 (plus 5 for India)
LUDA (Project EF4)	Chinese	3250/3960	433-1 × 42-0 × 15-1 132.0 × 12.8 × 4.5	6 HY-2 SSM, 4-130mm, 8-37mm, 4-25mm, 2 FQF-2500 ASW rocket launchers, 4 DC mortars, 2 DC racks	ST/32	1970–87	17
HARUNA	Japanese	4700/6300	501-11 × 57-5 × 16-8 153.0 × 17.5 × 5.1	2-5in, 1 ASROC, 6-12.75in TT, 3 HSS-2 helicopters	ST/31	1972–73	2
TYPE 42	British	3850/4350	410-0 × 46-0 × 19-0 125.0 × 14.0 × 5.8	2 Sea Dart SAM, 1-4.5in, 2-20mm, 6-12.74in TT, 1 Lynx helicopter	COGAG/30	1971–82	10 (plus 2 for export, 4 lengthened)
SPRUANCE	American	5826/7800	563-4 × 55-0 × 20-6 171.7 × 16.8 × 6.3	2-5in, 8 Sea Sparrow SAM, 1 ASROC, 1 SH-3 helicopter	GT/30	1973–79	31 (plus 4 derivatives)
GEORGES LEYGUES	French	3830/4200	456-0 × 46-0 × 18-0 139.1 × 14.0 × 5.5	4 Exocet SSM, 8 Crotale SAM, 1-100mm, 2-20mm, 2 ASW torpedo launchers, 2 Lynx helicopters	CODOG/30	1976–88	7
SOVREMENNYY (Project 956)	Soviet	6300/7850	511-10 × 56-9 × 21-4 156.0 × 17.3 × 6.5	8 SS-N-22 SSM, 2 SA-N-7 SAM, 4-130mm, 4-30mm, 4-21in TT, 2 RBU-1000, 1 Ka-27 helicopter	ST/30	1978–	In production (23 built or building)
HATSUYUKI	Japanese	2950/3700	432-4 × 44-11 × 14-3 131.7 × 13.7 × 14.3	8 Harpoon SSM, 8 Sea Sparrow SAM, 1-3in, 2-20mm, 1 ASROC, 6-12.75in TT, 1 HSS-2B helicopter	COGOG/30	1980–86	12
Frigates							
RIGA (Project 50)	Soviet	1260/1510	295-3 × 33-6 × 10-0 91.0 × 10.2 × 3.2	3-100mm, 4-37mm, 4-25mm, MBU-600 ASW rocket launcher, 2 DC racks, 2/3-21in TT	ST/30	1952–58	64 (plus 8 built for export and 4 in China)
TYPE 15	British	2240/2850	358-3x 35-8 × 14-0 109.2 × 10.9 × 4.3	2 Mk 10 Limbo mortars, 2-4in, 2-40mm, 8-21in TT	ST/36	1952–57*	23 (plus 4 Australian and 2 Canadian)

Class	Nationality	Displacement normal/full load (tons)	Dimensions overall (feet-inches) (metres)	Armament	Machinery/ Speed (kts)	Launch/ * Conversion dates	Numbers built
ST LAURENT	Canadian	2000/2600	366-0 × 42-0 × 13-2 113.1 × 12.8 × 4.2	4-3in, 2-40mm, 2 Mk 10 Limbo	ST/28	1953–56	7 (plus 13 derivatives)
DEALEY	American	1314/1877	315-0 × 36-8 × 11-10 96.0 × 11.2 × 3.6	4-3in, Weapon Alfa	ST/27	1953–57	13 (plus 5 to modified design in Norway and 3 in Portugal)
TRIBAL	British	2300/2700	360-0 × 42-3 × 13-3 109.7 × 12.9 × 4.0	2-4.5in, 2-40mm, 1 Mk 10 Limbo, 1 Wasp helicopter	COSAG/27	1959–62	7
LEANDER	British	2350/2860	372-0 × 41-0 × 18-0 113.4 × 12.5 × 18.0	2-4.5in, 4 Seacat SAM, 1 Mk 10 Limbo, 1 Wasp helicopter	ST/28	1961–71	26 (plus 2 for export, 6 built in Netherlands and 6 in India)
KNOX	American	3020/4066	438-0 × 47-0 × 25-0 133.5 × 14.3 × 7.6	1-5in, 8 Sea Sparrow SAM, 1 ASROC, DASH, 2-21in TT, 6-12.75in TT	ST/27	1966–73	41
KRIVAK (Project 1135)	Soviet	3075/3575	405-3 × 46-3 × 15-1 123.5 × 14.1 × 4.6	4 SS-N-14 ASW missiles, 4 SA-N-4 SAM, 4-76mm, 2 RBU-6000 ASW rocket launchers, 8-21in TT	CODOG/32	1970–81	21 (plus 19 derivatives)
IROQUOIS	Canadian	3551/4700	423-0 × 50-0 × 14-6 128.9 × 15.2 × 4.4	1-5in, 8 Sea Sparrow, 1 Mk 10 Limbo ASW mortar, 6-12.75in TT, 2 CHSS-2 helicopters	GT/29	1970	4
D'ESTIENNE D'ORVES	French	950/1250	262-0 × 34-0 × 10-0 80.0 × 10.3 × 3.0	2 Exocet SSM, 1-100mm, 2-20mm, 1-375mm ASW rocket launcher, 4 ASW torpedo launchers	D/24	1973–82	17 (plus 3 for export)
JIANGHU (Project EF3H)	Chinese	1586/1900	337-9 × 39-4 × 13-2 103.0 × 12.8 × 4.3	4 HY-2 SSM, 2-100mm, 112-37mm, 2 RBU-1200 ASW rocket launchers, 4 DC mortars, 2 DC racks	D/26	1975	25 (plus 3 for export)
KORTENAER	Dutch	3000/3786	427-0 × 47-0 × 14-0 130.2 × 14.4 × 4.4	8 Harpoon SSM, 8 Sea Sparrow SAM, 2-3in, 4-12.75in TT, 1 Lynx helicopter	COGOG/30	1976–82	10 (plus 2 for export and 10 derivatives)
OLIVER HAZARD PERRY	American	2648/3486	445-0 × 47-5 × 14-5 135.7 × 14.5 × 4.4	1 Standard SAM/Harpoon SSM, 1-3in, 6-12.75in TT, 1/2 LAMPS helicopters	GT/28	1976–88	51 (plus 6 for Australia, 6 for Spain and 8 for Taiwan)
MAESTRALE	Italian	2990/3250	374-2 × 42-9 × 27-5 122.7 × 12.9 × 8.4	4 Otomat SSM, 1-5in, 4 Albatros SAM, 4-40mm, 2-21in TT, 2 AB-212 helicopters	CODOG/32	1981–84	8
'MEKO 200'	German (for export)	2700/2994	372-5 × 46-6 × 13-7 110.6 × 14.2 × 4.1	8 Harpoon SSM, 8 Sea Sparrow SAM, 1-5in, 3-25mm, 6-12.75in TT, AB-212 helicopter	CODAD/27	1985–	7 for export plus 12 derivatives
TYPE 23	British	3500/4200	436-4 × 52-10 × 24-0 133.0 × 16.1 × 7.3	8 Harpoon SSM, 32 Seawolf SAM, 1-4.5in, 2-20mm, 4-12.75in TT, 1 Lynx helicopter	CODLAG/28	1987–	In production (13 built or building)

Machinery abbreviations:
ST = steam turbines; COSAG = combined steam and gas turbines; COGAG = commbined gas and gas (turbines); CONAS = combined nuclear and steam; GT = gas turbines; CODOG = combined diesels or gas (turbines); COGOG = combined gas or gas (turbines); D = diesel; CODAD = combined diesel and diesel; CODLAG = combined diesel-electric and gas (turbine).

Submarines

MODERN submarines were created, in their current form, in roughly the fifteen years after the Second World War. Developments in overall design since that time have been elaborations on themes which were well established by the early 1960s. The only major new development in hull or machinery since that time has been the low-powered, air-independent powerplant, intended to supplement conventional diesel-electric propulsion. The submarine weapon system, on the other hand, has changed enormously. In 1945 the targets were all surface ships; postwar, at least in the US and Royal Navies, the emphasis shifted to anti-submarine warfare (ASW). That transformed the problem, since a submarine must be located in three dimensions. Moreover, it placed a premium on passive sonar operation, since a submarine would surely give her position away if she 'pinged' her active sonar for long. At least the US Navy sought to use fully passive methods, including passive ranging (by triangulation). The main exception was fire control for the Subroc nuclear-armed missile, which had a range well beyond the capability of any passive ranger. In that case target range was estimated passively, then confirmed by a single strong ping before the weapon was fired. Less successful in developing passive systems, the postwar Soviets were far more interested in active sonar. They also emphasised anti-ship warfare far more than their rivals in the West.

Homing torpedoes

The weapons also changed. In 1943 the Allies and the Germans both introduced homing torpedoes, in the Germans' case to attack escorts, in the Allies' case to attack U-boats as they dived. By the end of the war the US Navy had a long range homer (Mk 28) to attack surface ships, supplemented by a short range defensive homer (Mk 27) intended to deal with escorts attacking the submarine. Later, Mk 27 was modified into an interim ASW torpedo, pending development of the more sophisticated active/passive Mk 35 (and its associated defensive torpedo, Mk 37).

The wartime weapons were fully passive; they homed on machinery and propeller noise. That was quite effective against surface ships. However, submarines were really noisy only when snorkelling or when running near the surface (where their propellers cavitated). Early postwar attempts at submarine ASW concentrated on snorkellers, on the theory that submarines transiting from their bases to their patrol areas would have to snorkel (or even run on the surface) for much of the time, simply to make good any significant distance. The submarine had limited overall endurance, set by food supplies and the crew itself, so time wasted on transit would detract from effectiveness in combat. Under these circumstances a submarine was not really too different from a surface ship, and both the Royal and US Navies developed ASW tactics using standard straight-running anti-ship torpedoes (set to run a bit deeper).

Once the submarine was well submerged, she could be relatively quiet, certainly quiet enough to evade most passive homers. The solution was an active pinger: the torpedo was aimed into the general area of the submarine, and then sought out its target. Hence the characterisation of Mk 35 (and Mk 37, which in effect replaced it) as active/passive. The current US Mk 48 also fits this category. Nuclear submarines in particular made the simple anti-snorkel homers obsolete, since they almost never made sufficient broadband noise to attract torpedoes.

The first important postwar British homing torpedo was the passive Mk 20, which existed both in escort (E) and submarine (S) versions. Because the surface platform was noisy, there was a real danger that the torpedo would turn and home on it. It was therefore designed to run

Early postwar submarine development was heavily influenced by the fast battery-driven German boats just entering service in 1945. Those furthest advanced were the coastal Type XXIII and the ocean-going Type XXI. The victorious Allies took over examples of these for trials purposes, and in 1958–60 the Germans themselves raised and rebuilt a sunken Type XXI, U-2540, which was recommissioned as the experimental submarine Wilhelm Bauer. *After testing the powerplant for the new Type 206 coastal submarines, the boat was transferred to the German Maritime Museum at Bremerhaven as an exhibit, as shown here.* (L & L van Ginderen)

An important wartime innovation was the schnorchel or snorkel, essentially a pipe which allowed air-breathing diesels to operate at periscope depth, so the submarine could run at a far greater speed than was usually the case on batteries alone. Being noisy, however, it had the disadvantage of making the submarine easily detected by sonar, and hence vulnerable to ASW torpedoes. Nevertheless, in the immediate postwar period the major navies made a priority of adding such devices to existing submarines. This 1949 photograph shows the wartime British Telemachus *raising what the Royal Navy called its 'Snort' mast.* (CMP)

out to a set distance before turning on its seekers. The submarine weapon listened all the way out, because the launching submarine could be quiet. Most early European ASW torpedoes were also passive. They were generally described as stealthy or discreet weapons, with very quiet electric powerplants, running relatively slowly so as not to drown out the target's noise with their own self-noise.

Torpedo attack always suffered from one major problem: the weapon is not too much faster than the target, so it is easy to miss (par-ticularly since fire control inputs are unlikely to be sufficiently precise). Homing in effect enlarged the target area to make up for imprecision, but it was not enough. The Germans invented, and the Allies developed, wire guidance to improve the torpedo's chances. The submarine, which tracks the target even after the torpedo has been fired, can steer the torpedo into a collision course with the target, taking target manoeuvres into account. To do that, the submarine fire control system must keep track not only of the target but also of the moving torpedo. Typically the torpedo is dead-reckoned: it is assumed that it has followed all the guidance commands sent down the wire. In a variation on this theme, some systems (such as those in modern German and US torpedoes) send the torpedo's sonar picture back down the wire. Wire-guided torpedoes entered US service in the early 1960s, and the Royal Navy's first such weapon, Mk 23 ('Grog'), became operational about a decade later. The Soviets followed some time during the 1970s, possibly as early as 1971 with a weapon called TEST-71. Wire guidance is now virtually universal for heavy torpedoes.

Submarine fire control

Second World War submarine combat systems concentrated on the attack of a single target. A submarine had relatively little capability to search for targets, and she could not attack several targets in quick succession. Navies varied considerably in the sophistication of their systems, but all were limited to fire control. For example, the US submarine's system was built around a Torpedo Data Computer (TDC). Given an initial estimate of target course and speed, the TDC projected ahead target position. Its estimates could be checked against periodic observations, *eg* by periscope or sonar. Target course and speed could be corrected to bring the TDC estimates into agreement with these observations. The TDC also solved the torpedo firing problem, calculating the gyro angle at which a torpedo had to be fired to hit the target moving according to its estimates. It automatically maintained correct gyro settings, so that torpedoes could, in theory, be fired as soon as the submarine came within range.

The TDC handled the final phase of an attack. In effect, the postwar theme was to elaborate the process of estimating target position before an attack. When that was applied to one or two targets, it was only a better way of doing the same thing. As it applied to many targets, it became a way of maintaining a picture of the situation from underwater, preferably with little or no exposure of masts (periscopes and radar) or use of active sonar.

For example, the main early postwar US submarine fire control system, Mk 101, added a section (an analyser) which estimated target range, course, speed, and bearing from a series of three sonar measurements, two of which could be passive. This section fed into a modified TDC, which could project target motion on the basis of either a straight or a curved (evasive) course (many older submarines were fitted with Mk 106, an analyser plus a slightly modified TDC). The step beyond was the realisation that initial estimates could be made entirely on the basis of passive sonar bearings (and, sometimes, the rates at which bearings changed over time), a technique called target motion analysis (TMA). TMA was initially a manual process. However, it could clearly be automated, a step the US Navy took with the Mk 113 system installed in *Thresher* and *Sturgeon* class attack submarines, and in most of its ballistic missile craft.

In theory, the original Mk 113 could conduct simultaneous TMA on four targets. That opened a new possibility. Using automatic TMA on multiple targets, a submarine commander could form a picture of the underwater and surface activity around the submarine, a sort of equivalent of a radar picture, without giving away the submarine's position by pinging with sonar. This sort of picture became more and more valuable as submarine passive sonar range increased (because sonars were working at lower frequencies). Also, as range increased, more and more non-targets (such as schools of fish or surface shipping) could be detected. A computer TMA picture could help sort them. On the other hand, automatic TMA calculations were not always successful. Data were never completely accurate, and the automatic calculators could be thrown off by a few bad pieces of data. Thus the US Navy, for example, generally demanded interaction between the operator and the computer, and ran a parallel manual TMA plot of the most important target. The US Mk 117 digital system, introduced in the *Los Angeles* class, provided a general-purpose computer amenable to TMA; the current BSY-1 or CCS Mk 2 greatly increases the number of localised targets.

British wartime submarines lacked an equivalent of the US TDC. They did have a simple 'fruit machine' computer corresponding to the US triangle-solver, but not connected to the tubes (the torpedoes were not automatically gyro-set and had limited gyro capabilities). The commander worked out a firing position and manoeuvred his submarine into place (relative

As for surface warships, the issue of fire control became far more significant after 1945. During the war British submariners had made do with the simple electro-mechanical calculator pictured here. Referred to as the 'fruit machine', it was nowhere near as sophisticated as the contemporary US TDC (Torpedo Data Computer), which formed the inspiration for much postwar submarine fire control development. (CMP)

to the target). He could not compensate for last-minute changes in target course and speed. British officers were much impressed with the TDC, and a new generation of submarine fire control systems (TCSS) were developed. TCSS Mk 2 had a position-keeper and remote gyro setters; it was broadly equivalent to the US TDC. Mk 3, installed in the first postwar submarines (*Porpoise* and modernised 'A' and 'T' classes), had automatic sonar inputs. An abortive TCSS Mk 4 (1955–56) was roughly equivalent to the US Mk 101. It incorporated a fully-passive (bearings-only) analyser unit. It was succeeded by Mk 6 for diesel submarines and Mk 7 for the first British nuclear attack submarines (HMS *Dreadnought* and the *Valiant* class). These were all electro-mechanical systems, difficult to adapt to different weapons. The Royal Navy had a peculiar problem. In wartime, as in the Second World War, it expected to use a mix of US and British weapons. Its fire control systems therefore had to be unusually flexible.

TCSS Mk 9 was the first British digital underwater fire control system, for nuclear submarines. It did not use a general-purpose programmable computer, and thus was somewhat limited in the range of weapons it could control.

The corresponding *Oberon* system was TCSS Mk 10/11.

The British situation was complicated by the requirement that nuclear submarines be suitable to escort surface units. Their fire control systems had to display enough of the tactical situation to permit the submarine to distinguish targets from the ships being protected. Thus the British became early advocates of computer-based systems capable of keeping track of multiple targets. In the mid 1960s a specification was written for a submarine action information system (in effect a track-keeper), DCA. It supported TCSS Mk 9 by providing it with data, but was not integrated with it. DCA entered service in 1973 aboard HMS *Swiftsure*. It could conduct automatic TMA on twenty-four targets, providing the submarine commander with a full picture of the situation around the submarine, derived entirely from passive sonars. The next step was to integrate the track-keeper with the fire control system. DCB was conceived as a DCA successor more closely integrated with TCSS Mk 9. However, Mk 9 could not support a longer range weapon, the new submarine-launched missile, Harpoon. DCB therefore required a completely new software-controlled fire control system. It entered service in 1976 aboard HMS *Superb* and was retrofitted into the earlier *Valiant* and *Churchill* classes.

TMA requires enormous computer power, so even the best modern systems do not localise more than a few targets, typically twenty to fifty, at a time. A submarine's sonars will generally detect many more, and may track many more, but that does not require nearly as much calculation.

The Soviets seem to have trailed the West in introducing such computer systems. Their main early postwar fire control system, Leningrad (for *Romeo* and probably *Foxtrot* class submarines), was roughly equivalent to the US Mk 101. Unlike Western systems, it could turn the torpedo through two successive angles. A submarine could therefore fire a series of torpedoes which would spread out and then follow parallel courses (contemporary Western spreads separated as they ran, so their chance of hitting a ship declined sharply beyond a certain range). Elaborate computer systems are certainly now in use, but submarines built for export retain the earlier analogue fire controls. For example, the current *Kilo* (Project 877E in its export version) can track only five targets, three of them automatically and two manually. Advertising brochures do not hint at any capability for automated TMA.

The Soviets did introduce a major new submarine weapon, the wake-following torpedo.

An upward-looking sensor, such as a small sonar, can detect the edges of a surface ship wake. The torpedo is set to pass through the wake, then turn after detecting the far edge. If the initial angle is right, the torpedo will have turned up the wake towards the ship. The next time it passes through (from the other side), it turns again. That brings it further up the wake. If it is fast enough, eventually the torpedo must pass under the target ship. The Germans were the first to try this technique, but they were not particularly successful, and postwar interest in the United States and abroad did not lead to production. The Soviets alone followed the idea to a successful conclusion. It was particularly attractive because no good countermeasure could be imagined: the wake is a very distinctive item. The first Soviet wake-following torpedo to receive much publicity was the fast long range 65cm (25.6in) weapon fired by recent submarines, but it now appears that virtually all Soviet anti-ship homing torpedoes are wake-followers.

Computer combat systems are now virtually universal among Western navies and submarine builders. Aside from US and British service systems, probably the most important have been developed by Signaal in the Netherlands (M8 and then Gipsy, employed for example in German export submarines) and Thomson Sintra in France (for French navy and export submarines; a French sonar system is used in the new Australian *Collins* class, which has a US combat direction system).

The fast submarine

The Second World War transformed the very concept of the submarine. Prewar submarines were essentially surface ships which submerged to hide. They relied on battery-driven electric motors when submerged. On the surface they were driven by diesels, which also recharged their batteries. At very low speed a battery submarine might remain submerged for two or three days, but she could not maintain much speed for more than an hour. Such a submarine could make good substantial distances (*eg* to close with a surface target) only on the surface. Once near (and ahead of) her target, she typically dived, loitered to await the target's approach, and then made her escape using up most of her battery charge at its maximum (one-hour) rate (she could not close in submerged at high speed without exhausting the battery, and hence her ability to escape). Since a relatively slow submarine could not go far even at the one-hour battery rate, escorts could often catch up with her as she tried to escape. If they could hold her

More radical than the fast battery submarine was the potential of hydrogen peroxide as an air-independent propellant. Under the guidance of Dr Helmut Walter, German development had been under way since 1940 but by 1945 there was no properly mature design ready for service. Postwar, only the British pursued the technology with vigour, building two small experimental boats, Explorer *and* Excaliber, *as fast ASW targets. Hydrogen peroxide was inherently unstable, and as a dubious tribute to its properties* Explorer, *seen here in April 1957, was nicknamed 'Exploder'. (CMP)*

down long enough, she would exhaust her battery and be forced to surface.

Before the advent of radar, a surfaced submarine was effectively invisible at night. The German wolf packs, thus, used U-boats essentially as night surface torpedo boats. Once the escorts had efficient surface search radars that was no longer practical, and U-boats had to attack submerged day and night. Late in the Second World War, many US submarine commanders adopted similar tactics (Japanese escorts lacked effective surface search radars).

Airborne radar made classical submarines obsolete. U-boats could be detected, day or night, as they formed up to get into attack position. The U-boats had somehow to run continuously (*ie* on diesels) without surfacing. The solution was the snorkel, a breathing tube through which the diesels could obtain the air they needed. It was not a new idea (the Dutch had adopted it prewar, and the US and Italian navies had experimented with it), but it had not been needed in the past. A submarine running on snorkel was quite uncomfortable, since the snorkel induction (intake) valve shut whenever a wave passed over it. With the valve closed, the diesels sucked air from inside the submarine. Snorkels equipped the U-boats from 1944 onwards.

It had long been obvious that any submarine capable of running submerged at high speed for a considerable time would enjoy enormous advantages. She could close in to attack a fast target, and still have enough endurance to escape. The higher the escape speed, the better

the chance that the escorts could not catch her to hold her down. For example, doubling escape speed would quadruple the area the escorts had to search.

As early as 1940, Dr Helmut Walter convinced the chief of the U-boat arm, Admiral Karl Doenitz, that the future lay with such submarines. He argued that batteries could not suffice; high power density demanded some sort of internal combustion engine, the submarine carrying the oxidant. Walter's candidate was hydrogen peroxide (often called high-test peroxide, HTP). Run over a catalyst, it decomposed into hot oxygen and steam. Fuel oil could be burned in the oxygen in a combustion chamber, adding energy. The resulting gas-steam mixture drove a turbine. Walter hoped that a properly designed peroxide submarine could run at high speed (up to 25kts) for up to ten hours. Since peroxide could not be generated at sea, a Walter U-boat had to have a full diesel-

battery conventional powerplant, to be used whenever full speed was not needed, or after the peroxide was exhausted.

Peroxide was very unstable. Walter planned to stow it in plastic bags in a second pressure hull slung beneath the main hull of his submarine, forming a figure-of-eight cross-section. By 1943 developmental problems were painfully clear. As an interim measure, Walter's streamlined double-hull boat was modified for conventional operation, the lower part of its figure-of-eight hull filled with batteries. The overall hull was already quite streamlined (compared with conventional craft), and very powerful electric motors were fitted. The resulting Type XXI 'electro-U-boat' could make about twice the underwater speed of a conventional U-boat, perhaps 15kts or 16kts. Like its conventional equivalents, it had a snorkel. A parallel coastal design, Type XXIII, was also developed. The Walter boat equivalent to Type XXI was designated Type XXVI. It was never built, but the Germans did complete several smaller Type XVIIs, each with a 2500shp turbine (Type XXVI would have had a 7500shp turbine).

The first Allied response to the fast battery submarine was the rapid streamlining of a few British 'S' class boats as targets to simulate the new threat. As can be seen from this 1948 view of Seraph, *the first such conversion, the reconstruction was not extensive, and since the machinery could not be altered the boat's performance did not nearly match that of a Type XXI. (CMP)*

The Japanese developed their own high-speed submarines, such as the *I-201* class, but their work had little or no impact on postwar thinking in any of the major navies. The Japanese programme seems to have been inspired by 1943 reports of German losses, but it is also fair to say that their prewar midget submarines were the first fast battery submarines to be built by any navy.

Type XXI was on the point of entering service at the end of the war (US submarine designers later argued that the boats were not really ready, and that they would have failed in service because their detailed design, *eg* hydraulic systems, were too complex). The few boats which began war patrols easily evaded Allied escorts, partly because their streamlined hulls were far weaker sonar targets than conventional submarine hulls. At maximum submerged speed the Type XXI was actually faster than many escorts, such as corvettes, particularly in anything like a rough sea. To make matters worse, boats armed with the new homing and pattern-running torpedoes might well have been able to attack convoys from outside the ring of escorts, beyond sonar range.

Diving depth

A second major postwar theme was deeper diving. Before the Second World War, most submarines were rated at about 300ft. Wartime submariners found that they needed much more depth to evade depth charges (the deeper the submarine, the longer the charges took to arrive, and the delay often allowed a submarine to slip out of lethal range). Furthermore, submariners discovered that surface-ship sonar range was severely limited when they dived beneath the surface acoustic or mixing layer ('the layer'). In the layer, sound velocity was constant, and sonar enjoyed its greatest direct-path range; below, the sonar beam bent sharply, and a submarine might become almost undetectable. In the Atlantic the layer was about 300ft deep in summer, but in winter it might extend down to as much as 600ft. Therefore, US and British postwar submarines were intended to operate at 700ft. That required new structural materials, such as high tensile steel in the US case. As it happened, the Royal Navy used a higher safety factor (the difference between crush and operating depth) than the US Navy (1.75 rather than 1.50), so British submarines very similar in design to their US counterparts were not cleared to dive as deep.

Deep diving required a new kind of torpedo tube. Existing ones used air pressure to force the torpedo out. Below quite a shallow depth, sea pressure would easily compress the air bubble behind the torpedo. One approach, which the Germans developed and the French adopted, was to use a piston to ram the torpedo out. The US and British navies adopted water slugs which, being incompressible, could push against water pressure. It appears that at least until quite recently Soviet submarines, however deep-diving, were equipped with air (pneumatic) torpedo tubes.

The alternative to such ejection tubes was to allow the torpedo to swim out under its own power. That was entirely practical with an electric weapon, and it minimised the drain (per firing) on the submarine's own power supply. On the other hand, a torpedo driven by an internal combustion engine (such as the US Mk 48 or the new British Spearfish) produces an exhaust, which is often toxic. If the torpedo tube fills with gas as the torpedo leaves, that gas may easily enter the submarine. Swim-out is therefore generally considered a poor option for such weapons. In any case, swim-out requires that

The German U-30, *a Type 206 coastal boat, fitted with external mine belt. Because German submarines have 'swim-out' torpedo tubes, they cannot eject some types of mine, and the external GRP canisters are IKL's ingenious answer to the problem.* (L & L van Ginderen)

water flow freely around the torpedo as it runs down the tube, so it must be narrower than the torpedo tube. The US Mk 37, designed to be fired by war-built submarines with pneumatic tubes, must have been one of the earliest swim-out weapons: its diameter was 19in, to fit a 21in tube.

The postwar German-built submarines all have large-diameter tubes specifically to allow torpedoes to swim out, because that eliminates the weight and complexity of ejection pumps or pistons. That simplicity did cause problems, however. The main Western submarine-launched anti-ship missile, Sub-Harpoon, is encapsulated but unpowered underwater: it is normally simply ejected under pressure. The Greek navy had to have its swim-out tubes modified for such ejection simply in order to use Sub-Harpoon. Similarly, mines would normally be ejected. In this case the usual solution is to mount a 'mine belt' externally, but that is to accept that mines cannot be checked or adjusted before they are launched.

The wartime Germans understood the value of depth, but it seemed to conflict with the desire for high speed. As an internal combustion engine, a Walter plant had to dump its exhaust products overboard (they could not be compressed for stowage). Thus it lost power as water pressure increased with depth. Walter expected his boats to run at about 50ft, *ie* just below periscope depth. The victorious navies wanted both speed *and* depth, and that required additional work. For example, the two British experimental Walter submarines (the *Explorer* class) were rated at 550ft (the last wartime type, the 'A' class, had been rated at 500ft), but it seemed unlikely that they could run their Walter engines below 400ft.

Early postwar development

At the end of the war, all three major allied navies (US, British, and Soviet) obtained examples of the Type XXI (two for each Western navy, four for the Soviets, who also obtained parts of twenty more), as well as badly damaged examples of the prototype Walter boat (Type XVII). Their reactions differed considerably.

The Western allies became aware of Type XXI in 1944, mainly by decoding Japanese accounts (radioed from Berlin) of such craft. The British promptly streamlined several 'S' class submarines (beginning with HMS *Seraph*, completed at Devonport in August 1944) to simulate them. Because the problem was so urgent, very little modification could be done. Neither motors nor batteries could be replaced. The hull could be considerably cleaned up, however,

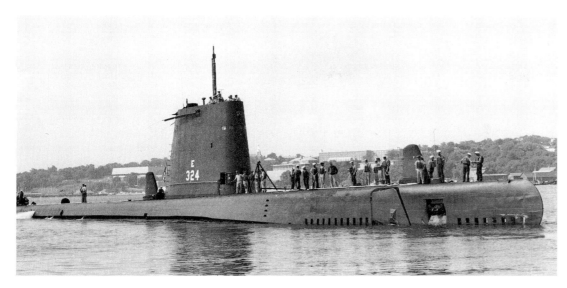

and *Seraph* (which was no longer capable of fighting) made 12.52kts at periscope depth, compared with 8.82kts before conversion (her resistance was estimated at 55 per cent of that of an unconverted craft). Converted 'S' boats were stationed at Bermuda to train both US and British ASW forces. At high speed they were so noisy that the British concluded that the best detectors might well be passive sonars. Apparently on this basis, in December 1944 the senior British submariner, Flag Officer Submarines (FOSM), concluded that there was little point in trying to duplicate Type XXI. Instead he wanted all effort concentrated on the 'ultimate' or 'true' submarine, capable of sustained high-speed underwater running.

Although it did not go far enough, a Walter boat would be far closer than a Type XXI to this

idea. When the British overran the German U-boat yards the following spring, they considered ordering one or more Type XXVIs from Blohm & Voss. The best they could get was a badly damaged Type XVII. They imagined that the Walter technology was quite mature, so in 1945 it seemed likely that the damaged Walter boat (renamed HMS *Meteorite*) could be placed in service in 1946 (this did not happen until 1950). The British 1945 naval programme included an experimental Walter submarine, which was intended as a prototype for an operational unit. Three modified 'A' class submarines of the 1944 programme were to have been replaced by operational Walter attack submarines provisionally designated the 'B' class. Half a century later, it seems that the problem was gullibility: the Germans seemed to be such technological supermen that everyone assumed that whatever they had put on paper could actually be built. Meanwhile, the British installed snorkels on board virtually all of their diesel submarines.

The US Navy feared that the Soviets would soon place the Type XXI in mass production.

Access to the British 'S' boats had ended with the war, but only tactical trials could reveal effective countermeasures to a fast battery-driven submarine. Thus the first US priority was to place both captured Type XXIs in service. They were a revelation. Far quieter than their US counterparts, they could out-run most existing escorts, particularly in any substantial sea. The US reaction, then, was quite opposite to FOSM's: fast battery submarines, which the British called 'intermediate', were well worth while.

Like early U-boats, Type XXI was not designed to last very long. The US Navy bought up all the spare parts (particularly battery cells) that it could, but it knew that its pair of Type XXIs would have to be retired within a few years. Development of a US equivalent received a very high priority. Meanwhile the US submarine designers investigated a possible US equivalent of the British 'S' boat conversion, using the much larger standard US fleet submarine as a basis. Work on a powerful new battery cell had already begun, for an abortive follow-on to the fleet boat. By late 1946 it was clear that a modified and drastically streamlined fleet submarine could exceed Type XXI underwater performance yet retain its full offensive armament. Conversions to this Guppy (Greater

Even the Guppy IA was relatively costly, so the programme was augmented by a more austere 'Fleet Snorkel' modernisation, which involved streamlining the fin but not the hull. The characteristic raked bow of the original fleet boats is evident in this view of USS Sabalo in September 1953. (USN)

Underwater Propulsive Power) standard were ordered; eventually fifty fleet boats were converted. Others received an intermediate 'fleet snorkel' conversion designed so that it provided part of the full Guppy outfit.

The early Guppies were extremely successful; they were actually faster than Type XXIs. Guppy conversion was possible because the US Navy used diesel-electric drive. All four diesels were connected to generators rather than, as in most submarines, to propeller shafts. On the surface the generators drove motors or were used to charge batteries. Although the fleet submarines were not designed for high underwater speed, they were intended to run very fast on the surface, so they had powerful motors (only parts of which were used underwater). It was simple to use the entire motor both submerged and surfaced, as long as enough battery capacity was provided.

Meanwhile, an entirely new deeper-diving (700ft compared with the wartime 400ft) design, the *Tang*, was put in hand. Although she was inspired by the Type XXI, *Tang* had a much more conventional circular-section pressure hull.

For the longer term, the US Navy invested in a variety of closed-cycle powerplants, including both the Walter plant and nuclear power. The goal was twice Type XXVI power (15,000shp) in a hull of roughly *Tang* dimensions, to reach Type XXVI speed (25kts). Work on most of these plants went very slowly, probably largely because the companies involved saw no civilian application for the technology. It seemed unlikely that the peacetime US Navy could invest enough to make such programmes worthwhile. Nuclear energy was the sole exception: the big electrical companies considered it well worth their own investment.

The British 1944 programme included three 'improved "A" class' submarines. It was soon quite obvious that they would be obsolete, so the Admiralty planned to build three more modern boats ('B' class). In July 1945 the Controller (responsible for ship characteristics) pointed out that the Walter engine was still immature; the new design should be adaptable

to a Walter or other closed-cycle engine when that became available. The Director of Naval Construction (DNC) interpreted this to mean that a British form of Type XXI (which, after all, was a hull originally intended for Walter propulsion) was desired. The main change would be deeper diving (to 700ft rather than the 500ft of the 'A' class). FOSM agreed for the moment, but found the maximum submerged speed (18–20kts) disappointing; a true submarine should make 25–30kts submerged. DNC developed a design for a fast diesel-electric submarine (17.75kts submerged for half an hour), but nothing came of it.

By the fall of 1945 FOSM's position had hardened. In March 1946 it was formally agreed that the single experimental submarine would be powered by a pair of Type XXVI Walter turbines (each of 7500shp), for a speed of 25kts; the 'B' submarine would be similarly powered (although it might have to be completed before turbines were available). No diesel submarine could manage the sort of performance demanded. *U-2518*, the more usable of the two British Type XXIs, was given to the French navy. On the other hand, HMS *Scotsman* was modified for much higher underwater speed, as a special ASW target. Batteries replaced her torpedo tubes and some of her diesels (she was fitted with the small diesel of a coastal 'U' class submarine). More powerful motors from an 'A' class submarine replaced her original motors. Her ballast tanks were re-profiled for better streamlining. On early trials she made 16.33kts at 50ft depth on 3200shp; she was expected to sustain 17kts for 40 minutes on her full 3600shp. She was reduced to 7kts on the surface. This was far short of the first US Guppies, which were credited with 19kts for 30 minutes. The extent of the sacrifice involved in the conversion seemed to confirm FOSM's view that

batteries and diesels could not provide really sparkling performance. That reinforced his bias towards Walter powerplants.

FOSM was not being altogether unreasonable. Britain was very nearly bankrupt. The British government was well aware that a whole range of new technologies was developing, but it could not afford to finance generation after generation of new weapons in quick succession (such as would be required of rapidly-developing technology). Clearly, each line of development would stabilise eventually, and the time between generations would stretch out to some affordable figure. By 1948 the British government (probably in agreement with the US government) decided that the chance of war would be small until about 1957, based on the assumed rate of Soviet reconstruction and also on an estimate of when the Russians would obtain the atomic bomb. Thus, 1957, the 'year of maximum danger', became the target date for modernising British forces. Procurement of interim systems, which would be obsolete by then, was strongly discouraged. Because FOSM hoped to have a prototype Walter submarine within a very few years, the fast diesel-electric type clearly fell into the 'interim' category. About August 1946 the three 'B' boats were cancelled in favour of a second prototype Walter submarine. Both were justified at least partly as targets for ASW forces.

By late 1947 it was unpleasantly clear that estimates of progress in the Walter programme had been over-optimistic. By this time Type XXI spares were in such short supply that there was little point in trying to refit the remaining British unit, *U-3017*. The British were also well aware of the spectacular success of the US Guppy programme. Although the Walter plant might well be the future ideal, war might come before it was ready. FOSM therefore approved

The first British postwar submarine design was the Porpoise *class, which first revealed an emphasis on silencing that was to be a marked concern in British ASW thinking for nearly half a century. This led to an early interest in passive submarine detection, and the* Porpoises *– the name ship of the class is shown at Malta in October 1966 – carried a fixed linear array down the length of the boat. This Type 2007 sonar was a successor to the Type 186 fitted in the postwar modernised 'A' and 'T' classes. (CMP)*

The Dutch Tonyn, *of the* Potvis *class. These vessels had a unique hull form, of three separate pressure hulls, two side by side with one above, in an attempt to increase internal volume. However, the long hull form produced more resistance than the new 'tear-drop' shape that became popular after the* USS Albacore, *and later high speed submarines – even if conventionally-powered – have shown a preference for the latter form.* (L & L van Ginderen)

an interim project. He was offered three alternatives: a new battery submarine; a 'T' class conversion (in effect a British Guppy); and an 'A' class conversion. The 'T' class would be the simplest to convert. FOSM wanted a new diesel-electric submarine designed in parallel, but DNC lacked sufficient design manpower. At an Admiralty meeting a 1948 programme was worked out: the 'T' conversion would be followed by the first new submarine (the *Porpoise* class) a year or two later. It would draw in part on US experience with the *Tang* class. Ultimately the 'A' class was also converted. The new battery submarine was the *Porpoise* class, the direct predecessors of the current *Oberon*. Work on the Walter engine continued.

The 'T' class conversion was complicated because, like other British submarines, it used direct drive: the diesels drove shafts connected to the motors (whose power was set by the relatively low speed requirement of pre-1945 submarine operation) and propellers. That left little room for replacing the motors. It was relatively easy to substitute 112 extra battery cells for an internal fuel tank. DNC estimated that a submarine so modified (and streamlined) could make 14.5kts submerged on 3000shp. That was hardly enough for FOSM and the Naval Staff. DNC had to double submerged power by adding a second 'T' class motor on each shaft – and another 14ft of pressure hull – for an estimated speed of 16.75kts. The battery matched that of *Scotsman*, but power consumption was roughly doubled, so that the 'T' conversion was credited with 16.75kts or 17.00kts for only 20 minutes. It seems likely that the enormous success of the Guppy made the British far more confident in developing the 'T' conversion.

The fast battery option was attractive partly because it was essential to have a modern submarine in which to incorporate new non-powerplant technology, such as sonars and control systems, pending completion of peroxide development. Once all those systems had been tested, they could be married to a mature peroxide engine – when that was ready.

Compared with the US design, *Porpoise* differed mainly in the attention paid to silencing.

As early as 1945 the British designers had decided that they could no longer connect their propellers directly to the diesels, since noise would travel up and back along the propeller shaft. They chose diesel-electric drive for their next submarine (which at that time was to have been a Walter boat). The diesel generator was sound-mounted to minimise snorkelling noise. When the *Porpoise*s entered service in the 1950s, the British argued that such submarines made the new passive long range sound detectors (the SOSUS system) obsolete. As it happened, the Soviets continued to use prewar-type direct drive in their postwar submarines, so the British fears proved unfounded (they finally adopted diesel-electric drive in the *Juliett* and *Tango* classes). Because their submarines were so very quiet, the British concentrated on passive submarine detection, to an extent far beyond that developed by the contemporary US Navy, achieving much greater ranges. Their different outlook was reflected in a different approach to passive detection. The standard British passive array was Type 186, a linear array running down the length of the submarine. The submarine turned to turn the array, but it could provide very accurate directional information at great range. The US equivalent was a much smaller BQR-4 array, operating at higher frequency, built around the submarine's bow. *Porpoise* had a more or less conventional hull, but the bow was sharply flared to provide lift to counteract a tendency to trim by the stern underwater.

The *Porpoise*s were conceived as an interim design; work on the British Walter engine proceeded. For example, the British expended much effort to slash the high cost of peroxide. By 1952 they saw two distinct lines of development: the fast Walter submarine with limited underwater endurance (6 to 10 hours) and a much slower submarine with several hundred

hours' endurance without snorkelling (300 hours at 5kts was suggested). The small Walter plant would virtually replace the submarine's battery. Since snorkelling inevitably exposed the submarine to detection, this sort of endurance might be very valuable to a submarine operating in the face of strong enemy ASW forces. The latter idea has been revived recently in the form of a variety of low-powered 'air independent propulsion' (AIP) powerplants. At this time FOSM was particularly attracted by the long-endurance option. The DNC was arguing that a nuclear submarine would be more valuable than even the best fast peroxide boat; it would be best to shift the peroxide team to developing nuclear machinery.

The British were already planning a specialist ASW submarine for their 1953 programme, so adding a slow Walter boat would greatly increase the overall design load (which already included the *Porpoise* and the fast Walter submarine). That proved unacceptable; DNC's proposal won out. The two experimental Walter boats survived, mainly because they had already been ordered and because they were badly needed for ASW development.

One other early postwar Western submarine design innovation deserves mention here: the Dutch triple hull. During the Second World War an exiled Dutch naval constructor, M F Gunning, realised that the internal volume of a submarine could be distributed among multiple separate pressure hulls; he proposed three (a main hull with two smaller-diameter ones slung on each side beneath it). The smaller hulls could accommodate, for example, batteries and motors. Alternatively, they could be used for Walter fuel and peroxide. Gunning tried to interest both the Royal Navy and the US Navy in his ideas, but ultimately only the Royal Netherlands Navy built his type of submarine (the *Potvis* class).

New hull forms

All of this suggests that the transition from the old submersibles to clones of Type XXI was relatively simple. It was anything but. As in the case of the Walter powerplant, the victorious allies imagined that Type XXI hydrodynamics solved all the problems of a fast submarine. The Germans glibly suggested that the deep hull (wrapped around the figure-eight section) was optimum, because it was roughly fish-shaped. They had tested such designs in a wind tunnel, but it emerged that they had never tested alternatives built around more conventional cylindrical pressure hulls, which were stronger and easier to build.

It turned out that conventional hull forms *and* that of Type XXI were inherently unstable underwater at high speed. They could easily porpoise, either broaching or diving unintentionally. Both US and British naval architects found they had to conduct special experiments to establish the appropriate hull forms and control techniques. The US Navy based its experimental designs on airships, which were broadly analogous to submarines. The David Taylor Model Basin tested a series of such forms as Series 58, concluding that the best submarine would be a short fat hull of circular cross-section. This configuration seemed impractical, because existing submarines, with their single decks, needed length to accommodate their internal components.

The British saw their experimental Walter boat as a means of testing control concepts, as well as habitability in a submarine heated by its Walter turbine. They also harked back to airship practice, and to their own experience of

very fast submarines (the 'R' class) in the First World War.

By 1949 the US Navy expected its closed-cycle programme to bear fruit in the near future, in the form of a 25kt submarine. Control problems were already evident in the Guppies; it was urgent that a very fast experimental submarine be built to test control surfaces and systems before the really fast operational submarine appeared. Since the experimental submarine did not have to accommodate operational equipment, she could adopt the new optimum hull form, which was the only way she could reach speeds comparable with those of the planned closed-cycle boat. USS *Albacore* was built. She was not, as some have thought, a demonstration of the new hull form for very high speed (about 26.5kts as completed); instead, she was designed to test control surface configurations. Her great success inspired a new generation of short fat submarines, which accommodated their equipment by adopting multiple decks: the nuclear *Skipjack* and the diesel-electric *Barbel* (which was conceived as an armed version of *Albacore*). The Dutch and Japanese navies produced their own versions of the *Barbel* design.

Unlike earlier fast diesel submarines, *Albacore* was inherently stable underwater. Since her crew did not have to concentrate on avoiding unwanted climbs and dives, they could concentrate instead on intentional manoeuvres. *Albacore* turned out to be wonderfully manoeuvrable in all three dimensions. As a consequence she easily evaded contemporary ASW units. For a time, it seemed that 'hydrobatics' would be a major consideration in future submarine design. Yet that did not happen. The problem was that, no matter how manoeuvrable, the submarine

had to operate in a very thin layer of ocean. At high speed she could far too easily crash through her collapse depth. Although crush depth could be increased, it could not be increased sufficiently to solve the problem.

For their part, the Soviets apparently considered duplicating Type XXI directly. That proved impossible. Instead, they redesigned two of their prewar designs, the medium range 'S' class and the long range 'K' class, roughly along German lines. They became Projects 613 (Nato designation *Whiskey*) and 611 (Nato *Zulu*). Production began in 1949. Alone among the major powers, the Russians had experimented prewar with a closed-cycle powerplant, a diesel fed by oxygen tanks. A small 'M' class submarine so powered was successful, and after the war this system powered thirty short range Project 615 (Nato *Quebec*) submarines. The Soviets also built a single Walter prototype, Project 617 (often called the 'Whale'). It was unsuccessful; it suffered a serious explosion while submerged to 80m (262ft). Few, if any, of the existing Soviet submarines were ever modernised with snorkels or increased battery capacity.

Prewar, the Soviets had the largest submarine fleet in the world, albeit largely for coast defence. In 1948 a Soviet admiral stated that Stalin planned to build a fleet of 1200 modern submarines. Most would probably have been *Whiskey*s, 236 of which had been completed when the programme was stopped in 1957. By that time follow-on designs were in production: Project 633 (*Romeo*), to replace *Whiskey*; and Project 641 (*Foxtrot*), to replace *Zulu*.

New roles for submarines

Given such numbers, Western navies concentrated on ASW measures, including new ones involving submarines. Any Type XXI clone could evade existing escorts. One possibility was to attack the submarines closer to home, at source. The US Navy, for example, justified the big new carriers it wanted to build after the war largely for their ability to strike at Soviet submarine bases. The other main means of attack

Following the success of the experimental fast conventional submarine USS Albacore, *the US Navy adopted the short fat hull for the very fast nuclear boats of the* Skipjack *class. The novel shape of the hull is apparent in this 1961 photograph of* Shark *at Malta; circular in section, it tapered at the ends to a snub nose and pointed tail, reflecting the airship shape that inspired it. Because the hull was optimised for high speed underwater, vessels with this form usually create a massive bow wave when running at even moderate speeds on the surface.* (L & L van Ginderen)

The largest single class of postwar Soviet submarines was the Project 613 medium range boats known to Nato as the Whiskey *type. Probably the most famous of the 236 completed was the unfortunate* Whiskey V *that ran aground off the Swedish naval base of Karlskrona in 1981, in an incident headlined 'Whiskey on the Rocks' by the tabloid press.* (CMP)

at or near source would be Western submarines.

Western submarine ASW strategy, then, began with patrols near Soviet bases. Because there were many possible bases, it seemed that very large numbers of ASW submarines would be needed. Through the first postwar decade Western passive sonars improved, so that boats could detect and close their targets from greater distances. The ASW submarines did not have to be so closely packed. They could form offshore barriers (eventually the barriers were pulled back into choke points such as the Greenland–Iceland–UK Gap).

Several other new submarine roles were tried. The two most important were missile attack and radar picket. A submarine was clearly the best (because most covert) way to bring missiles near a target coast, an idea the Germans conceived during the war. Postwar, both the US and Soviet navies developed families of missiles specifically for submarine firing. The US Navy concentrated on cruise missiles, fielding Regulus in the mid 1950s. The Soviets developed cruise and ballistic missiles in parallel. They fired the first submarine-launched ballistic missile, a converted army Scud, in September 1955.

For the US Navy, radar pickets were essential to fast carrier battle group operations. Conventional surface ships were likely to suffer badly from enemy air attacks, as off Okinawa in 1945. The wartime navy therefore conceived a submarine picket, which was developed postwar. It was a very difficult project, partly because so much electronics had to be squeezed into so little space, and partly because the radar antennas had to be made both pressure- and watertight: hence its code-name, Project Migraine. Even so, by 1950 pickets converted from wartime fleet submarines were in service. Their main defect was that they were too slow to keep up with the carriers; pickets would have been sent to carrier attack areas in advance of the

The second generation of postwar Soviet submarines can be represented by this Foxtrot *class diesel-electric boat, an improved version of the long range* Zulu. *The hull shows greater attention to streamlining than earlier types, but also a new emphasis on sensors, the unpainted sound-transparent areas being clearly visible at the bow and on the fin (below the bridge windows).* (MoD, Crown Copyright)

ships. The solution was higher power, either an adapted closed-cycle plant (a pressure-fired boiler was seriously considered) or, ultimately, nuclear power. Ironically, just as the ideal picket, the nuclear *Triton*, was completed in 1959, the submarine picket mission lapsed in favour of carrier-borne early warning aircraft.

The Soviets converted several *Whiskey* class submarines to radar pickets (*Whiskey Canvas Bag*). Their role is not altogether clear. It was probably to supplement Soviet continental air defence in areas subject to US air attack (there were also surface pickets, which survived the submarines).

Nuclear propulsion

In 1945 many submariners saw atomic power as the solution to the problem of the true submarine. However, it was clearly far from fruition. Work on the Walter cycle and its relatives was pressed ahead on the theory that a generation of such submarines would appear before any nuclear plant could be perfected. By about 1948, however, studies had convinced the then Captain Hyman G Rickover (who was in charge of the nuclear propulsion programme) in the United States that nuclear power was entirely practicable in the near term. It was clearly so much more attractive than the closed-cycle systems that they were soon relegated to backup status. Rickover was authorised to build prototype submarine reactors. To speed the process, he chose to build full prototype powerplants, and to build a real submarine powerplant in parallel with each prototype.

The main issue in such a design is heat transfer (often called cooling) from the reactor to a boiler in which steam is made (there was, and is, no satisfactory means of directly converting reactor heat or radiation into electricity). The three main alternatives were gas circulated through the core of the reactor, water, and liquid metal (in the US case, sodium). Gas and water had a great advantage: they could not become radioactive. Thus piping outside the reactor proper did not have to be shielded, and the boiler and turbine could be repaired underway. Gas and liquid metal could, in theory, carry far more heat than water, so they could make much hotter steam for a more efficient turbine.

Gas might even be used directly to drive a gas turbine. The British tentatively chose gas cooling about 1950, but found that a gas-cooled reactor was far too massive for submarine use (gas cooling was used in contemporary British power station reactors). Rickover had rejected it about two years before, and chose the two alternatives.

By 1953 it was clear that the simpler of the two, pressurised water (pressurised so that it could not boil within the reactor vessel), was preferable. The water inside the reactor served both to carry away heat and to moderate (slow down) the neutrons (to make the reaction possible). If, owing to battle damage or accident, the water drained from the reactor, the reaction would automatically shut down. It also turned out that the system was inherently stable. For example, if the water became too hot, moderation became less effective, and temperature fell back; if it became too cool, moderation became more effective, and temperature rose back up to the desired level. The only real defect was that the temperature rise within the reactor vessel was quite limited, so overall system efficiency was limited. Nuclear submarines would need relatively massive steam turbines, operating at

temperatures and pressures the US Navy had abandoned in the 1930s. By way of contrast, the liquid-metal reactor was inherently unsafe. Sodium reacts violently with water, so battle damage might well be catastrophic. It is also extremely corrosive. Moreover, sodium could not function as a moderator, so the reactor itself became more complicated. Its one great advantage was much more efficient heat transfer; it could drive a modern small high-temperature turbine. Rickover hoped that the problems could be solved, because he saw liquid metal as a possible key to really high engine performance. In fact the liquid-metal plant, installed in the second US nuclear submarine, *Seawolf*, proved unreliable. It was removed. Proponents of liquid-metal technology have long claimed that the problems could have been cured. Rickover probably lacked sufficient staff to develop both systems in parallel, so he killed the less attractive of the two.

The pressurised-water reactor was installed in a prototype submarine, USS *Nautilus*. She was far larger than a *Tang*, and the plant did not quite put out the planned 15,000shp (it produced 13,200shp), so she did not make the expected 25kts (she probably made about 24kts at

The world's first nuclear-powered warship, USS Nautilus, *on sea trials in May 1955. The advantage of range conferred by nuclear power was already obvious, but operational experience with this boat soon established that the speed of nuclear submarines would make them opponents of unprecedented difficulty for surface forces.* (USN)

The first Soviet nuclear submarines were dubbed the November *class in the West. Reportedly, they suffered reliability problems but with two reactors were fast, and their speed influenced the US Navy's requirement for a faster SSN, which eventually emerged as the* Los Angeles *class.* (MoD, Crown Copyright)

best, and was credited with something over 23kts). Even so, she was a revelation. For the first time in history a submarine could manoeuvre really freely against surface forces, with devastating effect. *Nautilus'* commander found that he could easily evade counterattack, but that his submarine was not quite fast enough to turn on her pursuers. Up to that time, the US submarine community had been impressed mainly with the long endurance associated with nuclear power. To reduce unit cost, the first production series (the *Skate* class) had only half the output of the *Nautilus* reactor, in a hull of roughly *Tang* size. They were much slower, about 19kts. Early tactical trials of *Nautilus* showed clearly that this was the wrong choice. The next class, *Skipjack*, had a modified *Nautilus* reactor (for 15,000shp) and an *Albacore* hull form, to reach about 29kts.

While *Nautilus* was being built, the US Navy was much impressed by her high cost. It seemed that the future submarine force would be a high-low mix of a few nuclear craft and larger numbers of modern diesel boats. Within a few years, however, it was painfully obvious that diesel submarines had little chance of engaging nuclear units. Nuclear submarines were so far in advance of the best diesel boats that there was little point in building the latter. Other navies found it impossible to take so drastic a step, but recently the Royal Navy has announced that it plans to sell off its remaining diesel submarines. One reason why the US navy avoided diesel submarines was that it generally planned to operate very far from home bases. Only nuclear submarines could transit at very high speed, and arrive in fresh condition. The Royal Navy proved this point when it sent five nuclear attack submarines to the South Atlantic in 1982, as the Falklands crisis intensified. They were fast

enough to be on the spot when the crisis exploded, yet they were covert, so their presence could not have inflamed the crisis. One of the five, HMS *Conqueror*, sank the Argentine cruiser *Belgrano*, the first (thus far the only) surface ship ever sunk by a nuclear submarine.

There was one problem. A nuclear reactor needed constantly running coolant pumps driven by generators, and its turbine had to be geared to the propeller shaft (the alternative, turbo-electric power, was not practical because DC motors of sufficient power were not available). The new narrow-band detectors (Lofar) could easily pick up the sustained and steady sounds of gearing and other auxiliary equipment. The British idea, of sound-mounting the engines (as in the *Porpoise*), was imported: later US nuclear submarines generally had their machinery mounted on rigid rafts which were sound-mounted to the submarine hull. The first such installation was in the *Thresher*, the prototype of later US attack submarines. She also introduced a big low-frequency long range spherical bow sonar (BQS-6, part of BQQ-2) associated with the Subroc anti-submarine missile. To clear space forward to accommodate it, the torpedo tubes were moved back from the bow. Finally, *Thresher* was built of a new high-

strength steel, HY-80, which increased her operating depth to 1300ft (the previous figure had been 700ft, unchanged since the *Tang*).

Thresher was followed by a long series of similar attack submarines (the *Permit* and *Sturgeon* classes). She was substantially larger than the earlier *Skipjack* (largely owing to silencing), but retained the same reactor. She therefore lost some speed, even though she was very carefully streamlined. The *Sturgeon*s were even larger, and their rated speed fell to 25kts. When *Skipjack* and *Thresher* appeared, the Soviet *November*s were not yet fully effective. It was assumed that they were no faster than *Nautilus*; US submarines enjoyed a substantial speed advantage. However, the *November*s had a much higher potential speed, thanks in part to their much greater installed power. By 1963 it seemed obvious that the rising curve of Soviet speed would soon cross the falling curve of US submarine speed.

It seemed likely that fast Soviet submarines would be able to intercept fast carriers (diesel submarines could not). Submarine escorts (which the British already advocated) might solve that problem. From about mid 1963, there was considerable interest in a substantially faster US attack submarine. Admiral

After the Permit/Sturgeon *classes, which stressed quietness and sensors over speed, the US Navy turned to the far larger* Los Angeles *design. The elongated hull (evident in this view of* Jacksonville*) did not have the relative hydrodynamic efficiency of the pure* Albacore *hull form, but these boats had twice the installed power of their predecessors, by courtesy of a new reactor, and were about 5kts faster. They were also fitted with a new digital combat system that considerably enhanced their effective firepower.* (L & L van Ginderen)

Rickover advocated installing a destroyer reactor, about twice as powerful as the then-standard submarine unit, in an enlarged *Sturgeon* hull. The resulting submarine would have been quite large, and the proposal was contentious. Many submarine designers, for example, argued that it would be better to wrap a more efficient hull around a more efficient powerplant driving contra-props. Rickover's proposal was finally adopted in 1968, after a *November* had dramatised the new threat to US carriers by intercepting USS *Enterprise*, en route to Vietnam. As built, the new *Los Angeles* class had both the new reactor and a new digital combat system (which was retrofitted into earlier craft).

Rickover personally disliked rafting (he considered it a poor engineering solution), and he strongly advocated development of the alternative, a high-powered turbo-electric drive. It was installed in only one submarine, *Glenard P Lipscomb*, and it was not very successful. Rickover did approve another solution to noise, the natural-circulation reactor (NCR). In it, the heat difference between the top and bottom of the reactor causes water to circulate, so that (at least at low power) no primary coolant pumps are needed. In the prototype NCR submarine, *Narwhal*, the reactor drove a huge low-speed (hence ungeared) turbine, and other measures were taken to minimise noise. NCR was inherently larger than a conventional reactor (it had to be taller to get sufficient circulation) and it was not used in attack submarines. However, a 35,000shp version was adopted for the *Ohio* class strategic submarines, for which silencing was particularly important.

From the *Skipjack* on, US practice was evolution rather than sharp changes from class to class. For example, *Thresher* began as a *Skipjack* built of the new steel, with a silenced powerplant and the new sonar. *Sturgeon* was a stretched *Thresher* with a bigger sail (to accommodate more masts, partly for surveillance). *Los Angeles*

began as a *Sturgeon* with a new powerplant. Within each class, quite considerable improvements were made with little external indication. For example, the original *Los Angeles* was limited to hull sonars and to twenty-six weapons with four torpedo tubes. She could not operate freely in ice because the planes on her sail could not be rotated to a completely vertical position. Successively improved versions gained twelve vertical-launching missile tubes (for Tomahawk strike weapons), a towed array passive sonar, retractable bow planes, anti-sonar coating (Special Hull Treatment), and radical changes in combat direction systems associated with new computers and consoles.

Eventually the growth inherent in the evolving standard type was wrung out. At the end of the 1980s the US Navy ordered the prototype of a new design, *Seawolf*, with twice the number of torpedo tubes (and twice as many torpedoes), a new combat system, and a much larger diameter hull (to regain the hydrodynamic advantage lost when the long *Los Angeles* hull had been adopted). At the time, *Seawolf* seemed to be the ideal Cold War submarine. When the Cold War collapsed, many questioned whether so large and expensive a submarine was needed. A new 'Centurion' design was conceived. However, it is by no means clear that any new submarine will be much less expensive than *Seawolf*, simply because the number of new submarines ordered each year has fallen so steeply. Each submarine must therefore bear a much larger fraction of industrial costs (overhead). The overhead costs may well far exceed costs associated with specific aspects of submarine capability, so the navy may well find itself ordering a far less effective submarine at a higher unit cost. As for sheer size, submarines are very cramped because of their basic physics. A surface ship has only about a third of her hull underwater, but even a surfaced submarine has virtually all of her hull underwater, so for the same displacement

the submarine has perhaps a third of the usable hull volume of the surface ship. If the post Cold War world demands more in the way of surveillance and capacity, the ideal post Cold War submarine is unlikely to be smaller than the ideal Cold War type.

Ballistic missile submarines

The most important application of nuclear power turned out to be to ballistic missile submarines. It transformed their mission. The original concept, both in the United States and in the Soviet Union, had been for the submarine to run in to attack an assigned target. She had no particular peacetime role. Indeed, she could expect detection and destruction if she tarried too long within range of the target. A nuclear-powered submarine, however, could loiter indefinitely within range, because she would not reveal herself by showing a snorkel. She could, therefore, function as a deterrent, always ready to fire. This peacetime role became absolutely vital to maintaining the nuclear balance between the superpowers. Unlike missile silos ashore, ballistic missile submarines (SSBNs) could not be targeted easily for a first strike, and thus offered an enemy no incentive to fire first.

The designers of such submarines had to solve several technical problems. First, the missiles could not be ignited until they left their tubes. Cut into the submarine's pressure hull, the tubes had to be of minimum diameter. They could not possibly leave enough space for

The very sophisticated US Seawolf *programme is unlikely to survive the end of the Cold War. Besides the prototype, a second boat has been funded, but smaller and nominally cheaper designs are already under serious consideration. This model makes the design look shorter than the* Los Angeles *class, but the hull diameter was increased in order to regain the proportions of earlier classes, which were more efficient hydrodynamically.* (USN)

The great advantage of the US Polaris missile over earlier submarine-launched ballistic missiles was that it could be fired from underwater. The first Polaris boat, the USS George Washington, *is shown loading a missile into one of sixteen tubes. The economical pattern of twin lines of vertical tubes abaft the fin was later adopted for SSBNs of all nations, including the Soviets (before the huge* Typhoon, *which has the sail abaft the missile tubes). (CMP)*

transmitted their reference line to the missiles via the straightest line in nature, a light beam.

US missile submarines carry their weapons in two parallel lines to provide space for the light emerging from the navigational equipment under the sail (where it originally had access to navigational instruments, such as a special star-sight periscope) and for an optical trolley. In other nuclear submarines, the reactor, the heaviest single item in the ship, is as close as possible to amidships; that is not possible in a strategic ballistic missile submarine. At least since the *Yankee* class, Soviet ballistic missile submarines have probably used much the same technology. So have the British, the French, and the Chinese, the other operators.

British and French nuclear boats

The Royal Navy was intensely interested in nuclear power. About 1955 work began on a British powerplant, but the engineers involved were transferred to the British civilian electric generator project. The Royal Navy then approached the US Navy. Admiral Rickover ultimately agreed to sell the after end of a *Skipjack*, which was married to a British bow section to form HMS *Dreadnought*. US reactor technology was incorporated in all later British nuclear sub-

missile exhaust to escape. The Russians, the first to build a ballistic missile submarine, installed elevators which lifted the weapons to the top of the submarine's sail. The submarine surfaced before erecting the missiles and then launching them, a process which could take as long as 45 minutes. Captain Harry Jackson, who had designed *Albacore* and who was assigned to the US Polaris programme, found a better way. He used a gas or steam generator to blast the missile out of the tube. Now the missile could be launched underwater. The blast provided so much momentum that it could punch through the surface. It could then ignite.

The British SSN Superb *in 1978. This second-generation design was significantly faster, deeper diving, and quieter than the preceding* Valiant *class, with a fuller hull form. The traditional British concern with silencing was manifest in the rafting of the machinery and pump-jet propulsion. A characteristic of British boats is the preference for bow hydroplanes over the US Navy's sail-mounted diving planes. (MoD, Crown Copyright)*

The other issue was fire control. A ballistic missile must be aimed at its target, pointed precisely before it is launched. The US Navy developed precise navigational systems, and

marines, although the extent to which they duplicate US powerplants is unclear. The Royal Navy always maintained that it had paid for the US reactor technology by providing the United States with the key rafting technique.

The United States never sold its reactor technology to any other navy. It came very close to selling *Skipjack*s to Canada about 1958–59, but the Canadians could not decide to buy within the year that Admiral Rickover allowed them. A draft agreement with the Netherlands, negotiated in 1958, was aborted. It is not clear whether France approached the United States for nuclear technology (a French gas-cooled reactor plant, planned for a submarine in the late 1950s, failed). However, the pressurised-water powerplants of the French strategic submarines essentially duplicate the US design (the French have always claimed that their plant was developed from US commercial powerplant technology, which in turn was derived from submarine practice).

More recent French naval reactors are quite different. They use less enriched uranium ('caramel'), which must be replaced about every five years (US-style reactors are now refuelled about every twelve years). The French also adopted a more compact arrangement in which the steam generators were integral with the main reactor. Their nuclear attack submarine, the *Rubis* class, is much smaller than a US or British type; it is sometimes characterised as a diesel submarine with a nuclear powerplant. Like a diesel submarine, it has electric propulsion (turbo-electric in this case). The other machinery is not rafted, and the very compact powerplant is sometimes criticised as too noisy.

Soviet nuclear submarines

The Soviets began work on submarine reactors in 1953, building a shore powerplant as a prototype. Their first nuclear submarine, Project 627 (Nato code name *November*), had two pressurised-water reactors rather than the one of US and British craft. It was apparently conceived as a strategic attack platform, to deliver a huge nuclear torpedo against Western harbours. The torpedo project was soon aborted, and *November* entered service as a conventional attack submarine. Her powerplant

The world's first nuclear ballistic missile submarine was the Soviet Hotel *class, completed in 1959–61. Three SS-N-4 missiles were carried in the enlarged fin and the first boats had to surface to fire them. However, this photograph depicts a* Hotel II, *which had SS-N-5 missiles, which could be fired from underwater. (MoD, Crown Copyright)*

was used in contemporary cruise missile (*Echo*, Project 659) and ballistic-missile (*Hotel*, Project 658) submarines (in the West it was called HEN, after the three classes). A follow-on reactor was designed for follow-on torpedo (*Victor*, Project 671), cruise missile (Project 666), and ballistic-missile (*Yankee*, Project 667A) submarines (the cruise missile design was abandoned owing to

the failure of the anti-ship version of the SS-N-12 missile planned for it).

Unlike the US Navy, the Soviet navy did not choose to stop building conventional diesel submarines altogether. *November* was roughly parallelled by continued *Foxtrot* production. Diesel versions of the cruise and ballistic missile submarines (*Juliett*, Project 651 and *Golf*, Project 629) were designed and built. *Golf* was apparently a direct development of *Foxtrot*, with much the same powerplant. *Juliett* was the first of a new generation, with a diesel-electric (rather than direct-drive) plant. Because the engine is not directly connected to the propeller, such a plant is amenable to modification; *Juliett*s later tested a variety of low-powered closed-cycle powerplants.

The Soviet navy always suffered from drastic political shifts. Nikita Khrushchev entered power convinced that only nuclear weapons made any real difference in war (he once said that he had no use for any submarine which did not launch nuclear missiles). Knowing of Soviet work on submarine-launched missiles, he became interested in counters to equivalent Western systems. The most spectacular was a very fast submarine, code-named *Alfa* in the West, intended to run out to the approximate position of a Western submarine and then hunt it down.

Unlike most submarines, *Alfa* (Project 705) was not intended to remain at sea for very long. She needed nuclear power to dash a few hundred miles at high speed. Speed was essential because, with each passing hour after initial detection, a submarine might move several miles. Beyond a point, search would become impossible. In theory, *Alfa*s would lie at their docks until a contact was reported, then dash out, attack, and return. They needed few crew-

The smallest SSNs in the world are the French Rubis *class. The early boats, like* Saphir *shown here in 1984, were configured for attacking surface warships, where their relatively noisy powerplant may not be at such a disadvantage. The later* Amethyste *group are modified for ASW, including a redesigned bow. (L & L van Ginderen)*

men, because nothing would be maintained on board. All repair work would be conducted at a home base.

To get high speed, the submarine had to be the smallest possible package wrapped around the most powerful possible powerplant. The obvious choice for a powerplant was a liquid-metal reactor, in this case cooled by lead-bismuth alloy. Radioactivity in the machinery spaces could be tolerated because no crewman was expected to enter them at sea. That concept of operation also drastically reduced the shielding requirement, to a thick bulkhead between the reactor and the forward part of the submarine. Turbo-electric drive was selected, possibly for silencing and possibly also because it allowed a more compact machinery arrangement (since components did not have to be in line). As it turned out, liquid metal was indeed more dangerous than pressurised water. A prototype plant in a modified *November* never worked properly, and ultimately had to be sunk in the White Sea. One of the *Alfa*s tried to start up before properly melting the metal, and ended up with a frozen and very radioactive reactor. Cut in two, she was described for years as the only submarine in commission simultaneously in the Northern and Baltic Fleets.

The other major new feature was a deep-diving titanium hull. Any submarine is always threatened by the possibility that the stern planes will accidentally lock in the diving position, causing an unintentional crash dive. The faster the submarine is moving, the deeper she goes before she can recover. *Alfa* was very fast, at about 43kts, so she had to be able to recover from a particularly deep crash dive. Her designers adopted titanium to provide sufficient hull strength without an excessive weight penalty.

Alfa is only rarely associated with Khrushchev's early days because the prototype did not appear until the late 1960s, but the vital initial work must have been done during Khrushchev's special Seven Year Plan of 1959–65, which was planned about 1956–57. Substantially smaller than most nuclear submarines, *Alfa* was often described as the prototype of future highly automated craft. In fact it was a unique project, obsolete in concept as soon as US submarine missile ranges increased beyond about 800 miles (so that running out to a datum was no longer a viable tactic).

Before 1959, Khrushchev saw the Soviet navy's main mission as strategic attack. However, in 1957 the first successful Soviet Intercontinental Ballistic Missile was fired. Two years later the army-oriented Strategic Rocket Forces was formed. The navy was told that its central mission was obsolete. It found a replacement: de-

A Project 670 (Nato Charlie *class) boat, originally designed for missile attack on carrier task forces. The bulbous bow section contains launchers for eight SS-N-7 anti-shipping missiles, a version of Styx that could be fired while the boat was submerged.* Charlie II*s carried the longer range SS-N-9. (MoD, Crown Copyright)*

fence against Western (mainly US) naval attack, particularly by carrier battle groups. Both cruise and ballistic missiles were to be oriented towards the new anti-ship mission.

In the case of ballistic missiles, the theory was that they would be fired to bombard choke points through which carriers would have to steam. A new ballistic missile, SS-N-6, was conceived for this mission; its main advantage over earlier types was its ability to be fired more promptly. A new SSBN, conceived to carry six such missiles, was redesigned to carry twelve, to provide a denser salvo (later it was redesigned again, as the *Yankee* class, to carry sixteen). Work began on a manoeuvrable ballistic missile, designated SS-NX-13 in the West, which would home on the characteristic radar emissions of the carrier. By the time this weapon was ready, the navy had been restored to the strategic mission, and it was unnecessary. Moreover, total numbers of naval ballistic missiles (which included SS-N-13) were now regulated by treaty, so there was little point in fielding a weapon which would reduce the more important strategic firepower.

The main available cruise missile was the long range (about 250nm) Shaddock (SS-N-3). It was far easier to adapt than the ballistic

weapons, first with pure command guidance and then with a terminal seeker. Work soon began on a shorter-range weapon, Ametyst, now known to the West as SS-N-9, and on a submarine to bring it close enough to hit fast carriers. The submarine had to be at least as fast as the target. Like *Alfa*, it had a titanium hull. In this case, however, the powerplant was a pair of pressurised-water reactors.

Neither the submarine, *Papa* (Project 661, nicknamed 'Golden Fish' because of its cost), nor the missile was available in time. As an interim step, a missile-firing submarine using the second-generation reactor was designed. Planned building facilities probably limited its overall length, so it had only a single reactor, which limited its maximum speed to an insufficient 24kts. Ametyst was not ready in time, so many of these submarines were armed instead with a submerged-launch version of an existing short range anti-ship missile, SS-N-2 (Styx, the submarine version of which was designated SS-N-7 by Nato). The result was Project 670, code named *Charlie* by Nato. When she was finally completed, *Papa* was so expensive (and apparently so unreliable) that she was not worth reproducing: *Charlie*s became standard. Nato called the second-generation reactor CVY.

By the time the *Charlie* and *Victor* programmes were well under way, the Soviet navy had experienced yet another gross policy shift. The monopoly of the Strategic Rocket Forces was broken; the navy's ballistic missiles were reassigned to a strategic role. At first they were considered second-strike weapons. The submarines had to approach the US coast in order to fire, and to do that they had to break out through Western naval forces, including ASW submarines. Quite aside from its newly restored strategic role, the Soviet navy acquired an important pro-submarine (PSW) role. Now its submarines had to deal with Western SSNs. To do that, the Soviets obtained details of the US Subroc/BQS-6 combination, a version of which they installed in the new *Victor* class torpedo submarine (Nato designated the Soviet missile SS-N-15).

The same combination probably appeared in a new diesel-electric submarine, *Tango*, which was apparently based on the *Juliett* powerplant. *Tango*'s project designation, 641-BUKI, suggests its close relationship to the earlier *Foxtrot*.

SS-N-15 had one major flaw: it could carry only a nuclear warhead. Soviet homing torpedoes were too large and too heavy to be accommodated within the standard 53cm (21in) diameter. Eventually, the Soviets developed light enough torpedoes for this purpose. Work began on a larger-diameter equivalent to SS-N-15 which

Currently the world's largest submarines are the Russian Typhoon *class SSBNs. These 25,000-ton vessels are believed to have two parallel pressure hulls within the broad outer hull. The twenty SS-N-20 ballistic missiles are housed forward of the fin, making the* Typhoon *the first SSBN to depart from the missiles-aft configuration of the first Polaris boats.* (MoD, Crown Copyright)

The anti-carrier role remained. In 1964 work began on a new long range cruise missile, SS-N-19, designed to exploit satellite-based radar and electronic surveillance. A submarine, probably loosely related to the abortive cruise missile craft of 1962, was designed to carry it: *Oscar* (Project 949). However, because the new submarines with 65cm tubes could carry the SS-N-9 successor, no direct descendant of *Charlie* appeared.

By the mid 1970s the standard torpedo/ ASW and strategic submarines had been in production for some considerable time, albeit in progressively modified forms. Pressure to shift to a new generation may have come in part from the realisation, through the Walker spy ring, that existing submarines were being tracked quite regularly by US and Nato underwater sound systems. Three new classes appeared roughly simultaneously: *Sierra* (Project 945), a *Victor* follow-on with a titanium hull; *Akula* (Project 971), and *Typhoon* (Project 941). Although it appeared to be another attack submarine (and thus an alternative to *Sierra*), *Akula* was primarily intended to carry torpedo-sized cruise missiles (SS-N-21s), a new weapon prob-

could carry either a nuclear depth bomb or a torpedo: SS-N-16. It was the first of a family of 65cm (25.6in) weapons which ultimately included a folding-fin version of the SS-N-9 successor, SS-N-22 (which is also carried on board *Sovremennyy* class destroyers). The Soviets also deployed 65cm torpedoes, both wake-followers to attack surface ships and ASW weapons. The new *Victor* class attack submarine was redesigned to carry four reloadable 65cm tubes plus two non-reloadable 53cm tubes (to carry straight-running nuclear torpedoes for snapshots back at submarines firing long range wire-guided torpedoes at them).

Meanwhile, work began on longer range submarine-launched missiles, the bearers of which could attack North America from within sea zones the Soviet navy could protect (the 'bastions'). The existing *Yankee* class design was

modified to carry them (Nato redesignated it *Delta*, but the basic submarine was unchanged: *Delta I* was Project 667B).

In the export stakes the runaway winner is the German Type 209, a conventional diesel-electric single-hulled coastal boat designed by IKL and built by HDW. Every navy of any size in Latin America operates them, and similar boats have been built for Denmark, Norway, Greece and Turkey. Recently, new markets have been opened up, including Israel and South Korea. (HDW)

ably inspired by the US adoption of Tomahawk in the 1970s.

Typhoon seems to have been conceived as a *Delta* successor, although it proved so large and expensive that *Delta* production continued after it entered service. *Typhoon* is unique among the world's ballistic missile submarines in carrying its missiles forward of the sail; it also has multiple pressure hulls within its envelope. The logic was probably inspired by the *Yankee–Delta* series. These submarines ran through several generations of missiles. Each time the missile changed, the amidships part of the submarine had to be redesigned to accommodate it. That affected the entire design. In a *Typhoon*, a redesign to accommodate different missiles would have fewer consequences.

Follow-on classes were in the design stage when the Soviet Union collapsed in 1991. The current Russian navy hopes to continue building nuclear submarines, but at a much more modest rate. It hopes to introduce two new classes either late in this decade or early in the next, a new attack submarine and a new strategic type.

Submarines for export

After the Second World War, many navies wanted to build up submarine forces. Numerous surplus US and British submarines were available, and through the early 1960s many modernised versions of these craft were transferred. By that time several countries were building new craft specifically for export.

Germany led. The designer of the Type XXI and Type XXIII, Dr Ulrich Gabler, became chief of a design bureau, Ingenieur Konto Lubeck (IKL). Initially he developed small submarines for the new West German navy, then for nearby Nato countries (Denmark and Norway), and then for export further afield (the first Type 209s went to Greece). The German boats were the only major Western type designed specifically for export, and not used by the navy of the building country. They did incorporate technology used by the German navy. The other major submarine exporters were Britain (mainly *Oberon*s) and France (*Daphne* and *Agosta* classes). The United States was unable to export submarines once its navy had decided to concentrate solely on nuclear craft (the only postwar US exports were small coastal submarines for Peru).

The Soviets exported numerous examples of their mass-produced submarines, initially *Whiskey*s and a few *Romeo*s and later *Foxtrot*s (for a time *Foxtrot*s were made specifically for export). Later they developed a new diesel-electric submarine specifically for export, although they retained many for their own service: *Kilo* (Project 877). It was the first Soviet short fat (*Albacore* form) submarine. The *Kilo* hull form seems to have been adopted largely to satisfy the two classes of Soviet customers: shallow-water navies (such as the Polish navy in the Baltic, or the Bulgarian navy in the Black Sea) and deep-water navies (such as the Indian navy). The former wanted short submarines, since the depth error associated with a given down-angle is proportional to length. The latter needed maximum internal volume, to accommodate fuel and stores. The multi-deck configuration satisfied both.

Norman Friedman

Submarines: Typical Classes, since 1945

Class	Nationality	Displacement surface/dived (tons)	Length × breadth overall (feet-inches) (metres)	Armament	Machinery/Speed surface/dived (kts)	Launch (*completion dates)	Numbers built
MODERNISED 'A'	British	1443/1620	282-0 × 22-3 85.9 × 6.8	6-21in TT	DE/19/15	1945–47	14 modernised
WHISKEY (Project 613)	Soviet	1050/1350	246-1 × 20-9 75.0 × 6.3	6-21in TT	DE/17/13.5	1950–57	236 (plus 21 in China)
TANG	American	1560/2260	269-1 × 27-1 82.0 × 8.3	8-21in TT	DE/15.5/18.3	1951	6
GUPPY IA	American	1830/2440	307-0 × 27-0 93.6 × 8.2	10-21in TT	DE/18/16	1952	12 converted
ZULU (Project 611)	Soviet	1900/2350	295-3 × 24-5 90.0 × 7.5	10-21in TT	DE/18/16	*1953–55	26
QUEBEC (Project 615)	Soviet	400/540	183-8 × 16-5 56.0 × 5.1	4-21in TT	DE/18/16	*1954–57	30
NAUTILUS	American	3533/4092	323-7 × 27-7 98.7 × 8.4	6-21in TT	N/—/23	1954	1
SKIPJACK	American	3070/3500	251-7 × 31-7 76.8 × 9.7	6-21in TT	N/—/30	1958–60	6
NOVEMBER (Project 627)	Soviet	4500/5300	363-9 × 29-5 11.0 × 9.0	8-21in, 4-16in TT	N/—/30	*1958–64	15
PORPOISE/ OBERON	British	2030/2410	290-3 × 26-5 88.5 × 8.1	6-21in TT	DE/12/17	1959–66	27
DAPHNE	French	869/1043	190-0 × 22-0 57.8 × 6.8	12-21.7in TT	DE/13.5/16	1959–69	25
ECHO II (Project 675)	Soviet	5000/6000	377-3 × 29-5 115.0 × 9.0	6-21in, 2-16in TT; 8 SS-N-3 missiles	N/20/23	*1962–67	29

Class	Nationality	Displacement surface/dived (tons)	Length × breadth overall (feet-inches) (metres)	Armament	Machinery/Speed surface/dived (kts)	Launch (*completion dates)	Numbers built
LAFAYETTE	American	7325/8251	425-0 × 33-0 129.6 × 10.1	4-21in TT; 16 Polaris/Poseidon missiles	N/—/20	1962–66	31
STURGEON	American	4246/4777	292-3 × 31-7 89.1 × 9.7	4-21in TT	N/—/25	1965–74	39
RESOLUTION	British	7500/8400	425-0 × 33-0 129.5 × 10.1	6-21in TT; 16 Polaris missiles	N/20/25	1966–68	4
YANKEE (Project 667A)	Soviet	8000/9600	426-5 × 39-3 130.0 × 12.0	6-21in TT; 16 SS-N-6 missiles	N/—/27	*1967–74	34
REDOUBTABLE	French	7500/9000	420-0 × 35-0 128.0 × 10.6	4-21.7in TT; 16 ballistic missiles	N/20/25	1967–82	6
TYPE 209	German (export)	1105/1230	178-5 × 20-3 54.5 × 6.2	8-21in TT	DE/11/21	1970–	49[1]
SWIFTSURE	British	4200/4500	272-0 (pp) × 32-3 82.9 × 9.8	5-21in TT	N/20/28	1971–79	6
CHARLIE II (Project 670)	Soviet	4000/4900	34-0 × 32-9 103.0 × 10.0	6-21in TT; 8 SS-N-9	N/—/24	*1973–82	6
LOS ANGELES	American	6000/6900	360-0 × 33-0 109.8 × 10.1	4-21in TT; 12 Tomahawk missile tubes in later units	N/—/31	1974–	62
VICTOR III (Project 671RTMK)	Soviet	4600/5800	347-8 × 32-9 106.0 × 10.0	2-21in, 4-25.6in TT; SS-N-16 and -22 missiles	N/—/30	*1978–91	26
OHIO	American	16,000/18,000	560-0 × 42-0 170.7 × 12.8	4-21in TT; 24 Trident missiles	N/—/25	1979–	18
KILO (Project 877)	Soviet	2325/3076	243-7 × 32-8 74.3 × 10.0	6-21in TT	DE/10/17	*1980–	34 (more likely)
OSCAR (Project 949)	Soviet	12,500/14,600	469-2 × 59-7 143-0 × 18.2	2-21in, 4-25.6in TT; 24 SS-N-19 missiles	N/—/33	*1982–	9 (to total 14)
TYPHOON (Project 941)	Soviet	18,500/25,000	562-7 × 75-0 171.5 × 22.8	2-21in, 4-25.6in TT; 20 SS-N-20 missiles	N/—/25	*1983–90	6
DELTA IV (Project 667BRDM)	Soviet	10,800/13,500	537-9 × 39-4 164.0 × 12.0	6-21in TT; 16 SS-N-23 missiles	N/20/24	*1984–91	7
AKULA (Project 971)	Soviet	7500/9100	377-3 × 45-9 115.0 × 14.0	6-21in, 2-25.6in TT	N/—/35	*1985–	7 (more likely)
HARUSHIO	Japanese	2400/2750	262-4 × 32-8 80.0 × 10.0	6-21in TT	DE/12/20	1989–	to be 8 total
VANGUARD	British	—/15,850	489-7 × 42-0 149.3 × 12.8	4-21in TT; 16 Trident missiles	N/—/25	1992–96	4 building

Machinery abbreviations:
DE = diesel/electric; N = nuclear.

Notes:
[1] Type 209 data are for the Greek *Glavkos*, the first sold. Total sales to date (some not completed): Argentina (2); Brazil (5); Chile (2); Colombia (2); Ecuador (2); Greece (8); India (4); Indonesia (2); Korea (6); Peru (6); Turkey (8); Venezuela (2).

4

Mine Countermeasures Vessels

IN 1945 minesweeping did not stop with victory: the wartime fields still had to be cleared, both in European and Asiatic waters. Well into 1946 the weekly total was about 50 ground and 350 moored mines, and the International Mine Clearance Board was not disbanded until 1952. It was probably just as well that the mine clearance work did continue, as it focussed the attention of navies on the lessons of the mine war and the many problems posed for the future. Estimates of the number of mines laid vary, but the following are of the right order.

Table 4/1: Mines laid

	Moored	Ground	Total
Northern Europe	97,000	23,000	120,000
Mediterranean	30,000	25,000	55,000
Pacific	30,000	21,500	51,500

Surprisingly few of these mines were cleared, perhaps some 30,000: the rest blew themselves up, became buried or otherwise became harmless, though survivors still turn up and may be lethal. The cost was high: the UK lost 521 merchant ships and 281 warships to mines and the mine countermeasures (MCM) task was demanding in ships.

Table 4/2: Allied mine countermeasures ships

	British	American	Total
Fleet sweepers	343	283	744
Coastal & auxiliary	1637	679	2460
Total	1980	962	3204

In home waters a peak of 949 vessels was reached by the Royal Navy in 1944.

The lessons drawn from the Second World War may be summarised as follows.

1. Large numbers of ships would be needed, further increased by the use of counters in mines.

2. Bigger minesweepers were too often used for ASW escort.

3. The moored contact mine was still very effective, particularly when fitted with anti-sweeping devices.

4. The efficient conduct of MCM operations needed HQ ships and support ships.

5. Pressure mines were unsweepable, and advanced combination magnetic/acoustic mines very nearly so.

6. Advance preparation was essential in material (ships and their equipment), organisation and most of all in training.

Types of mine in 1945

The potential enemy for the West, the Soviet Union, was known to possess a very large number of mines, mostly of the older, simpler types, but including a substantial number of advanced design. Mines available in 1945 are described below; the few types which have appeared more recently will be mentioned later.

Moored mines

Contact. The classical mine, first used by Russia in 1855, in its latest form had a number of horns which would break if hit, so firing the mine. To make sweeping more difficult, mooring cables were made heavier, fitted with explosive cutters to sever sweep wires, and even with ratchet devices to allow a sweep to pass through without severing the mooring.

Antenna mines. Introduced by the US Navy in 1918, this type had a long wire held upwards by a small float. If the copper wire touched a steel hull, the electric potential would explode the mine.

Moored magnetic and acoustic mines were in use by 1941.

Ground mines

A mine exploding on the bottom, up to about 30m (100ft) below the target, will cause much greater damage than one exploding in contact, often breaking the hull in half.

Magnetic mines. Used by the Royal Navy in 1918 off Belgium and off Russia in 1919. The small

In 1945 one of the most pressing problems after victory in Europe was to clear wartime minefields. Germany was charged with clearing those around her own coasts and in July 1945 the German Mine Sweeping Administration was set up, under British command but employing many ex-Kriegsmarine craft. Prominent among these was the wartime R-boat, and when a new class of inshore sweepers was required by the new Bundesmarine in the mid 1950s the resulting Abeking & Rasmussen design resembled the final R-boats in layout. A flotilla of these, led by Gemma *(M 1097) is seen entering Ostende in 1984. (L & L van Ginderen)*

One of the largest postwar MCMV programmes produced the British 'Ton' class coastal minesweepers. They were 'non-magnetic', being constructed of mahogany planking over aluminium frames, and some 200 were built in various forms in five Nato countries. Some vessels were later converted from sweepers to minehunters, and most were given enclosed bridges like that on the hunter Iveston *shown here in 1984. (L & L van Ginderen)*

Their signatures were too high for safety and they were unable to generate the power required. The wartime, wooden motor minesweepers (MMS) of the Royal Navy were limited to 60 tons of magnetic material, but even this was too much for safety in the future.

The eternal problem of quality versus quantity rose in acute form. The new ships would be very sophisticated but must still be cheap enough to build in numbers within peacetime budgets. Wartime building could not be relied on as the sweepers would be required on the first day of a war. The crews, too, would need to be sophisticated, and reservists would need lengthy training.

Western powers received a sharp reminder of the mining problem when clearing a path for the landings at Wonsan in October 1950. In an area of about 400 square miles there were some 3000 Soviet mines, mostly contact ones of 1904 design but including a considerable number of very sensitive magnetic mines which could even be fired by the metal engines of the US wooden sweepers. In sweeping a path, 225 mines were swept for the loss of four sweepers and a tug, while five destroyers were damaged.

Signatures

For the new generation, all signatures would have to be reduced to very low levels. All depend on depth of water, and sweepers needed to clear ahead of an amphibious landing needed exceptionally low values.

number of German mines laid in 1939 caused great problems until countermeasures were found. The British 1940 model used the horizontal rather than the vertical component of the magnetic field and also worked off the rate of change rather than the strength, making both sweeping and degaussing much more difficult. This mine was later adapted to double contact: the magnetic field would first have to increase, and the mine would fire as it decreased when the ship passed. This put the explosion in a more damaging position and was also much more difficult to simulate in a sweep.

Acoustic mines. Introduced by Germany in August 1940. Developments included change of sensitivity and the use of specific frequencies aimed at helping the mine to discriminate between a ship and a sweep.

Later in the war major navies introduced a number of tricks to make sweeping more difficult, and these were applied to both magnetic and acoustic mines. Delay clocks left the mine inert, incapable of being swept for up to twelve days after it was laid. Counters would explode the mine only after a certain number of signals (up to sixteen) had been received. The sweeper would have to make a large number of passes before it was certain that the counter had run out.

Combined magnetic/acoustic mines. The mine would be made live by a magnetic field, which had to be maintained, and then fired by an acoustic signature. The relative position of the

magnetic and acoustic fields, as well as their rate of build-up, had to be very carefully matched to sweep a mine.

Pressure mines. A moving ship will generate a suction below it which can be used to fire a mine. Several countries developed such mines but feared to use them while they could not be swept. Early German mines (Oysters) could be fired by long waves, but this was cured by combination with a magnetic trigger. There was (and is) no effective way of sweeping such mines.

By the end of the war, fields were laid with a mixture of mines, moored and ground, and of varying sensitivities, making mine clearance difficult, hazardous and very time-consuming. There was a growing fear that nuclear mines might be used.

Postwar MCM considerations

It was clear that converted fishing vessels could no longer form the bulk of the sweeping fleet.

A parallel programme to the 'Ton' class coastal sweepers was the smaller inshore design, built for the Royal Navy as the 'Ham' class. Also composite in construction, they were built in three series, the third represented here by HMS Puttenham, *being a foot longer. (CMP)*

Pressure. Below a certain displacement, the pressure signature is so low that it is hard to distinguish from waves. European navies have set the maximum size of their MCMVs at under 800 tons.

Magnetic. The starting point is to avoid the use of steel components as far as possible, implying, in the early years, wooden hulls and bronze fittings. Some magnetic items were unavoidable and a degaussing system was still necessary. The magnetic field perceived in the Earth's own magnetic field depends on latitude, and overseas operations require a mobile range to measure and correct the signature. Low magnetic materials tend to be expensive and the elaborate monitoring to ensure that the desired result has been achieved and maintained may prove even more expensive.

Acoustic. At sweeping speeds the main problem is the machinery noise. Engine designs were developed which, by careful balancing, were less noisy, and were further reduced by insulation. Noise transmission was then reduced by fitting flexible mountings under the engine and, in later generations, by mounting all the machinery on a raft, isolated from the hull and supported flexibly above the waterline.

Propellers are heavily loaded when towing big sweeps and are liable to form noisy cavities in the water. Gradually, from about 1960, propellers were put into service which were quieter. It was never easy to design a propeller to be quiet both when towing and when free-running at a higher speed.

Both magnetic and acoustic signatures can become degraded in service and repeated rangings are necessary.

Additional problems

Shock. In the course of its duties an MCMV will experience repeated explosions quite close and an occasional one very close. The shock will hit the hull and may deform the shell, perhaps causing it to rupture, between the frames, or even distort a whole panel between bulkheads. Both the hull and the gas bubble formed by the explosion will oscillate with periods measured in milliseconds, so that though initially the shell will be pushed against the frames, it will shortly afterwards experience a suction pulling it away from the frame.

The shock is transmitted through the hull to equipment and to the crew. The equipment is mounted on flexible mounts which can damp out the resultant motion, the mounts usually also serving as a noise insulation. Men can suffer broken legs or, if thrown against the deck over-

USS Endurance, *one of the* Agile *class of MSO (ocean minesweepers). This design, the largest of the immediately postwar American MCMVs, was wooden-hulled with non-magnetic fittings. Their Packhard diesels were selected before properly developed, and it was nearly a decade before all the teething troubles were eliminated.* (L & L van Ginderen)

head, fractured skulls; protective helmets are worn between decks in mined waters.

A full size section of a new design of hull is usually tested to destruction by shock. Equipment will be designed and tested to a lower level of shock than the hull. When completed, the first ship of a new class will be exposed to a shock loading which is a little less than that expected to cause damage, though a few weak points are usually found. The shock loads used for design and for testing are agreed within Nato.

Escape. One wartime lesson was that mess decks should be just below the upper deck and not too far forward for easy escape should a contact mine explode on the bow.

Seakeeping. MCMVs are small and their behaviour in rough seas can be lively. Pitch and heave depend mainly on length, and it was found that the 105ft (31m) wartime MMS were too short for open sea work and that later 126ft (38m) craft were only marginal. For work in exposed European waters a length of 40m seems the minimum, together with a good freeboard and draught. Several classes have been fitted with roll reducing devices. (Note that fins are ineffective under about 8kts and are not much help to hunters working at lower speeds.)

Minesweeping

Moored mines may be swept either using a sweep wire worked between a pair of ships ('A' Sweep) or, more usually, with a single ship streaming a wire from one or both quarters. The far end of such a sweep is supported from an 'Oropesa' float and the wire is kept at the correct depth by a kite or otter at both ends. If the sweep engages a mine mooring, the latter

will run along the sweep until it falls into a cutter, driven by a small explosive charge. In good conditions the swept width can be up to 265m (290yds).

Magnetic sweeps are much refined versions of the Second World War 'LL' sweep in which a heavy electric current (*c*3000 amps) is pulsed from buoyant cables towed behind the ship. Modern sweeps have the capability to reproduce varying magnetic wave slopes and field magnitudes. The generator required is large, upwards of 500kW, and the control system is elaborate. A path of some 60m (65yds) wide can be swept.

The towed acoustic generator can reproduce accurately the noise field of different ship types, matching frequency distribution levels and their rate of change. A monitor is also towed which measures the noise characteristics fed into the water and, through the control box, can adjust the output of the generator.

The drag of these big sweeps is considerable, and powerful ships are needed to tow them. Lightweight sweeps cannot be effective against all types of mine, but may be of use ahead of the main MCM force to reduce the risk to them (the precursor sweep).

The first generation of postwar MCMVs

As a result of the Korean War and the perceived Soviet mine threat, a very large number of minesweepers was built in Nato, mainly in the UK and USA, the remainder being derivatives of these designs adapted to local equipment. The British 'Ton' class coastal minesweepers were designed by W J Holt, RCNC, a keen yachtsman who had designed the wartime MMS, and they were seen by him as a development of the 126ft design as he had originally intended it, with two engines. Holt had also had experience of the US Navy's excellent YMS, and features from this vessel also appeared in the 'Tons', though Holt did not like the YMS form. The 'Tons' displaced 425 tons deep.

The 'Tons' had a high, half-length forecastle which provided accommodation and also kept the ship dry, a style copied in most later MCMVs. The unbalanced profile made them hard to control at low speed in high winds, which did not matter as sweepers but became important when they were converted to hunters, where control at low speeds is vital. They were designed round the novel Deltic diesel – light, powerful, compact and, it was to prove, reliable. They were built with a double layer of mahogany planking over aluminium frames, later sheathed with nylon.

The 'Ton' class represented the most costly building programme for the Royal Navy prior to the Polaris submarine force; 118 were built in the UK and 93 to slightly modified designs in Canada, France, Holland and Portugal. They have proved most valuable ships and have been used as patrol boats and hunters. Many remain in service though, with advancing years, maintenance of the wooden hull becomes costly.

The 'Tons' were too big for very shallow water work, and the 'Ham' class of 195 tons were built as inshore sweepers. The UK built ninety-three and more were built overseas. Their size allowed little scope for additional equipment and their life was short before being discarded or converted to auxiliary uses. Eleven 'Ley' class were built as minehunters but they were ahead of their time. The projected sonar did not materialise and they have had to rely on divers for mine disposal. A similar hunter derivative of the 'Tons' was cancelled.

The 'Tons' and the earlier 'Hams' suffered from an unforeseen problem. When the ship rolled in the Earth's magnetic field the aluminium loops formed by frames and deck beams generated an electric current (eddy current) which had associated magnetic fields. The problem was eventually solved using a sensor at the masthead which controlled a degaussing system, but the last 'Hams' (*2701* upwards) had the better solution – an all-wooden hull. An all-wood 'Ton' was designed but not built.

The ships of the contemporary US pro-

gramme had wooden hulls and were also of two sizes. There were ninety-three ships of the 755-ton *Agile* class (originally designated AM, but from 1955 MSO), of which fifty-eight were retained by the US Navy, and the rest transferred to other navies. They were bigger than the 'Tons' and had a more powerful magnetic sweep, and like the 'Tons' they had a long active life, three taking part in Operation Desert Storm. The US Navy retained twenty of the 159 ships of the *Bluebird* (or *Adjutant*) class and two of twenty-five slightly larger *Albatross* class. They were of 400 tons, slightly updated YMS. Both classes of US ships suffered from unreliable machinery.

Large numbers of both US and RN craft were transferred to other navies and many remain in service. The British programme is often criticised for being too numerous, as many never entered service. This criticism is unjustified: they were built as a war reserve, to be manned when needed.

Minehunting

Even while the first generation was building, it was realised that an increasing proportion of mines were unsweepable and that future mine clearance would depend on minehunting. Minehunting is easy to describe, but its success depended on the solution of several very difficult technical problems.

In the earlier minehunters, a high-definition

sonar was carried underneath the hull, the transducer being very accurately stabilised in order to keep the pencil beam on target despite the lively motions of a small minehunter. The suspect area would be searched with a moderately wide beam and, if a suspicious object was seen, the sonar would be switched on to an even higher frequency narrow beam to examine and classify the object. It was usually necessary for the ship to manoeuvre round the object to 'see' it from different directions, keeping outside the danger area for explosions (some 100m, 330ft) and inside sonar range, not much more than 200m (650ft) of early sets. The ship itself, some 50m (165ft) long, had to be manoeuvred precisely within this annulus despite tidal currents and wind.

If the object was classified as a probable mine, it would be examined by a diver, and possibly made safe and recovered or, more usually, detonated using a remote controlled mini-submarine. The most common of these is the French PAP, weighing about 800kg (1760lb) in latest form, including a 100kg (220lb) demolition charge, 2.7m long and 1.2m in diameter (9ft by 40in). It can operate up to 600m (1970ft) from the ship at a speed of 6kts and down to 300m (985ft), controlled by the ship's sonar. The PAP carries a floodlight and a TV camera giving positive identification of the mine. The charge is then laid alongside the mine and detonated after the PAP is recovered.

Minehunting is very slow. Except under the most ideal conditions, the search speed is likely to be under 4kts. Manoeuvring to classify a suspicious object takes time – and there will be many false alarms caused by saucepans, bits of pipe etc – while to launch a PAP, identify the mine, drop the charge and recover the PAP may take an hour or so.

Hunting is never 100 per cent certain, so several runs will be needed to ensure that an area is clear. There is also a high risk of the hunter passing over the mine, so it needs very low signatures and a high resistance to shock.

A number of ways have been tried to obtain the high manoeuvrability. The simplest uses conventional twin screws with precise control from electric or hydraulic drive, twin rudders in the slipstream and a large bow thruster. 'Active

The Belgian Aster, *one of the French-Dutch-Belgian Tripartite Minehunter programme, displays a couple of the French PAP (poisson auto propulsé) 104 mine-destruction submersibles on her quarterdeck (under the weatherdeck overhang). The ships of this class have electrically-propelled twin active rudders and bow thrusters for manoeuvrability while hunting, in addition to a normal single-shaft diesel for transit. (L & L van Ginderen)*

rudders' with a small propeller on the rudder driven by a small electric or hydraulic motor in a pod have been used in several designs. All are likely to be noisy, as to be quiet a propeller has to move a large mass of water slowly, and the axis of the propeller must be in line with the flow. Neither active rudders nor bow thrusters satisfy these conditions. The Voith Schneider vertical-axis propeller used in later Swedish and British hunters gives superb manoeuvrability but it has taken time to overcome its problems of mechanical and hydrodynamic noise.

The hunter conversions of the 'Tons' scored their major success when they used 193 sonar to clear of field of very advanced Soviet mines laid by Libya in the Red Sea in 1983.

The prototype 'Hunt' class MCMV HMS Brecon *in 1980. These combined hunter/sweepers are the largest British mine warfare vessels of the postwar period and are also the largest GRP (glass reinforced plastic) vessels in the world. They have been criticised for their cost, since so few could be afforded, but they are very capable, and proved their worth in the Gulf War. (MoD, Crown Copyright)*

Second generation MCMVs

The Royal Navy carried out a prolonged study into the style of future MCMVs from the late 1950s, examining many unconventional schemes such as bottom crawling tanks, paddle catamarans, etc. A relatively conventional solution was selected and, since there were very large numbers of simple mines in use, world-wide, it was decided that the new MCMVs should be able to sweep as well as hunt.

Signatures were to be much lower than in previous ships, demanding very large, slow running propellers which could be quiet under transit, hunting or sweeping conditions. The hull had to be non-magnetic and non-conducting, the latter ruling out metals and carbon reinforced plastic. Though other materials have been considered, the practical choice lies between wood (probably laminated) or one of several forms of glass reinforced plastic (GRP) construction. Arguments over the choice of material are confused because the relative costs of different forms of construction vary between countries, depending on the experience available.

The hull has to withstand severe and repeated shock loads, and the Royal Navy carried out a number of tests on large sections of different construction and a very much larger number of tests of individual panels. As a result it was decided to use a single-skin GRP hull stiffened by framing. There was still a considerable number of problems to be solved, of which only a few can be given even a brief mention.

The most serious was that the shell tended to separate from the frames under the tension loading during the second phase of shock loading. This was solved by using titanium bolts to hold them together. The glass was used in 'woven' form for extra strength, which also contributed to the fire resistance of the hull. The resin was chosen for minimum water absorption and, since it is dissolved by most paint strippers, a barrier coat had to be applied under the paint. Since GRP is non-conducting, all electrical equipment had to be individually earthed – and a lightning conductor fitted. GRP is transparent to electromagnetic radiation, and radios, radars etc had to be screened to prevent mutual interference.

To prove the design approach, a GRP replica of the 'Ton' class hull was built in 1972 and fitted with the machinery and other equipment from a 'Ton' being scrapped. The result, HMS *Wilton*, the first GRP warship, has been very successful in service, a small fire and two collisions helping to demonstrate the worth of GRP. She has, of course, also been shock tested. GRP construction was accidentally given a much more severe test when *Ledbury* of the succeeding 'Hunt' class suffered a major engine room fire with temperatures up to 900°C for four hours. Though there was extensive damage to equipment and systems, the GRP suffered only slight, localised damage, easily repaired, while it insulated neighbouring compartments from the heat of the fire. GRP construction in small numbers is never cheap, but the cost of the 'Hunt' class hull is only 7 per cent of the total cost. Non-magnetic equipment – bronze anchor cable, for example – is much more expensive than a GRP hull.

The cheapest form of GRP construction uses a sandwich with two skins of GRP separated by a foam filling. Foams have been developed which resist shock but, after an explosion or after a fire, there is no way of discovering how much of the foam has been affected without cutting the hull apart. Italy has developed a thick (140mm) monocoque structure, also to be used by the US Navy, which, though heavy, meets shock requirements.

Sapri, one of the Italian Lerici *Class MCMVs. The Italians have developed a thick monocoque construction technique for the GRP hull that requires no framing. This has been adopted by the US Navy for its new* Osprey *class.* (L & L van Ginderen)

Wood construction and, even more, its maintenance, is too expensive for most developed countries (except the USA). Non-magnetic steel has been used, though it is not clear from published information if the eddy current problem has been solved. It seems that its use is only economic in Germany, which has the right skills, making repair difficult for other countries.

The 'Hunts'

The design of the thirteen ships of the 735-tonne 'Hunt' class incorporates all the features discussed above. The two nine-cylinder propulsion engines and the similar pulse generator (all low-magnetic Deltics), together with three Foden diesel generators and other auxiliary machinery, are mounted on GRP rafts suspended from flexible mounts above the waterline. The GRP reinforcement of these rafts is arranged so that most of the fibres lie in the direction of the highest stress. A full-scale mock up of the whole ship in wood and hardboard over a steel frame was built in the shipyard to ensure that every detail was conveniently positioned.

At low hunting speeds the propellers are driven by hydraulic motors for silent and precise operation, and there is a large-diameter bow thruster. The small residual magnetic field is monitored by a magnetometer at the top of the mast, which controls an automatic degaussing system, further reducing the field. The 'Hunts' carry the full array of the latest versions of moored, magnetic and acoustic sweeps. A large section was tested to a high shock load, and *Brecon*, the first of class, has been exposed to operational loading. The 'Hunt' class hull is the largest piece of plastic ever built.

Support

The need to keep MCMVs small means that their capacity for self maintenance is very limited. The Royal Navy has created several Forward Support Units (FSUs), each of which is built into a number of containers, the number deployed depending on the nature of the operation and the location of the unit.

The final outcome of a long and convoluted design process, the US Avenger *class are a very large (1300 tons) but highly capable class of multi-purpose MCMVs.* USS Devastator *(MCM-6) was one of a squadron of this class visiting Ostende in April 1993.* (L & L van Ginderen)

The unit deployed to the Gulf in 1991 had sixteen containers for stores (200,000 items costing £1.5 million) with a computerised index, workshops, power supply and external communications. The living and sanitary containers were not needed as the unit was accommodated in an LSL rather than on shore. An FSU is manned by about 40 senior ratings.

A headquarters staff is needed to control the operation to ensure that coverage is complete, and this was based in a survey ship for the Gulf operation. Mobile ranges to check the magnetic and acoustic signatures against degradation and the effects of magnetic latitude will also be needed.

Other solutions

Belgium (10 ships), France (10) and the Netherlands (15) collaborated on the design and construction of a big class of 'Tripartite Minehunters' of 595 tonnes. Construction is very similar to that of the 'Hunts' but with GRP pins

Seehund 5, *a drone minesweeper of the German 'Troika' system. Each team consists of three of these unmanned craft, controlled by a specially converted coastal minesweeper during operations, although they can be manned while on passage. The German navy has eighteen of these drones.* (L & L van Ginderen)

instead of bolts. Their French sonar and disposal equipment is very similar in capability to that of the 'Hunts', though they have no sweeping gear. They have a single propeller and an active rudder, electrically driven while hunting.

The Italian *Lerici* design of 520 tonnes is fairly similar except for its monocoque, unframed hull. This design also forms the basis for the US Navy's slightly larger *Osprey* class. A number of ships similar to the Tripartite and *Lerici* classes have been built for other counties.

The US Navy completed the *Avenger* in 1987, the first of a class of eleven. She displaces 1262 tonnes and has a wooden hull made up of four layers of timber, sheathed with GRP. She has a variable-depth sonar for mine location which should give improved performance in bad conditions. *Avenger* was still suffering from teething troubles during Desert Storm, with unreliable machinery and equipment.

The *Avenger*s were designed for deep water and are too big for shallow water, and it was intended to supplement them with the *Cardinal* class of sidewall hovercraft (surface effect ships, SES), but the shock trial of a section was a failure. It is now intended to built ships of the *Osprey* class of 785 tons, based on the Italian *Lerici* design but bigger and with US equipment.

Soviet MCMVs

Little is known about Soviet MCM capability. They have built a large number of fleet sweepers, many with aluminium hulls, other steel, both of which would generate high eddy current fields. All are heavily armed and many act as ASW ships and hence are likely to have high magnetic signatures. Visible sweeping gear appears similar to Western equipment.

There is a considerable number of coastal types, many with wooden hulls. Most appear to be sweepers but some, without much visible equipment, are clearly hunters.

Other vehicles

Many alternatives to the conventional, displacement MCMV have been tried and a few even put into service. Since none of these has been generally accepted, their main characteristics need only be noted.

Helicopters. The US Navy has a number of Sea Stallion helicopters which have a valuable capability for visual location of floating and shallow moored mines. They can tow light sweeps or a side-scan sonar for precursor sweeping ahead of the MCM force. Precise track keeping is difficult and support costs are high.

Hovercraft. A fully skirted hovercraft is decoupled from the sea, giving it an inherently high shock resistance and a low acoustic signature which cannot be degraded in service and comes without the cost of special mountings. The air-driven hovercraft is exceptionally controllable and can follow a track better than a conventional ship, but it has a high fuel consumption and running costs are higher than those of ships. Every aspect of MCM operations has been tried full scale by the Royal Navy, but hovercraft have not been put into service.

In the route surveillance role the object is to confirm that a selected channel is mine-free, rather than to dispose of mines. The channel is searched using side-scan sonar at relatively high speed and the picture recorded is compared in a computer with 'yesterday's view'. Since the vehicle inevitably passes over any mine present, the hovercraft's near invulnerability and its low signature at speed make it particularly suitable.

The ERMISS (Explosion Resistance Multi Influence Sweep System) was distantly related to the hovercraft and was designed to reproduce all the signatures of a target vessel, including pressure, and to survive the resulting explosion without damage. Full-scale tests showed promise but also revealed problems which would have been very costly to overcome, and the project was abandoned.

Surface effect craft. These are better described by their original name of sidewall hovercraft, as the air cushion is held by two sidewalls and skirts are only needed at the ends. This reduces the cost of skirt maintenance but greatly reduces the noise and shock isolation of the true hovercraft. Existing SES have all suffered from severe motions in a seaway. Norway is building ten 500-tonne craft as the high transit speed is valuable along their lengthy coastline.

Troika. The German navy has built, and used in the Gulf, six units consisting of a control boat and three unmanned, remote control boats carrying sweeps. They have no hunting capability.

Catamarans. The catamaran has a wide clear deck on which to deploy gear, whilst its great stability makes it easy to add new items. This same excess stability leads to very high roll accelerations which can damage equipment and injure personnel. The two Australian catamarans of the *Rushcutter* class have been unsuccessful due to problems with weapon integration. A catamaran is being designed for the French navy.

Multi-role craft. The lesson of the Second World War, which remains valid today, is that MCMVs must be dedicated to that task. Crew skills are specialised and a GRP hull designed to resist shock is too heavy to be effective for high speeds. It is virtually impossible to reconcile high power with silence. A multi-role craft is likely to combine the faults of all.

DATS. Both the US Navy and the Soviet navy have developed 'active' anti-submarine mines. The mine is usually moored in deep water, close to the bottom, and will listen for a target. The target is then classified and located, perhaps by active sonar, and a torpedo (US Navy's Captor) or a rocket propelled missile is fired. The Royal Navy has devised a 'Deep Armed Team Sweep' (DATS) towed between a pair of simple, steel hulled sweepers, the sweep being automatically kept close to the bottom. Since these mines are programmed against submarines, a simple surface ship is not thought to be at risk.

The Australian catamaran minehunter Rushcutter *has proved disappointing in service and the programme has been curtailed. The peculiar seakeeping of the catamaran hull form causes problems, which is why so few have found naval applications.* (RAN)

Third generation MCMVs

During the 1970s the UK Ship Department devised a cheap minehunter to supplement the 'Hunt' class in the easier tasks. This 'Utility' minehunter was not built, but the concept led to a requirement for a 'Single Role Mine Hunter' which was designed and built by Vosper Thornycroft as HMS *Sandown*, benefiting from the experience with earlier generations of MCMV. It has a single-skin, framed GRP hull, but the framing is almost entirely unidirectional, omitting the expensive crossing joints, and new flexy resins have made it possible to omit bolts. The builders claim that test sections have withstood 'over four times the operational shock factor and over twice the survival shock requirements of the RN'. Large sections are pre-outfitted and dropped complete into the hull, the first time such a method has been used in a GRP hull.

The *Sandown* is propelled by two Voith Schneider vertical-axis units which give it exceptional manoeuvrability, while development has enabled her to meet the noise targets. Manoeuvrability in winds has been improved further by the aerodynamically balanced above-water profile. A variable-depth sonar is used which, with the transducer close to the bottom, has improved capability in bad conditions and against camouflaged or buried mines. Five are

HMS Sandown, *the first of the new Single Role Mine Hunters, demonstrates the manoeuvrability conferred by the Voith Schneider propellers. These economical GRP craft may be considered the only 'third generation' postwar MCMVs so far in service, and have found favour with the navies of Saudia Arabia and Spain.* (Vosper Thornycroft)

building for the Royal Navy, three for the Saudi navy and four under licence in Spain. The British version is a pure hunter, but light sweeps are fitted in the Saudi version.

Sandown has a data bus to integrate the control and functioning of weapons, navigation and of command and control, using the Nautilus system. *Sandown* was undergoing trials during the Gulf War which validated the thinking behind her design.

The Gulf War

Casualties during the Iran–Iraq war, including the USS *Samuel B Roberts*, showed the hazards of mining in the Gulf, and this was confirmed during Operation Desert Storm, with damage to USS *Tripoli* and *Princeton* showing also that the venerable contact mine remained a threat. Perhaps the only real surprise of the Gulf mine war was that well over 1000 mines, many of advanced design, were cleared without loss or damage to the MCMVs.

The first problem was getting to the Gulf. The European ships went – slowly – under their own power. The US ships, with much further to go and unreliable machinery, travelled at a higher speed on a heavy lift ship – surely the right way for slow boats to travel to war. During the fighting the only vessels in the combat zone were four US ships and five British 'Hunts', the latter being responsible for clearing a path ahead of the US battleships when bombarding.

The Royal Navy's FSU proved of great value, even to the US ships.

After the war, seventeen other European ships from France, Belgium, Holland, Italy and Germany joined in the clearance. Once again, hunting was shown to be slow, but it was now quicker to hunt moored mines than to sweep them. Floating mines proved difficult and could only be located visually, stopping most night work.

Conditions were not good for sonar but all types worked well, as did the mine disposal vehicles. The operation was greatly assisted by the US Global Positioning System (GPS), a satellite-based navigation system which gave a repeatable, positional accuracy of a very few metres. The British ships were given additional light anti-aircraft guns, but the rules of engagement forbad their use.

Lessons are most usually learnt from disasters, and it must be hoped that the success of the Gulf War does not conceal the lessons. These may be seen as the need for a numerous force of MCMVs, with well trained crews, controlled by experienced staff and properly supported.

The future

Mines are still a major threat to trade and, in the current unstable state of the world, perhaps even an increasing threat. Any small power, or even a terrorist group with access to a few elec-

tronics buffs, can devise a clever actuating circuit. Such threats require well designed material and well trained crews to counter. Peacetime navies are inclined to think of mine warfare as a minor, even ungentlemanly, task, but it is demanding in skills and in technology.

Any form of mine clearance is slow and hence a numerous force of MCMVs is essential. Many companies are developing self propelled 'fish' which run ahead of an MCMV, powered through an umbilical, locating mines and placing demolition charges. Such developments are very welcome but will have to demonstrate 100 per cent success before they can be used from 'craft of opportunity', and converted fishing vessels, which are noisy and lack shock protection.

It will always be easier to fit a new firing mechanism to a mine than to deploy a counter; the MCM force will always be playing against odds.

David K Brown, RCNC

Mine Countermeasures Vessels: Typical Classes, since 1945

Class	Nationality	Displacement normal/full load (tons)	Dimensions overall (feet-inches) (metres)	Hull	Armament	Machinery/ Speed (kts)	Launch dates	Numbers built
TON	British	360/450	152-0 × 28-9 × 8-3 *46.3× 8.8 × 2.5*	Composite (wood/aluminium)	1-40mm, 2-20mm	D/15	1952–59	118 (plus 93 derivatives)
HAM	British	120/159	106-6 × 21-0 × 5-6 *32.5 × 6.4 × 1.5*	Composite (later all wood)	1-40mm or 20mm	D/14	1952–58	93 (plus derivatives)
AGILE	American	637/735	171-6 × 34-0 × 13-1 *52.3 × 10.4 × 4.0*	Wood	1-40mm	D/13	1952–56	93 (inc transfers)
BLUEBIRD	American	360/400	145-5 × 26-6 × 7-0 *44.3 × 8.1 × 2.1*	Wood	1-20mm	D/13	1953–61	159 (inc transfers)
SCHUTZE	German	241/267	155-9 × 22-10 × 7-6 *47.4 × 6.9 × 2.3*	Wood	1-40mm	D/25	1958–63	30
VANYA (Project 257)	Soviet	200/250	131-7 × 25-11 × 5-7 *40.2 × 7.9 × 1.7*	Wood	2-30mm	D/16	1961–73	65
NATYA (Project 266M)	Soviet	650/750	196-10 × 32-3 × 9-10 *61.0 × 9.8 × 3.0*	Aluminium alloy	4-30mm, 4-25mm 2 RBU-1200 ASW	D/18	1970–80	35 (plus exports)
SONYA (Project 1265)	Soviet	—/450	160-1 × 28-10 × 6-11 *48.8 × 8.8 × 2.1*	Wood (plastic sheath)	2-30mm, 2-25mm	D/15	1973–80	65
HUNT	British	615/725	197-0 × 32-3 × 7-3 *60.0 × 9.8 × 2.2*	GRP	1-40mm	D/17 H/8	1978–87	13
SEEHUND ('Troika' drone)	German	91/99	81-9 × 15-2 × 6-0 *25.0 × 4.6 × 1.8*	Wood	Nil	DE/9.4	1979–82	18
TRIPARTITE	French-Dutch-Belgian	519/544	161-0 × 29-0 × 8-0 *49.1 × 8.9 × 2.5*	GRP	1-20mm	D/15 E/7	1981–90	35
LERICI	Italian	485/502	164-0 × 31-4 × 8-7 *50.0 × 9.6 × 2.6*	GRP	1-20mm	D/15 H/7	1985–	10 (plus 6 exports)
AVENGER	American	1100/1312	224-0 × 39-0 × 12-2 *68.3 × 11.9 × 3.7*	Wood	?	D/13.5 E/?	1985–	11 (plus 3 on order)
RUSHCUTTER	Australian	170/—	101-7 × 29-5 × 6-6 *30.9 × 9.0 × 2.0*	GRP	4-12.7mm	D/10 H/?	1986–87	2
OSPREY	American	—/851	188-0 × 34-8 × 8-9 *57.3 × 10.6 × 2.7*	GRP	1/2-12.7mm	D/12 H/?	1990–	Building (programme of 17)
SANDOWN	British	450/484	172-0 × 34-0 × 8-0 *52.4 × 10.4 × 2.4*	GRP	1-30mm	D/13 E/6	1991–	5 (plus 3 Saudi and 4 in Spain)

Machinery abbreviations:
D = diesel; DE = diesel-electric; H = hydraulic; E = electric.

Modern MCMVs have various forms of propulsors, usually driven by electric motors, through hydraulic thrusters or active propellers; where quoted above, the second figures relate to these special untra-quiet and/or precise sweeping drives.

5

Fast Attack Craft

URING the 1880s, Admiral Aube conceived a new strategy for the French navy in its unending rivalry with Britain's Royal Navy. Recognising that France was unable to challenge the might of the British by conventional means, he proposed the construction of fleets of small attack craft and submarines armed with the new self-propelled torpedoes. These, he claimed, would make the traditional blockade tactics of the Royal Navy untenable. At the same time large, specially designed raiding cruisers would attack Britain's seaborne commerce, cutting off her supplies of food and raw materials and, eventually, bringing about her defeat. Adherents of this new concept of naval operations referred to themselves as the *Jeune École* (Young School), with the implication that their concepts were the way of the future and previous operational philosophies were old-fashioned and redundant.

One of the immediate results of these theories was the construction of large numbers of steam-powered torpedo boats by the world's navies. The problem quickly became apparent; technology was simply not up to the task set before it. Torpedoes were short-ranged and low-speed; to gain an acceptable proportion of hits meant firing at very close range. The hull designs were small scale, very lightly built versions of those used in conventional types of warships. Reciprocating engines were still the only available propulsion machinery, which meant that the engines had to occupy most of the hull if the required speed was to be achieved.

The resulting craft were poor sea-boats and very vulnerable to gunfire. They were not even

very cheap, since their engines were disproportionately expensive and the light hull construction meant they had short operational lives. About the only real significance of these craft was that the defences planned against them – larger and more seaworthy ships armed with relatively powerful gun batteries – became the ancestor of the twentieth-century destroyer. These, armed with torpedoes of their own, did become significant threats to larger surface ships but were no longer the mosquito fleet envisaged by Aube.

Prior to the outbreak of the First World War, a series of advances in hull design and propulsion machinery, combined with the steady increases in torpedo range and speed, seemed to revive the possibility of building small, cheap fast attack craft (FAC) that would pose a significant threat to major surface units. The first of these jumps forward was the planing hull design. The basic concept of the planing hull was understood as early as the 1840s, but it took the development of lightweight, powerful internal combustion engines for it to become practical. At rest a planing hull is supported entirely by its buoyancy but, if it can exceed a critical (hump) speed, most of the hull lifts out

of the water, dramatically reducing resistance. This hydrodynamic lift force generated by the motion through the water is sufficient to balance between 60 and 70 per cent of the hull weight, reducing resistance largely to friction between the water and the planing surface.

Once engines sufficiently powerful to drive a hull beyond the hump speed were available, the motor torpedo boat became a practical proposition. The relationship between hydrodynamic lift and hump speed meant that, for geometrically similar boats, the critical speed rose in proportion to the square root of their length. Thus if a 60ft hull planed at 30kts, a similar 240ft hull would plane only at 60kts. Thus the new generation of torpedo boats would have to be small. The development of internal combustion engines as powerplants made the concept possible. The first of the type was built by the French engineer Campet in 1905. By the First World War a typical British 55ft Coastal Motor Boat (CMB) displaced 10 to 11.5 tons and could achieve 40kts when powered by two 375bhp engines.[1]

---

1. Dr Norman Friedman, *US Small Combatants: An Illustrated Design History* (Annapolis 1987).

At the end of the war the Royal Navy gave two of the specialist builders a relatively free hand to incorporate their own ideas into a prototype fast attack craft. Vosper's produced MTB-538, with a glued all-wood hull, from which was derived the 'Gay' class. Gay Bombardier, *shown here in April 1953, was the first to complete. They were hard-chine boats, clearly descended from wartime practice, and were the last British FAC with petrol engines, the following 'Dark' class having the new Deltic lightweight diesels. (CMP)*

These British CMBs achieved fame by torpedoing the Russian battleship *Petropavlovsk* in Kronstadt harbour during the intervention against the Bolsheviks in 1919. In reality, they achieved little in proportion to the resources invested in them. These not only included the cost of the craft themselves but the infrastructure needed for their operation. They needed to be carried to the scene of an action and picked up afterwards. Their light construction and high-powered, highly stressed engines made them short-lived and expensive to operate. They were unsuitable for retention by the cash-limited peacetime navies and the CMBs (together with their equivalents in other navies) were quickly discarded.

Development only resumed in the years running up to the Second World War. The British Power Boat company produced a successful motor torpedo boat design. This was adopted by the Royal Navy and subsequently used as the basis for the design of the US Navy PT-boats. The British Power Boat design used a different hull form. The CMBs had been designed with a substantially flat hull form carrying a step in the hull intended to break the suction of the water and help the boat rise to a planing position. The new MTBs had a hard-chine hull. In this design a shallow 'V' shape ran from the bows right aft. The same hydrodynamic forces lifted the hull into the planing mode, but the planing angle was much less extreme and gave the boat a more comfortable ride. This resulted in a better and more effective platform from which to fight. Hard-chine hulls also permitted a larger boat than the older design but benefited less from the planing effect. The craft were still too small to carry both an effective torpedo and gun armament though, and British Second World War FAC were equipped either for torpedo attacks (MTBs) or gunnery duels (MGBs).[2]

The Germans took a different course when designing their S-boats (*Schnellboote*). By accepting significantly lower speeds they could adopt a conventional round-bilge hull, build it toughly and equip it with diesels rather than the potentially explosive petrol engines. The larger boats could carry effective torpedo armaments backed up by substantial gun batteries. These quickly included powerful auto-cannon, derived from weapons designed for fighter aircraft. Although viewed as a regressive design at the time, this layout reflected a German appreciation that their boats would be on the defensive, protecting their assets against British attacks. In engagement after engagement across the North Sea, the German S-boats consistently outfought their British opponents.[3]

Disentangling the effectiveness of the FAC during the Second World War is difficult, since the literary accomplishments of MTB and MGB commanders far exceeded their military achievements. At least part of the problem with the British MTB and MGB units was that the officers commanding those boats saw them-selves as the leading edge of a new generation of naval officer, not hidebound by the useless and time-wasting traditions of the past. Part of this self-image was a tendency to dismiss proper after-action reports as useless paperwork, and few such accounts were prepared. No methodical analysis of engagements was performed and no common tactical doctrine emerged. As a result, no strong core of professional expertise was formed and few commanders learned by the mistakes of others.

An objective viewpoint strongly suggests that, as in the First World War, the resources expended on these craft were wasted and could have been more profitably employed elsewhere. The MGBs in particular proved to be a major disappointment. Although they carried quite heavy gun batteries, up to and including 4.5in guns, they demonstrated a serious inability to use that firepower effectively. The high speed of the craft, lack of proper fire control and severe vibration made it impossible for the gunners to concentrate their fire or to achieve a significant volume of hits. Slowing down to increase accuracy caused the craft to drop below their hump speeds and caused further speed reductions. This left the MGBs as very easy targets indeed.

Even where the FAC had fulfilled useful roles – for example barge-busting in the Solomon Islands by US Navy PT-boats – the task could have been better fulfilled by slower, more robust and better armed craft.[4] The FAC proved terribly vulnerable to air attack. German fighter pilots referred to British MTBs and MGBs as 'Eiders' after the ducks that sat on the water and allowed themselves to be shot up. By the middle of 1943 the growing presence of USAAF B-17 and B-24 aircraft had caused the Germans to install heavy batteries of auto-cannon on their aircraft to deal with the heavily armed and armoured bombers. These cannon batteries proved ideal for engaging FAC. Since German

2. David Cobb, *Warship Profile 7: HM MTB/Vosper 70ft* (Windsor 1971).

3. Dr G Hummelchen, *Warship Profile 31: German Schnellboote* (Windsor 1973).

4. *US Naval Operations in World War II*, Volume VI: *Breaking The Bismarcks Barrier* (Boston 1952).

Vosper, the leading British designer of fast attack craft, persevered with the short hull, increasing its smooth-water speed by the adoption of gas turbines. The Royal Navy maintained a Coastal Forces cadre, but most of Vosper's output was for export. The Libyan Susa, *shown running trials in 1968, was a notable first, being fitted for Nord SS-12 anti-ship missiles. These French-made missiles were short range modified anti-tank weapons, but produced the West's first FAC-M design. (Vosper Thornycroft)*

fighters rarely operated in appropriate areas, the number of British FAC sunk in this manner was not great, but when such attacks did occur, the MTBs and MGBs were virtually unable to defend themselves. The same problems of inaccuracy and inability to concentrate gunfire that were a serious limitation in anti-surface engagements proved fatal in anti-aircraft work. Although the boats carried theoretically powerful AA armaments for their size, including quadruple power-operated turrets with 0.303in machine guns taken from Defiant fighters, they were unable to put up any sort of operationally useful defence. This factor was to recur, in far more devastating form, half a century later.

Postwar Western attack craft

Following the end of the Second World War, most Western navies quickly disposed of their inventories of PT-boats, MTBs and MGBs. Except for four experimental craft, built to compare different hull designs and construction techniques, the US PT-boat fleet was quickly sold out of service. There was a revival of interest during the late 1950s in response to the proliferation of Russian torpedo- (and later missile-) armed FAC. The long gap in FAC construction had resulted in the appropriate design expertise being dated. After a series of design studies, the US Navy acquired twenty Norwegian-designed

Nasty class FAC-T in response to the PTF requirement. These had the merit of being available immediately. These PTFs were deployed to the Vietnam theatre, where they were utilised for SEAL missions and other covert operations.

This was the start of a long series of specialised riverine warfare craft optimised for troop transport and providing fire support in the Mekong delta and other inland waterways in the South East Asia theatre. In 1968, when the peak of force strength was reached, some 800 of these boats were in service. Many of these were handed over to the South Vietnamese, and others to Cambodia or Thailand, as the defeated US forces retreated from Vietnam.[5] In common with most other small craft operations, an objective analysis (conducted many years postwar) of the riverine campaign by one US ally indicated that the resources in both manpower and material invested in the riverine fleet were largely wasted and that their practical effect on Vietcong and North Vietnamese Army operations was negligible. However, the same analysis also pointed out that the technology available at the time did not permit other forms of operation in the area, so some result was better than nothing, and that massive resource commit-

ment in return for minimum gain was a common feature running through all US operations in Vietnam, whether on land or sea or in the air.[6]

In contrast to the virtual US abandonment of the FAC concept during the 1950s, the Royal Navy retained a core capability throughout the period. Their main rationale was seen as operations against Soviet forces in the Baltic, and even the English Channel if the much-feared Soviet breakthrough to the coast actually occurred. By 1959 the emphasis in British defence planning had shifted to a combined nuclear deterrent and East-of-Suez orientation which left little role for such craft. The boats had, like their predecessors, proved extremely expensive craft to maintain and support. In an era of tightening defence funds, these large expenditures on craft of highly suspect utility could not be justified.[7]

Some Western navies did maintain FAC fleets. Greece, Sweden and Norway all faced the problems of attempting to execute naval opera-

5. Major General William B Fulton, US Army, *Vietnam Studies: Riverine Operations*, US Department of the Army USGPO (1973).

6. *Lessons of the Vietnam Deployment XII*, Royal Thai Army SCHQ Monograph (Bangkok 1990). In Thai and not publicly available.

7. Eric Grove, *From Vanguard to Trident* (London 1987).

Sweden is one country which has continuously favoured fast attack craft for service in the restricted and island-strewn waters of the Baltic. However, the Swedish navy was quick to appreciate the need for larger designs than common in Western navies, and also retained an emphasis on gun and torpedo attack when missiles became fashionable. The big Spica *series culminated in the 335-ton* Stockholm *class (Spica III), which now carries SSMs, but also has a powerful gun and torpedo armament. This is the* Stockholm *in May 1983, with a 57mm gun and two 21in torpedo tubes forward. (L & L van Ginderen)*

The West's first public glimpse of Soviet missile boats came from propaganda photographs like this February 1962 picture of a flotilla of Project 183R boats, which came to be known to Nato as the Komar *class. The P-15 (Nato 'Styx') missiles were housed in the large tubes aft. (CMP)*

tions in restricted waters. Once rearmament was permitted, Germany also continued to explore the FAC concept, partly in response to the tactical conditions of the Baltic and off the Norwegian coast, where a combination of shoal water, very large numbers of small islands and narrow rocky inlets offered an environment inimical to the operation of major warships. These were the conditions where the virtues of FAC were strongly emphasised and their limitations minimised. In an environment where the FAC could hide in inlets or caves from prowling aircraft and dash out to launch their attacks, they seemed to have a future.

The problem lay in controlling the operations of the FAC. Experience during the Second World War had suggested that FAC required close control and co-ordination if they were to achieve tactical success. This had been one contributory factor to the successes of the German S-boats over the Royal Navy MTBs and MGBs. If the FAC attacked piecemeal, they could be easily defeated by larger warships. Only a co-ordinated attack by a number of boats was likely to be successful. In order to achieve this end, the Western FAC operators set up extensive shore-based control and co-ordination centres which could relay information out to the FAC and position them to maximum effect. As command control technology advanced, these networks were computerised and formed a key element in the deployment of FAC in Baltic, North Sea and Norwegian Sea areas.

The Royal Norwegian Navy introduced one key FAC design during this period, the *Nasty* class torpedo boat mentioned earlier. This was a lineal descendant of the MTBs and PT-boats of the Second World War, with a hard-chine planing hull. The *Nasty* class were designed as a private venture following a detailed analysis of Second World War planing hulls. They differed from the earlier designs in having a much wider hull in proportion to their length and in having a rounded hull section forward to reduce slamming. This was not very successful, and experience showed that their rough-water performance was little better than that of the earlier designs. In addition to US procurement, the Norwegian navy purchased twenty of these FAC, while Greece ordered six and Turkey two.

The Swedish navy followed a different course. The original postwar designs were close

derivatives of the US PT-boat concept with planing hulls. However, from 1950 onwards a new and much larger FAC design on the German S-boat model with a rounded displacement hull was built. A detailed comparison between the two designs showed the overwhelming superiority of the larger boats (which should have been expected given the experience of the Second World War). The new Swedish design, the *Spica* series, could carry both torpedoes and a powerful gun armament. In the tactical environment of the Baltic, this combined armament was deemed to be the most effective, and additional Swedish construction concentrated on the larger design. The Swedes also investigated the possibility of arming the new FAC with guided missiles. The *Spica* series were large enough to carry the weapons, but a careful evaluation of the relative merits of the system suggested that torpedoes and rapid-fire guns were more effective for the chaotic, short range actions likely to occur in the northern reaches of the Baltic. Sweden did develop an anti-ship missile, the RB-08 derived from a French target drone, but this was restricted to installation on frigates and was never considered for FAC installation. Only the introduction of a new generation of much lighter anti-ship missiles would see the installation of such weapons on Swedish FAC.

The advent of the Soviet missile boat

The Soviet Union did not follow this example. During the 1920s, the new Soviet Union was very poor and, quite clearly, ground forces had to have priority. This made the establishment of conventional fleets out of the question. A

Russian equivalent of the *Jeune École* grew up, favouring the construction of light coastal craft, submarines and land-based torpedo bombers operating in 'combined arms' fashion. This operational concept had to emphasise the construction of light torpedo craft since, at that time, only the torpedo offered a way for a very small, apparently inexpensive unit to hurt a larger and more powerful one. The FAC were backed up by 'guard ships' (SKR), a hybrid design featuring a combination of the attributes of torpedo boats and offshore picket ships. Where the Soviet model differed from the earlier French concept was that it envisaged absolute control over operations by shore-based command and control facilities. These would receive all contact data, and direct the forces available to it into position to attack the approaching enemy force. This concept ensured political control of the forces and appeared to make best use of the weak and ill-distributed resources available.

After the end of the Second World War, the Soviet navy went through several radical changes of plan. However, the coastal forces represented a direct continuation of prewar thinking. Very large numbers of motor torpedo boats were constructed, initially the wartime P-2 design derived from US-supplied PT-boats but quickly supplanted by the slightly enlarged and more seaworthy P-4. This was, in turn, replaced by the much larger 75-ton P-6 (Project 183) torpedo boat, armed with four 25mm anti-aircraft guns and two 21in torpedo tubes. A modification of this basic design was to revolutionise the whole basis of the FAC concept.

Following the Second World War, the Soviet Union had exploited captured German V-1 technology to design a series of anti-surface cruise missiles. In a series of iterations the pulse jets were replaced by ramjets and then by conventional turbojets. These large missiles were intended for attacks on land targets and were land-based, subsequent versions being designed to equip an abortive rocket-battlecruiser (Project 82R). However, in 1954 the Soviet Union started development of a surface-to-surface guided missile intended to equip smaller warships. In 1958, this missile entered service as the P-15 (Nato codename SS-N-2A) Styx, the first platform being converted P-6 FAC. Known as the Project 183R (*Komar*) class, these carried two P-15 missiles in inclined launchers replacing the torpedo tubes.[8] This interim conversion was quickly replaced by the much larger *Osa* class (Project 205) which mounted four P-15 missiles on a substantially larger hull.

For the first time, the FAC appeared to be a really viable weapon. The introduction of surface-to-surface guided missiles meant that the launch platforms did not have to close to suicidally short ranges to engage their targets, but could stand off and fire from long range. Initial Soviet estimates were that two P-15 hits would be required to sink a destroyer-sized target. However, the effective point defences carried by Western warships led the Soviet navy to expect a substantial number of missiles to be shot down; they calculated that as many as twelve would have to be fired to score those two hits. This would require three Project 205 class boats, leading to those craft being organised in tactical units of three hulls. Standard doctrine called for the dispatch of two such units to engage each target in the expectation that at least one would be sunk before it could fire.[9]

The engagement sequence relied upon the use of passive electronic surveillance to provide initial contact data. The Project 205 class missile boats were equipped with a directional electronic support measures (ESM) system with a large square antenna behind the main mast which provided sufficient accuracy for an over-the-horizon launch if necessary, but with a substantially reduced chance of success. The preferred technique was, however, to use the

The Egyptian navy had the first operational experience with missile boats when two of its Soviet-built Project 183R craft sank the Israeli destroyer Eilat *in 1967. Even after the expulsion of Russian advisors from Egypt, Soviet technology continued to play its part. For example, this 'October' class boat is essentially a Soviet 183R hull, built in 1975–76 at Alexandria and sent to Britain for completion. The machinery and missiles (Otomat) are Italian; the electronics and other equipment British. (Vosper Thornycroft)*

bearing data provided by the ESM equipment to key a sector-only radar search. By restricting the scan to a limited arc (rather than the full 360 degrees), and by limiting the transmissions to a few pulses, the Soviet navy hoped that the burst transmission would either be unnoticed or provide insufficient information to compromise the attack.[10] The Project 205s would then use the range, course and speed data obtained from the radar search to run into closer range (typically about 15 miles) and fire. The missile would then climb at 45 degrees to an altitude of around 400ft. When about 6nm from the projected position of the target, the conical-scan terminal radar seeker would switch on and the missile would make its attack at a glide angle of around 2 degrees. The P-15 warhead was a large shaped charge positioned behind the missile fuel tank. Thus the effect of a hit would be to blast burning rocket fuel into a gaping hole in the ship's structure torn by the shaped charge.

The original P-15 missile had fixed wings and could not distinguish between stationary and moving targets. It was thus very vulnerable to countermeasures. In 1964 the original version was replaced by the P-20 (Nato codename SS-N-2B) which had been originally designed to be fired from submarines (this version being designated SS-N-7 Starbright by Nato but retaining the P-20 designation in the Soviet Union). The most significant change in the new missiles was an improved homing seeker with an alternate infra-red guidance system. Standard load was three radar-homing and one infra-red on each Project 205. As a bonus, the requirement for launch from submarines had required

the adoption of folding wings. These permitted a much lighter and more compact launch tube, improving stability and reducing hull stress.

Although the system had already been in service for almost a decade, the SS-N-2 first arrived in public perceptions with the sinking of the Israeli destroyer *Eilat* in 1967. Four P-15 missiles fired from inside Alexandria harbour by two Project 183R missile boats scored two hits. The immediate result was a massive upsurge in interest in the concept of missile-armed FAC, and a major effort to develop equivalent systems. It was apparent that Project 183R and Project 205 missile-armed FAC (now designated FAC-M) had been supplied to a large number of states considered by the Soviets to be friendly to them. These were perceived as posing a serious threat to Nato navies – as indeed they did.

Reaction in the West

The appearance of these FAC-M in the Soviet Navy inventory and the sure, certain knowledge that their deployment would spread through the layers of Soviet client states and allies of steadily decreasing stability, induced a rapid Western programme of emergency countermeasures. In 1961 the US Navy had started design work on a

8. *The Roar of our Rockets: Russian missile and rocket development 1945–55* (Moscow, in Russian).

9. Dr Norman Friedman, *World Naval Weapons Systems* (Annapolis 1991).

10. Stuart L Slade, 'Through a Glass, Not Quite So Darkly', *Naval Forces* VI (1992).

The US fast gunboats of the Asheville *class were the product of a short-lived interest in such craft during the Kennedy era. They were employed in various roles, none central to the main concerns of the US Navy, but found some utility, for example, in simulating Soviet missile boats in Nato exercises. Two of the class are shown here in June 1979, the outboard vessel being* USS *Welch.* (L & L van Ginderen)

new generation of fast gunboats, the PGM or *Asheville* class. These were intended to provide patrol off the coasts of countries supporting hostile guerrilla forces, tracking coastal shipping, blockading gun (and, much later, drug) smugglers, engaging enemy small craft and supporting minor amphibious operations. It is obvious that Vietnam-type situations loomed large in this formulation. After the usual complex design process, the *Asheville* class emerged as 38kt diesel/gas-turbine powered ships displacing 225 tons standard and over 50m (164.4ft) long. They were originally armed with a 76mm (3in) rapid-fire gun forward and a 40mm Bofors AA gun aft.

This combination of high speed and relatively large hull offered an attractive platform for anti-FAC-M weaponry. The existing armament was clearly inadequate and, in the absence of purpose-designed anti-ship missiles, the US Navy initiated a programme of converting air-to-air and surface-to-air missiles to anti-ship work. At the cost of a speed loss of 3–4kts, the *Asheville*s were able to mount the new Standard-ARM interim anti-ship missile aft. These ships were never popular in the US Navy and were quickly withdrawn from service, most being transferred to allied navies. Ironically the recipients, perhaps more familiar with the harder ride and lower seakeeping standards of FAC, found them to be very satisfactory, and the basic de-

sign has been built in South Korea, Taiwan and Indonesia.

An appreciation of the intrinsic inaccuracy of guns mounted on FAC had led the French to offer an FAC armed with a modified anti-tank missile, the SS-12, to export customers. This would, they hoped, offset the inherent inability of the gun-armed FAC to shoot straight by using a guided weapon. When originally introduced, there had been few takers. Now a new generation of anti-ship missiles would be designed in the West with a new series of FAC to carry them.

Western missile designers followed a different tactical route from their Soviet counterparts. Exploiting the much more advanced level of electronic technology meant that the missiles could be made to fly much lower than the P-15 family (15–30ft rather than 450ft). This greatly enhanced the survivability of the individual missiles, so that missiles shot down would be the exception rather than the norm. The same higher level of technology also meant that the guidance systems could be more accurate and

less susceptible to countermeasures. Since the probability of multiple hits was now enhanced, the size of the warhead could be reduced accordingly, dramatically reducing the size and bulk of the missile. This smaller warhead was also made more acceptable by the fact that the Western missiles were largely aimed at opposing Soviet FAC-M which required far less damage to be counted as a mission kill. Of these new designs the most successful platform by far was the French (actually German-designed using S-boat technology) *Combattante* class, which sold extensively around the world. Its missile was to become almost synonymous with the anti-ship guided missile – Exocet.[11]

The 1973 October War between Israel and an Arab alliance saw the first actions between missile-armed FAC. Egyptian and Syrian Project 205 boats engaged Israeli Sa'ar boats (a derivative of the *Combattante*) armed with Gabriel missiles (a missile of rather mysterious antecedents – the airframe is certainly Israeli, derived from that of a command-guided missile called Luz, but the guidance system is suspiciously similar to that of the Italian Sea Killer beam-riding anti-ship missile, supplemented by an Israeli terminal active system). These engagements went overwhelmingly in Israel's favour. The P-15 and P-20 missiles failed to score any hits at all on the Israeli craft, while many of the Arab boats were lost. The reason for the lack of success was primarily that both the P-15 and

11. Dr D G Kiely, *Naval Surface Weapons* (London 1988).

The Iranian Gorz, *a French-built* Combattante II *type, representative of perhaps the most popular export FAC craft of the 1970s. Built for the pre-revolutionary regime of the Shah, which had both the resources and the political backing to obtain almost any Western high-technology equipment it fancied, this class carried American Harpoon SSMs rather than the Exocets sold with most examples of this design.* (C & S Taylor)

The South African 'Minister' class FAC-M is an Israeli Reshev *class (or Sa'ar IV type), the first three of which were built in Haifa. They are fitted with a locally modified version of the Israeli Gabriel SSM, known in South Africa as Skorpioen. The larger Sa'ar IV capitalised on experience with the combat-proven Franco-German boats derived from the* Combattante *that did so well in the 1973 October War; they also initiated the trend towards larger, more capable corvette-like coastal forces.* (South African Navy)

P-20 were designed to engage relatively large targets and their guidance systems had insufficient discrimination when used against the small Israeli FAC-Ms. The missile itself was too large and clumsy to engage the fast, highly manoeuvrable FAC-Ms. Finally the P-15 family of missiles require considerable warm-up time to stabilise the gyros before the missiles can be fired. Arab crews, under attack, failed to allow sufficient time for this; as a result the gyros tumbled on launch.

The results of these actions were as marked as the sinking of the *Eilat* five years earlier. The FAC-M enthusiasts hailed the small craft as being the new, all-conquering masters of the sea and asserted that navies possessing such craft would be able to prevent conventional warships from operating anywhere within reach of the FAC-Ms. Substantial additional numbers of these attack craft were sold in the Middle East, Far East and South America, with the German TNC series craft taking over from the French *Combattantes* as market leaders.

Second generation Soviet craft

Back in the USSR, a new generation of FAC-M were appearing. The first were the Project 1234 (*Nanuchka*) class missile craft. Western sources regarded these as being another new and radical step forward in naval design, but the fact that they carried the same type name as the older Project 205s, *Maly Raketny Kutr*, suggested that they represented an evolutionary development. This was indeed the case. Experience had shown that the Project 205s had inadequate seakeeping abilities and lacked proper defences against attack. The provision of a larger hull was intended to improve seakeeping abilities and

The first class that legitimately might be considered a missile corvette was the Soviet Project 1234, known as the Nanuchka. *Although displacing about 770 tons, more than twice the tonnage of the average FAC, their seakeeping was no real improvement; but they did carry a point-defence missile, SA-N-4, whose launcher was retracted into the forecastle (under the circular hatch in this view).* (MoD, Crown Copyright)

allowed the Soviet navy to push their inshore forces forward, particularly in the Baltic and North Sea, taking the battle to the German, Danish and Norwegian defences. Although the significance of the design was not fully appreciated at the time, Project 1234 was the first missile corvette.

The Project 1234 FAC-Ms were armed with a new missile, the P-50 (Nato designation SS-N-9). This was very much faster than the older P-15/20, and had a more advanced homing system and substantially longer range. The P-50 was originally designed to be fired from submarines and from the Project 1134A (*Kresta II*) class cruisers before that group of ships were redesigned on the building slips to carry the new 60-RU (Nato designation SS-N-14) ASW missile. Fired from the Project 1234 class FAC-Ms, it provided a long range component to supplement the short range P-15/20 missiles. The idea was that the P-50 salvo would disrupt and scatter the enemy formation while the Project 205s closed in and finished off the cripples with their P-15s and P-20s.

When the Soviet concept of shore-based command and control collapsed following the disastrous Okean '70 exercises, the necessity of having sea-based command ships became apparent. The Project 1234s were available to fulfil this requirement. These ships had not proved to be a successful design. Too much had been attempted on the limited displacement and the Project 1234 had shown seakeeping characteristics no better than those of the Project 205. Like the earlier design, their diesel engines had proved to be seriously unreliable, and there is some suggestion that the P-50 missile had proved to be of questionable tactical utility. The original plan of using these craft for forward deployment was untenable, and they had been relegated to fulfilling much the same inshore role as the Project 205. A new, improved successor class, the Project 1241 (*Tarantul*) class was becoming available. One advantage the Project 1234 boats did have was the possession of a

12. Major General Chaim Herzog, *The War of Atonement* (London, 1975).

surface-to-air missile system, the SA-N-4. This was to prove very necessary.

The answer to the missile boat threat

The Royal Navy had first become aware of the menace of the FAC-M during the Indonesian confrontation in the mid-1960s. At that time Indonesia was a Soviet ally and had already received Project 68bis (*Sverdlov*) class cruisers, Project 30bis (*Skoryi*) destroyers, Project 613 (*Whisky*) submarines and Project 183 torpedo boats. The probability was, therefore, that Royal Navy units operating in these waters would face the FAC-Ms at some time. In fact the Indonesian communist government collapsed before this could occur, but at the time the danger seemed very real. In home waters the Royal Navy would be expected to operate off the Norwegian coast as part of its Nato-assigned duties. This, too, offered potential for engagements with the Soviet FAC-Ms.

The Royal Navy, therefore, faced a more immediate threat of engagement by FAC-M than most other Nato powers – probably only the US Navy, threatened by the prospect of North Vietnamese-operated Project 205s, was in a similar position. The immediate and obvious answer to the problem was to build a new generation of FAC of their own. This was, indeed, the course promoted by some factions of the Navy planning staff and their allies in the UK shipbuilding industry. Throughout the early years of the 1960s, a concerted effort was made to divert shipbuilding funds and manpower resources away from conventional surface combatants and into the new FAC-M concept. On at least five separate occasions, efforts were made to divert naval construction funds away from surface ships into FAC-M construction.

Each time, these attempts were defeated by collaboration between the Treasury and the Royal Navy. The Royal Navy advanced the rationale that, in an environment where funds were restricted, such funding as was available had to be concentrated on primary tasks. For the Royal Navy, this meant anti-submarine warfare in the North Atlantic and power projection

in the East-of-Suez area. Fighting the Soviet FAC-Ms could, of necessity, be devolved to the German, Norwegian and Danish navies. Treasury support was obtained by pointing out just how expensive FAC-Ms were to operate when their life-cycle costs were taken fully into account and how their very limited operational flexibility meant that providing for other requirements would mean further additional expenditure. In each case, the rejection of the FAC-M construction plans led to a furious campaign in the media in favour of such projects. In their own eyes at least, those promoting this campaign were the heroic champions of a new age, challenging the aged, reactionary clique who refused, out of pure geriatric obstinacy, to see that the FAC-M was the invincible new wave of the future.

In fact the reason for the opposition to FAC-M construction was that the professional operational analysts in the Royal Navy had come up with a far more effective answer. At that time, Royal Navy frigates had started to carry Wasp helicopters as part of their ASW weaponry. This was purely a weapons delivery platform, carrying anti-submarine torpedoes to a point determined by the ship's sensors. Probably drawing on an institutional memory of how vulnerable its MTBs and MGBs had been to German fighters during the Second World War, the Royal Navy investigated the possibility of arming these helicopters with lightweight air-to-surface missiles to engage the FAC-Ms while the frigate stood off at a safe range. The French AS-12 missile was selected as interim equipment for this role.

A series of exercises revealed that this was indeed the right answer to the FAC-M, but a better platform/weapons system combination was required. The new platform was the Lynx helicopter, a much more capable machine than the diminutive Wasp, with its own radar and much greater weightlifting ability. Develop-

ment of the weapons system side was undertaken by British Aerospace in 1972. This drew on a very careful analysis of the characteristics of the FAC-M and exploited the weaknesses so carefully concealed by promoters of the concept. The maximum range of the missile was deliberately designed to place the launch platform well outside the reach of the point-defence guns and shoulder-fired missiles mounted on the FAC-M. However, by restricting the range of the missile to the least permitted by the above consideration, the bulk of the weapon could be kept to a minimum. Warhead size was also reduced to the smallest acceptable, since it was believed that the damage control capability of an FAC-M was virtually non-existent. Much lower levels of damage than those needed for ship-termination would result in a mission kill. If necessary the cripples could always be finished off later if the decision was that such sinkings were really desired. In many limited war/police action cases, actually sinking a ship could prove to be very undesirable in political terms.

These restrictions on range and warhead power were complemented by the adoption of semi-active radar homing. While this disadvantaged the launch platform by forcing it to illuminate the target throughout the missile's flight, semi-active radar was a much lighter technology yet more accurate than beam-riding, active radar or infra-red against small, fast, diesel-engined targets. It was also inherently less vulnerable to the level of jamming capability found on an FAC. The result of all these economies was that the Lynx could carry four Sea Skua missiles and fire them in salvo – presenting a threat which no FAC could counter. For the FAC-M nemesis had arrived.

After a long series of trials, the new missile, Sea Skua, was introduced into service in 1982. The first rounds were fired that year during the Falklands campaign. Eight rounds were expended, scoring eight hits, sinking an 8500grt

A smaller but improved successor to the Nanuchka *was the* Tarantul *(Project 1241). With combined diesel/gas turbine machinery, they were faster than the* Nanuchka*s by about 4–6kts, being credited with a maximum speed of 36–38kts. They may have been designed with exporting in mind, and a number were sold to client states, like the East German* Rudolf Egelhoffer *shown here in 1990.* (L & L van Ginderen)

freighter and crippling two patrol boats. Following this laudable debut, the Lynx/Sea Skua combination saw its first real action during the Second Gulf War, and, in doing so, destroyed the credibility of the FAC-M. The word 'massacre' is devalued these days, with every tactical reverse being so described, but its use to describe the two-day Battle of the Bubiyan Channel is precisely and literally correct. Not only were the British Lynx helicopters instrumental in destroying the Iraqi navy, but they did so without even being seriously threatened, let alone damaged or lost.

The first part of the battle took place as one phase of the series of engagements that formed Battle of Khafji. A convoy of Iraqi small craft (mostly Boston Whaler and Seacat types) carrying Iraqi special forces and escorted by three ex-Kuwaiti TNC-45 FAC-Ms were sighted heading south. Their objective was to land south of the fighting at Khafji and set up road-blocking ambushes to delay and harass troops sent to relieve the US Marines who the Iraqis believed would be trapped in the city. Three Royal Navy Lynx set to work. An initial problem was that the Sea Skua was designed to operate in the North Atlantic conditions of high sea swell. They therefore flew too high to hit the Boston Whalers. The escorting TNC-45s should, on paper, have been able to put up a credible defence, but their sophisticated Racal Cutlass ESM systems were non-operational following sabotage by the original Kuwaiti crews, and their modern Swedish fire control systems proved useless.

There was nothing wrong with the radars, but for a variety of technical reasons their tracking beam could not be held on target. On board the Lynx helicopters, the crews could hear the Orange Crop ESM system (ironically also made by Racal) detecting lock-on then almost immediately losing the lock. If a lock was held, a few gentle evasive manoeuvres were sufficient to rectify the situation. The Seaspray radars on the Lynx had no problems in holding their locks and the Sea Skuas crashed home. Twelve missiles were fired, scoring five hits, sinking two TNC-45s and crippling the third. The remaining small boats (seventeen in all) were trapped

in a bay. The Lynx called for a few stout-hearted friends and were answered by virtually every flyable helicopter in range. ASW Sea Kings and SH-60Bs, UH-1 and UH-60 troop transports and dedicated AH-1W and AH-64 gunships turned up and proceeded to chase the small craft around the bay with cannon, missiles, rifle fire and hand grenades until all were sunk or driven ashore.

Overnight the British frigate helicopter maintenance crews modified the guidance system on the Sea Skuas to allow the missiles to fly closer to the water. The next day four Royal Navy Lynx coached by a US Navy SH-60B (which had a superior search radar but no missile capability) went to work on a second Iraqi convoy. This was commanded by a Project 254 (T-43) minesweeper and comprised three Project 770 (*Polnocny*) class LSTs escorted by an ex-Kuwaiti TNC-57, the surviving TNC-45 and six assorted Project 205 FAC-Ms. The Lynx fired a total of 14 Sea Skuas, scoring 14 hits, sinking the Project 254, two Project 205s and the TNC-45 and leaving two LSTs and the TNC-57 dead in the water. Fixed-wing aircraft then swarmed over the convoy, finishing off the cripples. Even the Project 205s, armed with SA-7 and SA-14 surface-to-air missiles, had been unable seriously to threaten the Lynx, let alone prevent them from accomplishing their mission.[13]

The failure of the FAC-M concept as a naval equaliser capable of offsetting the power of conventional warships was utter and complete. A share of the extent of the Iraqi disaster can be explained by the poor material condition of their boats and the abysmal training standards of their crews. However, once these factors have been discounted, the fact remains that the fun-

damental reasons for the defeat of the FAC-Ms are inherent in the design of the craft and cannot be eradicated. Firstly, the lightly-built FACs vibrate too much as a result of the powerful engines installed and their rough ride in anything other than mill-pond conditions. This causes the tracking beams on the air defence fire control radars to wander off target before a firing solution can be attained. Secondly, the low silhouette of the boats, essential for their role, means that radars and ESM equipment have to be carried low. This limits their maximum coverage against low-flying targets. To make matters worse, the low mountings mean that the electronics are within the surface duct, a layer of warm, moist air trapped close to the sea surface. Radars and ESM equipment within this duct cannot detect targets flying above it. There is another disadvantage associated with radars carried low; the radar beam travels directly to its target but also reflects off the sea surface to the target and off the top of the surface duct to the target. This multi-pathing effect provides a series of ghost images with the radar fire control oscillating helplessly between them.[14]

This operational experience had confirmed the findings of the earlier tactical analysis by the Royal Navy. As predicted, the excessive vibration mentioned earlier had meant that anti-aircraft guns did indeed have very limited range and suffered severe problems in putting up a concentrated barrage. Shoulder-fired and pedestal-mounted missiles can reach further out, but beyond 5–6km they had, as predicted,

13. *Surface Combatants Market Overview*, Warships Market Intelligence Report, Forecast International (1993).
14. *Land & Sea-Based Radar Market Overview*, Radar Market Intelligence Report, Forecast International (1993).

The major surface ship's answer to the missile-armed FAC has turned out to be the helicopter equipped with its own air-to-surface missile. The Lynx helicopter with Sea Skua missiles was one of the great success stories of Western technology in the 1991 Gulf War. HMS Cardiff, *a British Type 42 destroyer that was very active during that war, is shown with her Sea Skua-armed Lynx during the operations to recapture Kuwait.* (MoD, Crown Copyright)

been ineffective. The assessment that helicopters engaging from outside this range would be virtually immune to counterattack had been confirmed. At one point it was hoped that electro-optical fire control systems would overcome these problems, but experimentation has shown that these, too, are adversely affected by the vibration and low mountings characteristic of the FAC-M.

Hydrofoils and sea sleds

During the 1970s, two additional technologies were adopted for FAC design. One, the hydrofoil, is basically an expansion of the planing principle. Instead of riding on a small portion of the hull, the hydrofoil rides on a wing mounted underneath it. This configuration was first tested in 1911 and immediately showed the potential to achieve very high speeds, in excess of 60kts. During the next fifty years a series of experimental and semi-experimental hydrofoil FAC designs were produced. They all suffered from the restricted range of weights which could be carried and numerous other design and operational difficulties.

Most navies that tried the design have found that the concept continues to have serious practical problems. These include extreme difficulties in tactical handling. There is a fixed minimum speed, below which the hydrofoil will not rise on to its foils. At these low speeds the hydrofoil acts as a very inefficiently designed displacement hull, further burdened by the drag of its foils. In some designs this can be mitigated, but the penalties still exist. At speeds high enough for the hulls to rise up on their foils, the craft suffer the same vibration and other limitations of conventional FAC. Operationally, hydrofoils

Like many advanced hydrodynamic concepts, the hydrofoil has proved difficult to adapt to the practicalities of naval service. Perhaps the most sophisticated design was a Nato programme in which the aircraft manufacturer Boeing took the lead. Rising costs eventually left only the US Navy willing to purchase the resulting PHM, and even then only six were built. USS Aquila (PHM-4) demonstrates the main features of this Pegasus class; the foils were computer-controlled and could handle quite rough seas without significant loss of speed. (USN)

Current trends in FAC design produce larger and more capable, but far more expensive, vessels. The Israeli Sa'ar designation was originally applied to 250-ton vessels (types I–III), then to the 450-ton Reshevs (type IV), while the Sa'ar V is a 1200-ton helicopter-equipped corvette, bearing little apparent resemblance to its predecessors – although the heavy anti-ship armament of eight Harpoon and eight Gabriel SSMs is a hint. Such vessels cease to be a cheap alternative to traditional surface combatants: just as the destroyer replaced the torpedo boat it was devised to counter, so the FAC-M has grown into the large surface combatant that was its original target.

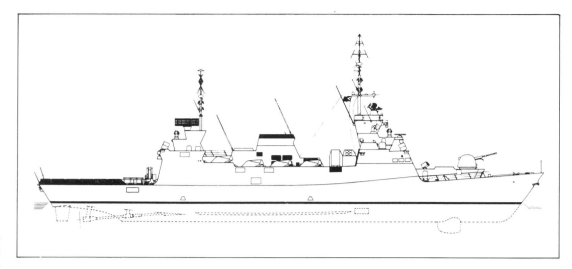

are difficult to dock and their foil systems are vulnerable to accidental damage. Experience has also shown that the foils themselves suffer from extremely severe erosion. These limitations far outweigh the theoretical benefits.

During the 1970s Nato started a programme to develop a common hydrofoil combatant, the PHM. This ran into the development problems summarised above, and the only tangible products were six craft operated by the US Navy. These were never regarded as successful and were finally used for drug interdiction in the Caribbean. Seven reduced versions of the design were built in Italy; these also were regarded as unsatisfactory and the concept was not pursued. Japan, however, took up the design as the basis for a class of hydrofoil missile boats. The Russians built a production series of hydrofoil craft in the 1970s and early 1980s, while the Chinese have built a hydrofoil based on the Project 205 design in very large numbers. In these cases, the configuration is restricted to special applications only and the craft are not regarded as being successful.

Another exotic displacement hull was the sea sled, also first tested in 1911. This has a hull shaped like a W. The bow wave runs into the tunnel and helps to lift the boat, while an air cushion formed underneath smooths out the hammering effect experienced with other high-speed hull configurations. The sea sled concept had some initial success but Royal Navy trials showed it to have inadequate buoyancy forward, to possess poor seakeeping characteristics and inadequate structural strength, and to provide a harder ride than was acceptable. The concept was revived in the mid-1980s by the Soviet Union with the Project 1239 FAC-M *Dergach*. This was designed to act as a flagship for Project 1241 FAC-Ms and thus required a large superstructure and copious electronics. A modified sea-sled-style hull seemed to provide the requisite combination of stability and deck space, but the resulting design was a failure as a result of the inability to get its electronics systems working

and the poor seakeeping characteristics of the design. For some years the Project 1239 remained a one-off experimental vessel but a sister-ship was recently completed.

Other exotic technologies have been tried in the FAC environment but none has proved to have military advantages commensurate with their practical limitations. These include surface effect craft (hovercraft) and wing-in-ground-effect craft. The latter are often the subject of awed praise from some quarters but in reality have been a signal failure.

Thus the current state of the art makes it appear that the existing hull technologies will continue to be used for small craft. The question is, then, how can the overwhelming limitations of the existing layout be ameliorated? The radar and ESM antennas must be carried high. Lightweight masts and advanced antenna technology can reduce the resulting penalties but not eliminate them; this drives the hull size up. The destruction of a craft by one or two hits from small missiles like Sea Skua is unacceptable, so the damage control capabilities must be improved; this drives hull size up. Point defences against missile attacks must be included; this drives hull size up. The hull requires additional strengthening and shaping to improve seakeeping characteristics; this drives hull size up. To escape the prowling helicopters, longer-range higher performance missiles with more sophisticated guidance systems are required; this drives hull size up. The new missiles require enhanced target acquisition and command control capability; this drives hull size up. To propel the larger hulls at acceptable speeds requires much more powerful engines and larger fuel tanks to feed them; this drives hull size up. While acceptable and militarily capable small missile-armed combatants with real combat value can be designed, they displace around 1200 tons, the size of a Second World War

destroyer escort. They can more accurately be called small frigates. The wheel has turned full circle once more.

Conclusions

This history and critique of the FAC concept illustrates a very important lesson. There are no absolute weapons, and the balance of advantage between attacker and defender is a shifting and insubstantial thing. On several occasions, significant advances in weapon and propulsion technology have given the appearance of making possible an equaliser; a small, inexpensive, highly lethal warship that will drive conventional fleets from the seas. On each occasion a clique of supporters has coalesced around the 'new concept', damning those who question its infallible lethality as hidebound reactionaries who are terrified that the 'new ideas' would upset their ivory towers.

In every case, be it the torpedo boat, the CMB, the MTB/MGB/PT boat or the FAC-M, as experience with the new design has grown and countermeasures have been developed, natural design evolution has turned the radical new concept into a minor variant of a traditional warship type. In every case, the hidebound reactionaries who have patiently argued that warships designed with regard to a broad spectrum of real military requirements and conditions will prove more viable and effective than those optimised for maximum performance in a very narrow part of the military and environmental spectrum have been proved correct. It is probable that within a few years new propulsion and weapons technologies will lead to a new generation of equaliser and the whole cycle will start again. History strongly suggests that such developments need to be treated with extreme caution.

Stuart Slade

Fast Attack Craft: Typical Classes, since 1945

Class	Nationality	Displacement normal/full load (tons)	Dimensions overall (feet-inches) (metres)	Hull	Armament	Machinery/ Speed (kts)	Launch dates	Numbers built
DARK	British	50/64	71-8 × 19-5 × 6-1 *21.8 × 5.9 × 1.8*	Composite	1-4.5in, 1-40mm; or 1-40mm, 4-21in TT	D/40	1952–58	19 (plus 7 export)
JAGUAR	German	183/210	139-10 × 23-4 × 7-6 *42.6 × 7.1 × 2.3*	Composite	2-40mm, 4-21in TT	D/43	1957–60	30
BRAVE	British	89/114	98-10 × 25-6 × 7-0 *30.1 × 7.8 × 1.8*	Composite	1-40mm, 4-21in TT	GT/50	1958–59	2
NASTY	Norwegian	70/76	80-4 × 24-6 × 6-9 *24.5 × 7.5 × 2.1*	Wood	1-40mm, 1-20mm, 4-21in TT	D/45	1958–63	21 (plus 10 export)
KOMAR (Project 183R)	Soviet	75/80	87-11 × 21-0 × 5-11 *26.8 × 6.4 × 1.8*	Wood	2-25mm, 2 SS-N-2 SSM	D/40	1958–61	c100 (plus c40 in China)
OSA I (Project 205)	Soviet	175/215	126-8 × 24-11 ×5-11 *38.6 × 7.6 × 1.8*	Steel	4-30mm, 4 SS-N-2 SSM	D/35	1959–66	c175 (plus c96 in China)
SPICA I	Swedish	200/235	140-1 × 23-4 × 5-6 *42.5 × 7.1 × 1.6*	Steel	1-57mm, 6-21in TT	GT/40	1965–66	6
ASHEVILLE	American	225/245	164-6 × 23-11 × 9-6 *50.1 × 7.3 × 2.9*	Aluminium	1-3in, 1-40mm, 2 Standard SSM	CODOG/38	1966–70	17
HUCHWAN (hydrofoils)	Chinese	39/45	71-6 × 16-6 × 3-3 *21.8 × 4.9 × 1.0*	Steel	4-14.4mm, 2-21in TT	D/50	1966–80	120 (plus exports)
NANUCHKA I (Project 1234)	Soviet	675/770	194-7 × 41-4 × 7-11 *59.3 × 12.6 × 2.4*	Steel	6 SS-N-9 SSM, 1 SA-N-4 SAM, 2-57mm	D/32	1969–76	16
COMBATTANTE II	French (for export)	234/255	154-3 × 23-4 × 8-3 *47.0 × 7.1 × 2.5*	Steel	4 Exocet SSM, 4-35mm, 2-21in TT	D/36	1971–82	30 (plus derivatives)[1]
TNC-45	German (for export)	228/258	147-4 × 23-0 × 7-7 *44.9 × 7.0 × 2.3*	Steel	4 Exocet SSM, 1-76mm, 2-40mm	D/40	1972–	Building (c40 to date)[2]
RESHEV (Sa'ar IV)	Israeli	415/450	190-7 × 24-11 × 7-10 *58.1 × 7.6 × 2.4*	Steel	4 Harpoon SSM, 6 Gabriel SSM, 2-76mm, 2-20mm	D/32	1973–80	10 (plus 9 export)
PEGASUS (hydrofoils)	American	198/241	131-6 × 23-2 × 6-2 *40.0 × 8.6 × 1.9*	Aluminium	8 Harpoon SSM, 1-76mm	CODOG/40	1974–82	6
TARANTUL II (Project 1241)	Soviet	480/540	183-9 × 34-05 × 8-2 *56.0 × 10.5 × 2.5*	Steel	4 SS-N-2C SSM, 1 SA-N-5 SAM, 1-76mm, 2-30mm	COGOG/36	1980–86	20
TYPE 143A	German	380/397	184-0 × 25-6 × 7-3 *57.6 × 7.8 × 2.2*	Composite	4 Exocet SSM, 1-76mm, 1 RAM point-defence missile	D/36	1981–83	10 (plus export derivatives)
FPB-62	German (for export)	—/632	206-7 × 30-5 × 9-5 *63.0 × 9.3 × 2.9*	Steel	1-76mm, 2-40mm, 2-20mm, 4 Exocet SSM, 1 Dauphin helicopter with AST-15 missiles	D/32	1986–	2 built for Bahrain

Machinery abbreviations:
D = diesel; GT = gas turbines; CODOG = combined diesel and gas (turbines); COGOG = combined gas or gas (turbines).

Notes:
[1] Customers include Greece, Malaysia, Iran and Libya; Israeli *Sa'ar I-III* similar.
[2] Customers include Singapore, Argentina, Ecuador, Thailand, Malaysia, Ghana, Bahrain, United Arab Emirates and Kuwait.

6

Amphibious Forces

AT the end of the Second World War the composition of the world's navies had changed vastly from what had been the typical order of battle in 1939. The need to conduct amphibious assaults against hostile forces led to the development of many new warships designed to transport men and material across the ocean and deposit them ashore, often in the face of determined opponents. The last fifty years have seen these warships grow in size, complexity and importance. As the major powers have shed overseas colonies, but not their international commitments, the need for amphibious warships has increased. Amphibious warships have also changed from ships capable of performing just one mission to ships capable of performing several.

The US Navy's 1945 amphibious fleet included thousands of ships, ranging from ocean-going attack transports (APAs), attack cargo ships (AKAs), dock landing ships (LSDs), tank landing ships (LSTs) and tank landing craft

(LCTs) to smaller landing craft vehicular and personnel (LCVP), utility landing craft (LCU), and infantry landing craft (LCI). During an invasion APAs, AKAs and LSDs would unload their supplies and troops into smaller LCIs, LCUs and LCVPs that would carry the troops on to the beach. LCTs and LSTs would steam up to the beach, opening their clamshell bows to allow tanks to drive ashore. Operating these ships had been honed to a fine art. The smaller navies had miniature versions of this, with LSDs, LSTs, LCTs and landing craft.

Many of the ships were extemporised merchant ship designs, hastily converted to their new roles. The speeds of the ships also varied. While some APAs and AKAs could steam at 20kts, most of the other ships were hard pressed to reach 11kts. This hindered the establishment of cohesive amphibious convoys.

Amphibious ship development since the Second World War has been dominated by the United States, although the former Soviet Union

and some of the smaller Nato navies have built innovative designs. The role of the United States in this field is largely a function of America being separated from the scenes of any major conflict by two oceans, leaving it with a requirement to have some means of lifting troops overseas.

Immediate postwar developments

While amphibious warfare was a major aspect of the fighting in the Atlantic and Pacific theatres of the Second World War, its demise was predicted by many leading military officials immediately postwar because of the atomic bomb. The July 1946 Bikini Atoll atomic bomb tests on decommissioned warships appeared to make future amphibious assaults impossible, because large concentrations of warships gathered offshore or troops on a beachhead would be ideal targets for mass destruction.

After witnessing the tests, senior US Marine Corps officials began an urgent programme to review and study future amphibious transport requirements. The officials considered the use of gliders, aircraft, submarines and helicopters. Submarines could not carry enough troops or cargo for a major assault, and aircraft required carriers for launching and fields for landing. Helicopters were the most practical option, because their speed allowed them to concentrate troops rapidly from ships widely dispersed offshore. The Marines had tested Pitcairn OP-1

Despite some highly original ideas – like a design with bow propellers that would beach stern-first – a fast tank landing ship (LST) could not be developed until the problem of the traditional clamshell bow doors was solved. Therefore, the first postwar American LSTs of the Terrebonne Parish *class looked similar to wartime vessels, although they were much improved in detail, with finer lines and reversible pitch propellers that gave them a 15kt speed. They also had increased capacity and more sophisticated landing arrangements, like a powered vehicle turntable, and bow doors, and a pontoon causeway. This is* Washoe County *(LST-1165). (L & L van Ginderen)*

uss Francis Marion *(APA-249), one of only two attack transports built in the 1950s. The design was based on a standard Maritime Commission 'Mariner' hull (C4-S-IA), and was fitted with flagship facilities. The ship could carry 1500 troops and embarked seven LCM-6, twelve LCVP and three LCP(L) landing craft. These ships were the last conventional attack transports, the role being taken over by a combination of helicopter carrier (LPH) and dock landing ship (LPD).* (L & L van Ginderen)

and Kellet OP-2 autogiros in Nicaragua in 1931, but the autogiros had little capability and the trials did not continue. In 1944 the Navy and the Coast Guard began using helicopters, and they showed more promise.

While the Marines were considering their assault requirements, the US Navy's General Board came up with their own future amphibious force requirements in November 1947. The Board's report called for sufficient fast lift for two Marine divisions, requiring twenty-four APAs, thirty-four LSDs (or six LSDs and twenty-eight 20kt LSTs), and four command ships. To solve the problems that cropped up with the amphibious force during the war, all the new ships would be designed from the keel up for amphibious warfare and all ships would be required to make a sustained speed of 20kts.

In December 1946 a Marine Corps board appointed by the Commandant, General Archibald Vandegrift, developed both a seaplane and a helicopter to move troops rapidly ashore from widely dispersed ships. The seaplane programme was plagued by mechanical difficulties, however, and by 1948 the Marines committed themselves to the helicopter option. The first experimental helicopter assault took place in January 1948, when 66 Marines were airlifted in five HO3S helicopters from the escort carrier *Palau* off the North Carolina coast. The helicopters could carry only three troops each, but an example had been set.

Similar exercises continued through 1951, and in that year, a board led by Major General Field Harris of the Fleet Marine Force, Atlantic, proposed converting *Casablanca* (CVE-55) class escort carriers to Marine helicopter transports as an interim step. Commandant General Clifton Gates also called for the building of a new class of dedicated helicopter carriers, each capable of carrying 1500 assault troops and eighteen 36-man helicopters.

The Korean War and its effects

While the helicopter tests were being conducted, the amphibious force received a tremendous boost in prestige. The Korean War

disproved the theories and beliefs that all future wars would be nuclear exchanges between the superpowers. When the Allies were pushed into the Pusan perimeter, only an amphibious landing could reverse the situation. The twenty-three LSTs that went ashore at Inchon provided ample proof that amphibious warfare was a vital element of seapower.

With the lesson of Inchon in mind, the 1952 budget provided funding for four *Thomaston* class LSTs, fifteen *Terrebonne Parish* class LSTs, two *Paul Revere* class APAs, and one *Tulare* class AKA. Two more LSDs were funded in 1953 and a final two in 1954. One *de Soto County* class LST was funded in 1954 and four more were ordered in 1955. The need to fund these ships was one reason the US Navy did not immediately order a large helicopter carrier. Navy objections that rotary-wing technology was not ready for a 36-man helicopter also delayed it. Navy plans called for more ships, however, and the 1955 Long Range Objectives study group called for having a mid 1960s amphibious force of four new flagships, six fast AKAs, eight APAs, sixteen LPHs, twenty-four LSDs and sixteen LSTs.

However, in May 1955 the Philadelphia Naval Shipyard began converting the escort carrier *Thetis Bay* (CVE-90) to the role of helicopter assault aircraft carrier (CVHA-1), installing a large elevator at the after end of the flight deck to carry helicopters between the hangar and flight decks. Her compartments and hangar deck were modified to carry twenty HRS helicopters and 1000 troops. *Thetis Bay* was recommissioned in July 1956 and joined the Pacific Fleet, where she proved that helicopter ships were practical for amphibious assaults. But her troop quarters were cramped and unit cohesion was broken so that troops could fill the existing berthing spaces.

Despite the shortcomings, Marine Corps officers found that *Thetis Bay* filled most of their requirements. To meet the continuing requests, the Navy began converting a second escort carrier, *Block Island* (CVE-106), in 1957. *Block Island* was to receive the same upgrades as *Thetis Bay*, but with a new designation, amphibious assault ship (LPH-1). Her conversion was cancelled in 1958, however, because rising conversion costs meant that the Navy would not get an adequate return during *Block Island*'s remaining service life. The new LPH designation was created in acknowledgement that the ship's primary role was as an amphibious ship, but it was also a political move, dictated by the opposition to more aircraft carrier construction from some Members of Congress and the US Air Force.

Purpose-built helicopter carriers

While the Navy was converting the escort carriers, it had drawn up the requirements for a dedicated amphibious assault ship. The requirements called for a simple engineering plant, the ability to carry nearly 2000 troops, and a ship that could be converted into an anti-submarine carrier, for helicopters using dipping sonars. (This requirement was used only once, between 1972 and 1974, when the *Guam* tested the feasibility of the Sea Control Ship [SCS] concept). The Marine Corps wanted the ship to have four take-off areas, but only three could be provided because of limited hangar deck space for helicopters. The new LPHs were also designed to be primary medical treatment facilities during an amphibious assault. Their medical facilities, better than those aboard almost any other warships, included three operating rooms and a 300-bed sick bay. The first ship, *Iwo Jima*, was ordered in 1958 and laid down in 1959.

Following Marine Corps experiments in 'vertical envelopment' using helicopters from converted escort carriers, a purpose-designed helicopter assault ship, or LPH, was ordered in 1958. The ships could carry 2000 troops and nineteen CH-46 helicopters or eleven of the larger CH-53s. They were intended to be convertible to ASW helicopter carriers, but, lacking catapults and arrester wires, they could not operate fixed-wing ASW aircraft. Shown here is the New Orleans *(LPH-11) shortly after completion in 1969. (L & L van Ginderen)*

While slightly longer than an escort carrier, she has much better helicopter maintenance facilities for the twenty medium helicopters she carries, and the 1900 Marines also have better berthing accommodations than aboard the converted escort carriers. Better habitability was a major concern, because Marines would make six- and seven-month deployments aboard the ships. The troop berthing aboard the new ships was designed to maintain unit cohesiveness, which was difficult to achieve aboard the converted carriers.

While the Navy was finishing the plans for the *Iwo Jima*, it became concerned at the lack of amphibious ships for the growing number of crises around the globe. As a short-term measure, three *Essex* class CVs, the *Boxer*, *Princeton*, and *Valley Forge*, were converted to amphibious assault ships in January 1959, May 1959 and July 1961. The three converted CVs, decommissioned in 1969–70, were expensive stopgaps. Even with half the engineering plant closed to save costs, they still needed a 1500-man crew, compared with the 500 men needed by an *Iwo Jima* class LPH.

The *Iwo Jima* and her sister-ships were much

less expensive to operate than the converted carriers, and they formed the core of deploying Marine Corps amphibious task forces from the mid 1960s onwards.

Combining different ship types

One of the major criticisms US Navy planners had of their amphibious vessels was the wide variety of warships required to perform an amphibious assault. During a typical assault, APAs would carry the troops to within a mile of the beach, lower their landing craft and send the troops ashore. Tanks, trucks, food, ammunition, and miscellaneous stores would be carried in AKAs, which used their own landing craft.

To rectify these shortcomings, US Navy planners issued a requirement in 1956 for a new multi-cargo and mission amphibious warship. The new design, designated amphibious transport dock (LPD), was based on the dock landing ship (LSD) design, but it emphasised troop and cargo capacity, instead of the LSD's docking capacity. The LPD has almost 65 per cent of an

APA's troop capacity and 60 per cent of an AKA's cargo capacity, while retaining an LSD's well deck.

The first LPD, *Raleigh*, was laid down in June 1960. Three *Raleigh*s were built before the Navy built twelve larger *Austin* class amphibious transport docks in the early 1960s. The first *Austin*s carry 930 troops; the last seven hold 840 troops, but they have an extra superstructure deck for flag operations and communications spaces, and they can carry a 90-man flag staff.

The *Austin*s have a small 58ft by 22ft hangar, which extends to 80ft. The hangar holds one utility helicopter, but six CH-46s can be accommodated on the flight deck during a deployment. The flight deck is formed by decking over a permanently closed well deck. The 168ft by 50ft well deck holds one LCU and three LCM-8 or four LCM-8 or twenty LVT. Two more LCM-6 or four LCVP can be carried on the flight deck and launched by a large crane at the after end of the superstructure. Forward of the well deck was 12,500ft of vehicle storage space. Because an LPD's well deck was enclosed, unlike the open well deck of an LSD, cargo could be transported without fear of water damage from high seas coming over the sides.

US Navy doctrine called for using LPH/LPD combinations, where an LPD might come within three or four miles of the beachhead to offload vehicles and cargo into her landing craft

The helicopter-carrying LPH could not embark landing craft so could not guarantee the support of troops on a beach in weather too bad for flying. The answer was a modified wartime LSD with greater emphasis on troop accommodation, which was classed as an LPD. The Raleigh *class was succeeded by the larger* Austin*s, the last of which were modified as amphibious force flagships. La Salle (LPD-3) was converted to a flagship for the Middle East station in 1972 and relieved by the* Coronado *in the early 1980s. The latter is pictured at Messina in 1983, showing the white paintwork adopted as a heat reduction measure by the Middle East flagships. (L & L van Ginderen)*

USS Sumter, *one of the* Newport *class that finally achieved the goal of a 20kt LST. This was realised by the novel landing system of a causeway lowered between the prominent gallows forward. The section of the bow above the knuckle opens to give the ramp a lower take-off point.* (L & L van Ginderen)

for transport ashore. At the same time, an LPH's helicopters would land on the LPD's flight deck to pick up troops for transportation ashore. The LPH/LPD combination was much faster than previous methods of troop embarkation, which required co-ordination between several types of ships.

Reaching the 20kt amphibious force

Constructing the large LPHs and LPDs was part of the improvement in amphibious capabilities of the 1960s, but the 20kt LST was equally part of the build-up. While most of the new ships of the 1950s and 1960s could maintain 20kts, the bow design of the LSTs prevented them from achieving a similar speed. Several radical designs for a new tank landing ship were considered during the late 1940s and early 1950s. One design had bow-mounted propellers and would turn its back to the beach to disgorge its tanks; others had false bows, but none of these advanced beyond the drawing board.

The *Terrebonne Parish* class LSTs had more space for troops, tanks, and cargo, hydraulic bow doors, heavier ramps, and a powered vehicle turntable. But they could only make 15kts. The *De Soto County* class LSTs could carry 634 troops and four landing craft on davits. They also had a 175ft pontoon causeway, two pontoon bridges, and an LCU as deck cargo for side launching.

Only when the clamshell bow doors were deleted did the US Navy reach its 20kt goal for LSTs. The *Newport* class, built in the late 1960s, had a conventional bow above the waterline that split into two 112ft bow ramps joined at their end by a cross-gallows. A causeway lowered through the gallows allowed vehicles to drive on to the beach. A tunnel through the superstructure provided an unhindered vehicle deck, while a stern ramp allowed vehicles to drive on to a pier or into landing craft.

Combining the flight deck and hangar of an LPH with the docking facilities of an LPD produced a very large ship. The Tarawa *class LHA was as big as many Second World War fleet carriers. One of the class,* Nassau *shown here, actually operated as a V/STOL carrier during the Gulf War, operating the Marine Corps' AV-8B Harrier jets.* (L & L van Ginderen)

Large amphibious assault ships

As the last units of the *Iwo Jima* and the *Austin* classes were being completed in the late 1960s, US Navy planners began considering ways to combine the best features of each of the two classes in the ultimate amphibious ship. Experience during exercises showed that the LPH's lack of a well deck for landing craft was a problem. Vertical assault was excellent for daytime assaults in good weather, but landing craft were still required for foul weather and transporting an assault force's equipment ashore. By 1965 there were proposals for a new ship combining the LPH's flight deck with the ability to carry twelve landing craft vehicle and personnel (LCVP).

With growing calls for a new amphibious assault ship, Chief of Naval Operations Admiral David McDonald asked in April 1965 for the planned sixth and final LPH, *New Orleans* (LPH-11), to be lengthened, with space for twelve LCVPs, two LCPLs, and 97 more troops. Scheduling delays at the Philadelphia Naval Shipyard forced a cancellation of these plans. As an interim solution, a seventh LPH, *Inchon*, was ordered in 1966 to a modified design, with davits to carry two LCVPs.

The solution to these shortcomings was a new amphibious assault ship, the LHA-1 *Tarawa* class. The requirements for the new class called for it to have an LPH's aircraft and troop-carrying capacity, and an LPD's docking, assault craft, and equipment capacity. The new ships were also to have the command and control suite of an amphibious flagship. A contract for the design and construction of nine ships was placed in May 1968, although four ships were cancelled in 1971. Although called an amphibious assault ship, the new *Tarawa* class were given the designation LHA.

Tarawa, commissioned in May 1976, is a quantum leap over previous amphibious ships. At 40,000 tons fully loaded and 840ft long, she is nearly the same size as a Second World War *Essex* class aircraft carrier. The 1900 Marines have better accommodation than they did aboard the LPHs. *Tarawa*'s 268ft by 78ft well deck can hold four utility landing craft (LCU) and three LCM-8 boats, or seventeen LCM-6 landing craft and forty-five LVTP-7 amphibious tractors. The well deck can hold one LCAC air cushion landing craft. There is an additional 30,000ft of vehicle storage space. The flight deck holds twelve CH-46 medium helicopters or nine CH-53 heavy helicopters, while the hangar deck can hold an additional thirty CH-46s or nineteen CH-53s. During Operation Desert Storm *Nassau* served as a V/STOL carrier, carrying twenty AV-8B Harrier jets.

A 300-berth sick bay with three operating rooms is provided. A 5000sq ft training and

USS Wasp, *the first of the LHD type derived from the* Tarawa *class, shows some modifications to Marine Corps doctrine. As the* Wasp*s are designed to operate fast air-cushion landing craft from over the horizon, the shore bombardment 5in guns of the earlier class have been omitted. There is also greater emphasis on aviation, the ships having facilities for Harrier V/STOL and ASW helicopters when required. Thus, with the shrinking numbers of fleet carriers available, the US Navy would be able to use the LHDs in a limited sea control role.* (Ingalls)

acclimatisation room with a controlled environment allows troops to adapt to the climate of their destination while exercising en route. Conveyors and cargo elevators rapidly move cargo within the ship, and a vehicle ramp allows trucks to drive directly from the vehicle garage or hangar deck to the flight deck. The LHAs are also the first amphibious ships to have a three-dimensional air search radar, the SPS-52, for long-range threat detection and limited fighter control. Three 5in guns are provided for shore bombardment.

The *Tarawa*s, *Austin*s, and *Newport*s were only part of the largest build-up of US amphibious forces since the Second World War. The Kennedy–Johnson era build-up, as it is often called (although actual ordering stretched between 1959 and 1971), saw the construction of five LHAs, seven LPHs, fifteen LPDs, five *Anchorage* class LSDs, five *Charleston* class LKA amphibious cargo ships, and the twenty *Newport* class LSTs. The *Anchorage*s and the *Charleston*s were built because Navy officials had become concerned that the new LPDs and LPHs did not meet all of the Navy's amphibious requirements.

The 1980s build-up

Despite the expansion of the 1950s and 1960s, the US Navy faced a problem during the late 1970s. Massive decommissions had left it short of its required strength to transport two and a half Marine Expeditionary Brigades, and mass obsolescence would mean that many of its amphibious ships would leave service during the 1980s. To stem this tide, the Reagan Administration began a major build-up when it entered office in 1981. By 1992 this third expansion had seen orders for six LHD class amphibious as-

USS Comstock *of the new* Whidbey Island *class LSDs. With a well designed for four LCACs, they also have a deck load of one LCM(6), two LCPLs and one LCVP. They can handle helicopters up to the size of CH-53s, but although fuel is carried for helicopters using the ship, there are no hangar facilities.* (L & L van Ginderen)

sault ships and twelve LSDs, and plans for a new LX multi-purpose ship.

The centrepiece of the new programme was the LHD, a modification of the *Tarawa* class LHA. One of the shortfalls of the LPH/LPD concept was that cargo still had to be off-loaded into slow, 10kt landing craft. To ensure timely arrival at a beachhead, this meant that LPDs and LSDs had to off-load within range of coastal missile batteries and guns. To correct this deficiency, the US Navy began testing two 45kt air cushion landing craft, JEFF-A and JEFF-B, in 1977. These tests led to orders, starting in 1982, for air cushion landing craft (LCAC) that could each transport one heavy tank or 60 tons of supplies ashore at 40kts fully loaded. However, existing LHAs and LPDs could load only one LCAC.

The *Wasp* class LHDs were proposed originally in the late 1870s, and some shipyards recommended building a modified version of the

LSD. As designed, the LHDs look similar to the LHAs, and have about the same troop capacity. But the LHD's two elevators are on the port and starboard sides, rather than on the starboard side and astern as on the LHA. They have 100,000sq ft for cargo and stores and 20,000sq ft for vehicles. The well deck can accommodate three LCACs.

The air wing is about the same size, but at Congressional insistence the LHDs have a secondary mission as Sea Control Ships. In their secondary role, the air wing will include twenty AV-8B Harriers and six SH-60B ASW helicopters. Because of shrinking Navy force structure, the air wing was modified in 1993, and future plans call for the *Wasp*s to carry five to ten AV-8Bs as part of their normal Marine Corps air wing. The Harriers would provide close air support in the absence of a normal carrier air wing. The LHDs also lack 5in guns.

The second major class, the *Whidbey Island*,

class LSD, were designed as replacements for the *Thomaston* class LSDs. Original plans called for using the *Anchorage* design, but this was changed to allow the new ships to carry four LCACs. This required a 440ft by 50ft well deck, larger than the 370ft by 50ft well deck of the *Anchorage*s. The well deck was not fully enclosed, to allow ventilation for the LCACs. Troop capacity was also increased, from 370 troops to 450 men. The Navy's plans also called originally for a new LPD class, but these plans were cancelled for budgetary reasons in the late 1980s. Instead, a cargo variant of the *Whidbey Island* is being ordered. This version will have only two LCACs but 40,000cu ft for cargo, compared with the 5000cu ft of the basic *Whidbey Island* design.

In 1992 the Navy announced plans to build twelve new LX class amphibious ships starting in 1996 to replace the fifteen LPDs, five LSDs, five LKAs and twenty LSTs built during the 1960s. Initial plans call for a 23,000-ton fully loaded ship, about 680ft long and carrying two LCACs, 900 Marines, and having 25,000cu ft of cargo space.

The investment in amphibious shipping paid off during Operation Desert Storm, when thirty-one amphibious ships served in the Persian Gulf region. Even so, this force was not sufficient to transport the full assault elements of two Marine Expeditionary Brigades. While no actual landings were carried out, the presence of large amphibious forces tied down thousands of Iraqi troops on the Kuwaiti shore and on the southern Iraqi islands of Warba and Bubiyan.

Command ships and fire support ships

The Second World War showed the Allies the vital need to have the amphibious command removed from the battleships and cruisers that traditionally had been fleet flagships. Requirements for shore bombardment often took these ships, in their gunfire support role, away from the optimum locations for exercising amphibious command, and despite their large size these ships often lacked the space required for a separate amphibious commander and his staff.

The command ships used during the Second World War were mainly merchant ship designs hastily converted during the war to amphibious

USS Blue Ridge, *one of two very sophisticated purpose-built amphibious command ships. Further construction was cancelled on the grounds that the new LHAs had satisfactory command and control facilities for amphibious operations. As a result they are currently employed as fleet flagships,* Blue Ridge *for the Seventh Fleet. She is shown at Yokosuka in 1985.* (L & L van Ginderen)

force requirements. Although they met most of the US Navy's requirements for the postwar years, the Navy saw a need for a new command ship class during the early 1960s to incorporate the advanced command and control systems entering service. A modified *Iwo Jima* class design, using the same basic hull and machinery but a different superstructure and internal layout, was chosen for the two LCCs, *Blue Ridge* and *Mount Whitney*, which were ordered in 1965 and 1966. The US Navy originally wanted to order four more LCCs, but the plans to provide the LHAs with sophisticated command suites meant that no more LCCs were required. In 1979 the *Blue Ridge* became flagship of the Western Pacific-based Seventh Fleet. *Mount Whitney* had already become flagship of the East Coast-based Second Fleet in the mid 1970s.

Converted LPDs are fulfilling most of the US Navy's other flagship requirements. USS *La Salle* was converted in 1972 to become flagship of the Bahrain-based Middle East force. In 1980 the *Coronado* was converted to serve as a relief flagship while *La Salle* was being overhauled. *Coronado* became flagship of the Pacific-based Third Fleet in 1986.

Only one fire support ship has been built since the war. Although design work on the *Carronade* began in 1948, she was only ordered in 1952 in the Korean War amphibious build-up. The Navy wanted a ship that could steam at 20kts and was capable of mass production, which was a costly requirement. Mass production considerations won, as the *Carronade* could steam at only 15kts and had only ¾in STS plate over her rocket magazines. She was commissioned in 1954, decommissioned in 1960, and recommissioned for Vietnam service between 1965 and 1972.

British amphibious warships

The United Kingdom had a different amphibious requirement in the immediate postwar era. Most of the overseas duties for British troops would be in Commonwealth nations or colonies, where there would be little need for opposed landings, and port facilities meant that troops could disembark from troop transports. The Royal Navy's amphibious force shrank considerably during the late 1940s. Many of its LSTs and smaller craft were on Lend-Lease from the United States and had to be returned, and with the overall cuts in British forces there was little funding or manpower to commission ships that would only be used during wartime.

Nonetheless, the Royal Navy's 1947 plans called for having a new LSD and nine LSTs capable of lifting a full brigade. These plans were revised in 1949 because of financial difficulties, and the new LSD was not built. The Royal Marines retained an interest in amphibious developments in the United States, and in April 1955 Major General C F Phillips, the Chief of Amphibious Warfare, asked that a requirement be written for two troop-carrying helicopters, one capable of transporting 33 men, the other able to lift 8 men. The helicopters would be carried aboard LSTs.

The July 1956 decision to invade Suez forced the Royal Navy to improve its amphibious assault capabilities. A decision was made on 25 September 1956 to convert the light fleet carriers *Ocean* and *Theseus* to interim LPHs capable of landing 450-man Commando units 15 miles away. Conversions were carried out, and the idea was tested off the English coast between 29 September and 12 October 1956. *Ocean* carried eight Royal Navy Whirlwind HAS 22s and two

The British commando carriers Bulwark and Albion at Aden in November 1962. The Royal Navy was an early advocate of the helicopter for amphibious assault and first employed the concept during the Suez invasion of 1956. The conversion of Albion, Bulwark and later Hermes to the LPH role proved invaluable in the troubled period of imperial withdrawal. (CMP)

a slightly smaller and modified version of the US Navy's LPD, the *Fearless*. The keel for a sister-ship, *Intrepid*, was laid down later the same year.

Fearless and *Intrepid* had well decks with space for trucks, tanks, and landing craft. The top of the well deck formed a flight deck, but, unlike the American LPDs, the British LPDs were not designed to embark helicopters normally, and the flight deck did not go all the way back to the stern. The *Fearless* class also carried fewer troops, berthing only 400 Royal Marines during normal operations, with room to embark up to 700 troops for short voyages. The construction of *Fearless* and *Intrepid*, and the conversion of *Albion* and *Bulwark*, allowed the Royal Navy constantly to maintain a version of the US Navy's LPH/LPD concept with the Eastern Fleet.

Fearless and *Intrepid* solved only part of Britain's amphibious shortfall. Many of the British Army's LSTs were obsolescent vessels left over after the Second World War and overdue for replacement. Because the LSTs were civilian-manned vessels used as logistics transports, the order for new ships was placed by the Ministry of Transport. The design for the new vessel was similar to a modified LST, with clamshell doors in the bow, but it also had a stern gate through which trucks could be driven. A helipad on the stern allowed the ships to carry a Gazelle or Lynx for patrol and light utility duties. The keel for *Sir Lancelot*, the first Logistic Landing Ship (LSL), as the new class was called, was laid down in March 1962. Four sister-ships were built during the next three years. Each could carry 340 troops, with room for a total of 534 troops for short transits; sixteen main battle tanks, thirty-four ground vehicles, and 340 tons of amphibious cargo, including 130 tons of gasoline and 30 tons of ammunition, could also be carried.

The new construction was not sufficient for troop and cargo lift requirements during the Falklands conflict. Two large luxury liners and seven roll-on/roll-off ships had to be taken from their normal civilian employment and sent with the Royal Navy's combatant forces, to carry the men and material required for the amphibious assault. The troops carried aboard the liners were transferred ashore by landing craft deployed from *Fearless* and *Intrepid*.

Whirlwind HAR 3s, while *Theseus* had six Army Whirlwind HAR 2s and six Sycamore Mk 14s. The capacity of the helicopters was limited, with the Whirlwinds carrying only 5–7 men and the Sycamores having a 3-man capacity. But the exercise went off successfully, and the first use of amphibious assault helicopters took place one month later, on 6 November 1956, when helicopters carried 415 troops and 22 tons of ammunition ashore in 90 minutes.

Following this operation, the Admiralty sought the permission of the British government to convert two carriers into LPHs. The Defence White Paper of 1957 made clear that rapid intervention forces were a necessary component of the British military. The obvious candidates for the LPH role were the light fleet carriers *Albion* and *Bulwark*, which were relatively new but could not be modernised to handle the aircraft of the 1960s because of a lack of funds.

Albion and *Bulwark* were converted to amphibious helicopter carriers in 1961–62 and 1959–61 respectively, losing their catapults and arresting gear but gaining facilities to maintain and support helicopters and Royal Marine Commandos. As modified, *Bulwark* carried 733 Royal Marines and twenty-one Wessex or Whirlwind helicopters, sixteen operational and five spares. *Albion* received a slightly different modification which allowed her to carry 900 troops, twenty-one helicopters, and four LCVP landing craft. During the early 1960s *Bulwark* was again modified to bring her up to *Albion*'s standards.

The decision to invest in an amphibious lift capacity also saw the revival of the LSD proposal in 1958. Because of the close ties between the US Navy and the Royal Navy, the British were aware of US plans to combine the missions of different amphibious ships into one hull. In July 1962 the Royal Navy laid down the keel for

Fearless *and* Intrepid *were the British version of the US LPD concept. The well deck is clearly demonstrated by this 1977 view of* Fearless *flooded down – the ship can transport four LCM(9)s in the well, and four LCVPs under davits amidships. When in commission both are usually assigned to the Dartmouth Training Squadron (for officer cadets), but both were available for service during the Falklands War in 1982. (C & S Taylor)*

Western European amphibious ships

Most of the Western European navies used former US LSDs and LSTs during the 1950s and early 1960s. This was particularly true for France, which began using small amphibious ships to transport troops in Vietnam almost immediately after the end of the war. However, during the 1960s the smaller Nato navies also began building amphibious ships with multi-mission capability. The French navy was the first fleet to build such ships. The 8500-ton *Ouragan* class LSDs were designed in the late 1950s and laid down in 1962. The design was different from the standard LSD, with the bridge to one side of a permanent helicopter deck forward of amidships.

The *Ouragan*'s primary mission is that of amphibious transport, for which she carries 250 troops for long deployments or 470 men for short trips. But the *Ouragan*s are also equipped to serve as floating logistics support and repair ships, with the 390ft long well deck able to dry-dock 400-ton ships. As transports the *Ouragan*s can carry two LCTs with eleven light tanks or trucks, or eighteen LCM Mk 6 landing craft. Other transport loads include eighteen heavy Super Frélon or eighty light Alouette helicop-

The latest French dock landing ship is the Foudre, *seen here demonstrating the anti-contamination pre-wetting system, part of the ship's NBC (nuclear, biological, chemical) defences. France has consistently maintained a small force for power projection in support of her overseas interests, and the amphibious ships are part of this capability. (DCN)*

ters or 120 light tanks. When serving as logistics support ships, the *Ouragan*s can carry 1500 tons of materials. During the mid 1980s the French navy began designing a new LSD, the 11,800-ton *Foudre*. The *Foudre* class will have most of the same capabilities as the *Ouragan*s, only they can carry up to 1400 troops in an emergency. The well deck can carry two LCTs or one P-400 type patrol boat.

Italy relied on former US amphibious warships longer than France, but when it began building its own ships it also gave them a multi-mission capability. Although two LPDs, *San Giorgio* and *San Marco*, were built between 1985 and 1988, the Italian Ministry of Defence only paid for *San Giorgio*. *San Marco*, built to the same design, was paid for, and is operated by, the Ministry of Civil Protection as a disaster relief ship, with a wartime amphibious capability. As LPDs the two ships can transport 450 troops, five CH-47 Chinook helicopters, and thirty medium tanks or three LCVPs. As disaster relief ships, the LPDs can hold about forty tracked vehicles, 99m³ of refrigerated stores and 300m³ of dry stores. The *San Giorgio*s have both a well deck with a stern ramp and clamshell doors in the bow, allowing cargo to be offloaded through either end. Even with the bow doors, the *San Giorgio*s are capable of steaming at 20kts.

Soviet amphibious warship developments

As a continental power, encircled by what it considered to be hostile powers, the Soviet navy saw little need for a large fleet of amphibious ships. Most Soviet amphibious operations during

A Soviet Ropucha *class LST. This is an early ship, later members of the class having shore bombardment rockets on the forecastle and four quadruple SA-N-5 or -8 point-defence missiles. Stern doors give these ships a ro/ro capability.* (MoD, Crown Copyright)

the Second World War were riverine operations, where small river craft transported troops to make hit-and-run raids or landings behind enemy lines. In these operations, ships that could operate along the shallow Baltic coast or in the numerous rivers of eastern Europe were far preferable to the transoceanic ships favoured by most Western nations. As a result, the end of the war found the Soviets with no specialised landing craft of their own. They had several requisitioned merchant ships used for troop transports, and they had acquired three Italian and sixty-nine German landing craft as war reparations.

Little happened to change this situation during the first ten years after the war. Emphasising a war against NATO, Soviet war plans had little if any requirement for the large ocean-going amphibious ships needed by the allied nations. Even through the late 1960s, the Soviet navy had very few amphibious ships for a fleet of its size.

The first purpose-built Soviet amphibious ships were the MP2 class medium landing ships, based on the German wartime MFP landing ships. Built during the mid 1950s, they could carry four tanks or 200 troops. They were followed during the late 1950s by the MP4 converted coastal motor transport ships. Both classes were intended primarily for amphibious operations along the Baltic and Black Sea coasts, where they could conduct encircling operations similar to those used during the Second World War.

Nearly all the Soviet amphibious ships built during the 1950s were capable of carrying only cargo, including tanks and armoured personnel carriers. Starting in the late 1950s, the Soviets began building the *Polnocny* class medium landing ships. The seven *Polnocny A* type had a very limited troop and cargo capacity, but the twenty-four *Polnocny B*s and nine *Polnocny C*s can carry 180 troops and six medium tanks.

The *Polnocny*s were followed in the late 1960s by fourteen *Alligator* class LSTs. The *Alligator*s can carry 300 troops and about twenty tanks. The seventeen follow-on *Ropucha* class LSTs had a smaller troop and tank capacity, of only 225 troops and 450 tons of cargo, but the *Ropucha*s have bow and stern doors, giving them a roll-on/roll-off capability.

During the late 1960s, Soviet military planners became preoccupied with the possibility of

war with China. At the same time, plans were prepared for the first of a major new amphibious programme, the *Ivan Rogov* class assault ships. The first ship entered service in 1978, and within one year was sent from the Baltic to the Soviet Pacific Fleet. A second ship, *Aleksandr Nikolaev*, entered service in 1983 and immediately joined her sister-ship in the Pacific.

The *Ivan Rogov* class are called Large Landing Ships by the Russians. Some Western observers have compared them with LPDs and mini-LHAs, but they have no real equivalent in Western navies. The ships are very well armed, with a twin SA-N-4 SAM launcher, two SA-N-5 launchers, a twin 76mm gun mount, and a twin 122mm rocket launcher. The armament, with its emphasis on shore bombardment and anti-air defence, suggests a recognition that the ship will have to operate in a high-threat environment, such as might be found along the China coast or the Baltic.

The troop and vehicle capacity of the class is large for their size. On a fully loaded displacement of 13,000 tons, and dimensions of 518ft by 80ft, it carries three *Lebed* air cushion landing craft or six *Ondotra* landing craft in her well deck. On a vehicle deck forward of the large superstructure, ten tanks and thirty armoured personnel carriers or trucks can be carried for the 500 troops accommodated. The superstructure has a large helicopter hangar that can be entered from both the front and the rear. Four Hormone C or Helix helicopters can be flown off flight decks fore and aft of the superstructure.

Vehicles could be disembarked through a stern gate or bow doors. The bow doors also showed that the Soviets had succeeded where

the United States had not, combining bow clamshell doors with a maximum speed of 23kts.

The Soviets were also the first major power to use air cushion vehicles as amphibious transports. During the early 1970s the Soviets began using *Gus* class surface-effect ships, which could carry 43 troops. The *Gus* class were followed by the *Aist*, *Lebed*, and *Pomornik* class air cushion vehicles, which could carry 100 to 200 troops or

The Ivan Rogov *is the prototype of the largest Soviet amphibious warfare vessel design. The photograph shows the stern gate of the docking well and the superstructure helicopter hangar, which also has access to a larger flight deck forward of the bridge. The ship can transport a complete naval infantry battalion of 500 and all associated vehicles.* (MoD, Crown Copyright)

After the war many Third World navies obtained ex-US or ex-British LSTs, but more recently many have received Soviet Polnocny *class landing ships instead. The Libyan* Ibn al Hadrami *is one of four Polish-built vessels of this class transferred in 1977–79 and is shown at Malta for refitting in 1983. These export versions have a helicopter deck forward of the superstructure.* (L & L van Ginderen)

one to four tanks for several hundred miles. Only the 87-ton *Lebed* class, which carry 120 troops, are small enough to be carried by the *Ivan Rogov*s.

Third World amphibious warships

Beset by tight budgets and the desire to have surface combatants and fast attack craft, many Third World navies have had little money left for amphibious warships. But this has not prevented some of these same navies from developing amphibious forces, using either locally-built warships or buying discarded warships from the major Western navies. Because small amphibious ships are easy to build, building these ships has also been seen as a way to develop an indigenous shipbuilding industry by many small nations.

Tank landing ships, tank landing craft and landing craft vehicles and personnel are the most commonly found landing craft in Third World navies. This reflects the large number of Second World War and Korean War era US LSTs and LCTs that were sold during the 1950s and 1960s, and the many *Polnocny* class medium landing ships that the former Soviet Union sold to its client states.

Those navies that have bought amphibious warships have often put them to many different uses. In many of the less developed nations, ships are the only means of transportation and communication with the more remote towns and villages. In nations with many small islands, such as Indonesia and the Philippines, amphibious warships are often employed as cargo and personnel transports to convey government staff and goods between the major islands and the smaller islands that lack landing strips for aircraft.

One of the few areas where amphibious ships have been used in the Third World has been the

Middle East. During the 1970s war of attrition, Israeli LCTs and amphibious transports conducted an amphibious raid along the Suez Canal, and during the 1982 invasion of Lebanon, Israel used the amphibious transport *Bat Sheva* and the *Ashdod* class tank landing craft to land troops and tanks behind enemy lines as they advanced up the coast of Lebanon.

Nigeria also used its single landing craft to stage amphibious assaults against Port Harcourt during the 1968–72 civil war. These 1971 assaults helped force the capitulation of the Biafran rebels.

The future of amphibious warships

Amphibious warfare continues to be a major weapon in the arsenal of naval planners. The US Navy's '. . . *From the Sea*' white paper, billed as

the successor to the Maritime Strategy, says that the US Navy's primary emphasis during the 1990s will be on warfare in the littoral seas and coastal regions around the world. Operating in these waters, it will work in conjunction with the US Marine Corps to open beachheads for the landing of heavier Army and Air Force units.

Both the Falklands conflict and the Persian Gulf War showed that amphibious landings can be carried out successfully, and that the threat of such operations can tie down large numbers of troops. Equally, the Falklands showed that letting amphibious forces decline can force a reliance on merchant ships that might not be available, while the Persian Gulf War showed that the threat of mines can be a major problem for amphibious planners.

Reports that Iraqi mines forced the US Navy to cancel a planned amphibious landing in

Despite falling defence budgets, the Royal Navy has retained a new LPH near the top of its priorities, and a new ship was ordered in 1993. This artist's impression depicts the new vessel, which is to be named Ocean *after the light fleet carrier that was the first to employ a helicopter-borne assault in action. The 20,000-ton ship will carry 600–700 troops and embark twelve helicopters.* (VSEL)

Kuwait have been widely publicised. Even if a landing was not planned, many small nations have seen that a low cost investment in mines can cause a major power to have second thoughts about such a landing.

Britain and France continue to believe in amphibious warfare. An LPH is high on the Royal Navy's list of future requirements, while France has plans for future LPD construction. Russia is having a difficult time operating her fleet, and with the new emphasis on protecting Russians, it is likely that amphibious operations will be restricted to traditional coastal flanking missions.

Most smaller navies will continue to build LSD-sized amphibious warships. These are small enough to be operated efficiently by many mid-sized naval powers, yet large enough to operate successfully at sea. And as long as sea transportation remains as cost-effective as it is, many Third World nations will rely on their amphibious forces for commercial transport.

David Steigman

Amphibious Warfare Vessels: Typical Classes, since 1945

Class	Type	Nationality	Displacement full load (tons)	Dimensions overall (feet-inches) (metres)	Armament	Machinery/ Speed (kts)	Launch dates	Numbers built
TERREBONNE PARISH	LST	American	5770	384-0 × 56-0 × 16-1 117.1 × 17.1 × 4.9	4-3in; 391 troops plus vehicles	D/15.5	1952–54	15
PAUL REVERE	AKA	American	16,838	564-0 × 76-0 × 26-0 172.0 × 23.2 × 7.9	8-3in; 1657 troops	ST/22	1953–54	2
BULWARK	LPH	British	27,000	737-9 × 12-0 × 27-0 224.8 × 37.5 × 8.2	8-40mm; 900 troops, 16 helicopters	ST/28	Converted 1959–62	2
IWO JIMA	LPH	American	18,000	602-3 × 84-1 × 26-1 183.6 × 25.7 × 8.0	8-3in; 2057 trooops; 11–19 helicopters	ST/23.5	1960–69	7
POLNOCNY C (Project 773)	LSM	Soviet	1150	266-8 × 33-1 × 6-9 81.3 × 10.1 × 2.1	4 SA-N-5, 2-30mm, 140mm RL; 180 troops, 250t cargo	D/19	1961–73	103
FEARLESS	LPD	British	12,120	520-0 × 80-0 × 20-5 158.5 × 24.4 × 6.3	4 Seacat SAM, 2-40mm; 400 troops, 15 tanks, 27 vehicles	ST/21	1963–64	2
SIR LANCELOT	LSL	British	5674	412-1 × 59-7 × 13-0 125.1 × 19.6 × 4.3	534 troops, 16 tanks, 34 vehicles	D/17	1963–67	6
OURAGAN	LPD	French	8500	489-0 × 71-0 × 15-0 149.0 × 21.5 × 4.6	4-40mm, 1-120mm mortars; 349 troops, 1500t cargo	D/17	1963–67	2
AUSTIN	LPD	American	16,900	570-0 × 84-0 × 23-0 173.8 × 25.6 × 7.0	8-3in; 930 troops, 500t cargo	ST/20	1964–70	12
NEWPORT	LST	American	8342	562-0 × 69-5 × 17-5 171.3 × 21.2 × 5.3	4-3in; 385 troops, 500t cargo	D/20	1968–71	20
BLUE RIDGE	AGC	American	19,290	620-0 × 108-0 × 27-0 189.0 × 32.9 × 8.2	2 Sea Sparrow SAM, 4-3in	ST/20	1969–70	2
TARAWA	LHA	American	38,761	820-0 × 106-7 × 25-7 250.0 × 32.5 × 7.8	2 Sea Sparrow SAM, 3-5in; 1903 troops plus vehicles	ST/24	1973–78	5
HENGAM	LST	Iranian (British-built)	2540	305-1 × 49-0 × 7-3 93.0 × 14.9 × 2.2	4-40mm; 700t cargo (inc 6–10 tanks)	D/14.5	1973–79	4
ROPUCHA (Project 775)	LST	Soviet	3200	370-8 × 45-9 × 9-5 113.0 × 14.0 × 2.9	4 SA-N-5, 4-57mm; 230 troops with vehicles, 450t cargo	D/118	1975–78	12
IVAN ROGOV (Project 1174)	LPD	Soviet	13,000	518-3 × 78-8 × 26-9 158.0 × 24.0 × 2.9	1 SA-N-4, 2-76mm, 4-30mm, 2-122mm RL; 550 troops, 30 APCs, 10 tanks	GT/23	1976–88	3
WHIDBEY ISLAND	LSD	American	15,726	609-6 × 84-0 × 19-8 185.8 × 25.6 × 6.0	2 Phalanx CIWS, 2-20mm; 440 troops	D/22	1983–89	8
SAN GIORGIO	LPD	Italian	7665	437-2 × 67-2 × 17-2 133.3 × 20.5 × 5.3	1-76mm; 400 troops, 5 helicopters	D/21	1987–93	3

Machinery abbreviations:
D = diesel; ST = steam turbine; GT = gas turbine.

7

Naval Auxiliaries

ONE of the many lessons of the Second World War was the increased need for naval auxiliaries. Auxiliary warships, including colliers, repair ships and tenders, had been part of many naval inventories since the beginning of the twentieth century, but the changing nature of naval warfare during and after the war created requirements for large fleets of many different types of auxiliaries.

Auxiliary warships have become so important that in two of the larger naval conflicts of the postwar era there have been nearly as many auxiliary warships as combatants taking part. During the Falklands conflict the Royal Navy sent two aircraft carriers and twenty-five surface combatants to the theatre of operations. Supporting these ships were sixteen Royal Fleet Auxiliaries and twenty-five merchant ships taken up from trade to provide supply and repair services. During operations Desert Shield and Desert Storm, the US Navy had eight aircraft carriers and sixty-eight surface combatants on station at various times. (Some ships were in theatre only for Desert Shield, others only for Desert Storm.) Keeping these ships filled with supplies and in working order required the efforts of twenty-seven naval auxiliaries and more than thirty civilian-manned Military Sealift Command auxiliaries.

Many of these auxiliary warships are designed for underway replenishment (unrep) or supplying a fleet on the move, but others are designed for fleet maintenance and repair support, providing most of the repair capabilities available from a major naval dockyard.

Central to the operation of any modern blue-water fleet is underway replenishment, demonstrated here by USS Cimarron *(AO-177), which is simultaneously refuelling the carrier* Coral Sea *and her* Leahy *(CG-16) class escort in 1981. The 27,000-ton* Cimarron *class has four constant-tension replenishment stations to port and three to starboard which can function at speeds of up to 15kts; they can transfer 408,000 litres of fuel oil or 245,000 litres of JP-5 aviation fuel per hour. The class is being lengthened to reach a full load displacement of nearly 38,000 tons. (L & L van Ginderen)*

Underway replenishment

Underway replenishment became critical with the wartime growth of aircraft carrier strike fleets. The ability of the US Navy's carrier task forces to strike rapidly across the Pacific Ocean and then retire, or to stay in an area to continue pounding targets, was dependent on a constant supply of fuel oil, aviation gasoline, ammunition and aircraft spare parts.

But non-carrier operations also required unrep ships. Britain's Royal Navy nearly had to give up the pursuit of the German battleship *Bismarck* in 1941 because the Home Fleet flagship *King George V* came close to running out of fuel. As it was, she and her escorts returned to port with their tanks nearly dry. As another example, Germany's raiding cruisers and pocket battleships relied on supply ships to keep them at sea for months on end.

Separated by two oceans from most of the fighting, it was the US Navy that led the way in the development of naval auxiliaries during and immediately after the Second World War. At the end of the war it had a vast array of oilers, ammunition ships, stores ships, stores issue ships, aviation supply ships, repair ships, destroyer tenders and submarine tenders.

Standard wartime procedures called for this supply fleet (or fleet train, as the Royal Navy referred to it) to operate hundreds of miles behind the battle fleet. Every three to five days the carrier task forces would race back from the front lines and meet the supply ships at a remote mid-ocean rendezvous.

The fleet train of 1945 was a vast organisation, with dozens of ships. The most important were oilers (AO), carrying the fuel necessary for fleet operations. Gasoline tankers (AOG) carried the aviation gasoline needed by the hundreds of aeroplanes in the carrier task forces. Ammunition ships (AE) carried bullets, bombs, shells and torpedoes. General store issue ships (AKS) carried the clothing, spare parts and repair tools needed by the combatants. Store ships (AF) had refrigerated and non-refrigerated holds for carrying foodstuffs. Aviation supply ships (AVS) carried supplies for the carrier's aircraft.

Once the task force and supply force had

joined up, the fleet train would begin to resupply the battle fleet. In operations frequently lasting nearly a day for a carrier and several hours for the destroyers, AOs would pull alongside the combatants and fire over highlines. Oil hoses would be passed along a trolley on the highline, connected to trunks in the fighting ships, and fuel would be pumped into their tanks.

After the oilers had completed their job, the AOGs, AEs, AKSs, AFs, and AVSs would come alongside the combatants and repeat the process, shuttling over pallets of bullets and beans by a trolley riding a highline. When the resupply process was completed, the supply ships would return to a major base, such as Pearl Harbor, to restock their holds, before steaming out to resupply the fleet again.

The rigs used by the resupply ships were rudimentary, forcing ships to steam within 40ft to 80ft of each other, with the consequent risk of minor collisions. Without a system to keep the highlines under constant tension, the height of the cargo lines varied as the ships moved closer to or away from one another. Sometimes, when ships closed quickly, the cargo ended up getting an unplanned soaking.

Most US Navy supply ships were conversions of the basic Maritime Administration T-2 and T-3 tanker and C-2 and C-3 freighter designs. Because they retained their merchant marine powerplants, many supply ships had a maximum speed of 11kts or at most 16kts, compared with the 25kts-plus speeds of the combatant fleets. Most had been modified to stock only one category of item, either food, fuel, ammunition, or spare parts.

With slow speeds and single-product ships performing the unrep mission, resupplying a carrier task force could take at least a day. Dur-

ing this time, the force was sailing on a steady course at a reduced speed, to allow the resupply to take place. This left the fleet vulnerable to any hostile submarines or aircraft in the vicinity.

The Germany navy found a way around some of these problems. Lacking a large merchant marine or navy, it built its fleet oilers to serve as multi-product replenishment ships, carrying fuel, food and ammunition in different holds.

Initial postwar developments

When the war ended and Germany's fleet was divided amongst the Allies, the US Navy received the *Dithmarschen* and the Royal Navy received the *Nordmark*. Renamed the *Conecuh* and *Bulawayo* respectively, each ship continued to serve as a multi-product supply ship. *Bulawayo* was withdrawn from service in the general early 1950s contraction of the Royal Navy, but the *Conecuh* served as a multi-product supply ship with the US Navy's Atlantic Fleet for nearly fourteen years between 1946 and 1960. Making regular deployments to the Mediterranean, *Conecuh* proved the viability of the multi-product ship, capable of dispensing several products to other warships.

On the basis of the *Conecuh's* first cruises, the US Navy considered converting the oiler *Waccamaw* to a replenishment oiler, or multi-product ship, in 1951. However, these plans were cut back when the massive recall of ships for the Korean War led to a shortage of funds and other warship construction programmes taking higher priority. Some naval officers also opposed the idea of building a multi-product replenishment ship because of fears that 'putting all the eggs into one basket' would be a mistake, in case the basket were sunk.

Because of the funding shortages and fleet

opposition, *Waccamaw*, instead of getting a full conversion, received just a modified refuelling rig in 1952. The new rig, designed for use in the stormy North Atlantic, allowed *Waccamaw* to maintain a greater distance from the ships being refuelled. Using winches on the resupply ship, the new rig allowed a constant tension and distance to be maintained between the two ships.

The construction of the massive *Forrestal* class aircraft carriers forced the US Navy to reconsider its replenishment capabilities. The first step, taken in 1952, was to order the first of five large *Neosho* class AOs with the new replenishment rig tested in *Waccamaw*. The *Neoshos* were among the world's first naval oilers built as such from the keel up (most previous US and foreign oilers were wartime conversions of tankers). With a capacity of 180,000 barrels of oil, the *Neoshos* had a cargo capacity nearly 50 per cent greater than the 120,000 barrels the wartime *Cimarron* class could carry.

Shortly after the *Neoshos* were ordered, the Navy ordered the first of five new *Suribachi* class AEs. Both new classes carried more cargo than their predecessors, and were faster, with a 20kt speed. However, carrier task forces were being designed to operate at even higher speeds, and a requirement for a fast multi-product ship was seen as the only way to provide the new attack carrier task forces with the supplies they would require. A requirement was accordingly issued in 1959 for a Fast Combat Support Ship (AOE).

Fast multi-product support ships

Combining all the capabilities of an AO, AE, AF and an AKS, the AOE carried nearly as much oil as an oiler, almost as much ammunition as an ammunition ship and nearly as much food as a stores issue ship. It was also to be fast enough to maintain the 25kt speed at which carrier task forces routinely operated. Several actions were considered, including modifying the *Iowa* class battleships then being decommissioned, or the axial deck *Essex* class aircraft carriers. Both these approaches were ruled out because the modification costs would have been too high to make conversion cost-effective.

Instead, a new design was chosen for what became the *Sacramento* class. The name-ship, ordered and laid down in 1961, represented a quantum leap in underway replenishment technology. At 750ft length, with a fully-loaded

Kilauea (AE-26), one of a class of eight 20,000-ton ammunition ships built at the beginning of the 1970s. Unlike earlier AEs, they were designed with helicopter facilities and usually embarked two UH-46 twin-rotor machines. (L & L van Ginderen)

Probably the most impressive auxiliaries in the world are the American Sacramento *(AOE-1) class fast combat support ships. These 26kt ships displace 53,600 tons full load, and although only four were built in the late 1960s, the design has been revived in modified form for a new class.* USS Seattle *is shown in June 1983 with two twin 3in guns replaced by Sea Sparrow SAM launcher forward. These high-value ships also have elaborate ECM defences.* (L & L van Ginderen)

displacement of 53,600 tons, she was larger than most Second World War battleships. The relationship to the battleships extended to the engineering plant of the first two ships, *Sacramento* and *Camden*, which each received half of the plant from the uncompleted *Iowa* class battleship *Kentucky*.

Their capacity fully matched the requirements. *Sacramento* carried 177,000 barrels of fuel, 2150 tons of ammunition and 750 tons of provisions, including 500 tons of dry stores and 250 tons of refrigerated stores. The new ships also had constant tension rigs allowing ships to steam 120ft from *Sacramento* at speeds as high as 20kts.

However, the most significant improvement in the *Sacramento* class was probably the inclusion of a hangar and a large flight deck capable of operating three medium helicopters, although only two UH-46 Sea Knights are normally carried. Helicopters added a new capability to underway replenishment. Carrying cargo on pallets slung beneath it, a helicopter could re-supply ships on distant escort stations. Using a helicopter also let the replenishment ship re-supply three ships simultaneously, two being connected by highline and a third getting vertical replenishment. Although the US Navy had been experimenting with vertical replenishment since the mid 1950s, previous efforts used either helicopters based on an aircraft carrier or helicopters operating from improvised flight decks aboard older supply ships. These ships had no

hangar facilities, so helicopters were constantly exposed to the elements, with a consequent increase in downtime for maintenance.

One year after the *Sacramento* was laid down, the US Navy laid the keel for the first *Mars* class combat stores ship. Combining the capabilities of an AKS, AF, and an AVS in one hull, the ships had five large holds, including two for spare parts, one for refrigerated stores, one for non-refrigerated provisions and one for aviation parts. They carried 25,000 types of spare parts in 40,000 bins and racks.

While the *Sacramento* class were under construction, the US Navy decided to build a slightly smaller multi-product ship, the *Wichita* class replenishment oiler (AOR). The AOR had a dual purpose. The limited number of AOEs

meant that the US Navy could not always guarantee having one with a forward deployed battle group. The *Wichita* class were also designed to fulfil the role of a multi-product supply ship to the Navy's ASW carrier groups. Because the ASW groups did not operate at the intense pace of an attack carrier group, a smaller ship was sufficient. The *Wichita*-class replenishment oilers each carried nearly the same amount of oil, 175,000 barrels, but their cargo holds were smaller, accommodating only 600 tons of ammunition and 500 tons of dry and refrigerated stores. In a cost saving measure that was later changed, the first six *Wichitas* were not given a hangar for their two helicopters, because the helicopter from the carrier could be used. When the seventh ship was ordered, in 1973, this omission was corrected, and hangars were fitted on either side of the funnel.

During the early 1980s the US Navy made all its replenishment ships capable of carrying multiple products. AEs and AFSs received one refuelling rig on one of their kingposts, to allow them to refuel other ships; AOs received eight refrigerated containers for carrying foodstuffs.

Savannah, *a* Wichita *class replenishment oiler or AOR. These multi-product ships are smaller versions of the AOE; they have four stations for fuel transfer and two for solid transfer on the port side, and three and two on the starboard side. They currently carry Sea Sparrow SAM and Phalanx CIWs for self-defence.* (L & L van Ginderen)

Sylvania *(AFS-2), the second of the seven* Mars *class combat stores ships, at Malta in September 1965. Along with the* Sacramento *class AOEs, the* Mars *class represented postwar ideas of how best to keep fast carrier task forces at sea. These vessels saw much active service in support of Task Force 77 off Vietnam between 1964 and 1973. (L & L van Ginderen)*

Resupply operations

Shortly after the *Sacramento* and *Mars* classes were completed, their utility was proven in battle. One AOE and one AFS operated with carrier Task Force 77 off Vietnam between 1964 and 1973. During a typical wartime operation a fast combat support ship would spend about twenty days off Vietnam, dividing her time alternately supplying the aircraft carrier task force off North Vietnam and the surface combatants off South Vietnam.

At the end of the three-week cycle, the ship would steam to the supply depot at the Subic Bay naval facility in the Philippines. After a four-day in-port period to take on more supplies, she would steam back to the task forces. If an AOE had to spend most of its time with the task forces, AOs, AEs, and AFSs would shuttle back and forth between the task force and Subic Bay. When they reached the vicinity of the task force they would resupply the AOEs, which would then replenish the combatants.

Underway replenishment operations are conducted by one of two methods, 'delivery boy' or 'grocery store'. 'Delivery boy' calls for the unrep ship to sail from warship to warship, while they remain on their assigned stations. 'Grocery store' works in the opposite manner, with the unrep ship assuming an assigned station, often in the centre of the task force, and other ships breaking off from their stations to rendezvous with her.

During the actual resupply operations, ships can either steam alongside, or the unrep ship can steam ahead of the ship being replenished. Most Western navies use the alongside method, since ships can steam at speeds as high as 20kts. This method is faster than the bow-to-stern method, but it requires skilled seamanship by the helmsmen and seamen manning the replenishment rigs on all ships involved. The alongside method follows the US Navy's Second World War practice of having the resupply ship send highlines to the ships being resupplied. These highlines are then used to send over tensioned lines carrying fuel hoses or span wires carrying palletised supplies.

Using the bow-to-stern method requires the unrep ship to drop a buoy carrying the end of a refuelling or resupply line. The ship being supplied steams to the buoy, picks up the supply line, and steams in the wake of the supply ship. This method restricts the ships involved to a maximum speed of about 5kts and it must be carried out in calm seas. The bow-to-stern method was long favoured by the former Soviet navy. Only during the mid 1980s did the Soviets begin alongside replenishment with any degree of regularity.

Other Western supply ships

The Royal Navy was one of the first Western navies to develop a fleet train. Hindered in the Pacific by the short range of its ships and the lack of an effective underway supply organisation, it realised it would need to develop such an organisation to operate globally in the postwar era. The Royal Navy operated the ex-German prize ship *Bulawayo* as a multi-product replenishment ship between 1945 and 1955. Following the successful experience with the *Bulawayo*, the Royal Navy laid the keels for their first AORs in 1954. The three 'Tide' class ships carried 13,000 tons of fuel and limited amounts of food, ammunition, and spare parts.

But most of the Royal Navy's replenishment ships through the 1960s were converted merchant ships, either tankers or grain and cargo ships with replenishment hoses or booms added. This changed during the 1960s, when the Royal Navy began building two types of replenishment ships, either oilers or fleet replenishment ships (AEFS), carrying ammunition, food, stores, and aviation parts. The first AEFS were the *Regent* and the *Resource*, which entered service in 1967.

Most smaller Western navies began building their first specialised multi-product replenishment ships during the early 1960s. Many of the smaller Nato navies had converted tankers to serve as replenishment oilers during the 1950s. The growth in Nato naval operations led to a need for more replenishment ships, and multi-product ships met the needs of these nations by eliminating the requirement for several types of ships.

The Canadian navy laid the keel for its first AOR, *Provider*, in 1963. Capable of carrying 12,000 tons of fuel oil, 900 tons of aviation fuel and 250 tons of dry cargo, she showed what could be accomplished on a hull no larger than that of a Second World War oiler. The Netherlands laid down an AOR, *Poolster*, in September 1962. *Poolster* carries 10,300 tons of supplies, including 8000 tons of fuel and 2300 tons of food, spare parts and ammunition.

Many of the Western replenishment ships were designed to perform other missions besides resupply. Three of the five French *Durance* class AORs have berthing space for 100 more personnel than they require, and flag facilities for a fleet commander. One *Durance* class oiler always performs this function for the French Indian Ocean fleet, and another often serves as the flagship for the Pacific squadron. The five ships carry differing amounts of fuel, oil, water, diesel fuel, provisions, spare parts and ammunition. They have also served as a prototypes for smaller AORs built for Australia and Saudi Ara-

The lack of suitable support was a mortifying experience for the British Pacific Fleet in 1944–45, and the postwar Royal Navy was quick to develop specialist replenishment vessels. The carrier Victorious *is shown in May 1967 between the fleet oiler* Wave Baron *(12,000 tons, built 1946) and the new combat stores ship* Lyness *(16,800 tons). With the end of British 'East of Suez' commitments, the three* Lyness *class ships were surplus to requirements and were sold to the USA where they are still operated by the Military Sealift Command. (CMP)*

bia. The two Canadian *Protecteur* class AORs can each carry four landing craft (LCVPs) and 60 troops, in addition to their normal crew. While the Canadian navy has seldom taken part in out-of-area operations, this is a convenient ability, in case a squadron must put troops ashore for civilian evacuation operations.

Because the small Western navies lacked the wide range of aircraft available to the United

The French AOR Durance, *first of a class of 17,800-ton multi-product replenishment ships. The ship has two replenishment stations on each side for either liquid or solid transfer, and full load is made up of 7500 tons fuel oil, 1500 tons diesel fuel, 500 tons JP-5 aviation kerosene, 130 tons distilled water, 170 tons fresh provisions, 150 tons munitions and 50 tons spare parts. (L & L van Ginderen)*

States, their AORs carried the same type of helicopters as their anti-submarine frigates and destroyers. This allowed them to operate as combatant members of ASW task forces, and not just as supply ships. Canadian AORs carry three Sea King helicopters, Dutch AORs carry three Lynx, and French AORs carry either two Alouette or Lynx helicopters.

Soviet and Chinese replenishment ships

In contrast to the Western emphasis on underway replenishment, the former Soviet Union displayed little interest in it through the late 1960s. Until the mid-1970s, most Soviet oilers

were modified civilian tankers. Many were not equipped for underway replenishment, instead preferring to dispense their cargo while at anchor in foreign ports or in the stern-to-bow method while steaming at 2kts or 3kts on very calm seas.

This changed during the 1960s, when the Soviets began to build six *Boris Chilikin* class AORs. They carried 13,000 tons of fuel oil and diesel oil, 400 tons of foodstuffs, 400 tons of ammunition, 400 tons of spare and repair parts and 500 tons of fresh water. The class had an interesting rig arrangement. The earliest ships could pass solid stores on either side forward, with liquids being passed on both sides amid-

The New Zealand replenishment ship Endeavour *was built to a Hyundai HDA-12000 standard mercantile design, modified for naval requirements. More ambitious navies have ordered versions of purpose-built auxiliaries from Western countries, but the mercantile adaptation is still the most common method of acquiring replenishment ships for Third World countries.* (RNZN)

ships and aft. The later ships could supply solid stores only on the starboard side forward, the port side being used for liquids.

The six *Boris Chilikin*s were followed in 1978 by the large AOR *Berezina*. At 40,000 tons fully loaded and 695ft in length, she was the largest unrep ship build outside the United States. *Berezina*'s cargo included 16,000 tons of fuel oil, 2500 tons of food, ammunition, and spare parts, and 500 tons of fresh water. *Berezina* was also well armed, carrying an SA-N-4 Gecko surface-to-air missile launcher, two RBU-1000 rocket launchers, and close-in weapon systems.

The Chinese did not build their first underway replenishment ships until the mid 1970s, when the *Fulin* class were constructed. The *Fulin*s, which had only one replenishment rig, were among the smallest replenishment ships in the world. The next Chinese replenishment ship class, the *Fuqing* class, entered service in 1981. The three *Fuqing*s had two liquid replenishment and one solid replenishment station per side. During a Chinese naval exercise in the South Pacific in 1984, the Chinese were observed to conduct underway replenishment with a much greater skill than many Western observers thought they would be capable of.

Third World supply ships

Many Third World navies operate one or two small oilers designed primarily to transfer oil, but with the capability to deliver other products as well. Many are former US Navy Second World War oilers transferred during the 1950s and 1960s. Some are small ships built to export designs in Great Britain, France or other European nations. Others were merchant oilers, modified by the addition of a derrick and boom arrangement to transfer oil to warships steaming alongside. In recognition of the needs of a modern navy, most of these small oilers, while primarily equipped to supply oil, can also carry and supply small quantities of ammunition and foodstuffs.

To save the costs of building an oiler, some Third World navies chartered tankers from their state oil companies. These ships were modified by the addition of underway replenishment derricks, booms and hoses, so they could perform their military mission if required. Using civilian tankers had many advantages for Third World navies. It saved the cost of building a warship that might see little use. It also allowed the ship to make a profit for her mer-

The largest Soviet fleet replenishment vessel is the Berezina, *a 36,000-ton one-off ship that can conduct refuelling operations alongside (single stations, port and starboard), or astern. There are two solid cargo transfer stations amidships, and vertical replenishment is carried out by two Hormone helicopters. Self-defence is provided by two twin 57mm forward, four 30mm 'Gatling' guns and a SA-N-4 SAM system abaft the funnels. Capacity is estimated at 16,000 tons of fuel, 500 tons of fresh water, and 2000–3000 tons of dry stores, ammunition and spares.* (MoD, Crown Copyright)

The US destroyer tender Cape Cod *(AD-43) is essentially a maintenance ship for missile cruisers and destroyers, with facilities to overhaul and repair everything from gas turbine main engines to missile guidance systems. They are said to carry 60,000 different types of spares in sixty-five storerooms. This is the latest tender design and is essentially similar to the L Y Spear class for submarines.* (L & L van Ginderen)

chant or navy owners when she was not needed for fleet operations. India and Peru both used this method to acquire fleet oilers.

Most navies that have one or two small replenishment oilers also have one or two small repair ships. This mirrors the other major trend in postwar auxiliary ship development, the addition of specialised repair ships and tenders to cater to a fleet's maintenance requirements.

Other fleet support auxiliaries

Repair ships and tenders

Most of the world's major navies already had repair ships (AR), destroyer tenders (AD), and submarine tenders (AS) in service before the outbreak of the Second World War. The increase in international naval operations following the war led to an expansion in the number of destroyer and submarine tenders and specialised repair ships.

By the mid 1960s, some of these war-built ADs and ASs in the US Navy and Royal Navy had been converted to care for the new nuclear-powered submarines and missile-armed destroyers entering service. The new equipment was in addition to the traditional full range of workshops, foundries, forges, electronic repair shops, optical repair shops, laundries, and large supply storerooms found aboard tenders (or depot ships, as the Royal Navy calls them).

Tenders have often been called on to serve as deployed flotilla, squadron, and fleet flagships during the postwar era. Several factors contributed to this practice, which took place in the US, Royal, and Soviet navies. Many tenders were fairly large and had the extra space to support a large staff. Tenders also were often called on to serve for long periods away from

One of six Soviet Don *class submarine tenders, designed to support eight to twelve boats. They also serve as flagships.* (MoD, Crown Copyright)

home port, supporting fleet units. But while deployed overseas, most tenders did not have heavy steaming schedules, allowing them to stay near land-based communications facilities or in safe anchorages.

Lack of a suitable cruiser led the US Navy to make the *Puget Sound* (AD-38) Sixth Fleet flagship in the Mediterranean between July 1980 and May 1985. As a flagship, *Puget Sound* accommodated 90 officers and enlisted personnel as flag staff. The cruiser *Belknap*, which assumed the duties in 1987, accommodates only 30 flag staff personnel, forcing some to be permanently left ashore in the homeport of Gaeta.

The British AS *Maidstone* served as the flagship for the Seventh Submarine Flotilla in Singapore during the 1950s and 1960s. As Britain withdrew from her overseas commitments and concentrated the Royal Navy in the North Atlantic, tenders were discarded.

But it was the Soviet navy that made the greatest use of ASs as deployed flagships. The six *Don* class and six *Ugra* class submarine tenders, commissioned during 1950–61 and 1963–72 respectively, all had the Vee Cone long range communications antennas commonly found on Soviet flagships. Because submarines were Soviet fleet units most frequently found out of Soviet home areas, using the *Don* and

Ugra classes as flagships made operational sense. These ships were often found in harbours from where Soviet submarines operated, such as Sollum, Libya; Cienfuegos, Cuba; and Cam Ranh Bay, Vietnam.

During the Cold War, a US AD and an AS would normally deploy for at least six months to the Mediterranean and the Western Pacific. Combatant warships and supply ships would come alongside every two or three months for ten to twenty days of intermediate-level maintenance (intermediate-level maintenance being above the capabilities of the ship's crew but below those of a shipyard).

Because of their similar roles, ADs and ASs are often built to common designs, with a few differences for their specific duties. The US Navy built four *Vulcan* class ARs, five *Piedmont* class ADs, and seven *Fulton* class ASs to a similar design between 1938 and 1944. This was repeated during the 1960s and 1970s, when the US Navy used a similar design for six *Samuel Gompers* class ADs and five *L Y Spear* and two *Simon Lake* class ASs. The Royal Navy built the *Maidstone* class submarine tenders and the *Tyne* class destroyer tenders to a similar design during the late 1930s.

The last members of these classes will not leave US service until the mid 1990s, and some

will survive in smaller navies until after the turn of the century, sixty years after they were built. While most of these ships were modernised during the 1950s and 1960s, only one, the submarine tender *Proteus*, was radically changed, gaining a new 44ft midsection containing additional workshops and storage tubes for Polaris missiles.

While most tenders were purpose-built or converted merchant ships, the Royal Navy used a *Majestic* class light fleet aircraft carrier as a repair ship for surface escorts during the 1960s in the Far East. *Triumph* was converted between 1958 and 1965, because the Royal Navy lacked a modern repair ship for its East Asian commitments and did not have the funds to modernise *Triumph* for carrier duties. During the conversion, repair sheds were built on *Triumph*'s flight deck, and repair shops were built on the hangar deck. *Triumph* could handle four frigates or destroyers simultaneously alongside, but after just seven years of service she was decommissioned in 1973, shortly after the Royal Navy ended its presence in the Far East.

Hospital ships

Few types of auxiliary warships have seen a resurgence once they pass from the registers of the world's navies, but hospital ships fall into this category. Many navies had several at the end of the Second World War, but most decommissioned their hospital ships, or returned them to their civilian owners if they were luxury liners taken over in 1939. The US Navy kept three hospital ships through the late 1960s. During the Vietnam War they alternated deployments off the coast. With helicopter landing pads at their stern, they could receive casualties less than an hour after combat.

When the US Navy established a forward-based destroyer squadron at Pireaus, Greece, in 1970, there was a proposal to send the hospital ship *Repose* to Pireaus as a dependent care facility. According to the plans, *Repose* would have provided all the services of a stateside naval hospital, both for the sailors and their dependants. These plans were cancelled because of the cost of converting the ship and the decision to terminate the Mediterranean forward homeport.

The Soviet Union commissioned its first two purpose-built hospital ships, the *Ob* and the *Yenisei*, in 1980 and 1981. With seven operating

The US hospital ship Repose *in 1960. One of a number of purpose-built vessels completed at the end of the war, the ship had beds for 800 patients and was air conditioned throughout.* (L & L van Ginderen)

theatres and 100 beds, they were smaller than most Western hospital ships. While no reason was advanced for their construction, the Soviet Union had operated several converted merchant ships off the coast of Angola as hospital ships for Cuban 'volunteers' wounded in the 'war of liberation'.

Just as the Soviet Union had taken merchant ships from trade for the Angolan war, Britain's Royal Navy was forced to rely on this step in 1982 during the Falklands War. The Peninsular and Oriental (P&O) Steamship company liner *Uganda* was requisitioned in April 1982 and equipped with all the facilities of a floating hospital. Sent to the Falklands as part of the Royal Navy's task force, she provided care for the British forces until July 1982, when she returned to the United Kingdom. *Uganda* was returned to P&O in 1984.

During the naval build-up of the 1980s, US Navy officials became concerned at the lack of hospital ships to support any amphibious operations. The last US hospital ship, *Repose*, was decommissioned in the mid 1970s and in poor material condition because of years of neglect. To remedy the shortage of hospital ships, the Military Sealift Command bought two tankers in 1983. During a three-year conversion, large prefabricated medical compartments were lowered into the tanker hulls.

Mercy and *Comfort*, as the two ships were renamed, each have twelve operating rooms, four X-ray rooms, 1000 beds, an 80-bed intensive care unit, a burn-care unit, and a 50-bed receiving area. The two ships are said to be among the best-equipped medical facilities in the United States.

One ship is based on each coast, with a small Military Sealift Command caretaker crew. During a crisis, each would be crewed by medical personnel from one of the Navy's hospitals, with reserve personnel taking the place of those

medical personnel sent to sea. *Mercy*, the Pacific ship, made a six-month trip to the Philippines in 1988 with a volunteer crew to provide medical care to the indigenous population. Both ships were also called up for operations Desert Shield and Desert Storm, although fortunately they had little work to do in the Persian Gulf.

Intelligence collectors

The growing use of wireless communications and the reliance on naval forces to serve as part of the superpower strategic equation led to a new naval auxiliary during the late 1950s, the intelligence collector. While most of the major navies have used various auxiliary and combatant ships to perform electronic and visual surveillance and intelligence collection, only the superpowers, particularly the Soviet Union, have invested extensively in a fleet of dedicated intelligence ships.

The first Soviet auxiliary intelligence gatherers (AGIs), began appearing off the eastern coast of the United States in the late 1950s. Most were converted deep sea fishing trawlers, sprouting several antennas. Fishing trawlers offered several advantages as AGIs. They had the range and endurance necessary to remain on distant ocean stations for several weeks at a time. The large holds for storing fish offered ample space for the electronic cabinets and listening spaces needed in an AGI.

The first AGIs to appear were the seven 500-ton *Lentra* class ships. Built in East Germany in the mid 1950s as trawlers, they were converted to AGIs in the late 1950s. The fifteen larger 700-ton *Okean* class AGIs were the first class to be built in large numbers specifically for the intelligence role. During the mid 1970s the Soviets built six 3500-ton *Primoriye* class AGIs, using a modified stern-haul fishing trawler design. The *Primoriye*s, which could process the

Balzam, the name ship of a class of three Soviet AGIs, or intelligence gatherers. The two plastic domes house satellite transmitting and receiving equipment and there are numerous direction-finding and intercept arrays. The ship is protected by a SA-N-5/8 SAM point-defence system. (MoD, Crown Copyright)

intelligence data they collected, were followed by the purpose-built *Balzam* class.

Soviet AGIs were stationed off US and allied naval ports, particularly carrier and submarine bases, to observe the entry and departure of warships, especially attack carriers and ballistic missile submarines. AGIs also followed the Western fleets, in particular the US Navy's carrier battle groups.

The US Navy used former destroyers and converted cargo ships for intelligence gathering. The USS *Liberty*, one of the earliest converted cargo ships, was attacked by Israeli aircraft and torpedo boats in June 1967 while conducting surveillance operations off the Sinai. The Israeli government said it mistook the ship for an Egyptian transport, but the ship had been intercepting Israeli communications at a time when Israel was about to finish off the Syrian armed forces on the Golan Heights. Thirty-seven American sailors died in the attack. The ship was decommissioned after returning to the United States.

The following January, another former merchant ship converted to a US Navy intelligence gatherer, the *Pueblo*, was attacked and seized by North Korean patrol boats. The North Korean government claimed that the *Pueblo* was violating its territorial waters. One sailor was killed in the initial assault. The remaining 82 US sailors were held prisoner until December 1968, when the US government signed a confession.

Because of the vulnerability of unarmed intelligence collectors, highlighted by these incidents, the US Navy began to rely primarily on surface warships with temporary intelligence vans, or submarines, to gather intelligence.

Weapons and sensor test ships

The rapid growth in naval weapons and sensors in the postwar era led to the creation of an entirely new type of auxiliary warship, the test and trials ship. However, no ships are built just as test ships. Often, a navy will take an active duty combatant, change her equipment suite for several months while she serves as a test ship, and return her to her original configuration when the tests are completed. The US Navy used this method to test the *Oliver Hazard Perry* (FFG-7) class combat suite aboard the guided-missile frigate *Talbot* (FFG-4).

But at other times an active duty combatant or auxiliary warship will be converted to serve solely as a test or trials ship, with no intention to return her to her original configuration when the tests are completed.

The earliest postwar test ship was the battle-ship *Mississippi*. Built immediately after the First World War, she served as a battleship through the Second World War and in 1951–2 was rebuilt to carry the Terrier surface-to-air missile, developed as part of the US Navy's Project Bumblebee. *Mississippi* fired her first Terrier missile in July 1953. Terrier's operational evaluation was performed aboard the ship between July 1954 and late 1955; *Mississippi* was decommissioned in 1958.

The most widely used test ship in the US Navy was probably the *Norton Sound*. Built during the Second World War as a seaplane tender, she was converted in 1948 to serve as a guided-missile test ship. During the 1950s she launched Aerobee, V-1, Loon, Lark, Regulus, Terrier, Tartar and Sea Sparrow missiles and rockets. Between November 1962 and June 1964 she was converted to serve as the test ship for the Typhon air defence system, carrying an AN/SPG-59 radar above the pilot house. Typhon tests ran up to July 1966, when the radar was removed. Between 1965 and 1967 *Norton Sound* test fired the Standard MR and ER missiles, which replaced Tartar and Terrier. In 1968 a 5in/54cal Mk 45 gun mount and Mk 86 gunfire control system were added. *Norton Sound* received the prototype Aegis air defence system in 1975, when a one-face AN/SPY-1 radar was installed. This was followed in 1981 by a pre-production version of the Mk 41 vertical launch system for Standard and Tomahawk missiles. By 1986, with the Aegis cruiser programme well under way, *Norton Sound* was redundant to fleet requirements and she was decommissioned.

The Royal Navy had also used former surface combatant warships as trials ships. The heavy cruiser *Cumberland* was converted to a trials ship in 1949–51. Her 8in guns were removed; two single 4.5in Mk 4 and two STAAG 40mm Bofors guns were mounted, along with a Mk 37 director. These systems were removed in 1953 and replaced by a 3in/70 Mk 6 aft, with an MRS 3 director on the bridge. She also received a 6in Mk 26 automatic twin mount in 'B' position. After testing new stabilizers and propellers in the mid 1950s, she was decommissioned in late 1958.

In 1971 the Royal Navy took the 'Battle' class destroyer *Matapan*, removed her weapons and installed additional electronics cabinets, and she was then used as the test ship for the Type 2016 bow-mounted and Type 2031 towed array sonars. *Matapan* was decommissioned in 1978 at the end of the tests.

The Landing Craft Maintenance Ship *Girdle Ness* was used as the Seaslug missile test ship. *Girdle Ness*, built during the Second World War to support landing craft, was modified between October 1955 and July 1956 by the addition of a triple Seaslug launcher and the associated radars. Missile tests began in 1957 and continued until 1961; in 1962 *Girdle Ness* became an accommodation ship.

France has used both old and new surface combatants as weapons and sensor trials ships. When the destroyer *La Galissonière* was commissioned in 1962, she tested the Malfon antisubmarine missile. France took a different path in 1979, taking the twenty-year-old frigate *L'Agenais*, removing most of her armament, and installing a DSRX 61 FLUTE towed array for trials. In 1985 the old frigate *Commandant Rivière* relieved the *L'Agenais* as the French navy's sonar trials ship.

The British missile trials ship Girdle Ness *leaving Malta in December 1961 at the end of nearly five years of development work with the Seaslug SAM system. The big triple launcher forward was modified into a slightly less substantial twin mounting when the missile went into service aboard the 'County' class destroyers, but the basic handling arrangements were worked out in this ship.* (CMP)

The French navy used a war prize, the former German transport *Mur*, for their guided-missile tests. Converted to her trails role in 1958–59, she tested the Masurca and Masalca surface-to-air missiles and the Malaface surface-to-surface missile during the 1960s. During the 1970s and 1980s she tested the MM 38 and MM 40 Exocet surface-to-surface missiles and the Crotale point-defence missile system.

Aviation auxiliary ships

Most Western navies did not build any aviation support auxiliary ships during the postwar era. The US Navy had three classes of seaplane tenders, all built during the war and decommissioned during the 1960s, when the Navy stopped operating seaplanes. However, the Royal Navy bought a ship for use as an aircraft auxiliary in 1984. *Argus* was a container/vehicle cargo ship that was chartered in May 1982 to carry aircraft to the Falklands. Purchased outright in March 1984, she was converted to support aircraft. For her new role, *Argus*'s vehicle cargo decks were made into a four-section hangar deck for eight Sea Harriers and three Sea King-sized helicopters. Three more helicopters can be carried on the flight deck, and two aircraft elevators connect the flight deck and hangar deck. Although lacking a ski-jump, *Argus* can be used for combat operations.

Civilian-manned auxiliary warships

The growth in naval auxiliary warship strength during the postwar era led some of the larger navies to organise civilian-manned organisations to operate their auxiliary fleets. These organisations, including the US Navy's Military Sealift Command and the Royal Navy's Royal Fleet Auxiliary service, used civilian merchant marine crews rather than uniformed personnel.

Operating these ships with civilian crews allowed major cost savings. When the US Navy transferred the *Missipilion* class oilers from the Navy to the MSC, the crew size decreased from 350 to 120 men because of the reduced need for bridge watchstanders. Civilian-manned auxiliaries were also less costly to operate because civilian merchant crews did not have the sea/shore rotation that navy personnel have increasingly come to expect since 1945.

One of the largest auxiliary fleets is the US Navy's Military Sealift Command (MSC). The MSC originally was organised in 1949 as the Naval Ocean Transport Service. It became the Military Sea Transportation Service (MSTS) in 1949. MSTS's merchant marine and naval crews manned the troop transports, cargo freighters and tankers used to transport US military personnel, their dependants, and Department of Defence cargoes throughout the world.

With a paucity of operational flight decks available, the Royal Navy has always been keen to transfer aviation training duties away from the main fleet. The Engadine, a specialist RFA-manned helicopter support ship, was built in the 1960s, but recently has been replaced by a converted container/ro-ro ship renamed Argus, seen here in her new role as an aviation training ship. As the mercantile Contender Bezant, this ship served as an aircraft transport during the Falklands War, but was purchased outright and given a major reconstruction during 1984–88. (Harland & Wolff)

During the late 1960s the growth of commercial air transports and the Military Airlift Command made the Navy's troop transports unnecessary, and they were decommissioned. The growth of commercial cargo carriers meant that fewer ships could transport more goods. In August 1970 MSTS changed its name to MSC, and ended the practice of having some ships manned by naval crews. This was followed by a change of mission in 1973, as the Navy began transferring its underway replenishment oilers to MSC control.

Britain's Royal Fleet Auxiliary has a much longer history. The service operated many of the support ships and fleet train ships for the Royal Navy during the Second World War. In contrast to the US Navy, which keeps its AOEs, AORs and most AEs under naval control, all of the Royal Navy's auxiliaries are operated by the RFA or the Royal Maritime Auxiliary Service, which operates harbour craft, tugs and survey ships.

Coast Guard organisations

The postwar era has also seen the growth of Coast Guard organisations in many nations. Most have been modelled on the US Coast Guard and prevent smuggling, control offshore pollution, ensure the accessibility of harbours, and perform offshore border patrol. In addition to the United States, Canada, India, and Japan also operate sizeable Coast Guards.

The future of naval auxiliaries

A replenishment at sea capability remains a high priority for many navies. The vast allied naval presence gathered for Operation Desert Storm, and the continuing requirements for out-of-area operations, have shown the continued need for ships with this capability. Even as most Western navies contract in size, underway replenishment ships remain high on their priority lists. The United States, Great Britain, Spain, and the Netherlands are all building modern unrep ships.

The tendency towards manning these ships with civilian merchant mariners is expected to grow among the major maritime powers, but not among the smaller nations. Most of the larger nations have enough jobless civilian merchant mariners to be able to afford this practice. Many smaller nations lack the merchant marine manpower pools to crew naval auxiliaries.

Repair ships will not be as high a priority, because of their less hectic operational schedule. Spending most of their time in port or at anchor, repair ships seldom endure the strains placed on surface combatants and amphibious ships, so existing vessels may survive for many years.

However, the growing interest in the offshore economic zones will create a steady need for hydrographic and oceanographic ships, and vessels of less capability than frontline warships to police them.

David Steigman

The US Coast Guard is the largest and best equipped of the world's maritime paramilitary forces. In wartime it has always had a frontline role, and its ships are designed with employment as auxiliary warships in mind. Most capable of the USCG's current inventory are the high endurance cutters of the Hamilton class, represented here by Chase. Combined diesel and gas turbine propulsion give these 3000-ton ships the high top speed of 29kts and a substantial range – up to 14,000nm at 11kts on diesels. (L & L van Ginderen)

Naval Auxiliaries: Typical Classes, since 1945

Class	Type	Nationality	Displacement full load (tons)	Dimensions overall (feet-inches) (metres)	Capacity	Machinery/ Speed (kts)	Launch dates	Numbers built
Replenishment ships								
NEOSHO	AO	American	38,000	655-0 × 86-0 × 35-0 *199.6 × 26.2 × 10.7*	180,000 barrels	ST/20	1953–55	6
SURIBACHI	AE	American	15,500	512-0 × 72-0 × 29-0 *156.1 × 21.9 × 8.8*	7500t	ST/20.5	1955–56	2 (plus 3 similar)
SACRAMENTO	AOE	American	53,600	791-8 × 107-9 × 38-0 *241.4 × 32.9 × 11.6*	177,000 barrels, 2150t munitions, 500t dry stores, 250t refrigerated	ST/26	1963–69	4
POOLSTER	AOR	Dutch	16,836	552-4 × 66-6 × 26-9 *168.4 × 20.3 × 8.2*	8000t liquid, 2300t dry	ST/21	1963	1 (plus 1 improved)
OLWEN	AO	British	36,000	647-8 × 84-0 × 34-4 *197.5 × 25.6 × 10.5*	18,400t fuel, 1720t diesel, 130t lub oil, 3700t Avcat, 280t Mogas	ST/19	1964–65	3
LYNESS	AFS	British	16,792	524-0 × 72-0 × 22-0 *159.7 × 22.0 × 6.7*	7782t	D/18	1966–67	3
PROTECTEUR	AOR	Canadian	24,700	564-0 × 76-0 × 30-0 *172.0 × 23.2 × 9.1*	13,100t fuel, 600t diesel, 400t Avgas, 1048t dry, 1250t munitions	ST/21	1968–69	2
WICHITA	AOR	American	41,350	659-0 × 96-1 × 33-1 *200.9 × 29.3 × 10.1*	175,000 barrels, 600t munitions, 425t dry, 150t refrigerated	ST/20	1968–74	7
BORIS CHILIKIN	AOR	Soviet	24,500	532-3 × 70-2 × 37-7 *162.3 × 21.4 × 11.5*	13,500t liquid, 400t munitions, 400t provisions, 400t stores	D/17	1971–78	6
DURANCE	AOR	French	17,800	515-6 × 69-5 × 28-5 *157.2 × 21.2 × 8.7*	7500t fuel, 1500t diesel, 500t JP-5, 130t distilled water, 370t stores and munitions	D/20	1975–87	6
FORT GRANGE	AFS	British	22,749	603-0 × 79-0 × 28-2 *183.9 × 24.1 × 8.6*	3500t munitions, food and spares	D/20	1976–78	2
BEREZINA (Project 1859)	AOR	Soviet	36,000	688-8 × 82-0 × 32-8 *210.0 × 25.0 × 10.0*	16,000t fuel, 2000t provisions, 500t water	D/21	1978	1
Tenders								
DON	AS	Soviet	9000	459-3 × 57-7 × 17-7 *140.0 × 17.7 × 6.4*	Logistic support for 8–12 submarines	D/17	1958–61	7
SAMUEL GOMPERS	AD	American	22,260	643-0 × 85-0 × 22-6 *196.1 × 25.9 × 6.9*	Can support gas turbine and nuclear surface combatants	ST/20	1967–83	6 (plus 5 similar AS)
Miscellaneous								
NORTON SOUND	AVM	American	15,170	543-3 × 71-6 × 23-5 *165.6 × 21.8 × 7.2*	Missile test ship, various configurations	ST/19	Converted 1948	1
BALZAM	AGI	Soviet	5400	346-0 × 50-9 × 19-0 *105.5 × 15.5 × 5.8*	ELINT equipment	D/22	1979–82	3
MERCY	T-AH	American	69,360	893-11 × 105-7 × 32-10 *272.5 × 32.2 × 10.0*	1000-bed ward, 80-bed intensive care, burns unit, etc	ST/17.5	Converted 1984–87	2
ARGUS	AVT	British	28,480	574-5 × 99-7 × 27-0 *175.1 × 30.4 × 8.2*	3500t diesel, 1100t avgas; 12 aircraft, 6 helicopters	D/19	Converted 1984–88	1

Machinery abbreviations:
ST = steam turbines; D = diesel.

Type abbreviations:
AO = fleet oiler; AE = ammunition ship; AOE = fast combat support ship; AOR = fleet replenishment oiler; AFS = combat store ship; AD = destroyer tender; AS = submarine tender; AVM = missile trials ships; AGI = intelligence gathering ship; T-AH = hospital ship; AVT = aviation training ship.

8

Nuclear Weapons and Navies

NUCLEAR weapons were probably the single most important influence on post 1945 navies. At first, in 1945, it seemed that the atomic bomb was the ultimate weapon, capable of levelling a city with a single blow. Many strategists accepted that future war would be a very short atomic blitz, and that even air defence might soon be irrelevant. Through the later 1940s it was realised that existing weapons, with yields of about 20 kilotons (kT), were powerful yet limited. A war fought with such weapons might continue for some considerable time. Naval forces might well perform their usual roles. Stalin's willingness to fight in Korea in 1950 seemed to show that atomic weapons had only limited deterrence effect, and that the Third World War, if it came, might not be altogether different from the Second. Western governments found this conclusion particularly unhappy because it implied that they would have to maintain massive forces, including large navies, to face the large Soviet military machine. In 1953, however, the United States demonstrated a new kind of weapon, the hydrogen bomb. It had about a thousand times the explosive power of the 1945 atomic bomb, and it really could do what the atomic theorists of that time had imagined. It could change war altogether. For example, it offered the possibility

that a few high-tech weapons, such as advanced bombers, could indeed deal with massive Soviet forces.

Ironically, unbeknownst to the West, the Soviets were finding it more and more difficult to field massive ground forces (largely because they were suffering from the demographic effects of their own massacres of the 1930s, plus those of the Second World War). Khrushchev came to power with exactly the same requirements as his Western counterparts. He too had to find some substitute for expensive conventional manpower; he too found that substitute in nuclear weapons.

On both sides, the advent of such weapons, and particularly of H-bombs, seemed to promise that any future war would be both short and extremely destructive. At first both sides imagined that the weapons would be used quite freely. The enmity of the Soviets was clearly quite deep and well-proven; surely they would use the most effective weapons they had. Soviet thinking was slightly more complex. It was taken for granted that the West would fall upon the Soviet Union to prevent its own destruction by the 'forces of history'. Khrushchev added the idea that nuclear weapons alone offered decisive results. That was generally read in the West to mean that they would be used from the outset.

However, it also seems fair to read Khrushchev's words (which his successors continued to use) to mean that such weapons alone could be decisive *against* the Soviet Union, whose vast territory and resources had precluded a German victory despite the manifold errors Stalin had committed before and during the war. He therefore became vitally interested in deterring the West from using nuclear weapons. As a corollary, should a war begin with a non-nuclear phase, efforts would be concentrated on destroying Western nuclear weapons and their platforms – including aircraft carriers and strategic submarines.

Nuclear weapons are clearly unlike all others in their capacity to inspire awe. What is often not realised is the extent to which governments insist on very tight control. For example, for many years it was believed in the West that all Soviet nuclear weapons were under specific KGB control (there is now evidence that at least in some cases the military service has custody, at least in peacetime; the KGB may, however, control vital elements of the weapon, which are not installed in peacetime). At least from the early 1960s, enormous effort has gone into preventing unauthorised use, even if the ship or submarine carrying the weapons is on the point of destruction. In the US case, the President must specifically authorise use, often by transmitting a special code. The Russians claim that they use an even more secure system, in which the military and the civilian authorities transmit separate codes which must be combined before a weapon can be released.

All such measures are both reasonable and operationally acceptable in the case of strategic weapons. However, there is little inherent difference between a bomb designed to flatten a city and, say, a nuclear depth bomb or the war-

Future naval war as anticipated in 1945: the hulk of the US light fleet carrier Independence *after exposure to atomic blast at the Bikini island test on 1 July 1946. The employment of weapons of such unprecedented power seemed to question every tenet of traditional naval strategy and tactics.* (CMP)

In a nuclear war, besides the effects of blast and electro-magnetic pulse (EMP), ships had to deal with the novel threat of radiation. Ships were designed to be commanded, and sometimes fought, from inside sealed citadels, while elaborate pipework allowed 'prewetting', to insulate the ship by letting the nuclear fallout flow off the vessel in the water sprays. As demonstrated by the British carrier Hermes, *this was a dramatic procedure, but careful attention had to be paid to the run-off of contaminated water, and it is noticeable that the flow from the flight deck scuppers is directly into the sea. (CMP)*

head of a nuclear-tipped air defence missile. Those weapons, too, are subject to elaborate controls. These efforts raise the interesting question of just how usable tactical nuclear weapons are, particularly for defensive purposes (such as ASW). As a consequence, at least in the West, professional scepticism as to the value of naval tactical nuclear weapons grew through the 1980s. However, many naval officers believed that only such weapons could deter the Soviets from using their own tactical nuclear missiles and torpedoes against Western navies. These weapons were removed from deployed ships under a 1991 agreement between President George Bush and President Yeltsin.

Ship design

Before their removal, they had real effects on Western warship design. Because they might not be released for use, every nuclear weapon had to have a non-nuclear counterpart. For example, in the US Navy the alternative to a nuclear depth bomb was usually a Mk 46 torpedo. Two tactical nuclear weapons *without* non-nuclear

counterparts, the Astor (Mk 45) torpedo and the Subroc missile, were retired precisely because they could not always be used. When they were carried, nuclear and non-nuclear weapons competed for space in the same magazines. Such space was inevitably limited. For example, some US frigates carried only eight Asroc anti-submarine missiles, in a simple box launcher. Each attack on a submarine required at least two of them. Carrying a pair of nuclear Asrocs (the conventional alternative carried a torpedo) would reduce the ship's ability to attack submarines by a quarter. Furthermore, handling nuclear weapons required special procedures. In the case of Asroc, that grossly increased the time taken to reload a missile, and the same procedure had to be followed whether or not the specific weapon in question had a nuclear warhead. Nuclear magazines also required special armed guards, even at sea.

A ship using nuclear weapons needed special design features. For example, even when exploded several miles away, a nuclear depth bomb would create a powerful shock wave. The ship had to be specially designed to survive it. Shock is a very subtle effect, and design provisions were often elaborate. Incidentally, the *lack* of shock-proofing made it very difficult to use Second World War hulls postwar. For example, it seemed obvious that cast-iron machinery mountings would fracture relatively easily. That was one reason the British postwar programmes to convert war-built destroyers to frigates were abandoned. Given the difficulty of true shock-proofing, many officers doubted that their ships would really survive the effects of their own nuclear depth bombs (projected by helicopter

or Asroc). Similarly, helicopter delivery of nuclear depth bombs was always considered quite hazardous, as the helicopter might be caught in the blast of the bomb (the Soviets estimated that a helicopter pilot delivering such a weapon had only a 50–50 chance of surviving).

Nuclear anti-aircraft weapons would create pressure and heat waves, quite aside from radiation. In the late 1950s the US Navy tried to deal with the problem by requiring that ships survive an overpressure of 10lb per square inch (psi). Hulls could already survive 50psi, but antennas could not. Superstructures had to be carried down into hull strength members so that they would not be swept overboard (that is why so many US surface combatants of the 1950s and 1960s have flat-faced bridges, which are upward continuations of major bulkheads). The Second World War *Cleveland* class cruiser *Atlanta* was converted to resemble a modern missile ship and subjected in 1964 to the shock wave created by a thousand tons of explosives. Many of her antennas did not survive, despite special design efforts. On the other hand, carrier strength standards were set by the perceived threat of Soviet nuclear anti-ship weapons. For carriers, the standard for overpressure was set in the 1950s by the pressure produced by a 5 megaton bomb burst over a neighbouring carrier in a dispersed formation.

More generally, navies became interested in means of shielding a ship and her crew from nuclear effects. The subtlest of these is electro-magnetic pulse (EMP). A large bomb exploded above the atmosphere creates a shower of very powerful electrical signals, comparable to (but much stronger than) those in a lightning storm.

The possible use of nuclear weapons at sea placed an even greater emphasis on analysing the effects of shock to produce more effective shock-proofing. In this postwar American test against the old destroyer Howorth *(DD-592), note the disturbance under the stern caused by the 'whipping' of the hull following the torpedo explosion amidships. It proved extremely difficult to counter such effects in existing ships, and postwar modernisation programmes were sometimes given up for just this reason.* (USN)

The resulting electrical shock can knock out electronic equipment, particularly modern solid-state units. However, any such unit completely enclosed within a metal cage (such as an unbroken superstructure) should be safe. Doors in superstructures can be recessed in metal passages which approximate wave-guides, and which therefore cut off EMP above or below some fixed frequency. Other anti-EMP measures included attempts to earth all exposed potential antennas, such as lifelines. The Soviets seem to have paid special attention to such efforts, and for years this was taken as evidence of a particular willingness to use nuclear weapons at sea. For example, they replaced their wire lifelines with glassfibre ones. That also reduced radar cross-section (during the Gulf War, the Royal Australian Navy draped radar-absorbing material over its lifelines); the metal lifelines also soaked up the energy of high-frequency radio signals, and thus substantially reduced the ships' overall radio range.

After the 1946 Bikini bomb test, US designers adopted funnel caps specially shaped to overcome the overpressure of a nuclear explosion. Ships in Western navies were fitted with special sprays to wet them down so that nuclear fallout would flow off. Sharp deck edges were adopted specifically to keep the radioactive water from flowing along the hull and thus contaminating the ship.

Nuclear strategy

Compared with their conventional predecessors, nuclear weapons offered navies infinitely more potential to affect events ashore. However, it was soon also obvious that a nuclear war would probably be extremely short. Classical naval strategy offers long-term assaults on an enemy: blockades, gradual envelopments around the enemy's periphery. Thus it seemed

The Australian destroyer Brisbane *during the Gulf War, with radar-absorbing covers to all her lifelines.* (RAN)

that the bomb gave overwhelming power but took away much of the traditional role of naval power. The realisation of this stark combination was probably most marked in Britain, particularly during the major defence review of 1957. It accounted for the decisions to scrap the reserve fleet and to wind up Coastal Forces. British anti-submarine efforts shifted from a mix of trade and naval force protection to an emphasis on the protection of Nato Strike Fleet carriers (including British units) which were to deliver nuclear weapons against the Soviet Union. To some extent, the starkness of the picture was relieved, for the Royal Navy, by the continuing need to police the Commonwealth.

The US Navy, which enjoyed more resources,

argued that matters did not admit so drastic a choice. Once the main enemy, the Soviet Union, had the bomb, neither side could freely use nuclear weapons. The US conclusion was not that maritime war would revert to its previous long-term character, but more that conflict between the two blocs would shift towards the periphery of Eurasia, where Western navies might operate relatively freely. As for Europe, after 1960 it became increasingly obvious that Nato would not welcome early use of nuclear weapons, which the Soviets also possessed. Thus even a major war might go on for some time (perhaps even to a conclusion) without involving nuclear weapons. That brought back a very real trade protection role, since the Nato forces fighting on land would need replenishment. Indeed, without protection for their sea communications, they might be unable to survive without using their nuclear weapons. Thus within two decades nuclear weapons came to form a vital backdrop to war, even though it was accepted that war itself might well be entirely non-nuclear.

At first the bomb was, if anything, overrated. Although the United States had very few bombs, the US and British governments assumed that Stalin would not dare risk war until he had enough bombs of his own. The central concept of the early postwar period was the target year for preparedness, the 'year of maximum danger'. The British remembered that, when Hitler's enmity became obvious in 1934, their government had estimated, with eerie accuracy, that war might come in five years (presumably this was a conscious reversal of the former 'Ten Year Rule', the assertion that war would not

The two naval contributions to a nuclear land war were provided by missiles or carrier-based bombers. The first viable nuclear attack missile was the Regulus I, shown being launched from the purpose-built USS Halibut, the only American nuclear-powered cruise missile submarine. Beyond is the Lexington, *at that time (1961) still an attack carrier. (CMP)*

come within ten years, which was widely credited with sapping British military power).

This time no one wanted to pronounce a Ten Year Rule. On the other hand, neither wartime ally was particularly anxious (or able) to remain mobilised after victory over Germany and Japan. Moreover, a future war would probably require investment in new technology. When would it be needed? It appears that both governments assumed that it would take Stalin about five years to manufacture enough bombs after he tested his prototype. After Stalin clearly showed his aggressive ambitions in 1948 (by overthrowing the Czech government), the two main wartime Western allies began to rearm. Their advisors estimated that Stalin could not have the bomb before 1952. That made 1957 the 'year of maximum danger', and the target for British naval and other military modernisation. When Stalin exploded his bomb in 1949, the crisis year moved up to 1954, and the US government planned massive rearmament, largely conventional, under a policy document called NSC-68 (the US rearmament for Korea, which was perceived as the opening move of Stalin's big war, was largely according to NSC-68).

Navies could offer two means of delivering atomic bombs to targets ashore: carrier aircraft and submarine- or ship-launched missiles. The US Navy naturally emphasised carrier aircraft while developing missiles to supplement them. The Soviets, who could not develop carriers, emphasised cruise and ballistic missiles modelled on German prototypes they had captured.

At about 10,000lb, the first atomic bombs were too heavy for existing carrier aircraft to deliver, and the US Air Force defeated a US attempt to build a carrier, USS *United States*, large enough to accommodate long-range bombers big enough to carry them (it scarcely wanted to lose its monopoly on nuclear delivery). Even so, the US Navy managed to develop a carrier capability with aircraft such as the AJ-1 (A-2) Savage and then the A3D (A-3) Sky-

warrior. Carrier modernisation, particularly the provision of steam catapults, was largely driven by the need to accommodate such aircraft. Moreover, from the late 1940s onwards, far more compact weapons were developed, eventually deliverable by fighter-bombers and by small carrier bombers, such as the A-4 Skyhawk. The new weapons could also be delivered by Regulus cruise missiles small enough to be fired from submarines, cruisers, and some aircraft carriers. A decade later the key to developing Polaris was the promise of a new generation of very light-weight hydrogen bombs, which could be lifted by a small solid-fuel rocket.

The significance of these nuclear weapons depended on US national strategy. The concept of *containment* was formulated in 1946–47: instead of trying to roll back the Soviets, the United States and her allies would try to deny them the two great nearby industrial centres of Western Europe and Japan. The Soviet threat was both military and economic: there was a real fear that building forces powerful enough to counter the Soviet military would so impoverish the West as to defeat it without war. It was generally assumed (incorrectly, as it turned out) that Stalin had not demobilised in 1945. The Soviet-backed coup in Czechoslovakia in 1948 and the blockade of Berlin a year later seemed to show that Stalin was willing to try his luck, even though as yet he lacked nuclear weapons (he almost certainly did not lack intelligence to the effect that the US nuclear arsenal was still extremely limited). A series of studies showed that enormous forces would be needed to counter the vast Russian army. The US Air Force argued that, armed with atomic bombs, its strategic bombers could win a future central war virtually single-handed; it argued that the navy should be reduced to a sea control force maintaining the security of its overseas bases (which might not even be needed once the intercontinental B-36 bomber entered service).

The Korean War suggested otherwise. The

The size of early nuclear weapons demanded large aircraft to carry them and the US Navy's A3D Skywarrior, initially designed for this purpose, remained the largest and heaviest aircraft regularly deployed to carriers throughout its long service career. An A3D-2 is shown landing aboard USS Ticonderoga (CV-14) in 1963, with another visible beyond. (CMP)

fare around the Eurasian periphery, where air bases might be scarce. This task, rather than the strategic attack envisaged in the late 1940s, largely justified the continued construction of powerful new aircraft carriers.

Tactical nuclear weapons

Free use of nuclear weapons clearly extended to dealing with enemy aircraft and submarines. The US nuclear build-up after 1948 eventually produced so much bomb material that nuclear depth bombs and nuclear warheads for the new Talos and Terrier anti-aircraft missiles (and even nuclear 8in and 16in shells) became available. Later the great question would be whether conventional weapons, particularly for anti-submarine warfare, could match the potential of the nuclear ones. For example, it was feared that no torpedo fast enough to deal with nuclear submarines could hear past the sound of the water rushing past its nose (the US Mk 48 solved the problem by running out at high speed until it approached the area in which the submarine was expected to be, then homing at lower

Soviets might well choose to fight along the Eurasian periphery, and the West could not really afford to abandon much of that area. Apocalyptic attacks on the Soviet Union would not be terribly appropriate. It seemed that traditional forces would, after all, be needed. For example, the US Navy began work on a new generation of non-nuclear tactical missiles such as Bullpup and bombs such as Snakeye and Rockeye. However, as the pre-1950 analysts had known, even a medium-sized conventional war like that in Korea was terribly expensive. In 1953 President Eisenhower entered office determined to avoid another Korea. The Cold War would probably last for many decades, and the United States could not afford periodic fiscal disasters. Because they were so destructive, a few nuclear weapons could do much the same job as numerous far more expensive conventional ones, drastically reducing the cost of preparing for war (there seems to have been little thought at first about the Soviet ability to match Western tactical nuclear weapons, thus deterring their use). Although he rejected the

air force's simple war-making concept, Eisenhower accepted a national strategy in which the United States would cut its costs by replying to Soviet aggression at 'a time and place of [its own] choosing', freely using tactical nuclear weapons. Naval tactical nuclear weapons, on board carrier aircraft, were clearly vital in war-

The perfection of the Aegis air defence system, with its ability to withstand saturation raids, has made the employment of tactical nuclear SAMs to destroy bomber concentrations less likely. The system first went to sea in the Ticonderoga *(CG-47) in 1982, and the panels of its SPY-1A radar can be seen on the bridge front and the hangar side in this view of the ship. (L & L van Ginderen)*

speed). Nuclear depth bombs were widely deployed, including to some Nato countries (under US control). They were more often intended for carriage by patrol aircraft than by shipboard helicopters.

In the case of air defence, atomic weapons were expected to complement conventional ones. Conventional anti-aircraft systems could not engage many targets in very fast succession. Thus the natural counter to such weapons was to concentrate bombers or missiles to saturate the defence. The existence of defensive nuclear weapons solved the problem, at least in theory, since a single nuclear explosion could destroy the concentration. Similarly, it appeared that once an anti-saturation system, Aegis, had been devised, nuclear anti-aircraft warheads could be abandoned. One reason was that a nuclear burst would create transient electronic blackout conditions, which might allow a follow-up strike to pass through defences unmolested (for example, radar could not see through the fireball). It might also produce short range EMP.

In a larger sense, there was increasingly a real question as to the circumstances under which nuclear defensive weapons might be used. The Soviets used both nuclear and non-nuclear anti-ship missiles; there was no simple way to distinguish the different versions of the same weapon. In theory, the US fleet might be allowed to use its nuclear weapons after the Soviets had used theirs in action (presumably in insufficient numbers to destroy the entire US fleet). However, there had to be a real fear that such use might be authorised in error, so that nuclear war would begin at sea (without much forethought), and then spread ashore; it might be that *any* use of a nuclear weapon would break the general taboo. Such fears made withdrawal of existing tactical nuclear weapons easier. After all, the ultimate deterrent to a Soviet nuclear strike on Western carriers was surely the threat of dropping nuclear weapons ashore, and those weapons need not come from the sea.

Nuclear warheads also seemed to be the only means of providing anti-aircraft weapons with effective anti-ship capability. The missiles could not easily home on surface targets, but they could be directed into the vicinity of those targets. In the US Navy, this argument was probably last made in connection with the abortive Typhon anti-aircraft system, devised about 1958. At about the same time the Royal Navy was intensely interested in a nuclear warhead for Seaslug. By the early 1960s improved semi-active homing made it possible for anti-aircraft missiles to hit surface ships, at least out to the horizon, and anti-ship capability was dropped as a motive for nuclear warheads.

Deterrence and flexible response

The US Air Force of the 1950s concentrated on its own apocalyptic war plan against the Soviets, which it argued would require thousands of weapons (most of which were now the much more powerful H-bombs rather than the A-bombs used against Japan in 1945). The navy could not possibly deliver anything like the nuclear tonnage the air force wanted, which the navy's leaders assumed was necessary. Naval strategic weapons, on board carrier bombers and missiles, could help dilute Soviet strategic defences and thus could make the air force's task easier.

In 1956, however, President Eisenhower was asked to authorise an increase in the number of

The advent of the submarine-launched ballistic missile, in the form of Polaris, radically altered what navies could offer at the strategic level. Because it could be launched from underwater, the launch vehicle was not only mobile but very different to track, vastly reducing the chance of significant losses to a first strike. This made Polaris a far more credible deterrent. (CMP)

US strategic weapons, largely for the air campaign. Although he did so, he was sceptical: he asked the army and the navy separately to evaluate the air force war plan. The new CNO, Admiral Arleigh Burke, was shocked to discover that the air force was assigning so many weapons to each target. Yet each could be killed only once. The navy could indeed match the level of useful destruction the air force offered. That was the real origin of the Polaris missile system. Regulus had been a relatively minor contribution to national strategic firepower; Polaris was conceived as a key element, quite equal to what the air force could wield.

Meanwhile, national strategy shifted in another way. In the 1950s, the United States built up forces mainly to deal with a possible Soviet military threat to Western Europe. It was tacitly assumed that any Soviet strategic threat to the United States could be dealt with: an immense sum was invested in the North American air defence system. However, from about 1956 it became clear that the Soviets were developing long range strategic missiles, against which defence would be impossible. Moreover, it was shown that the air force's own strategic bombers could not take off in time to avoid destruction by incoming attackers. US national strategy began to shift towards *deterring* a Soviet attack, either on Europe or on the United States. It also became clear that, at least in Eurasia, the United States could no longer expect to use tactical nuclear weapons. Any future medium war would be at least as expensive as Korea, as Vietnam showed.

As for Europe, it was clear that Nato could not fire nuclear weapons at the outset of any Soviet attack. It had to hope that the threat of escalation would convince the Soviets to stop. Eventually, in the mid 1960s, a doctrine of flexible response was agreed: Nato would initially resist without resorting to nuclear fire, but would be willing to escalate in advance of the Soviets, if need be. Nato would fire a 'nuclear shot across the bows' if the Soviets advanced despite its initial non-nuclear resistance. The Alliance partners were still quite unwilling to pay the high price of a conventional counter to the big Soviet army. One fear, only rarely expressed, was that Nato politicians would decide that the 'shot across the bows' should be a literal description: better to burst a nuclear weapon at sea than on their lands. In that case Nato might well suffer terribly. Surface ships are quite vulnerable to nuclear attack, so a nuclear war at sea would probably go much against the Alliance. It was never clear whether the Soviets would hesitate to use their own naval tactical nuclear weapons, which existed in great variety; but any Nato expression favouring early Nato use would surely encourage them.

By about 1980, many Americans had become convinced that no European war would ever escalate to a nuclear exchange, because both superpowers had far too much to lose. It might be necessary to fight a protracted Second World War-style conflict in the shadow of a nuclear threat. This was hardly a theoretical point, because it meant that a whole arsenal of tactical nuclear weapons was virtually useless, and that immense investments in non-nuclear capability might be necessary.

The policy shifts are obvious mainly in retrospect. Most of the central decisions were not widely discussed. In particular, the nuclear concepts of the 1950s promised that relatively few weapons would suffice. That was fortunate, since the guided weapons of the time were extremely expensive. They were also quite large, so ships of reasonable size could not carry very many. As nuclear use became less and less likely, numbers (*eg* magazine capacities) did not grow, because the weapons themselves did not shrink. Moreover, nuclear weapons always promised that wars would be short (if horribly destructive), so there was little need to maintain stockpiles or a national mobilisation base of the sort inspired by earlier conflicts. Remarkably, the decline of the nuclear weapons did not inspire any reversion to past ideas of lengthy and expensive war-fighting. Fortunately, the collapse of the Cold War protected the West from the discovery that limiting stocks to about thirty days' worth of ammunition (to contain costs) did not guarantee that a future war would not extend to day thirty-one.

Even so, some remnants of earlier ideas survived. US warships could not carry very many anti-aircraft missiles, so they were provided with a means of taking more on board at sea. That in turn much affected their design (open spaces for missile strike-down were required, and missile magazines had to load from above), and limited the dimensions of the missiles themselves. In practice, such transfers were extremely difficult, and were rarely carried out.

For the United States, naval nuclear weapons had another significance. The Soviets paid special attention to Western nuclear weapons, on the theory that they alone could bring decisive results in a major war (otherwise the sheer size of the Soviet Union would presumably stop any Western advance). Soviet strategy emphasised early attacks on nuclear-capable ships and aircraft, even if the war had not yet reached a nuclear stage (Western strategists thought more in terms of escalation from a non-nuclear to a possible nuclear stage, the theory being that both sides would draw back before they reached an uncontrollable nuclear exchange). Thus it could be expected that the Soviets would open the war with strikes against the main US nuclear-armed surface ships, the strike carriers.

From the 1970s onwards, Tomahawk cruise missiles presented an interesting alternative. Nuclear capability could now be dispersed over numerous surface ships and attack submarines. To eliminate US naval nuclear capability at the outset, the Soviets would have to track not just twelve or fifteen carriers, but some hundreds of ships. They probably would be unable to do so. Thus merely deploying a new kind of nuclear weapon drastically changed potential Soviet capability during the initial *non-nuclear* phase of a major war.

The US Maritime Strategy of the 1980s used another version of this logic. The only important Soviet naval asset was the fleet of strategic nuclear submarines (SSBNs). Westerners assumed that neither side would ever use its SSBNs. However, the Soviets might well use their attack submarines against vital shipping between North America and Europe. The Soviets expected to attack Western SSBNs, and assumed that Western navies would attack their own. They built up bastion defences, which necessarily included much of their own attack submarine force. The Maritime Strategy emphasised the attack on the bastions, in the hope that the Soviets would continue to defend them actively, reducing the threat to open-ocean shipping. This strategy in turn inspired the design of the US *Seawolf* and of the Sea Lance stand-off ASW weapon.

The other element of bastion attack was the announced intention to send a multi-carrier strike group into the Norwegian Sea. Given their view, that nuclear-capable ships were the first priority, the Soviets would have to attack the carriers with both submarines and land-based missile-firing bombers. Unlike other possible bomber targets (such as merchant ships or frigates), the carrier groups would be quite capable of destroying the bombers *in the air*,

The British carrier Eagle *with two of her Buccaneer strike bombers in 1964. The Royal Navy originally argued for nuclear bombs (and the Buccaneers to carry them) as a counter to the powerful Soviet cruisers of the* Sverdlov *class, but they clearly had limited land-attack possibilities as well. However, when the Royal Navy acquired the country's strategic nuclear deterrent, in the form of Polaris submarines, the Royal Air Force had enough political influence to get the replacement carriers cancelled.* (MoD, Crown Copyright)

before they could fire their missiles. Similarly, Soviet submarines not tied down in bastion defence would presumably be forced to engage the heavily-armed carrier groups, which would turn into killing zones (in effect, classic convoys). Thus the Soviet emphasis on nuclear weapons and on bastion defence could be turned to force them into early and potentially decisive battle, clearing the way for Nato shipping.

The air engagement idea in particular seemed practicable only because of the advent of a very high-capacity air defence weapon system, Aegis. Because Aegis seemed capable of dealing with any missiles fired by any bombers which did not fall early victim to the battle group's long range fighters, the carrier fighters could concentrate on the bombers (without Aegis, they would have tried, probably with few results, to shoot down the missiles once they had been launched). The point of attacking the bombers was that they were extremely capable, yet relatively few, their crews carefully trained and thus irreplaceable.

Britain and nuclear weapons

As in the United States, Britain's Royal Air Force bitterly resisted attempts to place nuclear weapons on board aircraft carriers. The Royal Navy was first able to obtain them, in the late 1950s, on the ground that they were needed to deal with raiding *Sverdlov* class cruisers. Clearly they provided much more in the form of a strike capability. Again as in the United States, the air

force ultimately did not mind a few weapons being carried by naval strike aircraft; how could they matter when it would take thousands to deal with the Soviet Union, and when the RAF alone could contribute many hundreds of bomber-loads? Polaris was a very different proposition.

The Royal Navy followed Polaris with enormous interest. Like its US cousin, the RAF used the central strategic mission to assert its dominance over the navy. About 1954 the Royal Navy began to argue that within a few years the RAF's fixed air bases would be easy targets for the coming generation of Soviet ballistic missiles, against which defence would be difficult or impossible. Soon only a submarine-launched missile, essentially invulnerable, would be a viable deterrent. The Royal Navy won this argument in 1962, when the Royal Air Force had to withdraw from deterrent operation as its next-generation stand-off missile, the US Skybolt, was cancelled.

By this time replacements for the war-built British carriers were nearly due. It is fairly clear in retrospect that Britain could not have afforded both the new carriers and Polaris without some massive defence cut elsewhere. Having lost its strategic mission, the RAF was the obvious candidate. It fought back successfully, and the British replacement carrier was cancelled in 1965. That undermined the weapons programme for carrier group escorts. It also eliminated the principal British anti-ship weapon, the carrier-borne strike fighter.

Nuclear weapons did survive in the Royal Navy surface force, in the form of a dual-purpose nuclear depth bomb, WE 177, which could also be used to attack tactical targets ashore. It was carried on board frigates (for delivery by helicopters) and on board the three light carriers, for delivery by ASW helicopters and Harriers. In the latter case it seems to have been conceived as a substitute for the much heavier conventional firepower which earlier and larger British carriers offered. During the 1980s, the Royal Navy generally argued that it had to retain nuclear depth bombs mainly to counter the threat of very high-performance Soviet submarines (particularly the *Alfa* class).

The Soviet perspective

The Soviet view was very different. In Stalin's view, the West would probably use naval forces as the United States had in the Pacific, to mount amphibious assaults around his long coastline. He wanted naval forces for three roles: offshore defence, raiding (which he could hope would divert Western naval attention), and attacks on the enemy's deep rear, *eg* the logistics base which would have to be built up in the United Kingdom. Direct attacks on shipping, the main Western fear, seem to have been a secondary consideration, at least at first.

Where the Western navies emphasised air and anti-submarine defence, the Soviets became intensely interested in guided anti-ship missiles (initially bomber-delivered) and in surface-to-surface missiles to attack fixed land targets. Stalin's interest in surface raiders (probably inspired by the effects of the *Tirpitz* on the Arctic convoys) led to orders for a series of battlecruisers (Project 82). By about 1955 this design had been modified, as Project 82R, to deliver surface-attack missiles, the early version of the later Shaddock (P-5, Nato designation SS-N-3). Submarines were developed for much the same purpose, to fire both cruise and ballistic missiles. None of these weapons was intended to attack other ships, although SS-N-3 was later modified for that purpose. The Soviets also developed nuclear-tipped torpedoes, both to attack carriers and to attack ports.

Stalin's naval programme was extremely expensive. In 1956 Khrushchev cancelled both the big raiders (Project 82R and the remaining units of the *Sverdlov* cruiser class) and the coastal

The commissioning ceremony for HMS Resolution *on 2 October 1967, the first of four Polaris SSBNs that carried the British nuclear deterrent from the late 1960s until the advent on the Trident submarines of the* Vanguard *class in the 1990s.* (CMP)

The Soviet Delta *class, developed from the* Yankee, *carried the new SS-N-8 ICBM, which could be fired from inside the protected bastion areas. This is a* Delta I, *which carried twelve missiles, but the larger* Delta II *could carry sixteen, like US SSBNs. (MoD, Crown Copyright)*

submarines. Submarine-borne nuclear missiles for land attack did survive. Khrushchev permitted construction of a class of small surface-to-surface missile cruisers (*Kynda* class, Project 58).

Then the Soviet navy felt the first of a series of shocks. In 1957 the Soviets successfully tested their first ICBM; the navy's monopoly on deep attack was finished. Khrushchev shifted that responsibility to a land-based Strategic Rocket Force (SRF). The navy argued that it had to concentrate more on countering Western carrier groups. It was given full responsibility for land-based anti-ship missile bombers. The cruise and ballistic missile programmes were reoriented to attacks on carrier battle groups and similar targets. For example, the ballistic missile submarine under design in 1959 had six missile tubes. That figure was doubled, so that the submarine would have a better chance of hitting a target while bombarding a choke point through which a carrier group would come (the submarine eventually emerged as the sixteen-tube *Yankee*, Project 667A).

The next shock came about 1964. As Khrushchev's power waned, his decision to shift all strategic firepower to the SRF came into question. Now the planned role of the new *Yankee* class ballistic missile submarines changed. Armed with missiles with a range of about 1600nm, they would be held in reserve during the early part of a nuclear war. To attack the United States, they would have to break out of their operating areas. A new generation of ASW-oriented ships would be needed to assist them in breaking out past blocking Western ships. For example, the torpedo-carrying SS-N-14 was adapted from a failed alternative to the

anti-ship SS-N-9. The new attack submarine (*Victor*, Project 671) was modified to fire SS-N-15, a Soviet version of the US Subroc.

The step beyond was a Soviet submarine-launched ballistic missile with such great range that it could be fired at the United States from *within* a protected bastion area: SS-N-8. The existing SSBN design was modified to suit, and the main role of ASW forces shifted to protecting the bastions. Within a few years, this shift had been exploited by the US maritime strategists.

France and China

Two other countries deployed naval nuclear weapons: France and China. France consistently saw nuclear weapons as a less expensive alternative to substantial modern ground forces. Her national strategy was to deter by offering an attacker steep escalation toward disaster. Although France could not support the sort of strategic forces fielded by the United States, in the French view she could buy just enough to make a direct attack quite unprofitable. Weapons went aboard strategic submarines as well as bombers, and in land-based ballistic missiles.

From the late 1960s on, the French navy itself was largely redirected towards supporting the ballistic missile submarines. For example, the open-ocean escorts built with Nato support in the 1950s (E 50 and E 52 classes) were replaced by *avisos* intended mainly to keep the estuary of the Gironde, through which the French strategic submarines passed, clear of Soviet submarines (these A 69 class ships were also intended to support French power projection operations in the Third World, the other major French naval mission). The major mine countermeasures programmes were similarly motivated. Later, French Super Étendard naval aircraft were equipped with nuclear weapons (bombs, then cruise missiles) described as 'pre-strategic', to be used to begin the escalation towards a strategic exchange.

In keeping with her concentration on the strategic role of nuclear weapons, France apparently never developed or deployed nuclear depth bombs. She probably had custody of some US weapons before she retired from the military element of the Nato alliance in 1966.

Finally, China has developed her own submarine-launched ballistic missiles and nuclear submarines to fire them. Clearly they were intended largely to balance Soviet power in the Far East. They were (and are) quite expensive, but it is too soon to say how much they cost China in terms of foregone conventional naval programmes.

Norman Friedman

France has not only built its own SSBN force (and the missile it carries), but also maintains an air-launched nuclear capability in the form of the navy's Super Étendard carrier strike aircraft. Four of these are shown in formation over the carriers Clemenceau *and* Foch. *(French Navy)*

9

Anti-Submarine Warfare and Weapons

BY 1945 the submarine had already clearly become the main instrument of a *guerre de course* of unprecedented effectiveness. In the Atlantic, German U-boats had demonstrated that a massed submarine offensive could only be defeated by a long, asset-intensive campaign directly to protect the transport shipping at risk. Japanese failure to put sufficient resources into shipping defence and to organise a proper convoy system spelled defeat by the American submarine campaign. The balance between main fleet operations to gain command of the sea and operations to exercise command had shifted to a more even balance between the two. Moreover, submarines were playing an increasingly important role in fleet operations themselves, where they had proved capable of acting as potent assets both in the surveillance and strike role. Anti-submarine warfare thus became a key – in some navies *the* key – post 1945 warfare speciality.

These trends were decisively reinforced by the advent of nuclear power in the mid 1950s. The nuclear-powered submarine (SSN) was a qualitatively different animal even from the fast battery drive submarines that had already pro-

voked the first postwar ASW revolution. Indeed, perhaps the SSN's only similarity to the diesel submarine was its capacity to submerge and its reliance on a similar range of weapons. The SSN's speed, underwater endurance and sensor capacity, all resulting from the availability of effectively unlimited power from the reactor, made it a submerged equivalent of the battleship, a true capital striking asset. ASW now had to be at the forefront of 'battlefleet' operations, directed at the neutralisation of SSNs by containment or destruction. The best counter to the SSN was another similar platform, confirming the trend to submarine-versus-submarine operations. If not killed by their own kind, SSNs could easily slaughter convoys and their escorts.

Finally, the advent of nuclear-armed ballistic and cruise missiles on submarine platforms added a wholly novel dimension to the ASW campaign. Submarines armed with long range missiles, especially if deployed against land targets, could not be countered by escorts as they had no need to risk engagement with those escorts. There was no alternative to finding needles in haystacks, never previously a very profitable way of using ASW assets.

This account will trace the development of ASW in the postwar era, concentrating first on the major ASW navies, those of the United States and the United Kingdom. It will then deal with an important ASW specialist, the Royal Canadian Navy, and conclude with a look at continental European and Soviet perspectives on the subject.

Countering the Type XXIs: the first ASW revolution

The Type XXI U-boat, soon copied by the victorious powers, more than doubled the underwater performance of the diesel-electric

During the Second World War it was found that an escort lost sonar contact with a submarine as it passed over the target to drop its depth charges, offering the submarine a chance for evasion. The answer was an ahead-throwing weapon, initially the Hedgehog spigot mortar and then the Squid. The latter could be mounted aft, firing right over the ship – as demonstrated in 1952 by the destroyer HMS Crossbow *– thus not interfering with gun armament or, more significantly, not exposing it to seas breaking over the forecastle. (CMP)*

submarine. As the Royal Navy assessed the situation in 1945, new ASW weapons and systems had to be able to cope with targets with submerged speeds of 15kts and diving depths of 1000ft. This required a complete new generation of fast escort vessels and new weapons and fire control systems for them. The problem was now analogous to that faced by the gunners for many years and the solution was the same, the adoption of an analog computer fire control system connecting advanced sonars that could cope with faster targets with longer ranged ASW projectors.

The most advanced shipborne ASW system in 1945 was the British combination of the Type 144 and 147 sonars and the Squid ahead-throwing mortar. Type 144 was a 'searchlight' sonar, with single, circular trainable transducer. Its main beam was horizontal in order to maximise search range, but this meant that targets were lost before they came within Squid's engagement range of about 375yds. To overcome this an extra downward facing rectangular 'Q' transducer had been added to provide distance and direction information for Squid. Depth information to set the Squid charges came from the long, thin 'sword' transducer of an additional 147 sonar. Just after the war, separate 144-based search and attack sets were combined in the experimental 160X system in the destroyer *Scorpion*, with the two transducers in a large 100in sonar dome.

The basic 144 system was developed in two directions. The combined search/attack searchlight sonar became Type 164, improved to give greater reliability, a wider range of frequencies and a 'ship's component mechanism', a device to remove from the bearing recording instrument the effect of the attacking ship's movement. Its maximum range scale in the attack mode was 1500yds. The other was 174, a 4000yd range search-only set with improved range and bearing recorders. The combination of the two, in-

tended for *Daring* class ships and new-build frigates not intended primarily for ASW, was known as 166. Type 165 was a version of 164 with a detachable rather than retracting sonar dome, intended to update former corvettes.

These sets came into service in 1950–51 but they were quite clearly only interim improvements. The definitive answer to the new fast battery drive submarine was the 170 sonar, an advanced set with a 'four square' divided transducer, two squares of which detected the target's depth and two its bearing, using the split-beam technique. This was stabilised against roll and pitch and trained and tilted electrically. It provided data for a long barrelled Mk 10 Limbo mortar. The sensor could track to 2000yds and the weapon could engage at 1000yds. After initial trials of the 170 in 1947–49 the destroyer *Scorpion* was fitted with the full system, including Limbo, and performed well on exercise in 1951. The following year the 'final prototypes' entered service in the first two Type 15 full conversion frigates. Mk 20 electric passive homing torpedoes were also under development to provide a capability that could exploit the sonar's full range. To provide an additional longer range search capability the 170 was combined with 174 housed in the same dome. The superior 170 was originally intended only for specialist Limbo equipped ASW ships, but it soon proved a necessity against modern submarines and was fitted to Squid equipped ships as well.

The threat from homing torpedoes with a range beyond that of existing sonars and the tendency for fast submarines to avoid detection by quickly passing through short range sonar beams both advised a long range search set, and in 1949 development began of Type 177, a medium-frequency electrically scanned search set with a range, depending on the conditions, of up to 18,000yds. Scanning sonars had a much higher search rate than mechanically rotated 'searchlights'. Type 177 was intended to work

HMS Relentless, *one of the prototype pair of Type 15 'full conversion' frigates, as completed in 1952. The ships carried the new Mk 10 Limbo mortar, a much improved and automated Squid (abaft the twin 4in gun, but with its barrels horizontal, not conspicuous in this view); they were also fitted to fire the Mk 20 ASW homing torpedoes then under development, but with the failure of this weapon the tubes were later removed. The ships reflected the experience of North Atlantic convoy battles, with an enclosed bridge, no weapons on the forecastle, and an extended weather deck. They were light on guns, with only two 4in and a twin 40mm Bofors, but their main battery was the heavy ASW weapon-load.* (CMP)

in conjunction with the 170 attack set. Unfortunately, by the time it entered service in 1957 its utility would have been greatly undermined by further submarine developments.

The US Navy also developed integrated ASW fire control. The Americans already had a scanning sonar, designated QHB, and this was integrated together with a large and complicated computerised Mk 102 analog fire control system and an 800yd range rocket-propelled depth charge called Weapon Alfa. Unfortunately the system did not prove altogether satisfactory, partly because of computer/sonar interface problems and partly because of problems with Weapon Alfa, both in terms of performance and late delivery. As a less capable fallback the US Navy still thought highly of Hedgehog, the ahead-throwing 260yd range spigot mortar developed by the British during the war. The US Navy's operational evaluation group assessed Hedgehog as 28 per cent effective against 26 per cent for double Squid (the Royal Navy, operating in more demanding conditions, considered Squid twice as effective as Hedgehog); a trainable version of Hedgehog was therefore developed and widely deployed postwar. Hedgehog was useful against submarines that suddenly appeared at close range.

The existing ship-launched homing torpedo, the short Mk 32, used as an active homing depth

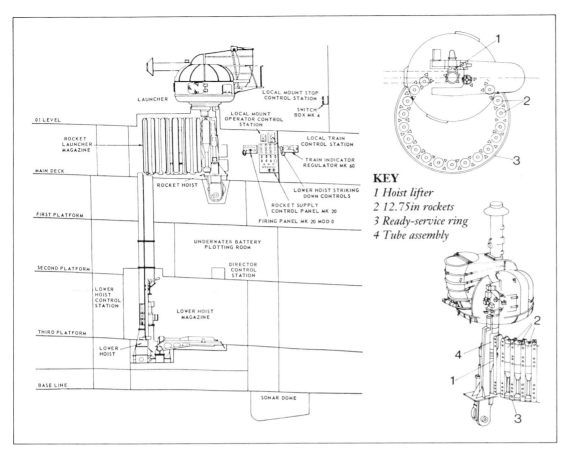

KEY
1 Hoist lifter
2 12.75in rockets
3 Ready-service ring
4 Tube assembly

A diagram of the US Weapon Alfa: an equivalent of the British Limbo, this was a traversing and elevating launcher for 12.75in rockets, which were fired at a theoretical rate of twelve per minute from a revolving ready-use magazine below. The system was very complex and difficult to maintain, and the US Navy upgraded the old Hedgehog as an interim alternative while a better weapon than both was developed.

operations. The Americans, who had never borne the brunt of the convoy battle in the Atlantic, were always ready to go even further in an 'offensive' direction and dabble in hunter-killer concepts. From 1943 onwards these had proved moderately profitable in the central Atlantic when SIGINT (signals intelligence), both direction-finding and code-breaking, had allowed escort carrier 'Hunter-Killer' groups both to hunt and to kill. Compared with escorting convoys at the height of the Atlantic battle it was highly asset-intensive, but, given the unwillingness of wolf packs to interfere with convoys, it was an attractive means of killing the hapless remains of the defeated U-boat force. The British and Canadians also went hunting for U-boats as a second best when it was not possible for various reasons to engage U-boats around convoys, using both shore-based maritime patrol aircraft (MPA) and surface groups.

By the war's end both carrier- and shore-based ASW aircraft had an array of sensors and weapons that would have been the envy of aircrew five years earlier: high frequency radar that could even spot snorkelling ('snorting' in British parlance) submarines, sonar buoys that could listen for underwater noise and transmit the results to the dropping aircraft, magnetic anomaly detectors (MAD) for localisation and classification of detections and homing torpe-

charge dropped over the side, was too slow at 12kts to deal with the Type XXI, as was its successor, the much lighter 15kt Mk 43. Much, however, was expected of the larger, faster Mk 35 homing torpedo fired from 21in tubes, a project which unfortunately died after an unsuccessful ten-year development programme. The related Mk 37 submarine torpedo, produced in both wire guided and free running forms, was pressed into service in surface ships in its free running version as a Mk 35 substitute. To exploit the expected performance of large homing torpedoes, sonar range was being pushed out correspondingly. A modified lower frequency QHB with a much higher scanning rate, SQS-4, was deployed in 1954. It could hold contacts out to 7500yds. A rocket-propelled version of the Mk 43, RAT, was developed and by 1956 the Atlantic Fleet destroyer force was calling for this to replace Hedgehog.

The war had been a triumphant vindication

of the close escort and support of fleets and convoys. As sufficient ASW assets became available the British began to use convoys in a highly offensive manner, routeing them through known U-boat concentrations to inflict attrition on the attackers. Convoys would be preceded by powerful support groups of well equipped 'escorts' designed to fight and defeat deployed submarine patrol lines and diminish the close escorts' task. These tactics have echoes in modern ASW

A Sikorski HSS-1 with 'dipping' sonar, May 1962. Putting a sonar aboard a helicopter increased the 'listening' radius, but this helicopter had a limited carrying capacity, so even if it were an effective 'hunter', it needed a separate 'killer'. This could take the form of another helicopter, but in practice was usually a surface ship. Later helicopters, with much increased payloads, could combine the roles. (USN)

One of the small 'K' class submarines built by the US Navy in 1950–52 as prototypes for a mass production ASW boat. Since quantity was reckoned a prime requirement, they were cheap, but attention was paid to quietness and they were given an effective passive sonar, for ambush-type operations. They were judged too small for the peacetime standard of habitability and their seakeeping also suffered from the small dimensions. (USN)

does that in some circumstances could give a much more certain chance of a kill than that achieved with depth charges. Keys to victory against the submersibles of 1943, the fixed wing aircraft lost relative effectiveness as the fast battery submarine undermined the effectiveness of both its sensors and weapons.

Maritime patrol aircraft and carrier-based ASW aircraft were still important to force submarines down and make snorkelling dangerous, but much was expected of the dipping sonar helicopter developed in the early 1950s. Dipping sonar had much better detection capacity than the contemporary sonobuoys against quiet underwater targets. ASW helicopters were, however, still relatively big machines carried in aircraft carriers and comparatively large surface ships, rather than on small escorts themselves. Only in Canada (see below) was the combination of the dipping sonar helicopter and the standard escort achieved successfully.

The helicopter could only carry lightweight torpedoes, which increased their importance even more as both air-delivered and surface ship weapons. A new electrically-propelled torpedo in the 450lb range, the Mk 44, was developed in the USA in the mid 1950s and was widely adopted. It had twice the speed of earlier lightweights (30kts) and its improved reliability meant that it could be widely deployed by surface ships as a more potent substitute for depth charges, with a range measured in miles (6000yds). When fired from a surface ship the torpedo was set to run into quieter water away from the launching ship to commence its circular search pattern for the target contact. The Mk 44, unlike its large finned predecessor, could be fired from a small 12.75in torpedo

tube. Mk 32 triple torpedo launchers became common sights on Western warships from the late 1950s onwards.

Submarine versus submarine

The problems faced by surface escorts in dealing with modern submarines led even the major Western navies to explore the potential of the submarine as a means of deploying a forward barrier to pick off enemy boats as they cruised on diesels towards their patrol areas. Submarines had the potential advantage of being able to choose the optimum depth for sonar performance. In 1948 ASW became the primary role of the British submarine force, although early exercises proved that the boats were not equipped with proper sensors or weapons for the task. It was planned to introduce Type 171 sonar, a submarine equivalent of 170, but after an initial installation it proved impossible to fit sufficient computer support into the confined spaces of a 1500-ton hull. Instead, passive techniques were concentrated upon, using both side arrays and bow transducers. Wire-guided torpedoes were intended to be procured to exploit these sensors, but they did not enter service until much later. Until then British submarines relied upon non-homing, high speed torpedoes; the slow and insensitive Mk 20 passive homer introduced in the 1950s was found only to be of use as an anti-escort weapon.

At the same time as the British, the Americans chose to develop the submarine as an ASW platform. It was found that using the JT hydrophone a quiet submarine could detect snorkelling boats at 8000yds, and new BQR-2 passive submarine sonar pushed this out to 20,000yds.

German technology was utilised to produce a 50-mile range, low-frequency passive set, BQR-4, that was fitted to special hunter-killer submarines (SSK). Existing boats were converted to SSKs and new small 'K' class vessels, intended for mass production for barriers, were built. Kills could be made either by the boats themselves or by supporting surface ships or aircraft. Until the mid 1950s and the delivery of passive homing Mk 35s and 37s the only submarine weapons available were straight-running weapons. Most American submarines remained general-purpose vessels, with ASW for the time being only one of their roles. Indeed, the relatively high levels of noise of early SSNs diminished their utility as ASW platforms.

The nuclear revolution

In 1955, the performance of USS *Nautilus* demonstrated that the techniques and systems coming into service would soon be almost as obsolete as their Second World War predecessors had already become. Five years before, the British Naval Staff, with its eye on hydrogen peroxide boats as well as forthcoming nuclears, had altered its requirement for new sensors and weapons to deal with boats capable of 25kts and diving down to 1500ft. This was too late to affect the basic design of Type 177, that was tested against *Nautilus* in prototype form in 1955. It was found that the set, with its slow search rate and narrow (80-degree) scanning, could not cope with fast-moving targets at close to medium range as it took too long for the sonar to move on to the next section. Although 177 was brought into service in 1957, the ships equipped with it were only dubiously effective against SSNs. Only in 1963–66 did the cylindrical transducer 184 enter service, with a wider all-round scanning and higher data rate – at a cost in maximum effective range, as available power had to be spread over 360 degrees rather than 80. Type 177's reliable effective range of 8000yds or so had already necessitated a re-think of weapons delivery, and by the time 184 was entering service British frigates were being equipped with manned anti-submarine torpedo-carrying helicopters (MATCH) of the Westland Wasp type as an

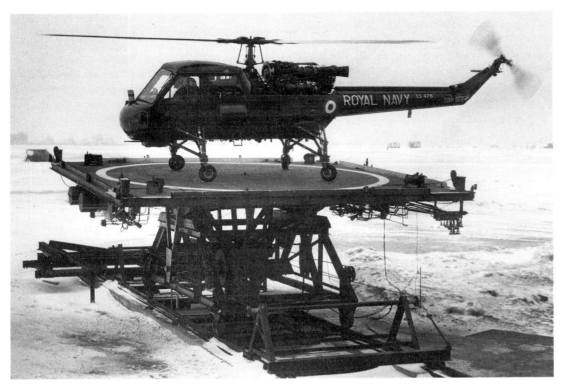

The British MATCH concept involved a diminutive Westland Wasp helicopter operating from small flight decks on relatively lively escort vessels. This required a high order of skill from pilot and ground crew, and the concept was worked out at the Royal Aircraft Establishment, Bedford, on a test rig that could simulate a rolling and pitching deck. A number of undercarriage configurations were tried, including suction pads, but the castoring, lockable four-wheel arrangement shown here was eventually chosen once a harpoon-like deck securing device had been developed. (CMP)

interim means of delivering lightweight torpedoes under control from the ship but at ranges of four miles or more.

The long term answer to the long range ASW requirement was felt to be the Ikara missile developed in Australia, which could drop a lightweight torpedo over a sonar contact at ranges of up to ten miles. In the end the British did not deploy Ikara widely and chose to emphasise the helicopter, since it also had other purposes (notably anti-fast attack craft missions with missiles) and could also more easily deliver other ASW ordnance such as nuclear depth bombs. A torpedo needs to be about 50 per cent faster than its target, and the nuclear submarine therefore made the Mk 44 obsolete. The answer was the Mk 46 with a hydrocarbon fuel engine and maximum speed against a submarine at periscope depth of 45kts at a range of six miles. This torpedo was deployed from 1967 onwards as a Mk 44 replacement, but in the meantime it seemed that nuclear firepower was the only sure answer to the SSN.

The first American 'Betty' nuclear depth charges based on the standard Mk 7 tactical bomb came into service for fixed wing ASW aircraft in 1955, but something more widely deployable was required. A lighter, small diameter Mk 34 warhead was designed for naval use, and entered production in 1958. It was deployed in the ASW role both as a 'Lulu' depth charge that could be carried by helicopters and

as a warhead for the ASTOR torpedo (see below). Some 2000 and 600 respectively were built of each type. The 1200lb Lulu had replaced the bulkier 2500lb Betty by the end of 1960. It was replaced in turn by the still lighter 500lb B-57 combined depth charge/strike bomb that entered service in the mid 1960s; all Lulus had gone by 1971. The B-57 was also put into the Nato stockpile for use by Allied maritime patrol aircraft. Britain began nuclear depth bomb development in the 1960s with a 600lb variant of its lightweight 'advanced tactical bomb', designated WE177C. This could be carried by MATCH helicopters, but does not seem to have been deployed at sea before 1971. By that time its utility had been rather overtaken by develop-

ments in conventional weapons and by the new strategy of 'Flexible Response' that cast doubts on the likelihood of obtaining early release of nuclear weapons merely to solve operational problems.

Nuclear ASW reinforced the existing emphasis on long range sensors. The SQS-23 surface ship sonar, with half the frequency of SQS-4, went into service in 1958. This was a 'reliable 10,000yd sonar' with a maximum range in optimal conditions of half as far again. Longer ranged weapons were also required. Not only was the original RAT too short ranged but it could not deliver its payload accurately enough for the Mk 43 to home. A longer ranged RAT 'C' firing a Mk 44 from a box launcher was combined with a proposed rocket-propelled nuclear depth bomb concept to produce ASROC fired from a box launcher. This proved very successful and was widely deployed in US and Allied ships from 1960 onwards, 12,000 being built over the next decade. The fire control system delivered the payload within lethal radius of the target, the lightweight homing torpedo's search pattern corresponding to the lethal radius of the nuclear depth bomb. Maximum range was 10,000yds, with a minimum range of 900yds (beyond Weapon Alfa's maximum). A new, lighter nuclear warhead in the

The operational mode for the US ASROC.

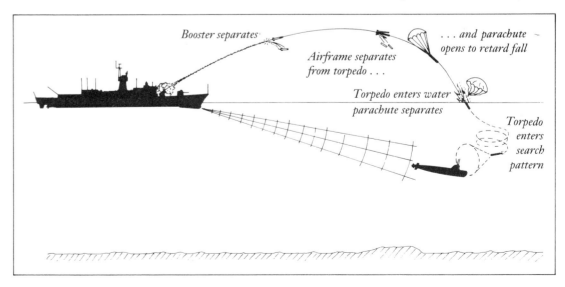

Booster separates

*Airframe separates
from torpedo . . .*

*. . . and parachute
opens to retard fall*

*Torpedo enters water
parachute separates*

*Torpedo
enters
search
pattern*

Tullibee was the US Navy's sole attempt at a nuclear-powered SSK, an updated version of the 'K' class, with the emphasis on very quiet, slow speed ambush tactics. The boat was fitted with a passive sonar ranging system called PUFFS (Passive Underwater Fire control Feasibility Study), recognisable from three large fin-like sonar domes. In this view of the boat as completed, the system is not yet installed, although two of the domes are visible; the third was fitted abaft the sail. (L & L van Ginderen)

low kiloton range, W-44, was developed for ASROC. Later substitution of the Mk 46 torpedo for the Mk 44 greatly improved the conventional variant of ASROC.

ASROC was expected to be too massive to retrofit into existing ASW ships. A more compact alternative means of distant weapons delivery seemed to be the drone helicopter. DASH (drone anti-submarine helicopter) was duly developed from 1963 and almost replaced ASROC, which was only saved by doubts over DASH's all-weather capability. It was as well that it was saved, for, after many ships had been modified with decks and hangars and yet more ships with control systems to operate other ships' drones, it was decided that the system was basically unsatisfactory. The drone loss rate was unacceptably high (over half were lost at sea) and there were terrifying stories of torpedo-laden drones out of control heading straight for the ships operating them – upside down! DASH was abandoned after less than a decade's service and the facilities in some ships were modified to handle manned helicopters.

In the late 1950s submarine ASW doctrine still emphasised slow speed, ultra quiet ambush operations. An accurate passive ranging sonar system, PUFFS, was developed to allow long range shots with the Mk 45 ASTOR, a nuclear-tipped wire-guided torpedo that entered service in 1959, whose W-45 warhead was detonated by command. PUFFS was fitted to conventional SSKs and to the first dedicated ASW SSN, the USS *Tullibee*. PUFFS proved unsuitable for use with regular nuclear boats because of streamlining and noise problems, and the only way they could normally use ASTOR was by tracking the target on active sonar, a tactically inadvisable method since it gave away their position.

Tullibee was not duplicated. Instead it was decided to build larger, faster general-purpose SSNs with her ASW capability. These were the *Thresher*s that appeared from 1962 onwards, followed by an improved, quieter *Sturgeon* class in 1966. Both *Tullibee* and the above classes had their bows filled by a massive sonar transducer, the BQS-6. This necessitated mounting the torpedo tubes amidships, canted outwards. These

boats also carried a passive low-frequency array around the forward part of the submarine, BQR-7, while a BQQ-3 passive classification system was mounted forward, amidships and aft. The whole suite was known as BQQ-2 and was associated with a Mk 113 digital fire control system and the Subroc nuclear missile. This allowed passive engagements with remotely fused nuclear warheads at ranges of 35–40 miles. Subroc first went to sea in 1966.

As for conventionally armed weapons, the wire-guided version of Mk 37 had become available in the early 1960s but had a range of only 9000yds. Moreover, the Mk 37 only had 10 per cent effectiveness against a target travelling at over 20kts. The need to provide non-nuclear alternatives to both ASTOR and ASROC became urgent as Nato moved towards strategies that emphasised conventional options rather than nuclear. Work had in fact started in 1956 on a long range, high speed ASW homing heavy-weight torpedo. A 35,000yd range 50kt torpedo finally entered service as the Mk 48 in 1971. Its kill probability against fast targets was assessed at 40 per cent and its advent into service saw the end of ASTOR, whose kill probability was assessed by submarine crews as 2, the target and the launching boat! ASTOR finally disappeared in 1976–77.

The British also saw their SSNs as primarily ASW systems, with a greater emphasis than the Americans on the support of task forces and convoys. The first of a new '2000' series of sonars, 2001, was developed for HMS *Dreadnought*, the first British SSN, commissioned in 1963. This was an active/passive set designed to operate at ranges measured in tens of miles

(detection of some targets was expected at as much as 60 miles). A passive array based on Second World War German practice had already gone into service in 1956 as Type 186, and conventional submarines eventually received an accurate 'split beam' primarily passive bow sonar as Type 187 in 1958. The major problem for British boats was not sensors, but the lack of weapon capability. Until the mid 1960s there was no usable 21in British guided ASW torpedo. The first generation wire-guided Mk 23 appeared finally in 1966, but was not properly mated to its associated fire control system until 1971. This also affected the ASW potential of the conventional boats that became customarily referred to as 'SSKs' as a mark of their new operational emphasis, as well as to distinguish them from the SSNs.

SOSUS, Lofar and HUKs

Submarines, with their ever longer detection ranges and inherent difficulties of integrating with other forces, helped to produce a new emphasis on hunting down enemy submarines. From about the time of the introduction of the SSN, however, other factors were pushing in the same direction. Not least was the capability of the SSN itself and its ability to attack even task forces and fast convoys from any direction. This made a protective 'ring of steel' seem an expensive option if technology offered other alternatives. Not that the SSN made hunting of a traditional kind any more attractive, given the ability of the SSN to dispense with snorkelling, to run carbon dioxide scrubbers to restore the air inside the boat and even to dispense with

From the first the British tended to see their SSNs as ASW systems, and were early advocates of quietness. HMS Dreadnought, *the first British nuclear boat, is silhouetted in the dawn light of the Malacca Strait while carrying out anti-submarine exercises with the Australian frigates* Yarra *and* Stuart *in October 1967. (CMP)*

much use of the periscope because of better sonars. SSNs were much more discreet than conventional submersibles but they did have one drawback, inherently greater noise levels. This made them vulnerable to long range passive detection, an operational technique that became possible in the 1950s in ways that had never been carried out before.

In the early 1950s both the British and Americans planned passive sonar bottom arrays for long range detection, but it was the latter who actually built a deployed system, SOSUS (Sound Surveillance System). This uses Lofar (low-frequency analysis and recording or 'Jezebel') narrow-band techniques to sense specific sounds in the ocean associated with the submarines of potential enemies. SOSUS was originally developed as Project Caesar in the early 1950s and detection ranges of up to 600 miles were obtained. Atlantic and Pacific 'Caesar' barriers were operational off the US coast by 1960. These arrays were part of a strategic ASW surveillance system that included the war-proven radio direction-finding surveillance car-

ried out from shore stations. In the 1960s and '70s arrays were deployed further forward to extend coverage into transit areas where submarines were usually better passive sonar targets. SOSUS became capable of cueing ASW assets, notably maritime patrol aircraft, into a circle of sufficiently small radius to make a hunt practical.

Lofar techniques also greatly increased the utility of sonobuoys to allow successful prosecution of contacts. The deployment of Lofar buoys was delayed by the use from 1957 of more precise explosive ranging techniques code-named 'Julie' (after a striptease artiste noted for 'making passive buoys active'). The first omnidirectional Lofar buoys were deployed by the US Navy in 1960, and buoys that could also be used in a 'Julie' mode were available by the mid 1960s. By the end of the decade directional Lofar (Difar) buoys were available to provide a passive accurate final localisation capability. Active sonobuoys also appeared at about the same time. This increased sensor capacity enhanced the effectiveness of carrier hunter-killer groups (HUKs) also.

In the mid 1950s older *Essex* class fleet carriers of the US Navy had been redesignated ASW

support carriers (CVS), with mixed fixed wing and rotary wing air groups as the centrepieces of a new generation of HUKs that could act on the information gleaned by the increasingly efficient ASW area surveillance system. These acted as potent counters against the newly developed missile-firing submarines of the Soviet navy as well as support units for the Striking Fleet. There were ten CVS groups in the early 1960s, but numbers declined until the type disappeared in the early 1970s. One reason for this was that with the deployment of the longer ranged P-3 MPA, the major role of the CVS fleet evolved into providing ASW support for carrier battle groups. In these circumstances it made economic sense to combine the CVS and attack carrier (CVA) role into one. The CVAs were duly equipped with fixed wing ASW aircraft, dipping sonar helicopters and new AIO arrangements to give them a general-purpose (CV) capability.

As the CVS died in the US Navy, however, the type was being reborn in Britain. There the need to deploy large dipping sonar helicopters spawned large helicopter carrying cruisers. These became ASW carriers much smaller than the huge American CVs. Despite the acquisi-

Until the advent of the four-engined P-3 Orion in the 1960s, the West's main maritime patrol aircraft (MPA) was the P-2 Neptune. MPAs lacked any effective area search method for locating submerged submarines, so these aircraft were usually cued by other means, such as SOSUS barriers, into areas precise enough for a dropped pattern of sonobuoys to have a fair chance of fixing the target; the aircraft could then carry out its attack. (USN)

The Whirlwinds of No 845 Squadron, the Royal Navy's first sea-going squadron of ASW helicopters with dipping sonars, joining Bulwark *in August 1957. As carriers became fewer, the Royal Navy sought to transfer the ASW role to large cruisers, initially converting the* Tiger *and* Blake, *but then instigating a series of studies which culminated in the current* Invincible *class, now rated CVS but described as 'through-deck' cruisers during their politically sensitive gestation. (CMP)*

tion of STOV/L fighters the operation of large ASW search-strike helicopters remained a key role for these ships. The airborne early warning helicopters with which these ships were equipped after the Falklands War also had an ASW utility with the technique of 'radar flooding' areas to keep conventional submarines submerged, so limiting their mobility and exhausting their batteries. Submarines could not distinguish the radar signals from these helicopters from those from Nimrod MPA equipped with the same radar.

Longer ranges and towed arrays

During the 1960s the US Navy introduced a powerful new active/passive low-frequency surface ship counterpart to BQS-6 in order to achieve ranges of 20–35 miles using bottom-bounce and convergence-zone techniques, *ie* bouncing sound waves off the bottom or exploiting the curved propagation properties of sound in water. The early SQS-26 sets were disappointing, but by the 1970s the sensor was working as designed and was fitted widely in cruisers, destroyers and frigates. A technique known as Passive Action Detection and Localisation (PADLOC) was evolved for use with both SQS-26 and SQS-23, using an additional transducer. An analog solid-state fire control system Mk 114 was developed to replace the digital Mk 111 as the link between SQS-23 and the ASROC torpedo weapons suite. Analog technology was reverted to in order to increase reliability. In 1972 an improved solid-state SQS-53 entered service in cruisers and in the large *Spruance* class ASW destroyers. This had better signal processing and improved passive performance in both broad and narrow bands. Steadily improved in succeeding years, the latest version has a stealthy active mode that spreads the pulse over a wider range of frequencies. The associated fire control system was Mk 116, fully integrated into the ship's general computerised combat system.

With a requirement for continental shelf operations, the British concentrated on improving the discrimination of their surface ship so-

nars, introducing their fully computerised but primarily active medium-frequency 2016 with the Type 22 frigates at the end of the 1970s. By that time detection ranges were being transformed by the application of long towed array passive transducers, combined with advanced computer techniques to process the data. These were capable of making narrow-band passive detections against relatively quiet targets at ranges in the 100-mile bracket. Deployed both in submarines and surface ships, the latter, with its ability to carry longer arrays, gave the surface escort of the early 1980s an ability to match and sometimes out-perform the submarine as an ASW detection platform that it had not possessed for a quarter of a century or more. Work on these arrays began in the USA at the end of the 1960s and they began to go to sea in the mid 1970s. At the same time the British put towed arrays into their submarines and, after trials in the late 1970s, the first 2031(I) surface ship arrays went to sea in 1982. Deployed in relatively quiet *Leander*s, they were able to exceed 100 miles in range, but the noisier Type 22s proved less sharp eared, despite better 2031(Z) equipment.

Passive operations dominated the Anglo-American ASW scene in the 1980s. The Americans introduced an impressive new SQQ-89 surface ship sonar and control system to integrate the passive performance of the latest versions of

SQS-53 with towed arrays and the sonobuoys of the light airborne multi-purpose system (LAMPS) helicopters carried in American escorts and replacements for DASH. These always relied on sonobuoys, at first monitored solely by the carrying vessels. Later LAMPS helicopters carried acoustic processors themselves to allow autonomous operation, if required. Such helicopters acted as effective prosecution assets for towed array detections, and in the Royal Navy the smaller MATCH helicopters began to be replaced by Sea Kings that could also prosecute contacts over long ranges. These helicopters also began to rely primarily on sonobuoys and the Sea King replacement, the EH-101, was conceived of solely as a sonobuoy platform (although a dipping sonar was later added). In addition, passive array contacts might be prosecuted by other platforms, *eg* carrier-based fixed wing aircraft or MPA. Indeed, this form of prosecution might well be more rapidly available if the contact was at extreme range. More than ever, towed arrays made ASW a multi-platform business.

The need to operate long range passive sensors in quiet water necessitated a reconsideration of ASW tactical and operational doctrine. Escort operations close to noisy ships, be they merchantmen or combatants, seriously degraded the effectiveness of passive sensors. In the 1970s the idea of a 'defended lane' began to gain some

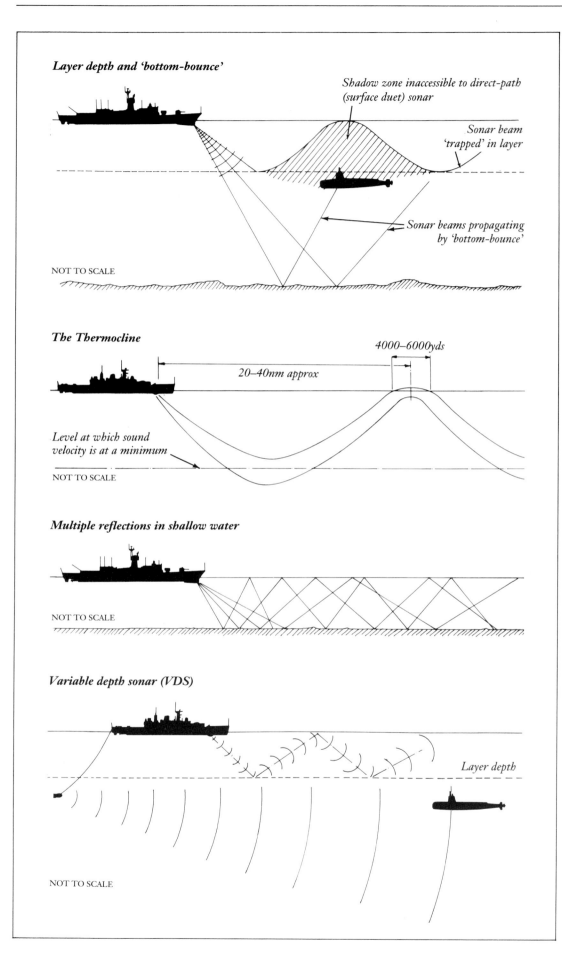

Layer depth and 'bottom-bounce'

Shadow zone inaccessible to direct-path (surface duet) sonar

Sonar beam 'trapped' in layer

Sonar beams propagating by 'bottom-bounce'

NOT TO SCALE

The Thermocline

4000–6000yds

20–40nm approx

Level at which sound velocity is at a minimum

NOT TO SCALE

Multiple reflections in shallow water

NOT TO SCALE

Variable depth sonar (VDS)

Layer depth

NOT TO SCALE

Sonar operating modes.

currency, and the beginning of the 1980s saw controversial experiments moving small convoys along such lanes protected with varying degrees of success by ASW assets using long range detection techniques. More universally accepted was the development of the Nato ASW Striking Force, a vanguard of the Nato Striking Fleet based around one or more British ASW carriers and made up of a number of towed array frigates and destroyers operating with helicopters, carrier-based ASW aircraft and MPA. The Striking Force was intended to engage Soviet SSNs and SSGNs before they could engage the Striking Fleet proper, as well as giving the Striking Fleet some idea of which water was free of the submarine threat.

The Striking Fleet was intended thus to engage and neutralise some of the Soviet subsurface 'battlefleet'. The rest was to be neutralised by forward operations by Anglo-American SSNs, using the pressure point of Soviet SSBNs to tie down most of the Soviet subsurface battlefleet in defensive operations. By the 1980s both the US and Royal Navies had developed ultra quiet SSNs equipped with advanced sensors and fire control systems and long range heavyweight torpedoes. The 6900-ton American *Los Angeles* class, designed originally for operations in support of high speed battle groups, had a displacement almost a third greater than its predecessor with double the installed power. This was delivered very quietly, however, and the boats carried a powerful BQQ-5 sonar suite capable of tracking many sonar contacts simultaneously using digital multibeam steering (DIMUS). The sonars consisted of a bow sphere and chin and towed arrays, with a second towed array in later models. The first boat was delivered in 1976. The improved Mk 117 fire control system was not available for the earlier members of the class, but it appeared in 1979 and was retrofitted into earlier boats. In the 1980s an integrated combat system, BSY-2, was developed as a replacement. This uses distributed architecture computer power to produce a more reliable underwater tactical picture with which the operator can interact more easily. It went to sea for evaluation in 1990. Although a stand-off missile system was considered for American SSNs, their weapons remained the Mk 48 torpedo that was improved to a 60kt 'advanced capability' (ADCAP) variant to counter high speed Soviet submarines in the early 1980s.

The British developed SSNs of increasing quietness in the 'S' class of the 1970s and the 'T' class of the '80s. Equipped with first Type 2001 and then 2020 bow sonars, plus flank and towed

The early US VDS installation SQA-8 aboard the destroyer John W Thomason. *The dark towed transducer body, with its stabilising fins, is visible, as is the heavy steel lattice lowering gear. Comparative tests favoured the SQA-10, which became the standard VDS for FRAM II destroyers.* (USN)

arrays, they also carried advanced electronic tactical fire control and data handling systems. The first TCSS, 9/DCA that went to sea in 1973, could track twenty-four passive contacts simultaneously, compared with the two–three possible using manual methods. It was later replaced by DCB with double the computing capacity. Sadly, weapons remained a problem for these excellent platforms. The Mk 24 Tigerfish wire-guided battery torpedo had serious reliability problems, even after it entered service in 1980; not until 1987 was the entire stockpile modified to a fully reliable standard.

Passive operations put a new emphasis on ASW torpedoes. Using nuclear firepower would cause reverberations that would blank out much of the effectiveness of passive sonars. Perhaps even more important were the problems of obtaining nuclear release in time to be of use. As mentioned above, this led to a move away from nuclear weapons in ASW thinking, especially in the USA. However, the need to hedge against torpedo unreliability led both Britain and America to keep a nuclear depth charge capability both for surface ships and MPA until the end of the Cold War.

Closing the passive sonar window

The main target of this panoply of passive sonar-based ASW was the relatively noisy Soviet SSN and SSGN force. Even before the end of the Cold War the latest Soviet boats were beginning to get too quiet for long range detection with existing equipment. Then the end of the Cold War at the beginning of the 1990s removed the threat as a major preoccupation for the two main ASW navies. The inherently quiet conventional submarine operating in relatively shallow water suddenly became the threat to counter. This put a new emphasis on active sonar operations, both using surface ships and helicopters. Instead of dispensing with dipping sonar as seemed likely at one time, modern ASW helicopters like the Merlin (EH-101), designed primarily as an advanced sonobuoy handling platform, were fitted additionally with new low-frequency long range dipping sets. Although the new British ASW frigate, the 'Duke' class, was conceived as an extra stealthy tug for 2031(Z), its main sensor might well turn out to be the 2050 active sonar with not only a lower frequency convergence-zone option compared with 2016, but also a software-based ability to reject bottom echoes and operate in shallow water at ranges of several miles. Towed arrays may still be useful – especially in broadband mode – but they will probably be combined with transmitters, including in multistatic modes with the transmitter on a mobile or fixed platform.

Variable depth active sonars (VDS) were used by the US and Royal Navies in the 1960s, but were not very popular because of handling problems and the tendency of both navies to operate in conditions where the ability of such sonars to be lowered below the thermal layer was less important. The Americans sometimes used VDS transducers in association with SQS-4 and developed a stand-alone SQS-35 for *Knox* class DEs that entered service in 1969. The latter soon became more important as towed array mountings, and the British also removed their Type 199 (the Canadian SQS-505, see below) from the *Leander*s that were fitted in the decade after 1969. VDS seems to be making something of a comeback as investment is channelled into active sensors useful in a broad range of water conditions. Britain began a project in 1991 to develop an advanced low-frequency VDS (Type 2080), but in 1993 this was jointly cancelled together with the projected British 2057 advanced passive towed array, and the concepts were combined into a new 'offboard system with a strong active element' designated 2087.

The surface ship/dipping helicopter combination will probably emerge as the key ASW systems of the late 1990s and early twenty-first century, with SSNs becoming less numerous and no more sophisticated. The magnificent American ASW-oriented *Seawolf* class SSN developed as the ultimate answer to the Soviet submarine is only being procured to keep the builders in business. This boat has a highly advanced BSV-2 combat system that integrates seven different sonar arrays and has enough computing and sensor power to require 570 kilowatts from the reactor – an interesting example of the power requirements for advanced underwater warfare, demands that only nuclear power can satisfy. It may well be the most sophisticated ASW platform to appear for some time.

The Canadian contribution

ASW remained the main priority of the Royal Canadian Navy after 1945, the Service operating in close co-operation with the Royal and US Navies. The RCN was responsible for two major contributions, VDS and the operation of large dipping sonar helicopters off small escorts. Work on VDS began in 1947, stimulated by the existence of the sound channel found between the warm surface and bottom layers off the east coast and the difficult shallow waters of the Gulf of St Lawrence. By 1958 SQS-504 had been developed, and on trials it demonstrated a range five times greater than the hull-mounted British 144 (5000–7000yds). It was incorporated in the Canadian escorts from 1961 and adopted by the British because it outperformed their experimental 192X. It was not entirely successful in service but the Canadians persevered and included a VDS in their SQS-505 sonar suite fitted to destroyers from the early 1970s onwards. Reported range in VDS mode is 27,500yds. Combined with a towed array it becomes SQS-510. Canadian sonars have done well on the export market, being used by Belgium, Greece, India, the Netherlands, and Portugal. A smaller, simplified VDS, SQS-507, was developed by 1968 for use by the experimental ASW hydrofoil *Bras D'Or*. This was an attempt to produce a unique high speed ocean-going ASW escort that could sprint and drift in support of convoys. As a novel concept it was a natural casualty of reductions in Canadian defence expenditure and was never fully developed.

A much more significant Canadian contribution to ASW was the early solution of the problem of operating large helicopters from destroyers. Experiments with a 'River' class frigate modified to operate a Whirlwind in 1956 led to the mating of the even larger CHSS-2 Sea King with the 2000-ton *St Laurent* in the 1960s to produce the first DDH. It was made possible by the 'Bear Trap' technique, which involves hauling down the helicopter. The early DDHs

had a hangar and flight deck for one CHSS-2; the DDHs of the early 1970s could accommodate two.

During the 1980s the Canadians developed their own CANTASS towed arrays and took a full part in ASW Striking Force operations.

Continental Europe and Japan

Of the Western European navies that developed ASW capabilities in the postwar era, the Royal Netherlands Navy was the most fully integrated into the CAN/UK/US ASW force, with skills equal to those of the others. In the 1950s the Dutch electronics industry allowed the development of a domestically produced range of 'searchlight' sonars. For their postwar ASW destroyers the Dutch copied the British concept of two searchlight sonars in a single dome, a CWE-10 surveillance set with a PAE-1 attack sonar. These were coupled with a pair of quadruple 375mm Bofors rocket launchers. After abortive experiments with large ASW torpedoes, the Mk 10 mortar/MATCH helicopter combination was adopted in the 1960s along with the related British sonar fit.

For their long range low-frequency sonar the Dutch chose a lightweight and compact American EDO design which was adopted by them as the CWE-610. Development began in 1963 for the Royal Netherlands Navy, and the set entered service in the mid 1970s in the *Tromp* class frigates. It was also retrofitted into the Dutch *Leander*s, which also received the associated

PDE-700 VDS. CWE-610 was replaced in the 1980s by the PHS-36 a low-frequency active/passive bow sonar related to the Canadian SQS-509. The Dutch also adopted towed arrays, first American and then French, and gave their escort-carried Lynx second-generation MATCH helicopters a dipping sonar autonomous search capability using French equipment. Dutch ships were able to take a full part in the Striking Force operations in the final decade of the Cold War. A combination of French and British technology was also used for the powerful 'Octopus' passive sonar suites developed for their quiet SSKs that were integrated alongside SSNs into the Nato forward ASW strategy.

The French navy, split between the Atlantic and Mediterranean and out of the Nato integrated command for over half the postwar era, has tended to follow its own path in ASW developments. The first solution to the short range escort problem was the active sonar/ASW torpedo combination carried in 1950s destroyers and frigates. The high speed 550mm (21.7in) heavyweight K-2 torpedo was not guided but was designed to deliver ordnance to a predetermined depth and distance. This was basically a torpedo equivalent of Squid, but doubts about its performance led to the addition of Bofors ASW rocket launchers. In addition a novel long range mortar was developed that could double in the shore bombardment role. Homing L3 torpedoes replaced the earlier K-2s in 1960.

In order to increase range, new higher capability 5KHz active sonars were developed in the 1960s, with quiet deep-diving conventional submarines the major threat in mind. A DUBV-

23 active set was combined with a large DUBV-43 VDS to obtain reliable direct-path ranges of 10–15km (6–9 miles). To strike at detections the Malafon ASW missile was developed as a stand-off delivery system for a new 533mm (21in) L4 lightweight torpedo. In the 1970s the French followed the British in fitting their best ASW ships with small helicopters, although they gave their Lynx aircraft a dipping sonar search as well as torpedo strike capacity. The French also persevered with the ship-launched torpedo, however, and deployed from 1971 a heavy 35kt battery-powered 533mm L5.

In recent years the French have designed and deployed towed arrays and adopted the American Mk 46 lightweight torpedo for their helicopters. The number of first rate ASW surface assets in the French navy remains very limited (less than a dozen), and the relatively low priority given to ASW is demonstrated by the building in the 1990s of 'frigates' with no ASW sensors. Although the French submarine force was given some ASW capacity with passive low-frequency arrays and both autonomous and wire-guided homing torpedoes, the decision was taken to build the first four French SSNs as primarily anti-surface platforms with less attention to quietening than would otherwise have been necessary. Only in 1991 did a quiet French ASW SSN appear, with the *Amethyste*.

The Italian navy concentrated on active sonar ASW in the Mediterranean, where the long range detections associated with Atlantic and Pacific waters are much more difficult. American active sonars, including VDS types when available, were used, coupled with ASW mortars of domestic design complemented from the late 1950s by licence produced lightweight torpedoes which the Italians themselves developed further. The latest Italian frigates carry the American DE-1164 combined medium-frequency hull-mounted and VDS sonar suite. Longer stand-off range was provided from the 1970s by 21in 'Kangaroo' wire-guided torpedoes carrying a lightweight torpedo payload. This was carried both by surface ships and submarines. From the late 1960s the Italians began to operate small dipping sonar and weapons delivery helicopters from frigates and destroyers. They were also pioneers in Europe of the

The Japanese have the only navy with destroyer-sized ships capable of carrying three Sea King helicopters. Shirane, completed in 1980, is one of a pair of ships improving on the original DDH concept first seen in the Haruna class. Besides the helicopters, the ships carry Asroc, six ASW torpedo tubes and an American SQR-18A TACTASS towed passive array, making them potent ASW platforms. (JMSDF)

ASW cruiser carrying larger numbers of these helicopters (first three, then six). Eventually this culminated in a through-deck ship with provision for twelve Sea Kings as well as – like the other cruisers – a hull-mounted sonar.

The West German navy's emphasis on shallow water operations close to home has meant that its ASW has emphasised active sonar short range operations. The German DSQS-21 developed in the 1970s by Krupp-Atlas was designed primarily for discrimination in cluttered water conditions. Bofors rocket launchers were the preferred short range weapon, while later lightweight torpedoes, both helicopter- and ship-delivered, became the normal weapons of choice. Like other mainland navies the Germans have given their Lynx dipping capability. It is no coincidence that these navies see more of a use for small 'dippers' than their deep-sea counterparts, as short range transducers are at a premium in difficult shallow water conditions.

One area where such ASW operations became important in the 1980s was around Scandinavia. Off the Norwegian coast it was important to clear the fiords in 'precursor operations' before the arrival of the striking fleet. This meant another challenge for the main Nato navies. Moreover, these forward operations meant that the Norwegians themselves had even more reason to emphasise the defence of coastal convoys through some of the most sonar-opaque and confused waters in the world. The Norwegian escort vessels were modernised with the addition of VDS to find targets for their indigenously designed Terne rocket-launched depth charge system.

In the Baltic, where sonar conditions verge on the impossible, Sweden tried to develop its ASW potential in the 1950s and into the 1960s by converting its older destroyers and torpedo boats into ASW frigates. Most retained depth charges as their main armament, but the three

later conversions in the early 1960s mounted Bofors 375mm ASW rocket launchers. These launchers were also mounted in the two destroyers built in the mid 1950s, but the four slightly smaller follow-ons had Squid. The Swedish submarine force also improved its ASW capability with improved sonars and lightweight 400mm homing torpedoes fired from special tubes carried in addition to tubes for heavyweight weapons. Apart from further SSK construction, the Swedes then rather neglected ASW until they began to be very concerned about Soviet submarine incursions in the mid 1980s. Serious ASW investment began once more, with missile FAC being equipped with high-frequency hull sonars and dismountable medium-frequency VDS. The land-based Vertol 107 helicopter force was doubled by transfers from the Air Force. These aircraft, designated HKP-4, are equipped with dipping sonar, depth charges and homing torpedoes. Swedish submarines also had their ASW role confirmed with advanced passive sonar suites and increased provision in new construction for improved lightweight torpedoes. A novel twist in Swedish ASW has been the development of weapons to inflict non-lethal damage and force submarines to the surface. The Type 422 torpedo has a reduced-charge warhead, and for helicopters and surface craft small depth charges and Elma rocket-launched harassment devices have been developed.

On the other extremity of the Soviet Union, the Japanese Maritime Self Defence Force had ASW as its main role, helping contain Soviet submarines and defend sea communications at ranges that grew to 1000 nautical miles from Japanese ports. The Japanese adopted American methods and technology and managed to make both Weapon Alfa and even DASH work better than it did at home. Both weapons needed replacement, however, and the 375mm Bofors

rocket launcher was adopted to supplant Weapon Alfa in the short range role and ASROC was more widely adopted to replace DASH (including fitting in 2100-ton DDKs, the smallest ASROC fitted ships in the world). The large Sea King helicopter was mated with the ASW destroyer, and lightweight torpedoes of American design were domestically produced for use by aircraft and surface ships. The Japanese developed a distinctive and compact DDH concept that went one better than the Canadians and put three Sea Kings on a 5000–6000-ton hull. The Japanese also built a fleet of SSKs for forward and barrier operations. Like later surface ships they were equipped with long range sonar suites and associated combat systems as good as any in the world. Japanese ASW forces work in close co-ordination with a comprehensive set of sonar arrays laid in the Japanese straits.

Soviet ASW

The Soviet navy was primarily concerned with anti-surface unit sea denial operations in the immediate postwar era. The main ASW role was the defence of larger surface combatants like cruisers, and destroyers were fitted with active sonars based on wartime British practice, ASW rocket launchers and depth charges for this role. Similar equipment was also part of the fit of smaller general-purpose guard ships designed to keep Soviet coastal waters free from hostile submarines that might be a threat to both naval and civilian shipping. This coastal defence task became more important with the advent of the first submarine-borne land-attack missiles. A new 1000-ton guard ship with improved ASW capabilities was designed for mass production. The Project 159 (*Petya*) first appeared in 1961. She was armed with new lightweight homing ASW torpedoes, 2500m range multiple rocket launchers and depth charges. The ships carried a new MF sonar (Hercules) and, together with the similar Project 35 ships (*Mirka*s) armed with longer range rockets, they were built throughout the 1960s.

In order to back up these smaller ships and to provide long range cover for planned missile ships, a new generation of destroyers, the Project 61 (*Kashin*) was procured, with ASW as an important part of their role. They could carry

21in homing ASW torpedoes as well as complementary 1000m and 6000m range rocket launchers. Even more impressive were two helicopter-carrying cruisers, the first of which was laid down in 1962. These carried fourteen dipping sonar helicopters and may have been intended to support a new missile-carrying large surface combatant. By the time they were completed, however, their role had changed. As with the Project 61s, it had become pushing the ASW defence zone out from the coast to counter the growing threat of the Polaris submarine. The helicopters were nuclear-capable, but the chances of the Ka-25 surviving the blast was officially put at 50 per cent. The primary nuclear delivery system was therefore a 16-mile range missile. The Type 61 'Large Anti-Submarine Ships' (BPKs), as they were designated on completion as a reflection of this new emphasis, carried Hercules sonars, but the helicopter ships carried a massive low-frequency Orion with a range of about 40km. Vega medium-frequency VDS was also fitted.

The programme of new more comprehensively armed Project 1134 ASuW rocket cruisers (*Krestas*), which were commissioned with the rather inappropriate designation of BPK, was stopped after four units and the rest of the class were built to a modified 1134A design with the SSMs replaced by torpedo-carrying ASW missiles. The latter were originally misidentified as SSMs (SS-N-10) but were eventually designated SS-N-14 in the West when their true purpose was belatedly recognised. Operating these ASW missiles was troublesome, as their range of about 30 miles was far beyond the range of the ship's Bull Nose MF sonar. The missiles had to be guided from information from two Ka-25 helicopters using dipping sonar ahead, and there was always concern that the missiles would down the helicopters. The ships carried only one helicopter each, a sign of the co-operative nature of Soviet ASW, and for closer range engagements carried heavy torpedoes and rocket launchers. The helicopter could

carry one of the two nuclear depth charges normally carried. A number of older ASuW missile ships built in the late 1950s were also equipped with the new sonar, torpedoes and rocket launchers and recommissioned as BPKs.

It had also been planned to build another type of ocean-going missile ship smaller than the 1134 but as large as the guard ship yards could build. This emerged as the Project 1135 BPK (*Krivak*) with its original SSM main battery on the forecastle replaced by the new ASW missiles. As this ship carried no helicopters, however, it could only fire at short range. These ships also carried the VDS adjunct to the Bull Nose, but this was less than a success, suffering great problems with lateral stability. They soon were relegated to guard ship work close to the USSR, supporting the new 'Small Anti-submarine Ships' that were produced in the 1970s as Bull Nose equipped 1000-tonners. These latter 1124s (*Grisha*s) were armed with torpedoes and rocket launchers.

The protection of their ballistic missile submarines was always a major role for Soviet ASW forces. During the 1970s this began to evolve from helping *Navaga* (*Yankee*) class boats break out to protecting *Murena* (*Delta*) class boats with missiles of full ICBM range survive as a strategic reserve in protected 'bastions'. Defending these became the core war fighting role of the fleet. This required area ASW operations in the so-called 'defended bastions'. The basic philosophy of the 1134 was continued in a new gas-turbine variant (the Project 1134B or *Kara*), while the helicopter cruiser was enlarged into a small carrier. Although ASW was downgraded to co-equal status with ASuW as the role for surface ships, a new generation of BPKs was designed in the 1970s. These Project 1155s (*Udaloy*s) carried two new Ka-27 dipping sonar helicopters to give an autonomous SS-N-14 targeting capacity as well as carrying a new longer ranged low-frequency Horse Jaw/Horse Tail hull/VDS sonar suite. The new VDS overcomes the old problems of stability by being saucer-

When they first appeared, the Soviet Krivak *ASW ships made a favourable impression in the West, but they were quickly relegated in their own navy to coastal guard ship duties. Their main weapon, four SS-N-14 ASW missiles, can be seen on the forecastle, and the large structure right aft houses the VDS. (MoD, Crown Copyright)*

The culmination of the cruiser-like Project 1134 BPKs of the Soviet navy was the gas turbine Kara class. Built for operations in support of the 'defended bastions' concept, they carried an extensive array of ASW weapons and sensors: two quad launchers for SS-N-14 missiles beneath the bridge wings, a helicopter aft, a VDS, plus ASW rocket launchers and ten 21in torpedo tubes. (MoD, Crown Copyright)

shaped and hung vertically over the stern. It may, however, only be usable in a sprint and drift mode, like the helicopter-style VDS used by the smaller Soviet ASW vessels.

Surface ships were, however, only one part of the Soviet ASW hunting force. Sonobuoys became available for helicopters and MPA from 1959, but they were not very efficient and were used primarily to prosecute contacts detected by other means. Helicopters used sonobuoys only when they could not use dipping sonar. From 1975 the Soviets had begun to seed Western submarine operational and base areas with sensors to collect signature information and a few years later deployed their first Lofar buoys, first carried in Bear-F MPA and later in helicopters. The Soviets also laid fixed acoustic sensors to help fence off the bastions both off the Kola and in the Far East, where water conditions are more favourable for long range detection.

The best way for the Soviets to counter Western intruders and to escort their SSBNs equipped with shorter ranged missiles out into the open sea was to improve the ASW potential of their own submarines. With the advent of the Trout Cheek passive array in conventional submarines in the 1960s the West assessed that ASW was now a key role for them. The noise of Soviet nuclear boats, however, greatly diminished their ASW utility. Even the Project 671 boats (*Victor*s) of 1968, equipped with low-frequency active/passive arrays and homing torpedoes, were too noisy to take on Western SSNs with much chance of success. Nuclear firepower was therefore an almost essential asset, and Soviet boats were equipped with a copy of Subroc

The Victor III *was the first Soviet SSN design to show a significant emphasis on noise reduction measures. They also deployed a towed array sonar from the bulb-shaped appendage on top of the rudder, clearly seen in this 1987 view.* (US Navy, by courtesy of John Jordan)

(SS-N-15) that had been compromised in 1964. In order to give a conventional weapons option, an enlarged missile with a torpedo warhead was developed. This necessitated fitting an improved 671PT variant (*Victor II*) with larger 65cm (25.6in) tubes and an enlarged combat system to exploit the longer (50-mile) range of the weapon. After seven of these, the design was modified once more with towed array as the PTM (*Victor III*), the first of which was launched in 1978. These boats were the first to display significant reduction in noise levels.

In the late 1980s Western ASW forces received a rude shock. The latest Soviet submarines were suddenly almost as quiet as theirs. The first such boat was the final PTMK batch of the 671s, launched from 1985. This disturbing trend, which undermined the passive sonar techniques developed to a high degree by Western navies, was continued in the two successor types, the 945 (*Sierra*) and 971 (*Akula*), both very quiet, especially the *Akula* with the rafted propulsion of its Western contemporaries.

So as the Cold War ended the Soviets had virtually caught up with the West in the primary anti-SSN platform at least. By concentrating resources, including skilled manpower, in the submarine service the Soviets had some counter to Western SSNs and SSBNs. They had also tried to exploit revolutionary non-acoustic sensor technology with laser radars on MPA and environmental sensors of unknown nature on SSNs. In addition they had worked on non-acoustic remote sensing for strategic surveillance. The latter proved too expensive to develop, however, and it seems most unlikely that the other technologies made up for a basic inferiority in sonar and computer technology that still existed in 1991 when the USSR ceased to exist. Much of the postwar technology used by the USSR for ASW was stolen via espionage. Soviet lightweight torpedoes were always bigger and heavier than their Western counterparts and were never used as standard surface ship armament as in the West. Surface ship towed arrays remained experimental many years after they had been deployed by Western navies, probably because of deficiencies in signal processing hardware. This, of course, reflected a fundamental deficiency in Soviet technology – especially information technology – that lay at the heart of the malaise that eventually brought the Soviet Union crashing down in ruin. In that sense, as well as in other more obvious ways, ASW lay at the heart of the postwar naval confrontation.

Eric Grove

10

Weapon Systems for Air Defence and Surface Warfare

THE weapons, sensors and associated tactics of anti-submarine warfare have been covered in the previous chapter, so this is confined to the weaponry dedicated to the other main naval roles, air defence and surface warfare.

Air Defence

Both in the United States and in Britain, air defence technology was driven by the needs of carrier screening, particularly in weather too bad to permit flight operations. It was generally assumed that, in the event of war, powerful Soviet shore-based naval air forces would attack Western warships and shipping both in the Norwegian Sea and in the Mediterranean, as the Germans and Italians had done during the Second World War.

Fleet air defence was, and is, conducted on three levels: area air defence, screening, and self-defence. In 1945 the only area (long range) weapon was the carrier fighter. Screening ships carried heavy guns, such as the US 5in/38, to deal with aircraft approaching the most valuable units. Shorter range automatic weapons were intended entirely for self-defence. Heavy gun range was so much shorter than fighter range that there was little conflict between the fighter and heavy gun zones. The logic of the combination was that attacking aircraft had to come very

close to their targets before they could drop their weapons. Only the fighters had much chance of actually destroying large numbers of aircraft, or of driving off attacks. Although guns did shoot down some aircraft, their main effect was to shake pilots sufficiently to make them miss. Thus the guns might be considered anti-missile (*ie* anti-bomb or -torpedo) weapons, even though their targets were the attacking aircraft.

This logic began to fail in 1943, when the Germans introduced guided weapons. Bombers could launch and guide them from well beyond gun range. That reduced the layered system to a single stratum, the fighters. Guns were useless unless they actually destroyed the incoming missiles, which was unlikely. In the Pacific a little over a year later, kamikazes had much the same significance. Again, gunfire was unlikely to throw the attack off (a dedicated pilot would simply steer into the heaviest concentration of fire).

Both in the United States and in Britain, it was understood by 1945 that the gun layer of defence had to be replaced by something far more lethal, most likely a guided missile. Ideally, it could have enough range to destroy a bomber before the latter came within missile-launching range (later, the missile became the most likely target). Thus in 1950 Terrier, then under development, was expected to be effective out to 10nm. Missiles were rather exotic technology, so the major navies continued work on a last generation or two of heavy anti-aircraft guns. Most of them were automatic replacements for earlier semi-automatic guns. Work on some such weapons had begun even before the Second World War.

AA guns and fire control

As early as 1937 Bofors began work on an automatic 6in/50, which ultimately equipped Swed-

The first generation of US missile frigates, four DLGs of the Farragut *class, displaying their twin Terrier launchers aft. This medium range SAM was one of a related trio of missiles – the other two being Talos and Tartar – known as the '3-T' Programme, which were the outcome of the wartime 'Project Bumblebee'. The large searchlight-like devices abaft the funnels are the cumbersome guidance radars for these early beam-riders: the inboard ship,* Preble, *still has the original SPQ-5, but the others have the improved SPG-55, which is slightly less bulky, and allowed the missiles to be controlled in the semi-active mode. (USN)*

A typical modern medium calibre gun, the US 5in Mk 45, a fully automated unmanned mount. Ammunition is loaded into the breech from below, restricting elevation to 65 degrees, but the weapon was not designed for AA fire, so this is no drawback. Since the gun will stand idle for long periods of time, reliability was essential and this was aided by a moderate rate of fire. In the ASuW and shore bombardment role for which the gun was designed, in any given period a heavier weight of shell can be delivered by a larger calibre, slower firing gun than a fast-firing smaller gun of increased complexity and potentially lesser reliability. (USN)

ish and Dutch cruisers. The US Navy began its relatively unsuccessful twin 6in/47 (ultimately for the *Worcester* class) before the war; it inspired the very successful triple 8in/55 (for the *Newport News* class). The Royal Navy was less successful with its dual-purpose twin 6in/50 Mk 26 (*Tiger* class). It also designed a very powerful single automatic 5in/70, which for a time was planned to arm a new class of cruiser-destroyers conceived as an inexpensive counter to possible Soviet surface raiders. For Project 82 the Soviets designed (and probably made in prototype form) a 12in/54 rapid-fire triple turret to fire nine rounds per minute (rpm) per gun compared with three for the earlier triple turret. The *Sverdlov* class cruisers, a developed version of the prewar *Chapaevs*, were armed with prewar-type semi-automatic 6in/57 guns in a turret designed in 1938. The only recent weapon in this category was the abortive US 8in/55 gun Mk 71, conceived about 1963 specifically for fire support, which could replace the forward 5in gun on board a *Spruance*. It may be revived during the 1990s. There have been several unsuccessful attempts to adapt army-type 155mm (6.1in) guns to destroyers, for much the same purpose.

The major navies continued to develop medium calibre dual-purpose rapid-fire guns. The US Navy developed its wartime 5in/38 into a higher velocity 5in/54, and placed a single automatic Mk 42 in production. It fired as rapidly as an abortive twin semi-automatic version. The Royal Navy continued to use a semi-automatic 4.5in Mk 6 designed in wartime.

Italy's OTO-Melara is one of the most successful exporters of naval guns, the 76mm/62 being a particular triumph, having been sold to, among others, two forces who traditionally prefer home-grown weaponry – the US and Royal Navies. This 3in gun was widely adopted elsewhere, and is shown here on the Dutch frigate Tjerk Hiddes; *the gun replaced the British 4.5in (114mm) twin Mk 6 originally fitted on these* Leander *derivatives. (L & L van Ginderen)*

France developed a twin semi-automatic 130mm (5.1in), but found ammunition production difficult. The gun was therefore adapted to take US 5in/54 ammunition, as *Modèle 1951*. In Sweden, Bofors developed a twin 120mm/50 destroyer weapon, adopted by Sweden and the Netherlands. This weapon was extremely impressive (it was almost adopted by the Royal Navy), but it was criticised at the time as being too noisy, too large, and not water- or flash-tight. An automatic 6in/50, used by Sweden and the Netherlands, was a prewar design. About 1956 the Swedish Admiralty asked Bofors to design a new 120mm gun for the next class of destroyers; the company proposed a single-barrel naval version of an existing automatic 120mm/46 field anti-aircraft gun. In the event, Sweden abandoned destroyers in favour of fast coastal attack craft. Russia had a twin 130mm (5.1in)/50

single-purpose B-13 destroyer gun. It was replaced in the postwar Project 56 (*Kotlin*) class by a German-style triaxially-stabilised dual-purpose semi-automatic 130mm/58 mount (56-SM gun), the guns of which elevate through the roof. This weapon was apparently planned for the abortive Project 82/82R.

The US Navy found Mk 42 too unreliable and derated it to about 20rpm. The next step was an unmanned mount, Mk 45, capable of much the same rate of fire but at limited elevation. The Royal Navy took much the same step with its 4.5in gun Mk 8. OTO-Melara of Italy developed a lightweight fast-firing (45rpm) 5in/54, again with an unmanned gunhouse. The Soviet Union differed from its Western competitors in developing an entirely new twin automatic rapid-fire (about 65rpm per gun) AK-130 130mm/70 mount, apparently largely

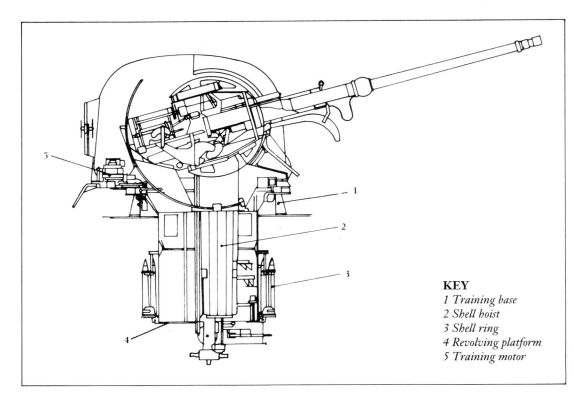

KEY
1 Training base
2 Shell hoist
3 Shell ring
4 Revolving platform
5 Training motor

The mechanics of the US Mk 75 (licence-built OTO-Melara 76mm/62).

The smaller automatic weapons survived. Bofors replaced its earlier 40mm/60 with a 40mm/70, versions of which are still in production. Italy imported the new weapon, and by 1960 Breda was making the twin 40mm under licence. Ultimately the company developed an entirely new mount with a much-modified elevating mass, as the Fast Forty. Bofors also developed a 57mm/60 as an intermediate step between the 40mm and the new 120mm destroyer gun. Several navies, such as those of France and the Netherlands, bought it. The company failed to produce a projected short 57mm, which could directly replace a 40mm/70 gun. Oerlikon, whose 20mm had armed so many wartime ships, developed more powerful 30mm and 35mm guns.

The Russians ended the Second World War with a 37mm/67.5 twin water-cooled gun (V-47M) derived from an earlier 25mm Bofors, and thus quite comparable (at least in mechanism) with the standard Western weapon. There were also air-cooled single and twin versions. These weapons were largely superseded in the postwar period by a quadruple 45mm/85 (SM-20-EIF) similar in layout to the wartime German *Vierling* 20mm (two barrels over, two under). This weapon in turn was superseded by an open-mount 57mm/70 in single, twin (ZIF-31B), and quadruple mounts (arranged like the quadruple 45mm). A new remote-controlled twin water-cooled 57mm/60 of 1961 (AK-725 or ZIF-72) armed many of the new generation of small surface combatants. The wartime and early postwar 25mm weapons were superseded by remote-controlled 30mm conventional (AK-230) and six-barrel Gatling guns (AK-630).

Fire control systems also changed. In 1945 the standard was a director equipped with a tracking radar. Typically, a target was detected by an air search radar, then designated to the director, which might scan to pick it up. The director incorporated an analog ballistic computer. Postwar, mechanical analog computers were replaced by faster electronic analog devices, which could handle the new jet targets. The US Mk 68, which controls 5in/54 guns, is an example.

In the 1960s a new class of integrated fire control systems appeared. They generally combined a fast-scanning search radar and an air tracker with a computer. The search radar worked in track-while-scan (TWS) mode. Each target it picked up was carried in its memory; by correlating target position on successive scans it could estimate target course and speed. Gener-

for surface fire. It replaced pairs of the earlier single 100mm gun, which in turn displaced a twin 76.2mm (3in)/60. It appears that in each case the main reason for up-gunning was to deal with surface ships.

The next step down was heavy anti-aircraft guns, whose shells were large enough to accommodate proximity fuses, but which were not considered large enough for surface fire. Wartime experience had shown that such fuses were essential to destroy targets such as kamikazes and missiles. Thus the US Navy developed an automatic 3in/50 to replace its Bofors 40mm guns. It designed a faster firing higher velocity twin 3in/70 as its ultimate anti-aircraft gun, but the mechanism proved too unreliable, and few entered service. The Royal Navy developed its own 3in/70 using the US ammunition and barrel (to ensure wartime supplies), but not the same mechanism. That proved fortunate, since its version (which survives in Canada) was far more reliable. The 3in/70 was conceived as a replacement for the existing twin 4.5in, but it was never so employed.

The prewar French heavy AA calibre was 100mm (3.9in). France ended the war with substantial stocks of old 130mm (5.1in) and ex-German 105mm (4.1in) ammunition. She briefly used the twin German 105mm and developed a new twin semi-automatic 130mm gun and a twin automatic triaxially-stabilised 105mm/60 to replace an existing French 100mm weapon. The 105mm gun was abandoned in favour of a single 100mm gun (standardised in 1953) com-

parable in size, weight, and power requirement to the Bofors twin 57mm, which France had adopted. The 100mm turned out to be a very fortunate compromise, because it was just large enough to be useful for surface fire. It therefore replaced not only the 57mm, but also, eventually, the 5in/54. In Italy, OTO-Melara developed a series of 76mm/62 guns, culminating in a very successful single mount.

The Russians ended the war with a standard single semi-automatic 100mm/56 mount, carried, for example, in *Riga* class (Project 50) guard ships. A shorter 51-calibre mount was used in *Kirov* class cruiser secondary batteries, and was planned for the abortive Soviet battleships and battlecruisers. A German-style twin triaxially-stabilised 100mm/70 mount (SM-5-1S) armed the *Sverdlov* class cruisers. It had no immediate successor. Instead, an entirely new twin 76.2/60 was designed. Planned for the abortive Project 82/82R battlecruisers, it first appeared on board *Kynda* class missile cruisers. Similar weapons armed most major Soviet surface combatants of the 1960s, such as *Krestas*, *Karas* and *Krivaks*. Then up-gunning began. *Krivak II* (1976) introduced a new single automatic 100mm/70 (AK-100), a weapon also mounted in the *Kirov* class cruisers and in *Udaloy* class destroyers (later versions of each mounted one twin 130mm in place of two single 100mm). In a parallel programme for small combatants, a single 76mm/60 (AK-176) replaced the twin 57mm guns on earlier versions of *Grisha* and *Nanuchka* (it armed *Pauks* and *Tarantuls*).

ally a scan rate of about 1 scan/sec sufficed for surface target tracking. No such scan rate could suffice for aircraft, so there was generally a separate air tracker. The main examples are the Dutch Signaal 'egg' (M/WM 20 series), the French Vega series, the Swedish 9LV series, and the US Mk 86. The Italian NA 10 series fits this category, but it was designed to extract video from an associated air search radar to cue its tracker; the tracker could also scan in surface mode. The Soviets were unique in adapting

TWS operation to air tracking (using much faster scan rates). Later they provided their TWS trackers with separate fine dedicated trackers, so they could handle only one air target at a time. Examples are the radars designated Bass Tilt and Kite Screech by Nato.

Western AA missiles

By 1945 it was obvious that guns were not sufficient; they could not reach out far enough.

Both the United States and Britain began work on radar-guided anti-aircraft missiles. First-generation systems were extremely large, both because of the sheer size of the missiles and because they required elaborate fire control systems. Thus they were perceived initially as cruiser weapons. The first Western series, the US Terrier, was placed aboard the heavy cruiser *Boston* in 1955. The more massive Talos also required a heavy cruiser (Terrier eventually went aboard small US cruisers, at that time called frigates). At about this time the British assumed that their broadly comparable Seaslug would require a 17,000-ton cruiser to be worthwhile (partly to accommodate the necessary radars and direction system). Projected ranges were 10nm for Terrier and 15nm for Seaslug. Terrier was eventually sold to the Italian and Dutch navies.

Both Seaslug and Terrier used similar beam-riding guidance techniques. A single radar tracked the target. The missile followed the tracking beam by measuring its position with respect to the tracking beam. The technique limited effective range. First, accuracy declined as the range increased, because the beam inevitably spread. Second, because the beam always pointed at the target, the missile flew an energy-inefficient pursuit course. In particular, it would not easily follow a manoeuvring target. Terrier was eventually modified for semi-active guidance, in which the missile seeks radiation reflected from the target. Accuracy increases as it approaches the target, because the signal grows stronger. In addition, the missile could estimate target speed by comparing the reflected signal with the radar signal. It could therefore lead the target, following a much more efficient path, and compensating more easily for target manoeuvres. Beam-riding and other command techniques are now virtually extinct in the West, except for short range weapons.

Semi-active guidance first appeared in the US Navy in Talos, a much longer-range (50nm at first, ultimately 125nm) complement to Terrier. Pure command guidance clearly could not put Talos on target, not least because the distant

While the surface-to-air missile was proving itself, many navies equipped their immediate postwar ships with automated AA guns. The French De Grasse, *for example, displays serried ranks of twin 5in guns backed by the new Bofors 57mm; fire control arrangements were also elaborate, with four large directors for the 5in guns and a similar number for the 57mm. Her near sister,* Colbert, *was converted to fire the Masurca SAM, a French equivalent of the US Terrier, in the early 1970s. (USN)*

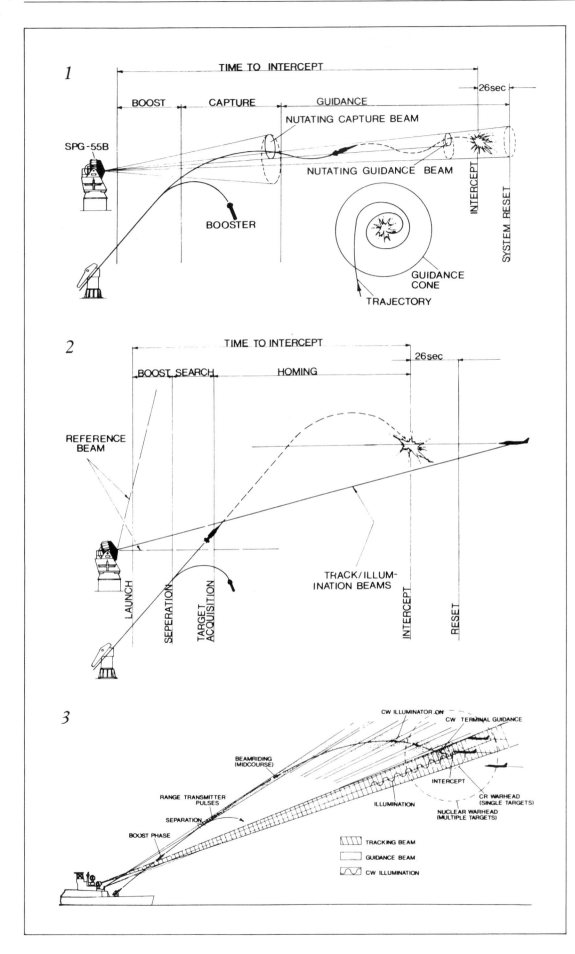

1. *Flight sequence of Terrier SAM beam-riding (in anti-aircraft mode). System reset is where the computer automatically adjusts the system if manual reset has not been performed. Beam-riding was retained even after semi-active homing was added to the missile's inventory, in order to achieve the positive control of nuclear-armed rounds required by US policy on nuclear weapons.*

2. *Flight sequence of Terrier/Standard SAM semi-active homing (in anti-aircraft mode). After target acquisition, missile follows an 'up and over' trajectory while maintaining a constant collision angle.*

3. *Continuous wave illumination as employed by the Talos long range SAM.*

target would seem so low; the missile would confuse the beam reflected from the sea with the beam it was intended to follow. The Talos system therefore incorporated a computer which steered the guidance beam to make the missile follow an up-and-over course. Only as it approached the target from above was the illuminator switched on. As it happened, this up-and-over course surprised enemy pilots in Vietnam, who were carefully watching for missiles approaching *from below*. Talos and Terrier both had nuclear versions.

It was painfully obvious that convoy escorts could not carry such weapons. About 1953 the British therefore pressed the US Navy to develop a small-ship guided weapon system, specially adapted to deal with low-altitude targets. It appeared in 1956 as the semi-active Tartar, intended to replace a single 5in/54 mount on a one-for-one basis. It therefore armed several classes of destroyers and frigates. Ironically, having asked for it in the first place, the Royal Navy never adopted this weapon. Tartar and its direct descendants were eventually sold to the Australian, Canadian, Dutch, French, German, Greek, Italian, Japanese, Pakistani, Spanish, and Taiwanese navies.

All of the early missiles were quite unreliable. Tartar was essentially the upper stage of Terrier, with a different (dual-thrust, *ie* boost plus sustain rather than sustain-only) motor. In the mid 1960s the US Navy carried out a 'get-well' programme in which the two missiles became versions of a new Standard Missile, Medium and Extended Range. Talos was also affected. As cured, both Terrier and Talos functioned effectively during the Vietnam War. Talos shot down a MiG-21 at a range of 65nm, and was considered so reliable that it (rather than carrier-based fighters) was used to cover the mining of Hanoi-Haiphong in 1972. The missiles in question were aboard the cruiser *Chicago*. Terrier was credited with several MiGs as well as a Styx

One of the most compact of the first generation SAMs was the US Tartar, which was originally designed to be capable of replacing a single 5in/54 gun mounting. It was a great success as a small-ship weapon, and was sold to about a dozen navies. The example shown here is aboard the French destroyer Kersaint, *a converted T 47. (French Navy)*

anti-ship missile (although postwar there was some question as to whether any such weapons had been present in Vietnam).

Ships designed to carry these missiles had to devote most of their topside space to the combination of search and fire control radars, open spaces to load missiles at sea (since magazine capacity was often no more than forty weapons per launcher), launchers, and the clear blast areas around the launchers. Any space dedicated to anti-ship weapons (generally torpedoes) was soon consumed by the ASW weapons described in the previous chapter. The Royal Navy in particular badly wanted its anti-aircraft missiles to have a secondary anti-ship capability. However, the guidance beam could not easily track a ship on the horizon. The Royal Navy did develop a dump mode, in which the missile was guided to a point roughly above the target, and then allowed to dive uncontrolled. However, it was generally agreed that the best way to provide a serious anti-ship capability was to provide a nuclear warhead, to compensate for any guidance errors.

The US Navy became intensely interested in anti-ship capability as the Soviets provided their clients with torpedo and missile boats in the early 1960s. It tested its standard anti-aircraft missiles in anti-ship mode, and was most gratified to discover that semi-active guidance worked against such targets. Although the missile warheads were ill-adapted to attack ships, a big missile hitting at supersonic speed was not too different from an earlier 14in shell. It could do terrible damage. This theory was proved correct when US missile ships engaged the Iranian navy in 1987, firing AA missiles as well as conventional anti-ship weapons (Harpoons).

A main limitation on these early missiles was limited target handling. A dedicated fire control radar had to track a target continuously from missile firing all the way to explosion. Ships could accommodate only so many directors, typically no more than four (all had to be on the ship's centreline, and superimposing more than two was generally impossible owing to topweight). That was acceptable against high-flying aircraft in the open sea, since a fire control radar (a fire channel) could be shifted to the next target after one was destroyed at maximum range. Near land or against low-flyers, each channel might well get only one chance per battle. That was the British experience in the Falklands, where the Argentines well knew the limitations of the semi-active Sea Dart system in *Sheffield* (Type 42) class missile destroyers.

As early as 1957 the main US anti-aircraft development agency, the Applied Physics Laboratory (APL) of Johns Hopkins University, sought a way out. Its solution was to combine a kind of command guidance with semi-active terminal guidance. The early missiles had no autopilots: if the guidance beam was turned off, they fell out of the sky. However, missile autopilots could certainly be designed. Moreover, they could be reset in flight by radio command. In theory, then, a missile could be ordered to fly towards the expected target position, and periodically adjusted to compensate for some target motion. When it got close enough, the missile could switch to the much more precise semi-active homing. Because no radar guidance was needed during most of the flight of the missile, several missiles could time-share a single fire control radar (the semi-active illuminator). The less time each illuminator spent per missile, the more targets the system as a whole could engage.

This type of operation required a new kind of radar. Existing missile ships used relatively imprecise search radars, which cued the fire control trackers. The tracker searched within a limited area defined by the search radar, locked on, and then guided the missile. Ideally, the search radar had to be more precise, so that it could minimise the time spent in illumination. To do that, it had to be able to check target motion periodically as needed, not only when an antenna swung back into the appropriate direction. APL wanted an electronically scanned radar, but its first attempt, a system called Typhon, failed mainly because radar technology was not yet mature enough. The current Aegis finally embodies the APL idea. Tracking by the SPY-1 radar is so precise that the illuminators neither search nor track: they are effectively slaved to the main radar, switched

on only for the last few seconds of missile flight. The missile is called SM-2 (SM-1 was the revised Tartar/Terrier).

Ironically, it turned out that SM-2 could be adapted to earlier missile fire control systems. Even given the time taken for the illuminator to acquire a target, the system offered far more firepower (more target-handling capacity) than its simpler predecessors. It is called the New Threat Upgrade (NTU). The new Anglo-French-Italian PAAMS missile operates like SM-2, except that the missile has an active seeker for the terminal phase. Because PAAMS was conceived mainly as an anti-missile weapon, its designers paid particular attention to violent manoeuvrability, using thrusters as well as wings.

The British never bought Tartar, but by about 1960–62 they were painfully aware that Seaslug was obsolescent. A variety of land-based missiles were considered and rejected. Work began on a British equivalent of Tartar, powered by a ramjet for greater range but still (in theory) small enough to fit a frigate or small destroyer). It eventually appeared as Sea Dart. Like SM-1, Sea Dart was limited to a single target per fire control radar. In due course a British equivalent of NTU was introduced as part of a general upgrade of the combat direction systems of Sea Dart ships, ADIMP. The Royal Navy also bought a much smaller anti-aircraft missile, the command-guided Seacat. It replaced the 40mm gun on a one-for-one basis, and could handle subsonic aircraft.

Tartar was too massive to equip frigates and auxiliaries. By about 1967 the US Navy was painfully aware that in many operations neither dedicated missile ships nor carrier-based aircraft could assure non-missile ships of protec-

A twin Sea Dart launcher aboard the British Type 42 destroyer Liverpool. *The system was given a severe testing during the Falklands War, where it performed well against long range targets, but, being limited to a single target per guidance channel, was easily swamped by large raids. (L & L van Ginderen)*

The first Soviet SAM, designated SA-N-1 by Nato, was a converted Red Army system. In this view of the Kashin class destroyer Obratsovy, *its relatively large stabilised launcher can be seen on the shelter deck abaft the twin 76mm gun; it has reloading hatches both fore and aft of the launcher (the latter partly obscured by the line of seamen). Control of the command-guided missiles is provided by the Peel Group track-while-scan radar on top of the navigating bridge.* (C & S Taylor)

tion. The solution was another semi-active missile, Sea Sparrow, an adapted air-to-air missile. It was very widely sold. Britain, France, and Italy also eventually produced small-ship close-in defensive weapons: command-guided Sea Wolf, command-guided Crotale Navale, and semi-active Aspide, respectively.

Soviet surface-to-air missiles

By the mid 1950s the Russians, too, wanted defensive weapons for their ships. The Soviet navy decided to cut its costs by adapting an existing ground or heavy fighter weapon. The standard medium range army missile, designated SA-3 by Nato, won out. Like Terrier and Seaslug, it was command-guided. The system was different. The Soviets favoured track-while-scan (TWS) radars for fire control, the radar scanning continuously while the operator picked out the target. Two successive target observations provided the system with estimated target course and speed. In theory, a TWS system could handle multiple targets with a single

radar, but in practice tracking would generally be imprecise. The Soviet systems tracked target and missile separately; the associated computer commanded the missile so as to close with the target. Nato designated the navalised SA-3 as SA-N-1. Its large-ship successor, also command-guided by TWS radars, was designated SA-N-3. It is unique among Soviet naval systems in *not* being an adapted army weapon. The small-ship command-guided system is SA-N-4.

The Russians faced exactly the same target-handling limitations as their Western rivals. SA-N-6, a large-ship system, was their equivalent of Aegis/SM-2 (actually based on the US Patriot system, which works rather differently). The fire control radar illuminates the target, and the missile transmits back the signal it receives. That signal is processed on board the ship, which commands the missile via an up-link. The combination ('track via missile') minimises electronics aboard the missile, leaving as much space as possible for a powerful rocket motor. A smaller SA-N-7 is the Soviet equivalent of NTU/SM-2. SA-N-9 is a modernised SA-N-4 fired out of a vertical launcher, but still command-guided.

There is also a class of very simple self-guided missiles, adapted either from hand-held infantry weapons or from infra-red air-to-air missiles: examples include the US Chaparral (used by Taiwan, adapted from Sidewinder) and the Soviet-bloc SA-N-5/8 (using the hand-held SA-7).

Close-in weapon systems

Beginning about 1970, guns began to return to prominence in a new very short range anti-missile role, as close-in weapon systems (CIWS). Because they need sufficient airflow over their control surfaces, missiles are ineffective *inside* a limiting range. As the *Eilat* incident (see below) showed, an incoming low-flying missile might provide its target with very little warning. There might well not be enough time to set up a missile, whereas a gun has no minimum range, although it certainly does have a maximum.

The first weapon of this sort was the US Phalanx, a 20mm Gatling gun provided with its own search/fire control radar. Phalanx automatically engages any target approaching its ships at high enough speed. It fires bursts of saboted rounds intended to hit the incoming missile (they are often called 'hittiles') and, hopefully, cause its warhead to go off. As in other guns, Phalanx must constantly correct its aim. The key to its effectiveness is closed-loop spotting. The radar tracks not only the target but also each outgoing burst, predicting whether the burst will hit the target. It corrects *before* the burst arrives near the target. Although Phalanx and its ilk are often described as putting up a 'wall of steel' between the ship and the missile, in fact they are aiming quite precisely. The Dutch 30mm Goalkeeper is in roughly the same class, enjoying somewhat greater effective range. Oerlikon and Breda now offer a twin 25mm

Gatling gun, Myriad; Mauser and Signaal offer a quadruple 27mm gun. There are also some other weapons on the market. It is not clear to what extent current Russian 30mm guns use closed-loop spotting.

Such guns are unlikely to begin hitting much beyond 1500yds. A missile has considerable momentum. Even if its wings are shot off, it will continue for some distance along much its original path. Some have therefore argued that hittile weapons are futile; they may well kill the target only to have its remains severely damage the ship.

The alternative is a larger round with a proximity fuse, which may be powerful enough to destroy a missile altogether, beyond inertia range. This approach is espoused by OTO-Melara (which considers its 76mm Rapido a viable anti-missile weapon), by Breda (using the 40mm Fast Forty in the Dardo system), and by Bofors (using the 40mm Trinity and possibly the 57mm Mk 2). The Italian navy seems to have agreed with OTO-Melara: its new *Mimbelli* class missile destroyers have single 76mm Rapidos where earlier ships had Fast Forties. The larger rounds may become even more attractive if, as seems likely, they can be provided with some form of command guidance. OTO-Melara is currently marketing just such a system for its 76mm gun. The US Navy is developing a higher velocity electro-thermal (propellant)

In the aftermath of the Falklands War, the British equipped a number of ships (notably the Invincible *class, and some Type 42 destroyers) with the US Vulcan Phalanx CIWS as a stopgap. After longer consideration, a preference for the Dutch Goalkeeper system was manifest, and it now equips the Batch 3 Type 22s. It can be seen forward of the foremast in this view of* HMS Cumberland. *(C & S Taylor)*

combustion gun (ETC) specifically to fire guided projectiles; a 60mm prototype is now being tested on a Phalanx mounting. ETC is valued because the propellant burns more slowly, accelerating the shell more smoothly and thus reducing the load on the electronics inside.

Some believe that no gun can fire quickly enough to deal with a missile which first appears at the horizon, and which may be supersonic. There is already a US proposal for an anti-missile laser roughly the size and weight of a 5in/54 gun. It may enter service early in the next century. If it replaces the shipboard gun altogether, however, it will also cost some very valuable current capabilities: shore bombardment and the ability to fire a shot across a bow to stop a ship. These are exactly the jobs needed in the sort of turbulent world disorder now in prospect. Yet the world disorder also involves many small countries which have invested in anti-ship missiles, and large navies will badly want insurance against sudden attack.

Surface warfare

The single really new postwar weapon was the surface-launched anti-ship missile, the lineal successor to the torpedo. Examples include the Soviet SS-N-2 Styx (P-15/P-20), the French Exocet, the Israeli Gabriel, the Franco-Italian Otomat, the Norwegian Penguin, and the US Harpoon. Usually guided by active radar (sometimes by infra-red or homing on a target's radar emissions), such a missile placed few demands on the ship or boat firing it. Because it often flew

at very low altitude, an anti-ship missile often provided its victim with little warning. Missiles of this type have been extremely popular with Third World navies.

The Soviets were the leaders in this process: they badly needed an equaliser to deal with what they imagined to be a major Western invasion threat (postwar *Whiskey* class submarines were part of the same effort). After 1945 they invested heavily in air-launched anti-ship missiles broadly related to wartime German work; the first operational weapon of this type was the beam-riding AS-1. In 1954 the Berezhniak design bureau (now known as Raduga), which designed AS-1, conceived a small radar-guided rocket, P-15 (designated Styx or SS-N-2 in the West). It probably entered service in the late 1950s, on board converted *Komar* class (Project 183R) and then *Osa* class (Project 206) missile boats. Range was about 20nm. A redesigned P-20 (SS-N-2C) had a range of about 90km (49nm). A simple fire-and-forget weapon which made few demands on the platform carrying it, Styx was widely exported. It offered the sort of anti-ship capability previously associated with torpedoes aboard motor torpedo boats, but with sufficient stand-off range to offer a good chance of success. The missiles were first successful against the Israeli destroyer *Eilat* on 21 October 1967. Although SS-N-2 had been known for some years (for example, US ships serving off Vietnam were equipped with countermeasures), this one incident seems to have brought home its potential. The most recent missile of this series is a big rocket-ramjet, 3M80 (probably also designated P-270; the Nato designation is SS-N-22), which arms *Tarantul* class (Project 1241) missile boats. It has been advertised but not yet exported.

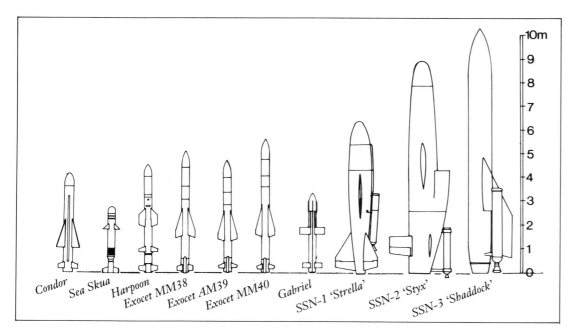

Comparative sizes of anti-ship missiles: Condor and Sea Skua are air-launched, the former by strike aircraft and the latter by helicopters; Harpoon, Exocet and Gabriel are typical Western ship-launched weapons; Strella, Styx and Shaddock show how much larger are the Soviet counterparts, which were designed with major surface combatants as their most likely targets.

The Chinese copied and then developed Styx in a variety of versions for air- and ship-launch as well as coast defence (FL-, SY-, and HY-series) before developing their own weapons, such as the current C-801 or HY-3 (which broadly resembles Exocet but is larger).

The main targets of the Western anti-ship missiles were generally fast attack craft, so warheads in the 500lb (227kg) or smaller class were quite acceptable in order to hold down size and weight. That was particularly important for missiles intended to arm destroyers and frigates, whose main roles were anti-aircraft or anti-submarine warfare rather than dealing with surface craft. The Soviets had much larger targets in mind; their minimum acceptable size was about twice that of a Western missile (500kg). That made for a much more lethal weapon.

Current Western ships generally carry four or eight anti-ship missiles, which might be considered analogous to the four or eight torpedoes of earlier classical destroyers. But the missiles are much less lethal: because they hit above the waterline, they are unlikely actually to sink their targets. For example, HMS *Sheffield* sank, not from the direct effects of an Exocet hit, but by flooding in a storm (through holes well above the waterline) after she had been abandoned and after she had lost most of her stability because her oil fuel had burned out and fire-fighting water was sloshing about her upper deck. Similarly, USS *Stark* almost sank not because of two such hits, but because she could not shed fire-fighting water, which was making her very unstable. Harpoon hits on fairly small Libyan and Iranian ships tended to disable them (often to burn them out), but not to sink them. The future may belong to a new class of anti-ship

missiles which dive to make underwater hits, or else to much more massive Soviet-style weapons (which can indeed tear ships apart).

By the time of the *Eilat* incident the Royal Swedish Navy already had its second-generation anti-ship missile in service. Its first was the command-guided Rb 315, on board a pair of destroyers, *Halland* and *Smaland* (it entered service in 1955, the first such weapon in the world). It was succeeded by the large radar-guided Rb 08, derived from a French target drone (CT 20), which first flew in 1966. In Norway, Kongsberg (now NFT) developed the unique infra-red guided Penguin.

In Italy, Contraves was already developing Sea Killer, a beam-riding anti-ship version of its Indigo anti-aircraft missile. Adaptation was relatively easy, since the anti-aircraft missile already rode a beam in three dimensions, whereas Sea Killer required control in only two (it used a radar altimeter to maintain altitude). Sea Killer sold poorly (it was adopted only by Libya and Iran), but its beam-riding guidance became part of a very successful weapon, the Israeli Gabriel. Gabriel was conceived as a response to the Styx which sank the *Eilat*. It began as an anti-ship version of a surface-to-surface command-guided missile, Luz, which was steered by joystick. Attempts to use Luz at sea failed, largely because the small boats firing it were far too lively for a human operator trying to stabilise a missile. The Italian beam-riding command system was acquired, and combined with semi-active terminal homing (the receivers are on either side of the missile). Because Luz had been designed for command guidance, its airframe left no space for the nose dish of an active radar seeker. The missile is joystick-controlled into the beam of

the mid-course guidance radar, then shifted to semi-active guidance on command.

Gabriel was extremely successful in the first missile-on-missile naval engagements in history, during the 1973 October War. These battles were a nice illustration of the strengths and weaknesses of such weapons. The Israelis knew that Styx had been designed specifically to attack large warships, and also that the boat firing it had to steer a steady course for some minutes while running up its gyros. They assumed that the Egyptian and Syrian crews of Styx boats would worry about their vulnerability during that straight run. Israeli Gabriel boats were equipped with long range chaff launchers, and their forward superstructures were covered in radar-absorbent material to reduce their radar cross-sections when viewed from ahead. Because it was command/semi-actively guided, Gabriel had only about half the effective range of a Styx, but the Israelis also believed that the human operators involved could overcome problems like electronic deception. Finally, the Israelis knew that the boats they faced carried only limited numbers of weapons, two for a *Komar*, four for an *Osa*.

The Israeli tactic was to run in, firing long range chaff to create false targets. Their opponents took that bait, and fired most of their Styx at the chaff clouds. Many went wild, since few if any boats stayed on course long enough to run up gyros. The Israelis hoped, too, that by reducing their boats' radar cross-section well below that of the chaff clouds they could evade any Styx which did not get caught in the false targets. That proved to be the case (a single Styx was shot down by machine cannon fire). Once the Styx had been largely exhausted, the Israeli boats closed in to fire their Gabriels. They were extremely successful, suffering no casualties at all while destroying the Egyptian and Syrian missile boat forces. Gabriel was widely exported, and both South Africa (Skorpioen) and Taiwan (Hsiun Feng I) made their own versions.

In France, Aerospatiale realised that a new missile market had been created. The company already made a radar-guided air-launched anti-ship missile, Kormoran. It combined Kormoran guidance, a motor already developed for the Anglo-French Martel air-to-surface missile, and the aerodynamics of another such weapon,

AS 30, to create Exocet. This missile, very widely sold, sank HMS *Sheffield* and the large container ship *Atlantic Conveyor* in the Falklands. It also damaged numerous tankers during the Iran–Iraq war. Like Styx, Exocet is a fire-and-forget weapon. The Italian-French Otomat is somewhat similar in concept, but larger, with greater range thanks to its turbojet engine. Unlike Exocet, Otomat Mk 2 (the only version in service) can accept mid-course guidance and is therefore more useful against distant targets.

Meanwhile, the US Navy began work on an anti-ship missile of its own, Harpoon. Harpoon was conceived as an air-to-surface weapon, to be carried by P-3 Orion maritime patrol aircraft. It was then recast as a dual-use weapon, to provide existing destroyers and frigates with a counter to Soviet anti-ship missiles. Unlike the small fast attack craft for which weapons such as Gabriel and Exocet were conceived, these ships already had missile launchers on board, and space was limited. Harpoon was conceived as a useful add-on, rather than as a main battery. It therefore had to fit the existing launchers, most notably the ASROC box and Tartar/SM-1 launchers, particularly the ubiquitous single-arm Mk 13. It had to be a fire-and-forget weapon, simply because such ships had no space for an additional fire control system. These considerations limited the size of the missile and, in effect, determined the size of its warhead. The result was extremely successful and widely exported. In addition to its air- and surface-launched variants, Harpoon has been produced in an encapsulated submarine-fired version, Sub-Harpoon. It was first used in combat against Libya in 1986, when it neutralised a Libyan *Nanuchka* class missile

corvette. Given its ancestry, it is ironic that most Harpoons are carried aboard surface ships, not in launchers with other types of missiles, but rather in standard separate canisters, typically in groups of eight (four point to port, four to starboard).

The Soviets produced a very similar turbojet-powered missile, Kh-35 (SS-N-25). It is likely to enter service in 1994; four such missiles can replace one SS-N-2, *eg* on board a *Tarantul*. Kh-35 is a substantial departure from normal Soviet/Russian practice, in that, like Western anti-ship missiles, it has a small warhead. As in the case of Harpoon, an encapsulated submarine-launched version is planned (but apparently does not yet exist).

Long range anti-ship missiles

At first the Western missiles were generally limited to the electronic horizon. They were aimed using either radar (which might see well beyond the horizon under ducting conditions) or electronic support measures (ESM). As range increased, some form of special over-the-horizon targeting became necessary. Many Western frigates and even corvettes carry helicopters for just this purpose. The Italian version of Otomat Mk 2 can be controlled directly by the helicopter (the French version, sold to Saudi Arabia, is controlled by the firing ship, which receives data from the helicopter). Thus the advent of missiles changed the shape of many ships, which otherwise would not have needed flight decks (since they were not intended mainly for anti-submarine operations).

Beside the short range weapons, the Soviets

produced an entirely different class of anti-ship missiles, of much longer range. When the Soviet navy was ejected from the strategic mission in 1959, it found a replacement: dealing with Western strike carriers. The only available long range missiles were strategic cruise (SS-N-3 [P-5]) and ballistic (SS-N-4) missiles. A new generation of strategic weapons, suitable for firing from underwater, was under development, the SS-N-12 (P-35) ramjet cruise missile and the SS-N-5 ballistic weapon. For each class the Soviets adopted a two-step approach, to provide interim and then more satisfactory capability.

Interim capability was provided by a substantial nuclear warhead, on the theory that, if the missile arrived anywhere near its target, it could cause substantial damage. In the case of the cruise missile, command guidance could place the warhead near the target. The launching ship or submarine tracked the missile as it flew out, correcting its aim point (this version was P-7). Because such guidance was not particularly satisfactory, as many missiles as possible were needed. The existing cruise missile submarine, *Echo*, was modified with a fourth twin launcher and with the necessary tracking and command systems. At the same time the surviving SS-N-3 surface platform, the *Kynda* class cruiser, was provided with similar electronics. These missiles were all fired well beyond the horizon. Target information was provided by a Bear-D bomber equipped with a large surface-search radar, designated Big Bulge.

Ballistic missiles could not be command-guided. They could be concentrated on a choke point through which a carrier battle group could be expected to pass. A new missile, which became SS-N-6, was designed; presumably its main virtue was that it could be fired much more quickly than its predecessors, arriving more promptly in response to intelligence. As in the case of the cruise missile, more weapons were much better than fewer. A ballistic missile submarine already under design carried six such missiles; its capacity was doubled to twelve (eventually it was redesigned again to become the sixteen-tube *Yankee* class strategic submarine).

The next stage was to provide each kind of missile with a seeker. That was relatively simple in the case of a cruise missile, although the design of the ramjet P-35, with its sharply pointed nose, did not lend itself to such modifi-

The US Harpoon was designed for minimum impact on the carrying ship, and being a fire-and-forget weapon needs little more than the space to bolt on the canisters (usually arranged so the blast is vented offboard). As such it can be carried by very small ships, as here demonstrated by the hydrofoil USS Pegasus. *(USN)*

cation. As a fallback, the guidance package was applied to the existing P-5, the guided version of which was designated P-25. In this version the missile relayed a radar picture back to the launching ship or submarine. The platform could not command it to attack any particular target, but it could use the picture to decide how to guide the next missile toward the target area. This version was not completely satisfactory, because P-25 was only barely transonic. A target could move quite far while it flew. Furthermore, the Bear-D provided the target with warning (for a time Western sailors said that two Bear-Ds in the morning presaged an attack in the afternoon). The Soviet plan was far more elegant. P-35 would have been teamed with a radar ocean reconnaissance satellite (RORSAT) or electronic ocean reconnaissance satellite (EORSAT), reporting down to a ship or submarine via a special data link (called Punch Bowl by Nato). P-35 was eventually designated SS-N-12 by Nato. By 1962 it was clearly less than successful, so a new missile, P-500, based on the turbojet SS-N-3, was developed. It was quite successful; its Nato designation is SS-N-19. SS-N-12 was eventually brought into service; it appeared only on board *Kiev* class carriers and *Slava* class cruisers.

For ballistic missiles, the Soviets conceived a manoeuvrable re-entry vehicle homing on radar emissions: Nato designated the missile SS-NX-13. Development was quite difficult; the missile was not tested until 1973. By that time the Soviet navy was once again much involved in strategic matters, and the Soviet Union had signed the first Strategic Arms Limitation Treaty. Every SS-NX-13, then, would crowd out a nuclear missile aimed at the United States. That was hardly a good bargain. Moreover, the

US Navy demonstrated a series of radar decoys clearly intended to derange SS-NX-13. This line of development was allowed to die out.

Both cruise and ballistic missiles differed from the small-ship missiles in a fundamental way. A small-ship missile relies on shipboard sensors. It is aimed out to a range and bearing *relative to the firing platform*. Because they began as strategic weapons, the big cruise and ballistic missiles were always aimed at geographical co-ordinates, not at co-ordinates relative to the ship or submarine firing them. That way they could take advantage of external targeting data, which would generally be provided in geographical terms (the word would be that the carrier was at some latitude and longitude, not 500nm from the ship bearing 060 degrees). This type of orientation has apparently survived in all later versions.

These were all very big missiles, far out of the small-combatant league. About 1960 the Soviets estimated that, because it was about twice as fast as SS-N-3 and would have its own seeker, P-35 would be about four times as effective. A new missile cruiser, Project 1134 (*Kresta I*) was designed to replace *Kynda*. It had to carry only four missiles, so more space could be allotted to defensive armament. In theory a few such ships would damage the target formation, then other ships armed with a smaller Ametyst or P-50 missile (SS-N-9) would close in to complete the attack. P-50 would have been carried both by a variant of the *Kresta* design and by a modified version of a coastal guard ship (SKR) then in design stage. The latter eventually became the *Krivak* class (Project 1135: at this stage, six missiles each). P-50 was in effect a small equivalent of P-25/35, sent out to a predesignated geographical point and then allowed to turn on

its seeker. Both P-50 and the P-5/7/25/35/500 series were developed by the Chelomei design bureau.

Events soon conspired against this plan. First P-35 failed. *Kresta*s therefore had to make do with four P-25s, which were much less effective. Then attention shifted to strategic warfare and ASW. The P-50 version of *Kresta* was redesigned to carry ASW missiles instead (SS-N-14s, developed from the abortive Berezhniak proposal for the P-50 specification). Similarly, *Krivak* was redesigned to carry a quadruple SS-N-14 launcher forward. A very large coastal attack boat, *Nanuchka* (Project 1234), was apparently designed to make up for the loss of coast defence P-50s in the *Krivak*s.

Cruise missile submarines were designed in parallel with these surface ships. P-50 itself suffered from protracted development, and as an interim measure Styx (P-20) was adapted to underwater launch (Nato called this version SS-N-7).

The anti-ship missile requirement did not, of course, vanish. In the 1970s the Chelomei design bureau developed a new fast missile, P-80, to replace P-50; it is carried aboard *Sovremmennyy* class destroyers. A folding-fin version, P-100, is carried aboard submarines equipped with 65cm torpedo tubes. Nato designates both P-80/100 and 3M80 as versions of SS-N-22, but as of mid 1993 there is every evidence that they are quite distinct weapons.

The US Navy fell into its own version of the Soviet long range anti-ship missiles almost by accident. About 1970 US submariners became very interested in a new concept – a big missile-firing submarine which might attack Soviet surface action groups. The Soviet navy had first brought surface ship concentrations into the Mediterranean in 1967, and there was real concern that they might destroy US carriers as the opening move in a war at sea. A big submarine might be able to hit them first. Otherwise, the carrier, so vulnerable to a first strike, would be the main US anti-ship weapon. This idea, for a long range supersonic anti-ship missile, was combined with a proposal for a very large nuclear submarine powered by a new 60,000shp reactor. There was also interest, both in the navy and in the air force, in a new generation

Four groups of twin canister launchers for SS-N-12 SSMs on the forecastle of the Soviet carrier Kiev. *The ship carries reloads, the total missile capacity being put at twenty-four, which suggests in terms of space a high priority for the anti-shipping role. The capabilities of the ship's V/STOL aircraft in that role are not great, so the missiles may be regarded as the main armament.* (MoD, Crown Copyright)

The Soviet cruiser Sovremennyy *carries the new SS-N-22 cruise missile in quadruple launchers in the usual position under the bridge wings. A folding-fin version is also fired by some recent submarines.* (MoD, Crown Copyright)

small strategic cruise missile. The cruise missile became particularly attractive in 1972, as the Strategic Arms Limitation Treaty (SALT) was being negotiated. Because it would exploit US advantages in electronics, the Soviets could not quite duplicate this weapon; it became both a valuable bargaining chip and proof that the Nixon administration, then in power, was not willing to concede strategic superiority to the Soviets. The Chief of Naval Operations, Admiral Elmo Zumwalt, feared that the big tactical cruise missile submarine would consume far too much of his budget. He killed it, but he let the missile survive in the form of a version of the strategic weapon. Since no new class of submarine was wanted, the new missile would have to fit the existing 21in submarine torpedo tube. It became Tomahawk.

In its tactical version, Tomahawk offered a range of 250nm, quite comparable to what the Soviets had in mind. Unlike the Soviets, the US Navy was unwilling to develop a dedicated targeting network (such as an equivalent of Bear-D or RORSAT) to support this essentially secondary capability: it was nice to have Tomahawk, but it was even more important to keep investing in anti-air and anti-submarine warfare, particularly since the budget was tight.

Tomahawk did differ from the Russian missiles in that it was fairly slow. It might take as much as half an hour to arrive at a target area. The US Navy was unwilling to accept any link between missile and launching ship or submarine, partly because links could be jammed and

partly because link activity would warn the target. However, in the half-hour of flight a target might move quite far. A Tomahawk searching for it might well pass alongside, only to be shot down.

A solution was found. Ships generally do not move randomly. If a ship's pattern of movement is known, its future position can be predicted with some confidence, over a period of hours, particularly if the ship has no warning that an attack is developing. A really powerful computer can keep track of surface ships over a very

wide area, predicting their positions using known characteristics. Those positions can be checked periodically. The navy established data fusion centres ashore. Tomahawk-carrying ships were provided with computers capable of maintaining a tactical picture out to beyond Tomahawk range, based on updates from ashore. On this basis they could aim their weapons. Because a Tomahawk might well find itself approaching a group of ships, the missile was provided with a passive radar detector (passive identification device, PID) so that it could pick out the highest-value target.

Unlike the Soviet system of tracking targets using bombers, the US system quietly collected information on all ships within a large area. No one ship could be aware that she was being targeted, so any Tomahawk would arrive as a surprise. The US system did depend largely on co-operation by the targets (*eg* on picking up their radar emissions from time to time), but that had to be accepted. The system worked. It was demonstrated during the Gulf War, when it was used to support the blockade of Iraq by tracking merchant ships approaching that country.

Norman Friedman

The US Tomahawk cruise missile in its anti-ship version.

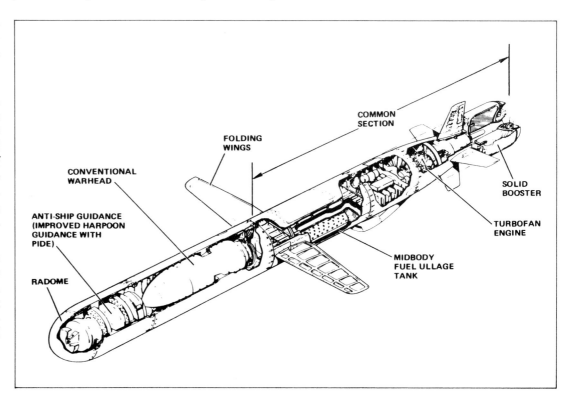

CONVENTIONAL
WARHEAD

FOLDING
WINGS

COMMON
SECTION

ANTI-SHIP GUIDANCE
(IMPROVED HARPOON
GUIDANCE WITH
PIDE)

SOLID
BOOSTER

TURBOFAN
ENGINE

RADOME

MIDBODY
FUEL ULLAGE
TANK

11

Naval Radars and Command Systems

THE naval use of radar evolved, in parallel with the land-based applications, just prior to the outbreak of the Second World War. US and British developments initially centred on the design of air surveillance equipment, while Germany made an early start in designing gunnery fire control sets. The heavy cruiser *Graf Spee* was equipped with such fire control radars at the time of her engagement by the Royal Navy; pictures of the burning wreck clearly show the antenna at the fore top. Indeed, a major incentive behind the British decision to purchase the wreck of the *Graf Spee* was the need to examine this equipment.

When radar development got under way in the mid 1930s the UK, the USA, Germany and Japan were on roughly level footing. However, Japanese researchers discovered that a radar pulse could be detected and its source localised from three times the range at which the return

echo could be received. Thus, they concluded, while radar was an interesting toy, it was of no military value. Japanese research and development effort concentrated on improving night-vision binoculars and other passive sensors, leaving the Japanese navy so far behind in radar technology that the gap could never be made up. As the US Navy developed both more advanced radar systems and, most importantly, the doctrine for the proper use of radar, the comprehensive radar fits of the US warships became of decisive importance. By the end of the war, most US and British warships carried a full range of surface search, air search and fire control radars. This rapid development had major design implications.

Prior to the Second World War ships were weight-critical. The fighting power of a ship was measured by the numbers of guns and torpedoes it carried, in turn determined by the

effect of the resulting topweight on stability. With the dawn of the missile age the situation changed, and warships became volume-critical. Missiles are relatively light in comparison with the volume they occupy, causing severe design challenges in finding sufficient internal volume to carry an adequate missile magazine capacity. The radars were also space-consuming, not least because their vacuum-tube technology was chronically unreliable and required the storage of large quantities of spares. These factors resulted in a generation of ships that were bloated in appearance and usually derided by the ill-informed. Modern warships are power-critical, their fighting capability being determined by their electronic sensors and command systems. These are major consumers of electrical power, the scale of which can be judged from the fact that if a US CG-47 class cruiser runs her SPY-1 radar continuously at full power, her unrefuelled range is cut from 7000 to 5000nm.

The importance of this sensor fit is usually neglected, at best being included as an after-thought. Most naval reference books list a ship's missile magazine capacity and the number of launch rails, yet rarely the number of guidance channels provided by the fire control radars. A modern warship lives or dies by its sensors. Of these, the most important, and undoubtedly the most expensive, are its radars. Area for area there are more radar systems on a modern warship than anywhere else on earth.

The silhouette of a modern warship is dominated by its electronic equipment and, with radars and ECM gear competing for topside space, sensor considerations often dictate the design of superstructure. The Russian destroyer Sovremennyy *is typical in this respect. Most prominent at the fore masthead is the massive Top Steer 3-D search radar with a Palm Front navigational/surface search radar ahead of it. Also distinctly visible are the small searchlight-like directors called Bass Tilt (abreast the bridge, for the 30mm gatling guns), and Front Dome (about the bridge, and abreast the main mast, for the SA-N-7 SAM system). Less evident are ECM and ESM gear, which also need space aloft. (MoD, Crown Copyright)*

The characteristic 'double bedstead' AKE-2 antenna of the British Type 965 radar, carried here by HMS Bristol. *This ship was the sole survivor of a planned class of carrier escorts, which were to have mounted a sophisticated Anglo-Dutch 3-D radar called Broomstick (Type 988), itself cancelled due to escalating costs. It was to have been carried inside a large dome above the bridge, whose flat top is a survivor of the original layout. The Type 965 was one of the last low-frequency search radars in naval service and survived until the 1980s in some ships.* (MoD, Crown Copyright)

Conventionally, naval radars are described by their frequency bands. Originally these were designated by a system devised during the Second World War, but advancing technology made this increasingly complex and difficult to use. The older system has now been replaced by a rationalised convention in which radar frequency bands are designated in a series running from A up to K. A- and B-band radars were common during the 1950s but have now largely been superseded by higher frequency systems. The last Western radar in this category was the British Type 965, which operated in the B-band. As frequency increases, the radar gains precision at the expense of range.

Also high-frequency radars have smaller antennas than low-frequency sets. Usually naval radars operate in the D-Band to K-band, with a few remaining systems in the A/B/C-bands and a very few higher than K-band. Other defining factors for radars are peak power, pulse repetition frequency (PRF) and pulse duration. The product of PRF and pulse duration is the duty cycle, the proportion of total time that the radar set is transmitting. This figure, multiplied by the peak power, gives the average radiated power of the radar. This average radiated power determines how well a given radar is able to detect a target. Because detection is cumulative, a large number of weak echoes will have the same effect as a small number of strong returns. The detectability of an individual echo is dependant upon the peak energy and on the duration of that return.[1]

The naval environment presents an especially difficult environment for radar operations. The relatively small size of ships means that large numbers of emitter antennas are close to each other and also to the structure of the ship. This results in mutual interference between the emitters and in distortions and false returns from the plating of masts and superstructure. Radars are also seriously affected by backscatter from the sea surface, a restriction that is particularly serious when attempting to locate or engage sea-skimming targets. At low frequencies (for example the B-band used by the old British Type 965 radars), signals reflected from the sea surface and the direct path signals can interfere constructively and destructively to form lobe patterns. Even the lowest lobes are at a considerable angle of elevation above the sea surfaces, restricting coverage against low flying targets. At high altitudes the lobing effect actually enhances range coverage. The lobing effect itself causes the targets to fade in and out of detection as they approach, and the ranges at which this occurs can be used as a measure of target altitude. These high-altitude characteristics were quoted (disingenuously – the real reason being that limited research and development funds had been switched to other areas, most notably electronic warfare and command systems) by the UK Ministry of Defence (MoD) as reasons for maintaining the Type 965 radar in service long after most other nations had switched to D- or E/F-band operation.

A radar's ability to distinguish objects at different ranges is a function of the pulse width, pulse duration and PRF. Since radars measure distance by the time differential between the emission of a pulse and receiving its echo, they cannot discriminate between a distant echo, received after the next pulse has been transmitted, and a near return received shortly after the original pulse has gone out. This problem, referred to as the second-time-around or STA, limits maximum effective radar range to half the effective time interval between pulses. Since radar signals travel at the speed of light (300,000 km/sec), this means that the unambiguous maximum range for a 1000pps radar will be about 150km. Thus a contradiction exists between probability of detection (attained by using a high PRF) and range of detection (best achieved by using a low PRF). Most shipborne long range surveillance radars use low PRF solutions, while radars used for fire control purposes use high PRF rates.

One technical solution to this contradiction lies in the use of pulse-doppler technology. This uses very high PRF rates yet typically detect targets well beyond their maximum unambiguous range. This is achieved because actual detection range is dependent upon output power, the product of peak power, pulse width and PRF. In effect the pulse-doppler radars are a compromise between operating at a pure frequency (continuous wave or CW) and pulsing. Pulse-doppler radars use shifts in the frequency of the return echoes to measure target velocity. Just as a pulse radar is limited in its unambiguous range, so a pulse-doppler radar is limited in its range of unambiguous velocities.

Many components of a radar set, for example the waveguides, can carry only a finite amount of energy before they break down. An overloaded waveguide will arc, resulting in no trans-

1. Dr Norman Friedman, *World Naval Weapons Systems* (Annapolis 1991).

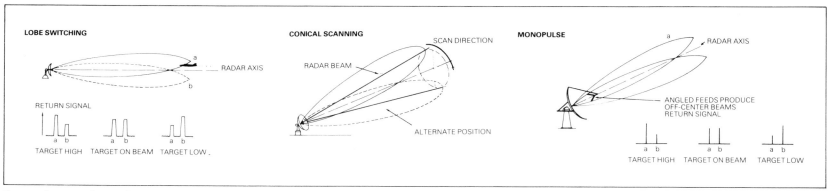

Some radar operating modes.

mitted signal. Since radar range depends on average power rather than peak power, a solution to this problem is to spread the power over a frequency-variable pulse (referred to as a chirp). The returned echo can be compressed into the equivalent of a very short, high intensity pulse. This approach also has advantages from the stealth aspect. These pulse-compression radars spread their energy over a series of frequencies using a short pulse in each. Although the aggregate energy may be large, there is relatively little peak energy in each. Since radar warning receivers and ESM systems work on peak energy, such receivers may find it difficult to detect these radars. A number of radars are deliberately designed to exploit this approach. Perhaps the ultimate is the Thomson-CSF Scout radar, which extends the pulse train effectively continuously across a range of frequencies. This class of radar is called the Frequency-Modulated Continuous Wave (FMCW) system.

Current technical developments fall into three areas. Firstly, solid-state transmitters are replacing the older valve units. This trend is quite distinct from the earlier shift from valve to solid-state technology for the radar control and data processing units. This left a single large vacuum tube unit, the radar transmitter, to be cooled and protected. Solid-state transmitters are now powerful enough to replace this unit, with substantial gains in reliability and system stability.

A second major development is the appearance of cheaper and more reliable forms of electronic beam forming and movement. Previously phase shifters were expensive and unreliable, so many radars used one-dimensional frequency scanning only. With the development of reliable and economic phase shifters, their use has become practical for a new generation of radar sets. This leads to the development of an active-array radar in which the elements of the antenna themselves transmit the signal. This eliminates the need to apply a phase shift to a signal produced by a single unitary transmitter.

Finally, there is the evolution of software-controlled transmission. Previously, pulse characteristics were defined by hard wiring which was extremely difficult to change. Although most radar sets have special war-only operating modes (WARMS), these too were hard-wired and, once compromised, could not easily be changed. The introduction of software control of transmitter characteristics enables those features to be changed easily and radically. Recognising the system using electronic support measures (ESM) is thus made substantially more difficult. It is still possible by a detailed examination of the pulse structure, but these techniques require orders of magnitude more effort.

Warship radars fall into four classes. These are the navigational radars, search radars, target acquisition radars and fire control radars. To this should be added a number of special-purpose sets: for example, precision approach radars permitting aircraft operations under adverse conditions, point-defence gun radars and a variety of others. Many radars may fall into two or more classes. For example, a small radar serving as a navigation radar on a missile cruiser may well also be the primary surface search radar on a missile-armed FAC or the fire control radar on an offshore patrol vessel (OPV).[2]

Navigational radars

Every ship in naval or paramilitary service, from the harbour defence motor launch or utility landing craft to the largest nuclear-powered aircraft carrier, has at least one navigational radar. At their simplest, these are ruggedised versions of commercial sets sold for use on privately-owned yachts. At the other end of the scale is a range of specialised military systems with capabilities approximating those of surface-search sets. The prime function of these sets is the provision of precise and accurate navigational data. In the military environment, this information is used for conventional navigation and collision avoidance, staging ambushes, minelaying

operations, inserting special forces and policing the seas in anti-piracy and anti-smuggling operations.

When used for these purposes, the situation where precise navigation is most essential is also where the dangers of the radar being detected by ESM are highest. This inherent contradiction is being resolved by the development of the frequency-modulated continuous wave (FMCW) radar. This exploits the fact that ESM equipment and the anti-radar missile function on peak power outputs. FMCW radars utilise a very low average power output of 1W, which compares very favourably with the 10kW peak and 10W average power of conventional pulse radars. Because of this low power output, the radar is only detectable from distances of 2.1km (1.3nm) or less. Also, in-service ESM receivers do not have the capability to decode the simple linear frequency modulator of this type of radar. FMCW radars have performances which compare favourably with similar conventional pulse radars, from 15km to 20km (9–12nm) for ships of 400 tons upwards. If the range of facilities offered by a military navigation radar is to be used, then it would appear that the FMCW system will become the norm for radars in this class.

Another approach to covert operation is to bury the radar transmissions within the mass of civilian traffic. Here the ruggedised version of civilian radars comes into its own. This end of the spectrum is exemplified by Racal's Decca 1226 – probably the most widely used maritime radar in the world. In a busy shipping lane, for example the English Channel or the routes off the coast of Southeast Asia, it is quite impossible to disentangle the warships using such radars from commercial traffic. One method used by maritime patrol aircraft in the Far East has been to fly straight at a suspect ESM contact and hope that a nervous captain turns off the ship's radar.

2. *Land & Sea-based Radars Market Review*, Radar Market Intelligence Report, Forecast International (Newtown, Connecticut 1993).

Search radars

These radars can be split into two groups, tasked with providing coverage against air and surface targets. Again there is considerable overlap between these two groups, with a number of sets being promoted as dual-purpose. In general, air-search systems operate in the D-band while surface-search sets operate in the E/F-bands. The design of a search radar allows it to sweep an area rapidly, with a high probability of being able to detect a target at greatest possible range. This requires the use of a broad search beam, in order to maximise the amount of pulses on the target per scan.

The Second Gulf War provided mixed signals on the use of air-search radars. In the northern Gulf, the defensive air control mission was allocated to the frigates and destroyers of the Royal Navy. This included ingress/egress control to and from Iraqi air space. It has been reported that the Royal Navy ships relied heavily on the extensive and highly sophisticated ESM equipment built into their integrated combat systems. Their long range Type 1022

The Type 1022 long range search radar of the British Type 42 destroyer Liverpool. *Originally called STIR (Surveillance and Target Indication Radar), the Marconi antenna is associated with a Dutch LW-08 radar receiver. On the mast platform is the Type 1006 navigational radar, surmounted by a topmast carrying ECM/ESM gear and a HF/DF aerial.* (L & L van Ginderen)

radars were considered to be secondary in importance.

Yet the low D-band Type 1022 revealed a previously unsuspected ability to acquire and track the much-vaunted USAF F-117 'Stealth Fighter'. HMS *Gloucester* routinely picked up all F-117 flights entering its area of responsibility at ranges of between 65 and 195km (40 and 120 miles). This was due to a combination of the hot, humid atmosphere, surface ducting and the surface of the sea reflecting radar energy scattered by the design of the F-117 back to the transmitter. HMS *Gloucester*'s radar operators quickly learned to distinguish the highly unusual 'flickering' radar signature of the F-117 from the mass of other transmissions. On at least one occasion such data, relayed to a Type 22 frigate, enabled the latter to lock her Sea Wolf missiles on to the F-117. This was done by the Sea Wolf fire control complex being alerted by the Type 1022 radars on nearby Type 42 destroyers. The target was then picked up using the Sea Wolf electro-optical fire control system, which was used to point the radar. Whatever the radar picked up from the position indicated by the EO system was assumed to be the target and treated accordingly.

There is a serious danger that emphasis on passive techniques will be taken too far. The fact is that, at present, there is no substitute for radar as an area surveillance sensor. Reliance on passive sensors is only viable as long as the opponents continue the indiscriminate use of their radar systems. As strict EMCON (emission control) techniques become universal, the role of ESM systems will, by definition, decrease. Even with modern ESM systems, it is relatively safe to allow radars to emit quick flashes at irregular intervals, although the risk goes up logarithmically with the duration and frequency of the transmission bursts. The challenge will be to gain as much information as possible from those brief, infrequent transmissions. This implies that the counter to ESM technology lies not so much in terms of the radars themselves, but with the command control system into which they are integrated. The next decade can thus expect to see integrated radar/C³I systems replacing the current generation of surveillance systems. The Swedish Giraffe radar already has such facilities built into its land-based variants, and these have been extended to the Sea Giraffe as the core of an integrated warship C³I fit. The US Navy's Aegis system is perhaps the leading example of an integrated air search/C³I system.

Increasing the radar range has a number of significant benefits in addition to the obvious advantage of increasing the area coverage of radar systems. ESM sets do not give accurate

bearings and provide only very approximate range data. Most ESM systems have a limiting bearing accuracy of 2 degrees, with accuracies of 6 degrees common. Thus if a radar set is detected at a considerable distance, the resulting information will be insufficiently accurate to permit a fire control solution to be developed. However, contact by the radar will be sufficiently precise to permit further action.

One possible route to increasing the range of radar coverage lies in adapting over-the-horizon (OTH) radars to shipboard use. OTH radars of the surface-wave type are best suited for this role. Upon transmission of vertically polarised radio waves close to a sea surface, electrical currents in the water cause adhesion of the radio waves to the water surface and thus travel around the Earth's curvature. It is also likely that the reflected energy will adhere to the sea surface for the return journey. Research on the systems has been orientated towards coupling specialised processing with standard HF communications equipment. Technical limitations, such as how to generate sufficient power at longer wavelengths, or how to build sensitive receivers and antennas of manageable size, had kept this alternative experimental.

Target acquisition radars

The role of these radars (also called target indication or TI radars) is to provide an intermediate level of capability between the broad-brush long range search and detection capability of the surveillance radars and the precise short range fire control systems. On paper the difference between a search radar and a target acquisition radar is that the former continually scans for new targets while the latter tracks specific contacts, handed over from the search system.

This class of radars was developed as a result of the very wide broad-beam characteristics of the early radar sets, such as the British Type 281, used during the Second World War. These were retained postwar, partly because insufficient funds were available to equip the Royal Navy with later, narrow-beam sets and partly because the wide beam meant more pulses on each target, extending the range of the radar (and probably explaining the success of Royal Navy radars in detecting the F-117). However, the contacts obtained lacked the precision required to point fire control radars and provided only the most minimal height-finding capability. The target acquisition set would refine the contact and gain altitude data by nodding. Effectively, the long range search set would acquire further out than the narrow-beam set, then trade this advantage for the

The main components of the US Mk 86 fire control system (for surface combatants like the Virginia *and* Spruance *classes) are the SPQ-9 target acquisition radar, inside the radome, and the SPG-60 tracking radar, whose dish antenna is below. (Lockheed Electronics)*

Type 992Q radar on the mainmast of the British Type 42 destroyer Liverpool. *An E/F-band radar, with fully stabilised antenna, it has a range of about 30nm on an air target. It functions as a general air search radar in Type 21 and 22 frigates, but is used for target indication on missile ships like the Type 42. (L & L van Ginderen)*

craft than 3-D pencil beam sets, and this could be of great importance as stealth technology spreads.

The US Navy does not agree with this assessment. They argue that the installation of too many radars on a limited area of superstructure results in blanking of search arcs and serious electronic interference between the sets. Interestingly, the *Perry* class missile frigates approach a European solution in that their Mk 92 fire control system includes a target indicating set which gains altitude data by helical scanning. However, the US Navy believes that when all the radars on a ship are merged by, for example, the US SYS-1 or its equivalent, the debatable advantages offered by target indicating radars become almost meaningless. In contrast, all the next generation of European AAW systems will retain the provision of a TI radar in addition to search and fire control sets.

The use of these radars highlights a major difference in electronic outfit philosophy between US ship designers and those in the rest of the world. The US Navy is unique in having the luxury of operating within concentric rings of defences many hundreds of miles deep, starting with the outer air battle and ending with the Phalanx point-defence guns. European navies do not have this luxury. Non-US warships rarely have more than two defensive rings surrounding them, and often only one. This makes it essential that each phase of the defensive system should operate at maximum efficiency, a consideration which they believe requires the provision of the separate target acquisition sets. This limited battle horizon also explains the limited ammunition storage on many Royal Navy warships, particularly the Type 42 destroyers. These ships would be unable to get off more than two or three salvoes in an engagement, totalling some 4–5 missiles. Thus a 22-round

added time taken for the TI radar to refine that contact and hand over to the fire control system.

At first sight, the evolution of three-dimensional and track-while-scan systems would appear to have eliminated the need for an intermediate level between search and fire control. The 3-D radars use pencil beams to provide range, bearing and altitude data precisely enough to point the fire control radars without an intermediate stage. These radars also provide zenith cover not possible with the search/TI combination. However, this merging of functions has not occurred outside the US Navy. Partly this is the result of the provision of a separate target indicating function being so firmly established in the operational doctrine of European navies. Also, many European navies believe that the dichotomy in roles between

search and fire control is so broad that the intermediate target acquisition radar, for example Type 996 on British Type 42 destroyers, remains essential. The new generation of 3-D target acquisition radars eliminate many of the time delays incurred with older systems. Royal Navy sources also suggest that experience in the Gulf has proved that the fan-beam search radars are much more capable of detecting stealth air-

The Perry *class FFG* USS *Aubrey Fitch. The ships of this class have a Mk 92 fire control system, using a licence-built Dutch WM-28 radar in the spherical radome over the bridge; target indication is via the separate STIR antenna between the lattice mast and 3in gun. The system controls both gun and missile, and can handle four separate targets. (L & L van Ginderen)*

magazine provides for at least four separate engagements prior to depletion. (Cynics suggest that this limited capacity also reduces the size of the magazine explosion when the ships are hit.)

If, as the Second Gulf War strongly suggests, stealth technology is of strictly limited value over the sea, the roles of target acquisition radars will be enhanced. If the stealth techniques used to get attack aircraft close to their targets undetected are shown to be relatively ineffective, naval attack aircraft will have to place greater reliance on stand-off weapons in order to engage warships. This, in turn, implies that the ships will have to acquire the attacking launch platforms at greater ranges. It also implies that designers of anti-shipping weapons systems will concentrate on designing performance into the stand-off missile rather than into the launch platform. Aerospatiale is already following this route by designing their latest versions of the Exocet missile to follow corkscrew trajectories from a variety of different attack angles. So successful has this programme been that the French navy has abandoned plans to install close-in gun systems on its ships and will rely purely on missiles for its anti-missile defences.

The next generation of anti-ship missiles will retain the complex evasive courses of the current weapons, but combined with high supersonic speeds and greatly increased ranges. After a detailed operational evaluation the Royal Navy concluded that gun-based anti-missile systems are ineffective against current sea-skimming missile threats, let alone against these advanced systems. Operational analysis has shown that a Goalkeeper 30mm close-in weapon system (CIWS) is likely to destroy an inbound 'today-standard' SSM less than 800m from the platform, while the 20mm Phalanx is likely to kill its target no more than 300m out. At these distances, wreckage from the missile will still strike the ship, causing widespread damage and fires. This is why the new Type 23 ASW frigates have not been equipped with gun-based CIWS.

An added threat is the development of the new Russian aero-ballistic anti-ship missiles fired from a rotary launcher on the Tu-22M.4 Backfire. These run in at over 90,000ft before diving near-vertically on their targets at a speed in excess of Mach 5. A saturation attack of this sort could easily be launched by one or two aircraft, dramatically increasing the threat posed by a small force of such aircraft in the hands of a Third World power. The advent of these new threats makes unacceptable the inherent hand-over delay between the radars (especially a problem on ships that do not have integrated combat systems).

Reaction times can be reduced by netting together existing radars, as in the US New Threat Upgrade (NTU). This has all the search radars on a ship feeding into a common computer combat system, the SYS-1, a technique completely dependant upon the provision of auto-detection and tracking. Automatic target detection is the key to automated combat system operation in that it maintains a constant alert status superior to any human operator. The disadvantage comes in its inability to match the sensitivity of the expert radar operator, working at a peak state of alertness. Here again is a fundamental difference in perception between the US design philosophy and that of Europe.

A European assessment (with which US radar designers profoundly disagree) is that US radar designers attempt to automate all possible functions on the basis that human judgement cannot be trusted. European practice, on the other hand, is to retain a considerable proportion of human influence within the decision loop, on the grounds that machines lack the inherent flexibility necessary for proper performance. This European assessment fails to recognise that the US Navy problem lies not in whether judgement can be trusted, but in handling the massive number of potential targets. The US Navy was faced with controlling a multi-phased battle stretching out to over 200nm, probably incorporating friendly and neutral contacts. In contrast, the European battle horizon is barely 50nm (limited by the range of on-ship missiles) and encompasses a much smaller number of potential targets.

This debate reflects some of the Royal Navy's criticisms of the Aegis system following operations during the Second Gulf War. British officers who have visited US Aegis ships believe that the system denies the radar operators access to raw radar data and places far too much reliance on the processing capability of the system. Aegis provides operators with the facility to select the rules for handling data, including changing the scan programme and blanking some targets to avoid system overload. One problem here is that there is a tendency to forget the rules adopted and to confuse synthetic video (which is much clearer and easier to understand) with reality. This was illustrated by the Cessna incident, in which a light aircraft was detected by a 2-D radar but not by Aegis, because the velocity filter rules in force washed the contact out. Such levels of automation have historically been unaffordable by European navies (which have learned, of necessity, to do without), and only the rapidly declining cost of computer power is making them available.

Data fusion is also affecting the target acquisition function. A good example is the destruction of Iraqi Silkworm missiles during the Second Gulf War. The coastal battery fire control radar was detected by HMS *Gloucester*'s UAA-2 Abbey Hill ESM system. The ship's action information system relayed this data to the Type 992 target acquisition and Type 909(I) fire control radars, directing them to the exact point where the missiles were expected to appear. The Silkworm appeared exactly where predicted and effectively flew into the Sea Dart missile fired at it.[3]

The natural progression from automatic target detection is non-co-operative target recognition (NCTR). In this technology, the sensor has the capability of distinguishing the nature of a target without requiring an IFF signal to determine whether it is friendly or hostile. One method of achieving this is blade count, another may be systems intended to spoof enemy aircraft into activating their IFF systems. Until very recently it was assumed that this type of technology would not be seen in a deployable form for many years. Reports from the Second Gulf War, however, confirmed that at least some US aircraft were fitted with highly classified systems of this type. Rules of engagement stated that potential targets would have to have their identity confirmed by two independent means, with NCTR being acceptable as one.[4]

Another approach to the target recognition problem is inverse synthetic aperture radar (ISAR). This is a very new technology and, up to the present, has only been used for identifying ships. To use this technique for imaging aircraft would require a massive increase in computing power and data processing technology which is not presently available. However, the increase in computer capability over the last decade has been so great that a number of radar companies now believe that ISAR will be a viable technique for aircraft recognition within a decade.

Synthetic aperture radars (SAR) achieve a very high level of resolution, suitable for imaging, from the motion of an aircraft along a given course. High resolution normally requires a very large antenna. A conventional radar scans as it is moved, thus, by the time it has been moved a significant distance, the radar is no longer looking at the same scene. SARs do not scan but stare in the same direction. This means that pulses emitted at any point on the SAR's flightpath contribute to the radar picture. The

3. Antony Preston (ed), *NAVINT* (8 November 1991).

4. Dr Norman Friedman, *Desert Victory: The War for Kuwait* (Annapolis 1991).

accuracy of the picture so compiled is a product of the aircraft's speed along a flightpath, the distance it travels and the integration time. The result is limited by the amount of memory built into the SAR, since later images have to be compared with earlier ones. SAR gives spectacular results but can look only sideways. Targets tend to be straight ahead.

ISAR solves this problem by using the motion of the target rather than the platform. The results lack the quality attained with SAR but do provide sufficient definition for profile recognition. Perhaps the most interesting use for this feature is in the Russian SS-N-22 anti-ship missile. This has an ISAR homing head which relays the target image back to the launch platform by a video datalink (either directly or via an intermediate relay station). The operator can then either confirm the missile's decision to attack a specific target or override it and order the SS-N-22 to search again. This technique has obvious advantages in defeating decoys and other countermeasures approaches.

The shooting down of the Iranian Airbus over the Arabian Gulf in July 1988 is a highly complicated case where the importance of displaying the targeting information obtained in a concise and unambiguous form is combined with the difficulty of ascertaining the intentions and capability of the target. This was an enormously complex situation in which, even if the target and its course had been unambiguously identified, the pilot's intentions remained unclear. He could, for example, have been about to attempt a kamikaze run – a hypothesis supported by the presence of Iranian surface craft (in this context, a diversion) and the distant but relevant presence of an Iranian P-3 Orion (in this scenario a target spotter and airborne control). The *Vincennes'* radar operators were attempting identification friend or foe (IFF) by behaviour patterns, a notoriously tricky operation, and, given the volume of data, it is understandable that they made a mistake.

One possible means of resolving this problem is the widespread adoption of colour displays. The use of multi-colours allows the presentation of a clear, easily assimilated picture but can cause problems with the significant number of colour-blind people. Displays can now present alphanumeric representation of electronic bearing lines and variable range markers, and range-adjustable intrusion alarms against potential collision dangers. The problem this raises is just how much information from a display can be

assimilated by an operator – after all, the display is there to support decision-making. Colour, which permits up to three times as much information to be displayed, is often opposed on exactly that ground.

Fire control radars

These highly precise short-range radars, operating in the I/J- or K-bands, are the teeth of the ship's radar system. These are the radars that steer missiles to their targets and provide the range and bearing solutions for both anti-air and anti-surface gunnery. As a result of this tactical role, fire control radars require precise tracking, and thus a narrow radar beam, which in turn means that the radar can scan only a fairly narrow area with any kind of efficiency.

These radars are being faced with two major threats. One is the danger of counterattack by anti-radar missiles (ARMs) such as HARM or SIDEARM. Means to counter this include spreading operational frequencies to cover additional bands, and the L-band and even M-band are being investigated in this respect. The use of intermittent operation is also a possibility. Here, being on a ship has distinct advantages. Most modern ARMs have the ability to store the last known position of the radar and to proceed to that point for attack. Although a 30kt ship is slow by missile standards, this speed can be sufficient to put enough space between the radar and the missile's destination to ensure a

Refurbished SPG-55B radar directors for Terrier SAMs in American DLGs. The pointed radome reveals a Cassegrain feed system, in which power fed from the rear of the antenna is reflected off a secondary antenna in front of the main reflector. Such a system blocks less of the antenna than a more conventional feed would do. SPG-55B controlled both beam-riding and semi-active homing missiles. (Sperry)

clean miss. A further point is that the missiles tend to home in on the emitting antenna, raising the possibility of making that antenna as cheap and easily replaceable as possible with multiple redundancy where practical. As a result recent fire control radar designs place the radar antenna as far as possible from anything valuable and use computing power to resolve the resulting parallax problems.

The ARM threat has caused many European radar designers to question the wisdom of installing the SPY-1 Aegis antenna in the bridge structure. The US position is that the threat represented by anti-radar missiles is overstated, since the nature of the missile means that it flies in a highly convenient flightpath for interception. Also many characteristics of the SPY-1 radar are not fully understood by European designers. Amongst these is the ability of the SPY-1 to scan in a random pattern that an ARM will find difficult to understand – an ability a conventional antenna cannot emulate. Furthermore, the SPY-1 activates for only the last few seconds of the engagement. This feature was adopted as a result of mass raid handling requirements but has valuable anti-ARM implications.

The changing nature of the threats facing modern warships, particularly in the Nato navies, is also likely to affect the development of fire control radars. The shift from superpower confrontation to regional conflict has meant that the danger from mass swamping attacks, containing perhaps hundreds of air-to-surface missiles, has gone. The likely opponents in a regional conflict just do not have these resources. The dangers from land-based attack using conventional iron bombs can be largely ignored unless the crews are specially trained for such attacks or the circumstances are highly unusual – crews used to attacking land targets find it impossible to adapt to trying to hit a target skidding all over the sea at 32kts while firing back with a heavy concentration of guided and unguided weapons. It could be argued that ships do have to come in and support land operations (this coming under the definition of highly unusual circumstances), in which case they are far less mobile. However, when precisely this situation emerged during the Falklands campaign, the majority of the damage inflicted on the Royal Navy was scored by the trained maritime pilots of the Argentine navy, not by the air force pilots thrown into the breach.[5]

The danger is from single salvoes of advanced missiles fired at dawn or dusk in the hope that one or more may leak through the defences. The recent revelation of the new family of Russian aero-ballistic missiles fired from a rotary launcher has alarmingly increased the

5. A R Burden, M I Draper, D A Rough, C R Smith and D L Witton, *Falklands – The Air War*, British Aviation Research Group (Twickenham, Middlesex 1983).

Soviet warships were notable for a multitude of radar and electronics systems. The modern destroyer Bezboyazenny has a Top Plate 3-D air search radar on the fore top, surrounded by three surface search/navigational radars; above the bridge, in the radome, is a Band Stand radar for the SS-N-22 SSM, with a Kite Screech radar director for the 130mm guns behind; Front Dome directors for the SA-N-7 SAMs face outboard, while the superficially similar Bass Tilt for the 30mm Gatling guns faces forward. (L & L van Ginderen)

plausibility of this attack pattern. The political implications of such a hit in a regional conflict are likely to be out of all proportion to the real damage caused (the effects of the destruction of the cruiser ARA *Belgrano* and the destroyer HMS *Sheffield* in the Falklands campaign are cases in point). The requirement therefore will be to defeat limited attacks with a high degree of confidence.

However these problems are resolved, it remains difficult to see how radar fire control can be replaced. No other sensor has the range, precision and poor-weather performance. Electro-optical, infra-red and laser techniques are now being integrated into fire control complexes in order to provide complementary back-up and alternatives to the radar, but the radar remains prime and is likely to stay that way. The case where British Type 22 frigates locked Sea Wolf missiles on to the F-117s is a good illustration.

Russian radar equipment

The USSR produced some effective equipment as well as some ineffectual systems. Semiconductor technology and processing power are two deficiencies which severely constrained options available to the Soviet defence industries. Often relying on vacuum tubes instead of integrated circuits, Soviet equipment is not very easy to use or maintain. Soviet radar designers reputedly placed a high value on making radars workable in varying conditions and by operators with widely disparate levels of ability. Although

this was not achieved in their older systems, newer developments have begun to accomplish this goal.

Just prior to their collapse, the Soviets developed their first naval phased-array radar, designated Sky Watch by Nato. This was reported to have been installed on the last *Kiev* class helicopter carrier, the *Admiral Gorshkov*. In fact this installation (and that on the aircraft carrier *Admiral Kuznetsov*) was 'for show' only and consisted of antennas with no electronic components. An inspection of the *Admiral Kuznetsov* revealed that none of the electronic suite had been installed or showed any sign of being ready in the foreseeable future. Subsequently, very close-up photographs of the antenna arrays showed that they consisted of slabs of concrete. It is now apparent that very serious software development problems had prevented the radars being completed. Funding for the programme was eliminated in 1990, and the aircraft carrier *Varyag* had its superstructure redesigned to accommodate more conventional radars.

The one-radar ship

With four classes of radar and the largest modern warships carrying as many as fifteen to twenty separate radar systems, the complexity of the set-up has become of considerable concern. The sheer number of radars and other electronic systems raises problems of mutual interference. The number of missile launchers on a ship is predicated by electronic interference between the missile guidance beams, not by space,

weight or cost. A resolution to this problem may be a move to a 'one-radar ship', where many functions are combined into a single set.

A first step on to this route has been taken with the evolution of the so-called multi-functional radars. However, the multi-functional radar, due to its very nature, is a bundle of compromises and thus is in need of support from other sensors, including additional radars. One problem is the fact that these radars are expected to handle simultaneously something of the order of 200 targets, while at the same time providing surveillance coverage. When carrying out long range volumetric searches at high data rates, the processing requirements are such that very little excess capacity can be left for other tasks. The same high processing capacity requirements result from the low-level detection and tracking efforts. This is not an insoluble problem, since processing power is now inexpensive and getting more so daily. However, there is still no sign of any navy attempting to move to a one-radar solution – the latest US design, the DDG-51 *Arleigh Burke* destroyers, retain separate navigation radars (SPS-64), missile guidance illuminators (SPG-62), air-search/target acquisition (SPY-1D) and surface-search (SPS-67) sets.

This reluctance is due to the fact that, even as the processing capacity requirement is resolved by natural technology evolution, there is a more fundamental problem with the concept. Even the best-designed, best-equipped and best-crewed ships get hit. Off the coast of Vietnam the USS *Worden*, a guided-missile cruiser, was mistaken by an F-4 fighter for an enemy SAM site. A single Shrike ARM was fired by the F-4. The missile worked perfectly while the cruiser, detecting the missile but assuming it was aimed at a hostile target, took no defensive measures. The resulting explosion shattered the ship's electronic installations and wrecked the Combat Information Center (CIC) leaving the cruiser dead in the water and defenceless. Fifteen years later HMS *Broadsword*, engaged in operations off the Falkland Islands, was strafed by an Argentine Dagger. A single 30mm shell struck the bridge.

Western warships tend to have fewer individual radar systems than Russian equivalents. The latest US surface combatant, the Arleigh Burke *(DDG-51) is built around the SPY-1D radar of the Aegis system, whose fixed arrays are positioned around the bridge. However, the ship has separate SPS-67 surface-search and SPS-64 navigational radars on mast platforms, as well as SPG-62 radar illuminators for the missile systems.* (USN)

With unerring precision it severed the ship's main databus, again effectively knocking out every single electronic system on the ship.

The one-radar ship is appallingly vulnerable to damage of this sort. A single lucky hit on the waveguides, databus or any one of a number of similar components could soft-kill the whole ship. Such a hit need not be from any high-tech weapon – an RPG-7 would do the deed as well as a HARM. Finally, the positioning of the radar to provide all-round coverage is quite impossible and would so severely restrict the rest of the design that the naval engineers preparing the drafts would not find it acceptable. As a result of these many limitations the concept of the one-radar ship probably will not survive.

Integrated combat systems

If a one-radar ship is undesirable (though technically feasible), the other route by which operational efficiency can be maximised is to integrate the output of all the ship's sensors via a common system. The design of common systems reflects the requirements placed upon all warships. These are the need to achieve sea control (guaranteeing that friendly ships stay afloat) and sea denial (ensuring that hostile ships do not). In pursuit of these tasks, warships must continue to go in harm's way. It is not sufficient for emphasis to be placed on ensuring that a warship survives – the purpose of its existence is to wreak havoc on the enemy. In radar terms, this means it will have to carry extended range radars to detect potential threats, multi-channel, long range target acquisition radars to localise, isolate and engage such threats, and improved, integrated fire control radars to defeat attack and to engage hostile platforms. Radars will become even more closely linked with the ship's integrated combat systems and associated with other sensors to maximise situational awareness.

The problem with this situation is that the sheer volume of data generated by a ship's sensors within the modern naval combat environment is beyond the capacity of manual plotting techniques. Without integrated command systems it is impossible for the crew of a modern warship to process, analyse and act upon the data presented to them within the timeframe available to them. Over the last two decades, modern anti-ship weapons have radically reduced this timeframe, while the advent of supersonic anti-

ship missiles and new internal-combustion-powered torpedoes promises further reductions during the course of the 1990s.

The earliest form of combat system automation was the introduction of the CIC during the Second World War. The aircraft carrier battles of 1942 had quickly shown that existing command control capabilities were quite inadequate to handle the large numbers of aircraft involved and to plot the necessary interceptions. Repeatedly, small groups of aircraft penetrated the fighter screens to damage or sink the opposing aircraft carriers. The US Navy responded by establishing a specific area into which all sensor and other relevant data would be fed. At first, this was a very improvised affair. In new-construction ships, a single compartment was designated as being the CIC and the original operators would lay the space out according to their own experience and prejudices. This included the design of the plot, on which the battle situation was manually mapped out (using grease pencils). Effectively, each CIC was customised and no standardisation existed – a factor that led to major differences in capability between apparently identical ships.[6]

Originally designed as an aid in controlling

---

6. John Monsarrat, *Angel on the Yardarm: the Beginnings of Fleet Radar Defense and the Kamikaze Threat* (Newport, Rhode Island 1985).

An early example of the need to transfer data was provided by Project Cadillac, a postwar American attempt to establish operational airborne radar pickets. This Avenger carried an APS-20 radar in the belly radome with a data link to a carrier or radar picket ship, which could thus benefit from the aircraft's far greater radar horizon. (Grumman History Centre)

air battles, the CIC concept proved its value during the vicious night surface battles around Guadalcanal. The introduction of the CIC and growing experience in its use is generally held responsible for the US Navy first equalling and then surpassing the Imperial Japanese Navy in night-fighting techniques. As the war progressed, CIC layouts became more standardised and the system rapidly matured. However, by the late 1950s the manual techniques used in the CIC had been overtaken by tactical developments, particularly with regard to aircraft and air-launched missiles. The initial step was to automate the CIC using the computer technology available at the time. Examples from this era include the British ADA (Action Data Automation) and early versions of the US NTDS (Navy Tactical Data System).

These systems began as computerised track-keepers, with raw radar data being fed into a computer which drove a display system. The computers did not process the track data, and all tactical decisions remained the province of the

7. S E Morrison, *US Naval Operations in World War II*, Vol XIV: *Victory in the Pacific* (Boston 1962).

CIC officer. Subsequently, the tracks generated were treated as computer files permitting the automated calculation of fighter intercept vectors and indicating which targets required particularly urgent attention. Operators still entered targets manually, and there were no dedicated trackers. Instead, the computer formed a track based on a sequence of entered radar blip positions.

Tactical data systems of this type are limited by their computer capacity. The maximum number of track files that can be held is determined by character-string length, since each file must

be designated by a distinct character string. Thus, an 8-bit computer has an 8-character string, giving a maximum of 256 distinct character strings. The total is limited by word length since the address is generally one word. These figures are independent of the amount of memory held within the computer. There are ways around this problem, but they tend to be messy.

Additional shortfalls are caused by incompatibility problems within the electronic systems. A review of weapons and computers reveals a wide range of operating clock speeds and word lengths (8, 16, 32 and 64 bits all being quite common). Linking such dissimilar equipment can cause exceptionally serious problems. For example, when the cruiser USS *California* went to sea on her early trials, it was discovered that the entire weapons suite was inoperative due to software incompatibility. This defect took almost a year to correct, during which time the ship was incapable of combat operations.

The next step onwards from these early computerised systems was to provide the facility to transfer data, and later a tactical picture, between ships. Again, this grew from experience during the Second World War. Faced with the Japanese kamikaze attacks in 1944–45, the US Navy started to deploy radar pickets along the threat axis. This system was quickly expanded to include combat air patrol elements by those radar pickets and early attempts at establishing airborne radar pickets (Project Cadillac).[7] The combat direction system was already turning search radar output into tracks, and the establishment of links permitted track correlation

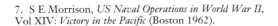
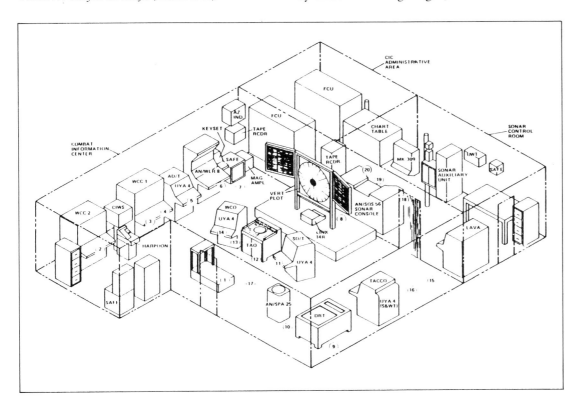

The layout of the CIC (Combat Information Center) in a Perry *(FFG-7) class frigate.*

between ships and allowed the transmission of targeting data.

This requirement resulted in the evolution of a family of Nato-standard datalinks. Link-11 was established as the means of data transfer between ships equipped with NTDS-like combat direction systems. In some cases, most notably the Royal Navy, a modified version designated Link-10 was adopted on technical and financial grounds. A few such RN ships carried both Link-10 and Link-11, these serving as gateway ships between the Link-10 and Link-11 networks. The Royal Navy subsequently adopted Link-11 fleet-wide, and the last of the gateway ships, HMS *Bristol*, has been decommissioned. A second group of datalinks, Link-4, Link-4A and Link-4B, was established for data transfer to aircraft, while an additional system, Link-14, was devised for use by ships without a combat direction system.

Obviously, this inter-ship linkage would work most effectively if there was a level of commonality between the combat direction systems of different Nato navies. This led to the US distributing the NTDS system widely within Nato, forming the basis of the earliest variants of the French SENIT, Italian SADOC and German AGIS, PALIS and SATIR systems. The British had already started to move down a different route with ADA, and a combination of this technology with NTDS gave rise to the first iteration of the Dutch SEWACO family. This level of standardisation was short-lived, and a steady divergence between US and European practice began. Much of this growing differential was due to the differing contractual arrangements between the countries. In the US, the sensor producing company tended to be prime for the combat direction system, resulting in the systems being orientated around the sensor in question. In the UK, in particular, prime contractorship for the design of the combat system was placed in the hands of independent third-party specialists in systems integration, which resulted in the system being less closely tied to any single sensor technology.

The US Navy also faced a highly difficult situation in that the sheer size of their fleet meant that any radical developments in command and control facilities would incur enormous expenses as the changes in system architecture were extended across the fleet as a whole. For US requirements, NTDS worked, and worked very well, reducing the incentive for a radical change in technology. Instead, the basic combat direction philosophy of the early generations of the NTDS was progressively refined and enhanced with automatic data entry facilities and more powerful computers. In con-

trast, European command system designers included more and more non-combat-related functions within the command systems so that automation, under the control of the command system, spread throughout the ship. These subsystems included combat area synthesis, integrated communications systems, ship control, damage control, maintenance and other ship operation functions. Symptomatic of the rapid divergence is that US commentators assume that combat direction system and command system are synonymous terms, while, in European usage, the combat direction system is but one of a number of subsystems making up the overall integrated command system.

As experience with the new command control facilities was accumulated, the limitations of relying on a single, centralised computer was seen to have serious effects. While a warship has an expected hull life of twenty-five to forty years, depending on how severely she is used, her weapons and sensors will become outdated and require replacement at least once during this period. The centralised computer systems are inflexible, and their intolerance makes even minor changes to the weapons suite an expensive and potentially difficult task. The effects of battle damage also have to be considered. The case in which HMS *Broadsword* was effectively disabled and knocked out of action by a single 30mm shell has already been mentioned. Any centralised combat system is extremely vulnerable to a single 'catastrophic' hit of this type. It may not even be necessary physically to damage the system, for if smoke, heat and toxic fumes from nearby fires make the CIC/Operations Room uninhabitable, the effects are the same.

However, while the costs of computer power and data storage remained high, these limitations had to be accepted. The same costs also restricted the extent to which the desired additional functions could be included within the combat system. Even as late as the FF-1052 *Knox* class frigates, US warships did not automate their ASW plots or integrate them with other ship functions (indeed, this class still does not do so). This situation changed during the early 1980s when the micro-electronic revolution dramatically reduced the costs of both computer power and data storage. The net result was the rise of the fully distributed combat systems now entering service around the world.

The development of micro-computer technology made it possible to include sufficient processing power within each operating terminal to permit it to stand alone from the main system. Thus, it was possible to dispense with the central computer entirely, and design a modular system in which each operator console

would have its own individual responsibilities, with data being shared, transferred, or rerouted via one or more databuses as needed. The result was a revolution in combat system design. The modular nature of the distributed architecture made it easy to upgrade, modify or re-equip a warship. Battle damage control is greatly eased since the reconfigurability of the system means that, for example, it is the work of a few seconds to reassign the navigational console on the bridge to take over the functions of the AAW console burning in the CIC (in recent equipment, this is done simply by inserting the appropriate authorisation card into a slot).

In situations where subsystems habitually work closely together, they are usually linked on a more permanent basis, using what are known as local area networks (LANs). In these, the equipment forming the LANs is linked by inexpensive data interfaces with the LANs themselves feeding into a databus. In modern designs additional back-up communications routes into the databus are provided and the databus itself is replicated to provide insurance against failure or battle damage. The resulting system can be compared with a spider's web, wherein the destruction of a single node does not destroy the integrity of the whole (the analogy should be taken too far, since it is quite possible that a single hit will take out most of a LAN). A distinction is often drawn between systems making extensive use of LANs but still retaining some degree of centralised computer power (referred to as federated systems), and those using wholly distributed architectures. This was once a valid distinction but the immense flexibility of modern command systems has blurred the difference almost to vanishing point. In the latest generation of distributed command systems, the difference between federated and fully distributed owes more to operational practices and concepts than to physical arrangements, and the same system may exhibit either set of characteristics in different navies, different ships, or even at different times on the same ship.

The introduction of distributed architecture has been matched by a radical improvement in the databus systems available. The latest generation of digital databus systems uses fibre optics cabling rather than the traditional copper wiring. This decreases weight significantly, as well as improving safety because it eliminates the fire and toxicity problems inherent in the insulation used with copper wiring. An example of new-generation databuses is the Dutch SEWACO VII system installed on the new *Karel Doorman* frigate class, which uses three separate high-capacity databuses for voice, data and video communications. All three communication

Holland's highly developed electronics industry has served the Dutch navy well. The latest Karel Doorman *class have a high proportion of Dutch electronics, including the new SEWACO VII data system. This is the* Willem van der Zaan, *the second of the class, on sea trials.* (RNethN)

modes are regarded as being absolutely essential for the correct and proper function of a European-style fully-integrated command system.

The need for ships to carry fully integrated combat systems has been aggravated by the blurring distinctions between various tactical scenarios. For many years it was standard practice to have separate AAW (anti-air warfare), ASW (anti-submarine warfare) and ASuW (anti-surface warfare) systems. Quite apart from the fact that this meant duplicated and inefficient data handling and processing facilities, voids were left where threats crossed the inter-system boundaries. For example, a warship engaging a submarine is quite likely to be suddenly subjected to attack by a salvo of subsurface-to-surface missiles. To defeat this attack in the very short time available requires input from the ASW system (giving the location of the firing point), the AAW installation (tracking and engaging the missiles), and the EW fit (to jam/decoy any leakers). If these systems are not integrated, it is unlikely that the ship under attack could respond quickly enough for its survival.[8]

A major part of the problem is that modern countermeasures techniques mean that no single sensor technology can provide a full and accurate picture of the developing tactical scenario. Moves to enhance a ship's reaction time and generally to improve her fighting ability mean that data from all available sensors (including radars, ESM, acoustic, optronic, and the seaman with binoculars standing on the

bridge) must be fully and comprehensively integrated. This implies full provision for data, voice and video transmission. In order to ensure that the onboard weapon systems receive this data quickly and accurately, these systems must also be fully integrated into the data net. As efforts to integrate weapons, sensors and ship handling into one package have continued, the combat system has come to dominate ship design.

A further driving force behind the development of combat system technology has been the need to improve integration between different platforms within a task group. This is driven both by the result of the tactical necessity of exploiting the differing capabilities of group members, and the essential need to extend detection horizons to the maximum possible. Thus, the efficient and timely transfer of data between ships, and between ships and aircraft, is vital. This requirement is intensified as ships sustain hits, and combat damage partially or totally disables their systems. Under such circumstances, it may be necessary for one ship to supply surveillance or targeting data to another.

A final influence on the introduction of command system technology has been the rising cost of manpower. This factor is both financial (the wages of the crew now represent the majority of a ship's running costs in Western navies) and tactical (the space taken up by the crew accommodations reduces that available for other functions). The use of efficient command system technology can sharply reduce the crew requirements on a modern warship, a prime example being the reduction of crew complements from 250+ personnel to fewer than 180 on board Royal Navy frigates. This rise in manpower costs was the primary driver towards incorporating ship maintenance, handling and

navigational facilities within the system. As an additional benefit, the integration of sensor data and ship control greatly increases the efficiency of evasive manoeuvres.

It is now generally accepted by the naval community outside the US that the advantages of a fully distributed combat system are such that this approach has displaced the older centralised system in most applications. The only exceptions occur where financial constraints prevent the adoption of the distributed concept. With these exceptions, the distributed system now reigns supreme, and it is the driving force behind the definition of the weapons/sensors fit for a given warship proposal. This has now led to the point where future Royal Navy warship programmes are likely to have the command system/systems integration team as the prime contractor, rather than the shipyard actually building the ship. Naturally, this trend is being fought by the shipbuilders.

The US Navy has lagged behind in following this trend. The European command control system industry attributes this to emphasis on integrating the operations of numbers of ships rather than integrating the activities within each vessel. US perceptions, however, differ. The fully distributed systems now dominating the non-US naval market use their computer power inefficiently and are not as powerful as they appear. This is a limitation accepted by European designers. Having experienced the problems caused by having inadequate computer power in a command system, all European command system designers ensure that there is a massive excess of processing capability in their

8. *C³I Systems Market Overview*, Forecast International (Newtown, Connecticut 1993).

Although based on the US Arleigh Burke *class, the Japanese Aegis destroyer* Kongo *differs in many aspects of the sensors, as might be expected from the country which leads the world in so many applications of electronics. A major improvement is offered by a new integrated command system.* (JMSDF)

architectures. The new Royal Navy Outfit DNA Command Management System, now in final development for the Type 23 frigate, uses less than 30 per cent of its available computer power.[9] If some of the excess is lost as a result of the relative inefficiency of distributed systems, so what? Computer processing power is inexpensive these days and, in the context of European navies, the benefits are worth the cost. Another very significant point is that distributed systems are substantially more expensive than a centralised equivalent and, in a navy as large as the US fleet, this is a very important consideration.

There is also an in-built US preference for a single, centralised track-keeping computer. This ensures the most efficient use of computing power for this purpose. While US command control within any single warfare area, AAW, ASW or ASuW, is excellent, the ability to handle multi-dimensional threats is demonstratedly inferior to the standards set by the British or some other European countries. During the Second Gulf War, US Navy officers visiting the British frigates and destroyers deployed in the Persian Gulf were astonished by the sophistication and capabilities of the Royal Navy command systems (which the British themselves considered obsolescent – the US admiration coming as a considerable surprise). More recently, the Canadian *Halifax* class frigates (which also have a very advanced integrated command system on the borderline between federated and fully distributed architectures) were the subject of extensive praise from Admiral Tuttle, who held them up as an example for the US Navy to emulate.[10]

Perhaps the most interesting comment on the difference between the US Navy and European approaches was made when the Japanese purchased the Aegis system for their new *Kongo* class destroyers (a derivative of the US *Arleigh Burke* design). One of the major design changes made by the Japanese was the installation of a new, fully distributed command management system, OYQ-6, in the ships. The Aegis combat

direction system is considered to be only a single subsystem to the overall command system.[11] US sources regard this as a job-creation programme for the Japanese electronics industry; European combat systems designers recognise the modification as making the *Kongo* class much more formidable warships than their US cousins – an advantage which may well be lost by the discovery that the *Kongo* class are built largely to merchant rather than naval standards.

As the operational environment for the US Navy shifts from superpower confrontation to a more varied and unpredictable one with a wide variety of threat levels, the US Navy will have to make some important and far-reaching decisions as to its requirements. An early attempt to design a distributed command system for submarines failed, but the architecture has been

adopted for the BSY-2 combat system on the SSN-21 *Seawolf* class submarines. There is some suggestion that future iterations of the *Arleigh Burke* design may have a fully distributed and integrated combat system.

Soviet command systems

The Russian approach to command control was very different. Early developments were associated with the threat from the US Navy's aircraft

9. Stuart Slade, 'Type 23 Command System, Myth and Magic', *Naval Forces* (6/1991).

10. Stuart Slade, 'Canada shows US Navy the Way Forward', *Naval Forces* (5/1992).

11. Tohru Kizu (ed), *Ships of the World* (various editions including 2/1993). Published in Japanese.

The Soviet cruiser Aleksander Suvorov *taking part in the mould-breaking worldwide naval exercise Okean '70. The old system of shore control was so discredited by its performance in this exercise that a whole new emphasis on seaborne command and control was to develop* (USN)

carriers. The proposed counter to these was the development of the *Kynda* class (Project 58) rocket cruisers. These were originally designed as Euro-strategic missile ships tasked with attacking shore targets in Europe and along the Mediterranean coast. Their reassignment to engaging naval targets placed a far greater strain on the command-control and targeting functions, one which the tight designs of the ships could not accommodate. The answer, as always with Soviet systems, lay in establishing a tight shore control of the ships (a control already implicit in their previous strategic rationale).

An extensive shore-based communications intercept and direction-finding network named Krug was established and assigned the preliminary role of threat warning and broad target location. This approximate data would be relayed to the new Bear-D reconnaissance aircraft, which would take over prime responsibility for precise target location and would also act as airborne relay points so that target data from Krug could be transmitted to the rocket cruisers. Bear-D would also act as an airborne waypoint so that radar video data could be datalinked from the SS-N-3 missile and from the aircraft's radars down to the Project 58, and target selection information relayed back to the missile.

When the ability to course-correct missiles in flight was introduced, this was accommodated by the installation of the Plinth Net datalink/tracking system. At the airborne end there is evidence to suggest that the Big Bulge radar on the Bear-D is also a dual function radar/directional datalink, possibly utilising back-to-back antennas within the housing. This contention is supported by the use of Big Bulge on the Ka-25 helicopters deployed on Project 1134 (*Kresta I*) cruisers, these having an airborne datalink relay as their primary function.

In parallel with the development of rocket cruiser command control technology there was a new approach to the problem of ASW. At that time, the only sonar available to the Soviet navy was a high-frequency searchlight system derived from the US Navy QCB system, obtained under Lend-Lease. This provided relatively solid coverage against slow-moving targets at short ranges. However, the searchlight mode of operation meant that a fast, well-handled submarine could evade contact completely. The platforms available, the Project 159 corvettes, were descended from the traditional Russian 'guard ships' and were small, poorly armed and had limited internal volume. They could neither carry a more capable sonar nor process the data from such a system.

The Russian solution to this problem was to integrate the capabilities of a large number of small ASW ships. The results of individual sonar searches by these ships were fed back to a shore-based command control point. They were then consolidated to give a circle of probability within which the target should be located. Initially this process was performed using manual tracking techniques, but the procedure was soon computerised. Once the circle of probability had shrunk to an acceptable degree, the guard ships would simultaneously fire their RBU-6000 rocket launchers into the circle. The parallel with land-based artillery fire control techniques' is readily apparent. A key requirement is that the RBU salvo should be fired simultaneously into the circle. This was achieved using a dedicated datalink called Fig Jar by Nato. Fig Jar and its associated fire control computer were deployed extensively throughout the Soviet navy.

This operational technique was adequate as long as the proposed enemies were conventional submarines operating close inshore. The appearance of the Regulus strategic cruise missile and then the early versions of Polaris required the reach of the ASW forces to be extended and the area of coverage expanded. This requirement led to the development of the *Moskva* class (Project 1123) helicopter cruisers. These substituted shipborne helicopters for the small sub-chasers. The shore-based command and control computers were moved on to the Project 1123 ships and designated the 'Second Captain'. By the time the Project 1123s entered service, Regulus had been withdrawn from service and the major threat was seen as the Polaris A-1 missiles fired from the Mediterranean. It was this environment that restricted the production of the Project 1123 to two ships and caused them to spend most of their life in the Mediterranean, rather than any alleged shortcomings in their seakeeping ability or design. The adoption of the Project 1123 design was paralleled by the installation of ASW fire control computers and Fig Jar datalinks on the *Kashin* (Project 61) destroyers, resulting in these ships being redesignated Large Anti-Submarine Ships (BPK).

As the Soviet navy gained experience in high seas operations, there was also provision of a significant enhancement in shipboard command and control installations. The basic command structure remained unchanged, with the land-based command and control facilities based around the Krug intercept system being in overall control of the ships and with the Bear-D aircraft providing more detailed target location and communication link facilities. However, the new Project 1134 cruisers had an enhanced local control capability. This utilised a version of the 'Second Captain', a threat prioritisation system, determining which targets should be engaged first and which functional areas of the Battle Information Post would be brought on line at any given time.

In 1970 the Soviet navy conducted its first world-scale operational manoeuvres under the title Okean '70. This was viewed in the West as a most impressive demonstration of the Soviet navy's new-found ability to conduct blue-water operations. Okean would be regarded as a watershed in naval development and the first clear challenge to Western naval supremacy. In the eyes of the Soviet navy, Okean was an unmitigated catastrophe. Intended to demonstrate growing capability in the new naval forces, the real lesson was that the whole concept of shore-based control was so deeply flawed that the effectiveness of the ships and their weapons were negated. In simulated engagement after engagement the Soviet command control system responded so slowly that the forces involved were 'unable to fulfil' their functions (Soviet-speak for getting blown out of the water). Attempting to control the forces from shore was an unmitigated disaster, with the task groups flailing around in an unco-ordinated manner. The rocket cruisers were unable to respond to surface threats quickly enough, and would have died with their missiles still in their tubes. Even the ASW forces proved incapable of fulfilling their design roles, and their operational practices were quite inadequate to cope with the level of technology and tactical expertise exhibited by Soviet submarines. Heads rolled.

The key factor was seen as being an overriding requirement to get the main fleet commands to sea. This would require dedicated flagships with sophisticated computer facilities to control task group operations. Experience had already shown that the concept of the Second Captain with a single large centralised computer was not supportable. The volume and variety of tasks required overloaded the system, negating much of the efficiency of these ships and explaining their poor performance in Okean. A new architecture was developed in which a single large centralised computer (the Second Admiral) would be the overall driver of the combat system. This would receive generalised directives from shore command and would supervise the operations of three subordinate combat systems, Second Captains covering the AAW, ASuW and ASW warfare areas. Each of these subordinate Second Captains would be brought on line as required.

This new architecture was bulky and required a much larger platform. A significant driver was the provision for electrical power to drive the electronic systems (and their cooling circuits). This was a perennial Soviet design shortcoming, with the Project 1134B (*Kara*) cruisers suffering frequent 'brown-outs' as a result of inadequate power supply provisions. The incorporation of the new combat system and the correction of other deficiencies in the earlier Project 1123 (*Moskva*) ships had led to the design of a larger air-capable ship, the Project 1143 (*Kiev* class). Purely by chance, the Project 1143 design could be easily modified into an anti-submarine flagship. The modifications involved the provision of a substantial further increase in computer and datalink power.

The availability of the Project 1143s as flagships offset some of the worse failings of the Project 1134A ships. The design of the combat system on the Project 1143s meant that the datalinks available could be used to control the Second Captains on those ships (much as the Second Admiral controlled the Second Captains on its own ship), offsetting the poor facilities available within those systems. It is apparent that the destruction of the Project 1143 flagships would be extraordinarily damaging to the tactical capability of the fleet. They would have to be heavily defended and their true purpose obscured as much as possible. Thus the increasingly heavy anti-aircraft batteries of these ships is not indicative of some profound tactical insight on the part of the Soviet navy, nor is it a sign of the inexperience of their design teams.

Once the true role of the Project 1143s is understood, the paramount need for the best possible defences against attack falls naturally into place.

The introduction of the at-sea flags for the rocket cruisers required even more extensive control facilities. The basic Project 1143 hull form was utilised in the design of an exceptionally powerful nuclear-powered rocket cruiser, the Project 1144 (*Kirov*) battlecruiser. Nuclear power was selected in order to provide sufficient electrical generating capacity to power the command control computers and their associated cooling systems. These followed the same pattern as established with the Project 1143 ships, with a large central computer 'waving the baton' over three smaller Second Captains, each dealing with a specific warfare area. Elaborate datalinks were built into the system, both for strategic communications to shore-based headquarters and for tactical communications between the ships of the task group, target location and airborne relay aircraft, submarines and the new families of RORSAT and ELINT satellites. This enhancement was particularly concerned with the proper exploitation of satellite data.

The latest Western command systems

Ironically, the US Navy was being pushed towards adopting a similar systems architecture by a set of rather different motives. When it adopted the anti-ship variant of the Tomahawk

cruise missile, the extended range of the weapon forced it to consider means of providing over-the-horizon targeting. This was provided largely, but not completely, by intelligence available ashore. About 1974, the US Navy decided to establish shore data fusion centres (FCCs) which transmitted data to a corresponding at-sea system (the TFCC) for combination with own-ship and own-fleet information. This data fusion was then used to form a targeting picture for the Tomahawk weapons control system. The link between ship and shore was designated OTCIXS, the equivalent submarine system being SSIXS. The British adopted a similar system for targeting Sea Eagle-equipped Sea Harriers, the data fusion/command system being called OPCON. Although, in both cases, the sea-based terminal provides far more information than in the Soviet system, the similarities in the basic architecture are striking.

The new generation of C³I equipment is based on software-driven computer networks.

A close-up of the Soviet 'battlecruiser' Kirov. This class introduced a level of electronic control facilities previously unknown in Soviet ships, as a response to the perceived need to transfer command and control to sea from the discredited land-based system. The importance of the electronics in the design can be gauged from the fact that nuclear power was considered necessary in order to provide enough electrical generating capacity for the massive computers and their cooling systems. (MoD, Crown Copyright)

As these systems have developed, the cost of hardware has dropped radically, while the developmental cost of software has risen in proportion. This curve has now reached the point where software costs account for approximately 85 per cent of the total cost for the individual system. Yet, once written, software costs virtually nothing to replicate. Since the computer terminals themselves are relatively low cost items, it makes good sense to distribute full software capabilities as widely as possible. A good example of the efficacy of this approach came during the naval blockade of Iraq. The US Navy had constructed a statistical model of ship movements as part of the Tomahawk anti-ship missile system described above. This model was also usable to track merchant shipping in the Persian Gulf. Combined with an off-the-shelf commercial terminal (classified as a tactical aid rather than a combat system so that military standards were not required) and fed with data from numerous sources including P-3 Orions equipped with ISAR (inverse synthetic aperture radar), this system made the blockade tight. More than 200 of these packages were shipped to the Gulf and effectively given to anybody who wanted one.

Royal Navy nomenclature provides an interesting insight into the evolution of command systems. The earliest integrated systems (ADAWS and CAAIS) were referred to as being action information systems. As additional capabilities were added to the systems and they became the keys to fighting the ships, the nomenclature was changed to command systems. Systems of this type, including the Royal Navy's Outfit DNA and the Canadian SHIN-PADS, represent the current state of the art. These command systems are supported by a command support system which is responsible for strategic and planning data but which operates within a much slower timeframe, and an operational information system which distributes data throughout the ship.

In future Royal Navy warships, these three subsystems will be merged to form a single combat management system which will tie all the data-producing and using areas of the ship within a single integrated whole. These reflect a growing perception that naval operations in the 1990s will require 'a multi-role vessel operating within a severe multi-dimensional threat environment'. Artificial intelligence probably will be further exploited in order to reduce crew workloads, while Ada will be adopted as the standard computer language. Finally, additional attention will have to be paid to the specific requirements of the user. The Royal Navy has adopted an unusual top-down approach by which the total requirements for the system are set at an early stage. However, task allocation to humans or computers does not occur until the system design has matured to a suitable level.

This outline of command control systems is, of necessity, brief. A few salient features stand out. One is the disastrous effects of trying to impose land-orientated strategic and operational concepts on naval forces. The Soviet

Representative of the newest generation of Western surface combatants, the Canadian patrol frigate Toronto *running trials. These ships have an elaborate C³I electronics fit, including the home-grown CANEWS electronic warfare outfit, overseen by an advanced integrated command system. Ironically, for a naval force with a clear appreciation of the value of command and control, Canada's is the only major navy to have suffered 'service unification'. If anything, modern command systems emphasise the unique nature of sea warfare and any erosion of this distinctive approach is likely to prove disastrous in combat.*
(Canadian Maritime Command)

navy, in its own eyes and confirmed by its own exercises, was incapable of performing its operational roles until it started to evolve its own distinctive strategies optimised for the unique conditions of naval warfare. The lesson is a salutary one that should be borne in mind by those championing 'joint command' and 'service unification'. Another is how the emphasis on combined arms tactics (involving co-operation between surface ships, aircraft and submarines) led to the development of datalinking facilities of bewildering complexity. Complexity on this scale inevitably means vulnerability to attack. On the other hand, the new generation of fully integrated command systems are now combat proven and have shown themselves to be stunningly successful. They will undoubtedly be the salient feature of all future warship designs and the real measure of how effective those ships are at their primary purpose – wreaking havoc upon the enemy.

Stuart Slade

12

Naval Electronic Warfare

NAVAL electronic warfare is as old as the earliest deployment of electronics systems on warships. The first recorded instance of electronic warfare took place during the Russo–Japanese war in 1905. A Japanese radio operator on board the battleship *Mishima* intercepted strange Morse code signals. He was able to determine that these originated from the Russian flagship *Petropavlovsk*, and, by manipulating his own aerials, to get a bearing on that battleship's position. He also discovered that he could blank out the Russian transmissions by holding his own Morse key in the down position.[1]

During the First World War the Royal Navy

The destroyer escort radar picket conversion USS Lansing *in 1963. Built to support the Continental Air Defense organisation, effectively as offshore radar stations, the ships were vulnerable to attack, and so were given priority for ESM equipment.* Lansing *carries the early WLR-1 electronic intelligence system in the dome on the main mast yardarm.* (US Navy)

introduced the first systematic monitoring of enemy radio communications. An extensive shore-based system of radio receivers monitored traffic between German naval headquarters and ships of the German Navy. The intercepts were used to analyse the patterns of transmission and their relationship to events, as well as to decipher the contents. Intelligence gained by this early signals intelligence (SIGINT) effort led to the successful interception and defeat of the German fleet at the Battle of the Dogger Bank. This engagement revealed to the Germans that their communications were compromised and subsequently deceptive measures were taken to hide the fact that ships were at sea. One such technique, transferring ship call signs to shore stations, was used just prior to the Battle of Jutland, to hide the fact that the German High Seas Fleet had put to sea.[2] This is an early example of a problem which persists to the present day – intelligence gained by SIGINT is often so valuable that its use compromises the means by which it was gained.

The First World War experience gained by the British in signals intelligence was to have another long-lasting effect. The Royal Navy developed an immense respect for the power of these techniques and, from the 1920s onwards, paid an inordinate amount of attention to radio discipline. Standard British doctrine was (and remains) to restrict radio transmissions to the minimum absolutely essential.[3] When radar was introduced, this discipline was extended to that technology also. A benefit of this policy has been that modern Royal Navy warships carry electronic surveillance equipment of very high standards. However, an objective assessment must be that this policy has been overplayed. The absolute limits applied to electronic emissions have serious operational consequences and have resulted in unnecessary losses. It is even possible that the loss of HMS *Hood* could be partially attributed to this, since she went into her final action with her radars turned off.

The 1920s and 1930s saw British cruisers tasked with 'trade protection', patrolling vast areas of ocean. Prior to the development of

radar, the only long range sensors available to detect enemy commerce raiders were onboard seaplanes and radio interception and direction-finding (DF). The latter, used to locate the raider's radio messages and distress signals from attacked merchantmen, would be used to key searches by the seaplanes. Admiralty requirements specified that the ships should be able to intercept wireless communications within a 950-mile radius. For this the cruisers required tall masts to extend the interception horizon as far as possible and long aerials to provide accurate bearings on the medium and long wave radios then used. A major part of the heavy cruiser reconstruction programme of the 1930s was to provide hangars for seaplanes to assist in the trade protection role.[4]

Providing for these requirements became a major design driver and explained the 'stately' profile of the British ships as opposed to their sleek, low-slung American cousins. This requirement to carry ESM antennas high and to provide for accurate direction-finding has persisted to this day and is, once more, becoming a significant design driver on modern warships. The US Navy used flying-boats and fleet submarines for strategic scouting, with the heavy cruisers using their DF equipment for tactical surveillance during the run-up to an engagement. As a result, the US cruisers were designed to operate in close proximity to the battle fleet, and their low masts permitted intercepts only within a 300-mile radius.[5] Later during this period, the US Navy developed a string of high-frequency direction-finding (HF/DF) stations around the Pacific to provide strategic surveillance of the Japanese fleet. Ironically, the US

1. David Warner, *The Short Victorious War: The Russo-Japanese Conflict 1904–5* (London 1973).

2. Arthur Pollen, *The Navy in Battle* (London 1918).

3. Dr Norman Friedman, *British Carrier Aviation* (London 1988).

4. Alan Raven and John Roberts, *British Cruisers of World War Two* (London 1980).

5. Dr Norman Friedman, *US Cruisers: an Illustrated Design History* (Annapolis 1984).

An American ESM system of the 1970s, called 'Hip-Pocket II' and tested in the missile destroyer Hoel. *The system included the ALERT II ESM gear; a Passive Engagement System, which automatically identified threats and displayed them in the CIC; a Shipboard Infra-red Surveillance System; a Dual-Spectrum Imaging Sensor for improved target detection; an Infra-red Threat Acquisition and Verification System; and an active-passive range-gated TV camera (with laser for ranging and low visibility operation). The SPS-10 surface search radar was modified for better low angle tracking with incoming target alarm (ITA) and video clutter suppression (VCS). There were also elaborate passive infra-red defences, including a system to spray the ship's side with seawater to reduce IR emissions. (USN)*

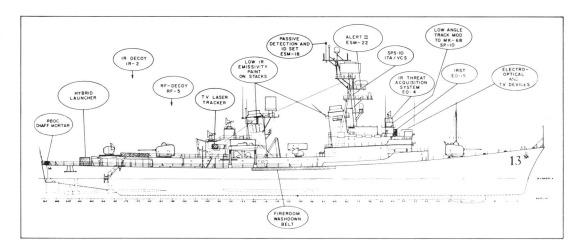

Navy had serious reservations about the efficiency of HF/DF until decrypts of transmissions made during their big fleet manoeuvres showed how well the Japanese were doing.

The earliest examples of specific radar-orientated electronic intelligence (ELINT) operations took place in the Pacific. In August 1942 US Marines discovered a crude Japanese radar on Guadalcanal. This was a Japanese Navy Type II early warning radar. This chance discovery gave birth to the idea that an electronic reconnaissance effort was needed to find the extent to which Japanese forces in the Pacific were radar-equipped. Work began at the Naval Research Laboratory in Washington, DC, to develop an intercept receiver suitable for both airborne and shipborne use. This new system was first deployed on the submarine uss *Drum*. She was assigned specifically to search for enemy radar signals with her rudimentary equipment 'when the crew was not otherwise engaged'. She returned from the cruise off the Japanese coast with the first ELINT log of Japanese radars. This mission was the ancestor of a long series undertaken by the US submarine fleet. These have continued up to the present day, with US and British submarines continuing to use their ESM systems to probe and record radar systems of potential (and actual) enemies.

As the Second World War progressed, Japanese destroyers started to carry radar warning receivers to warn them of US Navy surface search and gunlaying radars. Initially crude, these were rapidly developed to provide octantal bearings on those radars and to differentiate between search and fire control modes.[6] German submarines running the gauntlet of Allied aircraft in the Bay of Biscay also started to carry radar warning receivers.[7] On the Allied side, warships threatened by the new German Fritz-X and HS-293 guided bombs were equipped with jammers for the search radars and radio controls involved.[8]

Postwar developments

Immediately after the end of the war, the naval electronic warfare effort was cut back. In the late 1940s the overwhelming power of the US Navy faced little credible surface threat. The Soviet navy was weak and ill-equipped, so little effort in countering its limited effectiveness or in procuring operational versions of the latest jamming equipment could be justified. As a result of the pre 1950 cutbacks in expenditure on conventional forces, combat-tested electronic warfare (EW) equipment was removed from the ships and stored in order to reduce maintenance requirements. What little effort there was tended to be unappreciated and poorly managed. This situation started to change in the early 1950s, partly as a result of the Korean War revealing that significant non-nuclear forces were essential, and partly as a result of the slow re-emergence of Soviet naval power. Interestingly, both US and British assessments identified 1957 as the 'year of maximum danger' when the Soviet Union was expected to launch its attacks. Recently released Soviet archives strongly suggest that this assessment was, in Stalin's time at least, entirely accurate.

The threat that started to emerge was not, however, from surface ships. The Russians had captured a substantial amount of guided-missile technology from the Germans, including details of the Fritz-X and HS-293 bombs. These were introduced into service by the Russians, who pursued the line of development with the aim of producing extended range stand-off weapons. The long range Tu-16 Badger was an early platform for these anti-ship missiles, with a medium range equivalent, the Tu-14, supplementing it for operations closer to the Russian mainland.[9] An initial response by the US Navy to meet the air threat was to exploit the technology developed during the Second World War. In the

early 1950s, intercept systems and the TDY jammer started to reappear in the fleet and were installed on a large number of ships. Problems were experienced in developing a more advanced jammer, apparently related to the jammer tube technology, which had difficulty in staying with the target frequency. This problem was only resolved in the late 1950s by the introduction of the carcinotron.

By 1958, the first of the long range Russian anti-ship missiles, the AS-1, had entered service and its existence, though not the precise details of its performance, was known to the US Navy. In response, the US Navy started to equip destroyers and frigates with SLR-1 ESM equipment and ULQ-6 false target generators to protect against missile attack. The design and operational doctrine of these systems was weak; they were difficult to use and were of limited effectiveness. Many commanders believed that using the jammers increased the chance of attack. The ULQ-5 systems, installed on many US Navy escorts, were 'blip enhancers', intended to decoy inbound missiles by making the aircraft carrier indistinguishable from its escorts. By implication this resulted in the loss of expendable escorts, not irreplaceable carriers. Land-based listening posts were built around the periphery of the Soviet Union and their work was supplemented by the ELINT mapping operations carried out by submarines and surface ships.[10] The appearance of Soviet AGIs festooned with intercept antennas was first noted in the Baltic

6. Hansgeorg Jentschura, Dieter Jung and Peter Mickel, *Warships of the Imperial Japanese Navy* (London 1977).

7. S E Morrison, *US Naval Operations In World War II*: Volume X: *The Atlantic Battle Won* (Boston 1956).

8. S E Morrison, *US Naval Operations In World War II*: Volume IX: *Sicily, Salerno, Anzio* (Boston 1955).

9. Steven Zaloga, *Target America* (San Francisco 1993).

10. *Land & Sea Electronic Warfare*, E W Market Intelligence Report, Forecast International (Newtown, Connecticut 1993).

An early British ESM system, UA-4, is visible on the foremost mast of the submarine Aeneas *about 1970. From right to left, the other masts are the small cross-section attack periscope, the binocular search periscope (for optical range-finding), Type 955 search radar, snort (snorkel), and a whip radio antenna.* (C & S Taylor)

and in the Norwegian sea in around 1957–58. By 1960 they had spread across the Atlantic and were a constant companion to Nato task groups. their presence led to an early appreciation of the virtues of emission control (EMCON) for warships, again the Royal Navy taking a much more serious, and probably excessive, view of this requirement.

During this period, the shattered countries of mainland Europe had far more urgent priorities than the development of EW capabilities, while the British were immersed in the problems of dismantling the Empire while adjusting to grossly reduced resources. Even as late as 1960, many British warships still carried the same electronics fits as they had mounted in 1945. The lack of a distinct need for surface EW tended to slow development efforts.

However, the Soviet navy faced a different situation. During the early 1950s the Russians were constructing the *Sverdlov* class (Project 68bis) cruisers. These were originally designed as the first instalment in Stalin's plans to construct a balanced high seas fleet. With Stalin's death in 1953, those Project 68bis cruisers at early stages of construction were scrapped. Admiral Kuznetsov conceived a strategy of using the remaining ships as raiders in support of submarine campaigns against transatlantic supply routes. In this role, their main enemy was seen as radar-equipped maritime patrol aircraft. The cruisers could not use their own radars without exposing themselves to detection, so they would have to rely on ESM equipment to detect and evade the prowling P-2s and Shackletons.[11]

Captured German U-boat radar warning technology was exploited to answer this requirement. By 1956 the design effort led to the introduction of the Watch Dog radar warning system for surface ships. It was partnered by a very similar system intended for submarines, designated Stop Light A. By the late 1950s and early 1960s, emphasis had changed to the construction of rocket cruisers and anti-aircraft destroyers to defend Soviet waters against the US Navy. The first ships to reflect this were the *Kynda* class (Project 58) rocket cruisers and the *Kashin* class (Project 61) anti-aircraft missile-armed destroyers. The significant factor was that these ships were intended to seek out and engage enemy task forces, not to evade contact. In this new environment Watch Dog on its own was inadequate and an active jamming capability was needed. Two jammers were designed to meet this requirement, a broad-band noise jammer (Top Hat A) and a deception jammer (Top Hat B).

While the Project 58 and Project 62 designs were being finalised, another new concept was being introduced. Designed for operations in coastal waters, the *Komar* class (Project 183R) had introduced the SS-N-2 Styx missile into service. This had given small fast attack craft a much greater degree of striking power. The Project 183R missile cutters were a hasty adaption of the earlier *P-6* class (Project 183) torpedo boats and were intended to fire their missiles over open sights. They were succeeded by the custom-designed *Osa* class (Project 205) missile cutters, which carried four missiles in place of two. The engagement sequence favoured by these new craft was to use ESM to gain a rough bearing on a target formation. This would cue the radar to perform a rapid sector search of that location to determine target course and speed, after which the Project 205s would run in and fire. These tactics required a new directional ESM receiver covering the high G-, H- and I-bands. The new system, with a large, radar-like antenna giving a bearing accuracy of around 2.5 degrees, was mounted on the rear of the mast of the Project 205 missile cutter.

The capability of the new breed of craft was revealed by the sinking of the Israeli destroyer *Eilat* by a Styx missile attack in 1968. This was the time when US involvement in the Vietnam War was at a peak, and there was considerable fear that the US warships supporting the military operations would be subjected to short range surface- and air-launched anti-ship missile attack. In fact this threat never materialised, but the danger seemed very real at the time. The US response was to develop a new auto-reaction anti-missile system, SAMID (Ship Anti-Missile

Integrated Defence). This was primarily a doctrine and training programme using a minimum of new hardware and was applied only to ships deployed off Vietnam. A longer-term development of this programme would have seen the introduction of new command control facilities and defence systems, but fell victim to post-Vietnam defence economies. It evolved into the DPEWS (Design-to-Price EW System) programme, which was eventually won by Raytheon with SLQ-32. A much-developed version of this set is still the primary EW system on US Navy warships.[12]

The development of missile-armed fast attack craft emphasised the closer proximity of the European forces to the potential battle zones and the need to secure advance warning of intentions. This led to greater emphasis placed on EW techniques. In particular, it was appreciated that the European navies faced a bloody close range brawl in the North Sea, Baltic and English Channel rather than a blue-water engagement. However, the dramatic economic improvements in Europe during the 1950s had made funds available for the modernisation of the armed forces. The provision of radar warning equipment, jammers and chaff launchers therefore received greater priority. The Royal Navy in particular started the development of comprehensive EW fits to its ships, firstly installing integrated ESM/electronic countermeasures (ECM)/decoy capability, then further integrating those systems with the overall command system of the ships. Interestingly, the installation of EW equipment took priority over modernisation of radar fits. During this time the Royal Navy overtook the US Navy in EW technology and operational technique, a position which it has retained to this day.[13]

From the Nato point of view, the prime concerns were the threats posed by Soviet submarines and by missile-armed long range bombers. The US Navy, mainly orientated to fighting in a blue-water environment, still placed little emphasis on its EW capability, preferring to rely on the concentric rings of active defences around its carrier groups. This strategy recognised the fact that electronic warfare defences required an extensive foreknowledge of enemy equipment, and in particular of the WARMs (WAR-only operating Modes) available to that equipment. Also, when faced with the possibil-

11. Stuart Slade, 'Through A Glass, Not Quite So Darkly', *Naval Forces* (6/1992).

12. Dr Norman Friedman, *The Naval Institute Guide to World Naval Weapons Systems 1991/92* (Annapolis, Maryland 1991).

13. Dr D G Kiely, *Naval Electronic Warfare* (London 1988).

The Side Globe antennas on a Soviet Kara *(Project 1134B) class missile cruiser.* (By courtesy of John Jordan)

ity of nuclear attack, a hard kill obtained by active defences was considered essential. This philosophy is illustrated by the design of the WLR-1 ESM system installed on US warships. This is an ELINT system and scans too slowly to provide adequate radar warning capability. Where such facilities are required, an additional radar warner is often added.

As the Cold War progressed and the Soviet navy moved on to the high seas in the middle 1960s, the Project 58 rocket cruisers were viewed as ill-balanced ships, showing the results of excessive land-orientated thought in their design. Although originally designed as strategic platforms, the Project 58s were effectively regarded as floating coastal defence missile batteries with the Project 61 destroyers as their protective anti-aircraft missile sites. Operating on the high seas had caused a fundamental rethink, the result of which was the *Kresta I* (Project 1134) rocket cruisers. Prominent down the sides of the superstructure were eight massive antenna housings, four on each beam. Named Side Globe by Nato, these were very high powered, mechanically-scanned highly directional noise jammers. The Side Globes were horizontally paired, with the antennas on each side of the ship providing 360-degree coverage. One pair covered the L-band, one the S-band, one the C-band, and the last pair the X-band.

Internally, Side Globe consists of two side monopulse DF units with a larger and stronger central horn being the ECM emitter. The two DF arrays are used to acquire accurate bearing data and are offset a few degrees from the central ECM unit to permit a wider working beamwidth. The complete assembly rotates as one unit, so when the measured amplitude from the incoming signal is equal in the DF channels, the central ECM emitter is bore sighted and ready to do its deeds. This arrangement has two very significant advantages. By equipping the ECM emitter with a related monopulse DF unit, a rapid look-through and bearing check is permitted. Secondly, having separate DF and ECM antennas in a common array (assuming there is sufficient isolation between them), the DF section can continue to track through own jamming. In passing, the jamming output from Side Globe is exceptionally dangerous and exposure is fatal to humans within 40–50ft of the arrays.[14]

Throughout the 1960s and early 1970s, improvements in technology enhanced the capabilities of the EW systems installed on warships. As transmitters improved, the ability to generate powerful, stable jamming signals was enhanced. Receiver techniques have also improved dramatically. Vacuum tubes were replaced by solid-state devices; circuit boards improved the way equipment was built, enhancing both durability and reliability. Electronic data processing, although in its infancy, began to open what has proved to be a flood-gate of new capabilities. Perhaps the most significant was the progressive replacement of analog systems by their digital equivalents. The immediate result was a massive increase in the capability of ESM systems to track and identify signals, with the accessible threat libraries containing hundreds, then by the late 1970s thousands, of signatures, rather

14. Stuart Slade, 'Without Glasses And A Bit More Brightly', *Naval Forces* (3/1993).

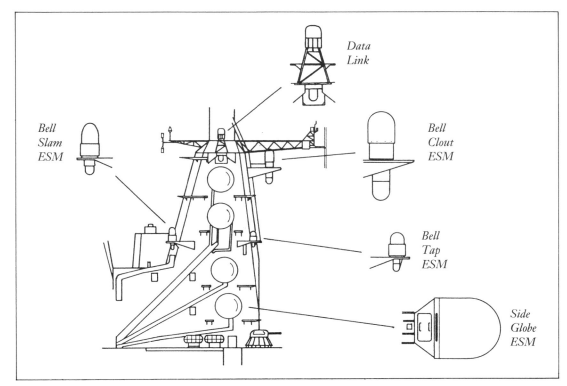

The ECM/ESM equipment of a Soviet Kresta II *(Project 1134A) missile cruiser of c1970.* (John Jordan)

than a mere ten or twenty. In the US, most of the work was applied to airborne jamming and ELINT collection developments while the limited operational philosophy and weak interest by surface forces continued. The technological foundation was laid and command appreciation of surface EW began to follow. In Europe the new technologies have been applied across a broad span of the EW spectrum. This resulted in the development and operational deployment of large numbers of land- and sea-based electronic warfare systems.

During this period, the Soviet EW doctrine was thrown into chaos when the US Navy started introducing Ku-band attack aircraft radars (on the A-6 and A-7) into the inventory. These operated in frequencies not covered by the existing Soviet EW systems, and meant that the ships were fundamentally defenceless against them. The situation was remedied by taking the basic Watch Dog system, adding two extra tiers of receptor horns to cover the additional frequencies required, and placing the whole unit in a new radome. This approach had the virtue that the new system could replace Watch Dog, saving topweight and space. It was designated Bell Shroud by Nato and was paired with a pair of jammers entitled Bell Squat A and Bell Squat B – effectively these being Top Hat with their frequency coverage extended to the K-band.

The first recipients of the new system were the Project 61M destroyers obtained by conversion of the older Project 61 ships. The Project 61M conversion entailed the installation of four rear-firing SS-N-2 missiles and enhanced electronics. They were intended for use as tattletales, trailing US task groups and identifying key targets within those groups. In this role they were at particular risk from the new attack aircraft, and it is not surprising that they had a high priority for the new Bell Shroud/Bell Squat system. Bell Shroud and Bell Squat have remained the standard destroyer/frigate intercept/jammer system equipping the *Sovremennyy* (Project 956), *Udaloy* (Project 1155) and *Krivak* (Project 1135) classes.

The Bell Shroud/Bell Squat system was not installed on the rocket cruisers and other ships fitted with the Side Globe and related equipment. These received three stand-alone fast-reaction defensive systems with an ESM receiver in the housing above the platform and a jammer in the radome under the platform. Bell Clout covers the C-band; Bell Slam the S-band (it is not known if the Nato designations reflect the frequency coverage by design or happenstance) and Bell Nip the Ku/Ka-band. At this time, Bell Tap was also further modified with a similar dedi-

cated jammer to act as a stand-alone covering the X-band. The latter can be seen in this configuration on the Project 1234 (*Nanutchka*) class missile corvettes, and a comparison with the original installation on the Project 205 is an interesting example of design evolution.

The appearance of a new generation of rocket cruisers armed with the new SS-N-12 and SS-N-19 long range high-speed surface-to-surface missiles introduced new requirements to the Soviet EW portfolio. These powerful ships could not rely on external targeting for their missiles while the range parameters of the new missiles far exceeded the radar horizon. A new sensor, designated Rum Tub by Nato, filled the gap. This is a high-precision long range ESM system using technology obtained from the British UAA-1, Dutch Ramses and US SLQ-32 systems. A combination of advanced lens and processing technologies meant that Rum Tub could provide target acquisition data

Right: A close-up of the superstructure of the Soviet helicopter carrier Baku *(since renamed* Admiral Gorshkov*), showing the array of ESM equipment.* (By courtesy of John Jordan)

Below: The Nato designations of ECM/ESM equipment of the Baku. (John Jordan)

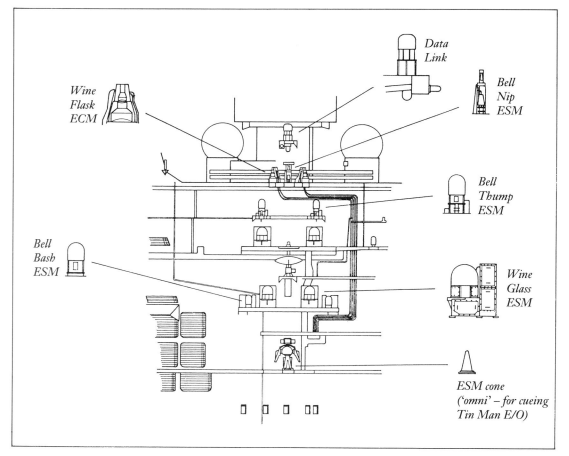

over ranges compatible with the new surface-to-surface missiles.

After forty years of postwar development, the state of warship electronic warfare has now stabilised. Most ships, whether Russian- or Western-designed, employ three different categories of EW systems: decoy dispensers, jamming devices and electronic intercept equipment. There are also a few anomalous systems including electro-optical countermeasures intended to blind optronic or FLIR equipment and/or their operators.

Decoy and dispensers

Decoy dispensers were originally designed to fire chaff clouds to seduce inbound anti-ship missiles from their target. In this role they have three distinct modes of operation. Firing at long range, the launcher provides an inbound missile with multiple targets. This dilutes the attack on the genuine target, giving shipboard point-defence systems a better chance of dealing with the attack. At intermediate range the chaff clouds are intended to seduce the missile guidance system away from the ship and into the decoy cloud, resulting in a clean miss. Finally, as a last-ditch measure, the chaff clouds can be used for centroid seduction. The seeker in an anti-ship missile generally homes in on the centre of the target's return, seeing the ship as a complex mass of point and corner reflectors. A large cloud of chaff can be used to distort the ship's return so that the apparent centroid is moved up and away from the real centroid, causing the missile to pass above or astern.

Conventional chaff is being increasingly circumscribed as missiles become more and more intelligent. Long range chaff decoys can be easily countered by the inclusion of MTI within the missile guidance programming. The chaff clouds will move more slowly than the ship and the movement is likely to fall into a different pattern. A modern radar homing seeker can take advantage of these differences to sieve out the chaff clouds from the genuine targets. Many modern chaff launching systems counter this by providing recommendations on the optimum course to be employed if full advantage of the chaff clouds is to be taken. An intelligent missile seeker will attempt to counter intermediate range seduction by range-gating the target echoes. Using this approach, a narrow band of returns around the expected target's position is defined and any echoes from outside this gate are ignored. These provisions are countered by the use of an active ECM system which uses range-gate pull-off techniques to move the missile's seeker into the chaff cloud some distance

from the ship. Centroid seduction is best countered by setting the radar altimeter on the missile to keep the flightpath at the lowest practical altitude.

All current types of expendable decoys are launched by either mortars or by rocket. Mortars and their ammunition, for example the US SRBOC system, have the advantage of being more compact. They are, however, inherently short ranged and the launchers have to be strongly built in order to withstand the impact of firing. These weight penalties are very severe, since they must not only include a robust launcher but also considerable strengthening of the ship's superstructure around the firing point. On the other hand, rockets have a much more flexible range bracket, require only the simplest launch rails and transmit virtually no firing stress to the ship's structure. Their major disadvantages are the need to provide protection against the rocket exhaust on firing and the reduced proportion of the projectile weight represented by payload. Both rocket and mortar chaff dispensing systems are available in considerable variety, but the current trend is strongly towards the rocket solution.

Defences based around decoy dispensers can be confounded by firing a stream of missiles, prolonging the period of the attack over several minutes. This quickly exhausts the ready-use supply of ammunition. Also a re-attack mode is now available for anti-ship missiles which could mean that a missile may have to be decoyed more than once. Since most existing decoy dispensers are loaded manually, a process taking some considerable time, these developments can only be countered by increasing the number of ready-use rounds held in the launcher. The earliest naval decoy launchers were single barrelled; but this has been systematically increased until the average is around twelve rounds per launcher, with the number of launchers increased from two to six per ship. The Israeli navy uses 24- and 48-barrelled launchers and is introducing a 72-barrelled launcher on its most recent construction. These are, however, designed to give one, two and three salvoes of twenty-four rockets respectively, rather than sustained firings over a long period. As the number of rounds per launcher is increased, mortar-style systems become even less attractive and the push to rocket-based systems is reinforced.

A different approach to the problem of providing prolonged decoying capability has been the development of towed floating decoys. The leading system in this category is the Royal Navy's Rubber Duck. The Royal Navy first adopted this as an emergency fit for the Falklands campaign, and subsequently extended the fit

throughout the surface fleet. Ironically, Rubber Duck was originally copied from a Soviet system. In spite of being seen since the early 1980s, the Soviet floating radar reflectors spread slowly through their fleet and many high-value platforms still have not received their scheduled outfit. Rubber Duck has also been adopted by the US Navy, under the designation SLQ-49, where it is in very widespread service. The original concept has gone through successive upgrades, improving its efficiency and reliability. The latest version, DLF-3, is currently undergoing trials.

Another threat to the viability of decoy launchers as an anti-missile defence lies in the steady improvement in the performance and flexibility of missiles. In 1982 the enquiry into the sinking of the destroyer HMS *Sheffield* by an Exocet missile indicated that visual warning of the missile attack could provide, at most, 20 seconds warning. Since the chaff cloud decoys required some 15 seconds to deploy from firing, this meant that the crew had, at best, five seconds to see the threat, classify it and initiate the launch procedure. This is just not possible. Since 1982 the speed of the inbound missiles has increased somewhat, while improvements in the design of radar altimeters has meant that the missiles can fly much closer to the sea. This means that a visual alert system is already non-viable and will become impossible when the next generation of supersonic sea-skimmers enters service.

Thus the provision of a separate rapid response warning radar system (RWR) for the chaff launchers is essential. Indeed, without such a facility chaff dispensers are just so much wasted topweight. A number of suitable RWRs are already available; these include Matilda (produced by Thorn-EMI) and Shiploc (produced by Thomson-CSF). The need to keep weight and cost to a minimum has meant that these detectors are prone to a high false-alarm rate and are best used in conjunction with a full-scale ESM system. The engagement pattern then becomes the ESM system triggering the chaff dispenser RWR when it picks up the missile launch platform search radar. The chaff dispenser RWR then fires the chaff launchers when it picks up the missile homing head. Direct triggering of the chaff launchers by the main ESM system is not regarded as being a viable solution due to the time taken for the full-scale equipment to analyse and classify the threats. It is also desirable to reduce the workload on an already heavily utilised system.

A matter of particular concern to Soviet tactical doctrine was the dangers presented by electronic interference between the large

Modes of Deploying Chaff Decoys

1. Confusion. *Effective against search and target indication radars during the search and selection phase. Chaff provides a number of false targets, which prevents or delays the selection of the real target.*

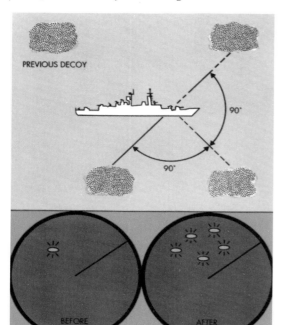

2. Distraction. *Used against radar and infra-red homing missiles during the target search phase. A threatened vessel surrounds itself with decoys, so that when a missile commences its preprogrammed search of the target area it will pick out a decoy before reaching its target vessel.*

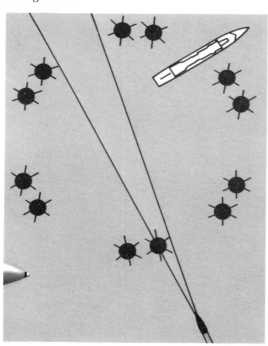

3. Dump/Range Gate Pull Off/Stealing. *Chaff decoys are deployed by vessel at short range (a) in co-ordination with an onboard jammer, denying range information to the 'locked on' missile (b); the vessel then ceases jamming (c), and the missile is 'dumped' on to the chaff decoy (d).*

a.

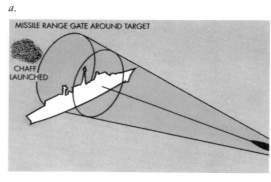

b.

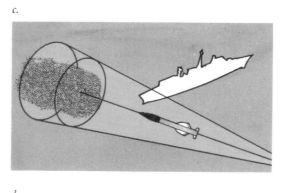

c.

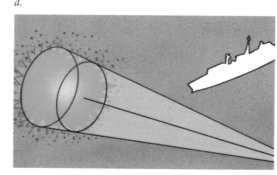

d.

4. Seduction/Centroid. *This provides a large and attractive decoy to a 'locked on' missile in close proximity to the threatened vessel, which then manoeuvres to draw the missile from the real target to the centre of the decoy. (ML Aviation Ltd.)*

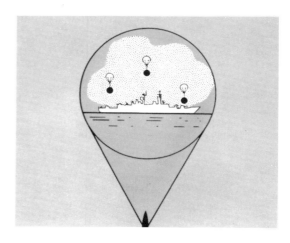

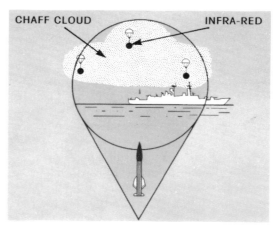

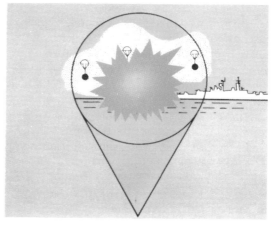

number of systems on their ships, and in particular the dangers of chaff clouds degrading the efficiency of other defence methods. The sequencing function of the Second Captain is regarded as being of primary importance in avoiding these problems. The late development of chaff launchers by the Russian navy and their correspondingly early development of offboard decoys all relate to Russian concern with this aspect of electronic operations.

The existence of other guidance methods means that a radar warning receiver can no longer be relied upon to give infallible warning of a missile approach. Other technologies have to be utilised. The most promising is the use of infra-red search and tracking systems which pick up the plume of heat generated by the missile's engine. This can actually be detected while the missile is still over the visual and radar horizons, adding priceless seconds to the alert time. The French navy already has a system of this type, Vampir, in service, while the Royal Navy is presently installing a derivative of the British Army's ADAD infra-red detector on its frigates. Systems in this category are designed to give 360-degree 24-hour coverage with light wavelength filters to reduce the number of false alerts. As laser-guided missiles become more common, it is probable that laser warners will also become part of the standard decoy dispenser alerting package. Naturally, in these cases the software programming of the dispensing system is designed to ensure that the correct munition is fired to counter a specific threat.

Finally, the attention given to the decoy dispenser and its alerting system should not divert attention from the ultimate reason for the system – its payload. In addition to electronic counter-countermeasures (ECCM), traditional chaff clouds can also be defeated by the use of secondary guidance methods or alternatives. Numerous anti-ship missiles have an infra-red guidance back-up to their primary radar seekers, while others use imaging infra-red or optical command guidance. Few modern decoy launchers are now restricted to chaff rounds. Nearly all offer infra-red decoy flares as an alternative payload, while smoke and thermal smoke rounds are becoming more common. Smoke rounds originally developed for armoured fighting vehicles may become increasingly important as a counter to laser-guided and optronic missiles. With the disappearance of steam turbine ships, traditional means of laying smokescreens are no longer possible (gas turbine and nuclear-powered ships cannot use the oil spray technique). However, the growing sophistication of missile homing heads is driving the decoy operators to adopt the concept of active expendable jammers.

An example of the latest rocket-propelled chaff system, the British 102mm Super Barricade. The smaller 57mm version has already proved more effective than a mortar-launched system. (ML Aviation Ltd.)

These are effectively lightweight disposable jammers installed within a decoy round and kept airborne for a period of several minutes by a parachute or hovering rocket.

The chaff used in decoy rounds has also changed radically over the last few years. The aluminium foil once used has been displaced in the latest systems by metallised glass fibres. These provide greatly enhanced bloom time, remain airborne for considerably longer and are much lighter, resulting in greater quantities being packaged into smaller rounds. A telling example of the advances made in this area occurred in the Arabian Gulf. It was discovered that a 57mm chaff rocket launched from the Barricade system on a British minehunter gave a chaff cloud four times as effective and much longer lasting than a mortar shell loaded with conventional chaff from the SRBOC system on a US frigate.

Jammers and other active systems

Active countermeasures can employ a wide range of tactics, from simple noise jamming through to false-target transmitters sequenced to confuse scanning radars. Noise jamming can be used to blot out signals over a wide range of frequencies (barrage jamming), the Japanese radio operator on the *Mishima* being the first to use this technique. This variant of noise jamming can be defeated by increasing the trans-

mitted power of the emitters to 'burn through' the jamming signals. Since the signal energy is spread over a wide band, the proportion on any one frequency is relatively low and burn-through energies can be reached at acceptable levels. A more subtle countermeasures approach is to concentrate the jamming energy on a particular narrow frequency band (spot jamming). This will normally be determined by the ESM equipment. The preferred option when dealing with spot jamming is using frequency agility to hop away from the jamming signals. As the frequency of the radar increases, the broader becomes the range of frequencies through which the system can hop. This complicates the task of the jammer in attempting to follow the hops.

A more elegant and effective jamming procedure is deception jamming. Deception jamming usually depends upon measurement of the radar PRF, scan rate and pulse width. For this data the jammer is dependent upon a companion ESM system. Since radars have finite side-lobes (*ie* cannot concentrate all their emitted energy or their reception in one direction), jamming signals can always enter via those side-lobes and appear to be coming from the direction in which the radar is pointed. Once a false echo has been generated it can be used to confuse the searching radar in terms of range (range-gate pull-off) or in bearing (by exploitation of the side-lobes). There are also multi-antenna anti-monopulse techniques. Variations in PRF are a simple counter-countermeasure, since the radars can be programmed to reject signals which do not

Current French electronics, as carried on the topmast of the cruiser Colbert. *From the top down, the four-masted aerials are the Telegon communication intercept equipment; the circular antennas are the directional part of the ESM system (the 'omni' for the system is the tall radome below); the flat circular radome houses the ARBB-32/33 jammer.* (Thomson-CSF)

conform to a precise preset pattern in PRF variation.

Naval jammers can also be divided into responsive and repeater subgroups. Responsive jammers measure the frequency of a received signal, digitally store and process the data, then set an oscillator to provide the desired response pattern. This can be continued after the received pulse has ceased and need not be at precisely the received frequency. Using this technique, a responsive jammer can be programmed to execute specific frequency shift patterns. Responsive jammers are, therefore, of great value in defeating frequency-agile radars. However, the response time of these jammers is limited by the time taken for the oscillator to reach the desired frequency. This could be between 100 and 250 nanoseconds, depending on the band width covered.

Repeater jammers are much simpler analog devices. They amplify the received signal, then emit a jamming pulse with or without a time delay. These jammers are usually built around frequency memory loops (FML) which may be coaxial cable, waveguides or an acoustic delay line. These store an exact replica of the received pulse. The received pulse is fed into the line and a memory switch is closed a set time after the beginning of the pulse. The jammer taps the FML and amplifies it to produce a replica signal. Unfortunately, as the pulse circulates within the delay line it gradually decays as the signal is degraded by noise contamination. Because no frequency measurement needs to be made, the response from a repeater jammer can be made extremely quickly. They are therefore best suited to jamming fire control radars and missile homing heads which use high pulse rates.

Regardless of the type of jamming and the generation system used, effective jamming requires that the jamming beam be concentrated on to the target. This requires that the jammer antennas must be paired with a tracking system. In some cases, for example the Thorn-EMI series of jamming systems, the tracking and jammer antennas are combined. The US Navy's SLQ-32 system goes one stage further and combines the initial detection, target tracking and jamming functions into a single antenna array. Although the tracker can function as a search antenna, its beam is too narrow for efficient search. A more usual solution is to have a separate coarse direction-finding system for initial detection. Another approach to the tracking problem is to combine the jammer antenna with a tracking radar, a system proposed by the French for a number of their fire control complexes. Proponents of this particular solution claim that it is of particular use where the jam-

mer is optimised for disrupting fire control radars. The arrangement means that locking the fire control radar on to its target automatically places the jammer in the correct alignment to degrade the enemy fire control system. As with many other systems, this arrangement is claimed to be 'in production for unspecified clients', a phrase that usually translates as 'collecting dust in a warehouse'.[15]

The time at which jamming should be initiated is the subject of heated debate. One argument stresses the importance of initiating jamming of hostile target acquisition radars at the earliest possible moment. This forces missiles launched with less than accurate targeting data to turn their seekers on earlier and to search a much larger area to acquire their targets. By implication they must also fly higher to search efficiently. There is also evidence that long range jamming enhances the effectiveness of chaff clouds and ship manoeuvres in evading attack. Supporters of this approach point out that active jamming can be performed indefinitely without running out of munitions. However, another school of thought suggests that this long range jamming is counter-productive in that it can be detected by hostile ESM systems and can actually be used to localise the jamming platforms. Jammers present exactly the same hazards in operation as do the radar systems they counter – their emissions can be detected by passive means from ranges considerably greater than the effective range of the system in question. Thus, just as a ship using its radars reveals its position, so does any ship initiating active jamming procedures.[16]

Thus, for all of the range and sophistication of jamming techniques available, the deployment of active jammers on warships is a contentious issue, with spirited debate as to whether the jammers are worth installing and, indeed, whether they do not represent a more serious threat to their platform that their utility warrants. The tactical and operational significance of this debate ultimately depends upon the circumstances involved. If the ship has already been detected, localised and placed under attack, the emissions of its jamming systems will not compromise it any further. Under such circumstances, attempting to jam target acquisition, fire control radars and missile homing heads is viable, although the desired results may be achievable by other means. If, on the other hand, a ship has not been detected and attempts to use jamming systems to prevent localisation by hostile radars, the emissions of the onboard jammers will achieve the opposite effect and highlight its position.

Much here depends upon the relative levels

This 1985 view of the destroyer escort Fraser *displays the main elements of the Canadian CANEWS electronic warfare system. The SRD-502 COMINT equipment is carried on the topmast with the ESM gear on struts either side of its lattice section. The stub mast supports the jammer, and the lattice between the funnel and the TACAN (Tactical Air Navigation) beacon. (L & L van Ginderen)*

of technology of the combatants. A sophisticated ship faced with a primitively equipped opponent with a poorly trained crew can use jamming techniques with devastating effect, while the same approach would be massively counter-productive against a ship equipped to a comparable or superior level of EW technology operated by well-trained and experienced personnel. This also points to the need for continuous training of crews in EW technique and a corresponding requirement for both shore-based and shipboard simulators.

15. Comprehensive details of current electronic warfare systems and a more detailed account of their operation are to be found in *The Naval Institute Guide to World Naval Weapons Systems 1991/92*, by Dr Norman Friedman. This is essential reading. *Jane's Radar and EW Yearbook* purports to cover the same ground but contains many inaccuracies and the information provided is often badly dated. It cannot be recommended.

16. William R Bigas, 'Electronic Warfare for Naval Systems', *Naval Forces* (6/1991).

Another area of concern lies in the jammer transmitting a radar-like signal. This is vulnerable to exploitation by anti-radar missiles (ARM) used in the so-called home-on-jam mode. Home-on-jam is sometimes presented as being a radical or mysterious technology, but is nothing of the sort. It is simply an extension of the already well-known and widespread anti-radar missile systems. Although the fact is not widely advertised, all ARMs have an intrinsic home-on-jam capability, while this facility is built into most of the large Soviet air-to-surface and surface-to-surface missiles as an alternative to radar and/or IR homing. The attack pattern here is to use either a mixture of normal and home-on-jam missiles or, as in the Soviet case, to provide the capability to switch from one homing mode to the other in flight.[17]

The counter to home-on-jam is to move the jammer off the ship completely and package it into a decoy round. This concept, the offboard expendable jammer, is mentioned briefly in the section on decoy dispensers. The Russian navy was the first to introduce an active offboard decoy system, using a twin-barrelled 150mm heavyweight launcher fed from a below-decks magazine. This system was originally believed to be purely a chaff launcher, but it is now known to be a launcher for offboard active decoys with chaff launching forming a secondary – but still significant – role.

In Western navies, two approaches are being explored. The first is to package a relatively sophisticated jamming package into a decoy rocket and fire the round, one-on-one, against individual missiles leaking through active defences. The decoy round deploys a parachute and uses blip enhancement and seduction jamming to lure the inbound missile away from its target and into chaff clouds. This concept is best illustrated by the GEC-Marconi Siren system and forms the basis for the Royal Navy's DLH programme. A second route is to install the jamming package on top of a platform that can be controlled to emulate the movements of a ship. This has been adopted by the US/Australian team behind the Nulka/Winnin system. This system can also be used to fake out search radars by giving a totally false idea of the potential target's course and speed, with the result that the missiles fired head off on a totally incorrect tangent. Both concepts have met with development problems resulting from the need to package sophisticated electronic components within a lightweight unit of restricted weight. Neither Siren nor Nulka is yet in service.

A GEC-Marconi Siren decoy round being loaded on to its launcher aboard a British frigate. (GEC-Marconi)

The limited role of jamming systems, the hazards presented by their use and the availability of the offboard jamming solution all strongly point to a reduction in the importance of these systems. However, the jammers do retain considerable tactical value in deflecting attacks on their platforms and in supporting strikes by jamming defence systems of hostile platforms. During the 1990s, the existing large, complex and expensive jammers will be replaced by new, lightweight systems which exploit advanced electronic technology to reduce costs dramatically while reducing capability to a much lesser degree. The emphasis in warship fits will partly switch to acquiring and perfecting the new offboard expendable jammers and partly to a major enhancement of passive ESM capability.

ESM systems

The electronic surveillance measures equipment fitted to a modern warship is rapidly becoming the ship's most important sensor. ESM provides a covert and unobtrusive means of gathering data on the tactical situation and on the hostile forces that are either threats or potential targets. During the Second Gulf War the Royal Navy frigates and destroyers tasked with the control of entry into and egress from Iraqi airspace used their UAA-2 Abbey Hill ESM systems for this purpose, regarding their Type 1022 and Type 992 radars as being of secondary importance. HMS *Gloucester* and HMS

Cardiff performed so efficiently that the British ships were awarded full EW control for all naval operations in the northern and central Gulf. This was a convincing demonstration of the fact that the 1990s will be the decade of the passive ESM sensor.

ESM coverage is both offensive and defensive, providing passive detection of naval and airborne threats well over the radar horizon, and also, where the level of capability provided is, sufficient, over-the-horizon targeting (OTHT) for missiles. The attack warning function requires coverage of the I-, J- and K-bands used by fire control radars and missile guidance seekers. OTHT targeting requires coverage of the D- and E/F-bands used for air and surface search and, preferably, screening of HF communications facilities. An intriguing example of the importance of the latter capability is the installation of an elaborate COMINT facility on some Korean destroyers linked to a TACAN navigation beacon. In the coastal waters off Korea, radar is virtually ineffective for picking up the small craft used by North Korean infiltrators. The COMINT installation picks up their radio communications with high directional accuracy and the destroyer's onboard helicopter is used to investigate the contacts. This is exactly the intercept procedure used by the British cruisers in the 1920s and 1930s, mentioned earlier.

ESM equipment can be divided into wide-

17. *To The Roar of Our Rockets* (Moscow 1992).

open and narrow-beam scanning types. A wide-open detector will pick up very short signals but is claimed to lack sensitivity in any one direction and will also lack directional precision. A narrow-band scanner will provide good directional data and may achieve great sensitivity, but with a finite scanning rate will miss very short burst transmissions. Effectively, an ESM system can scan either in bearing or frequency, or use some compromise in between these two extremes. British practice is to adopt wide-open detectors using fixed antennas and to measure signal direction by phase comparison. This is sufficient to provide bearing accuracies of 0.5 degrees, more than adequate for a missile firing solution. Up to the early 1980s, US policy was to use rapid scanning directional antennas. The current standard ESM system in the US Navy, SLQ-32, is a wide-open system which uses electronic scanning to form numerous narrow beams simultaneously. In theory, this provides a very good compromise between the demands of good frequency coverage, sensitivity and high bearing accuracy. In practice, it is reported not to have worked well. The Second Gulf War highlighted the extent to which British warships outperformed their US (indeed all Allied) cousins in the EW role, and suggests that the design philosophy adopted by the British may become more widely accepted.

The primary function of an ESM receiver is to determine the main parameters of an intercepted emitter, including the bearing, intensity, frequency, pulse width, PRF, scan rate and frequency hopping pattern (if any). These data are then compared with a threat library, the emitter identified by comparison with known parameters or marked down as previously unknown, and the operator informed accordingly. In some cases the data are immediately conclusive – Royal Navy UAA-2 operators found the signature of the US SPY-1 radars so specific that it could be identified instantaneously. In other cases, the presence of similar radars on friendly and hostile platforms (Cyrano IV on the Mirage F.1 being a good example) or the adoption of war-only modes made the contact highly ambiguous

and identity had to be resolved by course and motion analysis or the use of other sensors. Here, the future holds a very serious problem in the development of software-controlled radars. These have a high inherent flexibility to emulate other radars, opening up a whole new range of counter-ESM techniques.

Parameter determination can be conducted by a number of different types of systems. One is a broad-band crystal video receiver (CVR) which can respond to a wide variety of signals within a specified band width. It can identify an intercepted signal by frequency band but cannot tell where within that band the signal is located. CVRs are very simple and lightweight and are not suitable for serious ESM duties. They are best used as radar warning receivers, set-on receivers for decoy launchers and for platforms too small to carry proper ESM. They are also very useful as back-ups for occasions when the primary ESM system is out of action as a result of technical malfunction or battle damage. CVRs are also ideal to be held in store as emergency upgrades for ships about to go in harm's way.

A second approach is the tunable receiver, also known as the scanning superheterodyne receiver (SHR). A narrow tuning band sweeps through the receiver's band width. If the sweep is very rapid compared with the duration of the signal, that signal will be detected and identified. If the transmissions are sufficiently compressed, there is a strong possibility they will be missed. Sweep rates achieved in SHRs can range from a few GHz/second for mechanical systems to 1 GHz/microsecond for electronically scanned

equipment. However, modern radars typically employ pulse widths of a few microseconds, degrading the efficiency of even the electronically scanned systems.

The third common technique for emitter parameter analysis is instantaneous frequency measurement (IFM). These receivers are open to the entire frequency band all the time and have a very high chance of intercepting a signal. They tend to be less sensitive than an SHR because they have to respond to a broad frequency band (as a rule of thumb, sensitivity is generally inversely proportional to channel width). IFM is becoming increasingly common in shipboard systems as the British argument that excessive concentration on sensitivity is counter-productive receives greater acceptance. The main drawback with IFM is that, since a finite time is required to process each intercepted signal, the system may be unable to cope with a string of intercepts in quick succession. This problem is not insoluble, but does increase the complexity of the system.

The key parameter determined by an ESM system is the bearing of the threat. An octantal bearing is adequate for radar warning purposes, while for many years a bearing accuracy of about 6 degrees was regarded as adequate for ELINT operations. It was no longer adequate with the growing use of ESM for OTHT, and an angular resolution of 2 degrees was demanded. Even this is now regarded as obsolescent, and the latest British and European ESM systems offer a combat-demonstrated angular resolution of 0.5 degrees. In the Arabian Gulf, HMS *Gloucester*

An example of a recent European EW system can be seen on the Dutch frigate Witte de With. *The Sphinx ESM system is disposed around the top of the plated fore mast (just below the DA-08 search radar); COMINT communications intercept equipment is carried on the lattice topmast. The other electronic equipment visible are the STIR-18 fire control radar for the Sea Sparrow SAM (on the fore mast platform) and STIR-24 fire control for the Standard SAM above the bridge, with a ZW-06 navigational radar forward of it. (L & L Ginderen)*

used equipment of this standard to provide targeting data on inbound Silkworm missiles. Three techniques are used to provide directional data. These are interferometric, monopulse and single-directional antenna.

Interferometers are the oldest form of direction-finding device. They consist of a series of omni-directional antennas, each of which detects a signal with a slightly different time delay depending on the signal bearing. The classic design, known as an Adcock, consists of two pairs of crossed vertical loop or half-wavelength wide antennas. The assembly can be rotated to give a bearing, this taking about ten seconds, or the bearing can be obtained by sampling the antenna with a rotating goniometer, cutting the time taken to about three seconds. The time taken to get a bearing can be cut to about half a second by grouping the antenna elements into two subgroups which are used to drive the two plates on a CRT. If a computer comparator is used, a bearing can be obtained almost instantaneously. A further design stage is to form more than two beams by using a circular array and using a goniometer to sample the relevant sections of the array. This provides greatly improved directivity at the expense of all-round simultaneous coverage. This array was originally developed by the Germans during the Second World War as the 'Wollenweber' and was very widely adopted postwar for land use. This type of array has now become virtually standard and is preferred by Soviet designers, who have adopted it extensively under the name Krug. A more modern version uses computer-generated preformed beams sampling all directions simultaneously.

Monopulse direction-finders compare the strength of signals as they are detected by a series of antennas orientated in different directions. These antennas are usually spirals or broad-band cones. Monopulse DF is used extensively in wide-open systems for warships, and the monopulse arrays can easily be seen on the masts of British frigates, usually just underneath the main search radar. Where installations on warships are concerned, monopulse techniques are usable only against radar wavelengths, since the individual antenna must be large enough (in wavelengths) to generate non-overlapping beams. The requirement for DF against HF, VHF and UHF radios requires a different design solution.

In contrast to interferometer and monopulse units, directional antennas have a narrow pattern and scan over the direction of an incoming signal. This provides a much greater gain, resulting in increased range, but coverage of a given signal is intermittent. The current trend is to rely upon monopulse for radar direction-finding and to reserve high-gain equipment for trackers associated with jammers.

Once obtained, there are a number of ways in which the parameters of intercepted radars can be displayed. Tabular presentation has the advantage of being compact and relaying the most detailed data, but has the disadvantage that few operators can easily visualise the tactical situation from the text presentation. A graphical presentation is required. The two most common conventions are polar and cartesian.

Polar presentation places the ship in the centre of a north-top circle with the bearing represented realistically and the frequency represented from the outside of the circle inward. These frequencies are not represented in order, but in a sequence intended to give an indication of threat level. Thus a wandering search radar would be on the perimeter of the circle, while a lock-on missile homer would be close to the centre. Polar presentation has the advantage of being quick and easy to assimilate but the disadvantage of being highly misleading to those not skilled in the EW arts. Non-specialists tend to interpret distance from the circle centre as range from the ship, not decreasing level of threat.

Cartesian display puts the intercepted data on a graphical chart with the bearing running along the bottom, with north at the centre and frequency running vertically. This is the method preferred by the Royal Navy, on the basis that it gives a trained operator a more immediately useful picture of the situation. Most of the latest EW systems have software provisions for both conventions and either can be selected according to doctrine or the operator's personal preference. The use of colour is also of great assistance. The current Royal Navy convention is to designate hostile forces in red, friendly forces in blue, neutrals in yellow and unidentified in white.

Even the most advanced electronic warfare equipment will not perform correctly unless it is properly located within the ship. Effectively this means that the need to place the ESM antenna in optimum positions drives the design of the superstructure. On this basis the degree to which superstructure design is dictated by ESM antenna placement is a very good pointer as to the priority placed on EW by the design teams. It is noticeable that the ESM fits on British ships are far more extensive than on US warships, and that a number of subtle design compromises have been made by British designers to ensure that the ESM antennas are carried in the optimum positions – high and providing uninterrupted 360-degree coverage. Most US warships carry their SLQ-32 antennas low,

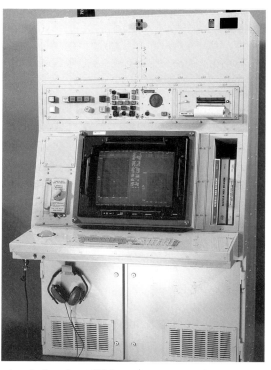

A typical modern ESM operator's console, for the GEC-Marconi Mentor system.

either on the superstructure or, as on the CG-47 class cruisers, actually fitted to the superstructure sides. This degrades the performance of the intercept and jamming systems owing to multipathing, and limits the intercept horizon. Worse, wooding caused by the superstructure and masts eliminates coverage directly ahead and above, creating dangerous blind arcs.

ESM technology has become even more significant with the introduction of long range anti-ship missiles. These require over-the-horizon targeting information. Radar ESM intercepts are one major means of obtaining this information; communications intercepts are another. The latter have recently become the centre of intense interest with the discovery that timing the arrivals of ground and sky waves can provide surprisingly accurate range data. The delay between the arrival of the ground wave and sky wave is due to the extra distance covered by the sky wave in reflecting off the ionosphere; as long as the altitude of the ionosphere is known, determining the range becomes a very easy calculation. The one piece of information required from outside the ship is the ionosphere altitude, this being obtainable from the meteorological services. Systems using this technique include the Israeli NATACS and the US SSQ-108(V)2, the latter becoming widely used within Nato.

Intrinsic within the concept of using ESM for target data is the absolute necessity of building up comprehensive libraries of threat radars.

This has resulted in a hugh effort, involving AGIs, submarines (often penetrating waters where angels would definitely fear to tread!), long range ferret aircraft, and surveillance satellites. As knowledge of ESM technology has spread, more and more navies are starting signature gathering operations of this type. The situation has been immensely complicated by the collapse of the Soviet Union and the exponential growth in regional instability. Nations now have to face the possibility of facing equipment they would previously have regarded as 'friendly', or even their own kit, sold in more amicable times. All of these sets will have WARMS which may require identification at very short notice. Many nations may lack the ability to design their own equipment but are able to modify kit supplied from outside, again increasing the signature identification task.

These factors suggest that modern, software-controlled threat libraries will be absolutely essential. During the Second Gulf War, some ESM and radar warning equipment was found to be virtually useless because the threat libraries were hard-wired and had to be returned to the manufacturers for modification. This particularly affected the range of low-cost systems sold on the export market. Fortunately, the British systems and most of their US equivalents were software-controlled and could be modified very fast. One source intimate with the effort has indicated that the US had far superior signature gathering capabilities, while the British had equally superior facilities, in the form of Marconi-designed Merlin Composers, for processing that data into threat library entries for common use.[18] Combining these two strengths proved massively effective and proved that economising in this area was extremely dangerous for those who had to rely on the equipment.

Electro-optical and FLIR decoy systems

In recent years missiles using laser-designation, laser beam-riding, TV, imaging infra-red (IIR) and other optronic guidance systems have started to appear in the anti-ship role. These are not subject to decoy by the EW methods described in previous sections. The emergence of the missile-armed helicopter as a primary threat to missile-armed fast attack craft has caused considerable concern in navies relying on such craft for the major part of the striking power of their fleet. Although the missiles are usually radar guided, such helicopters use electro-optical systems, predominantly Forward Looking Infra Red (FLIR), as the main means by which they can locate their targets. This avoids alerting the targets by over-use of the main radars. The provision of means to counter such electro-optical systems would seem to be essential if the FACs are to regain some measure of operational freedom.

FLIR jammers employ an intense modulated infra-red light. If such an IR source is sufficiently intense, the FLIR will see some of it, even when it is looking at another part of the scene. It is, after all, attempting to detect weak sources of IR radiation and some leakage is unavoidable. Since the flashing light is out of phase with the FLIR scanning cycle, the FLIR will associate these leaked flashes with other portions of its scan. If the scan rate and flashing rate of the jammer are in the correct ratio, the field of view of the FLIR will be covered, negating its use as a sensor. This type of jamming is quite common against conical-scan infra-red guided air-to-air missiles. In the case of the systems used at the Battle of Khafji during the Second Gulf War, the jamming was negated by a technical fix changing the FLIR scanning rate. The FLIR jammers currently available will become ineffective as staring FLIRs become cheaper, and thus wider spread. However, given the importance of FLIRs as a search, target acquisition and weapons guidance system, the development of means to jam such equipment is likely to be of growing importance.[19]

A second approach to the problem of optronically-guided missiles is to attack the guidance system itself. Many anti-ship missiles are guided to their targets by the guidance system tracking the relative positions of the target and an infra-red flare located in the rear of the missile. This opens a countermeasure window. If the target shines a sufficiently bright infra-red source at the missile operator, the guidance system will mistake it for the flare and the guidance system will be negated. Such jamming systems are already commercially available, most notably from the French, and were used by Iraqi forces.

The final approach to the electro-optical countermeasures problem has been developed by the Royal Navy. In 1989 it was revealed that a laser 'weapon' had been fitted to Royal Navy warships for over seven years. Indeed, the system, initially referred to as the Laser Dazzle Sight, was used in combat during the Falklands campaign and subsequently during British naval operations in the Arabian Gulf during the First Gulf War. The system is now known to be designated 'Outfit DEC', reflecting its origins in fire control laser technology.

Although Outfit DEC is still covered by British security restrictions, additional details on the system and its use are now becoming available. Outfit DEC works in three modes. In the first, it can be directed at the sea surface in front of an inbound optronically-guided missile. Reflections from the sea throw up a wall of laser light which burns out the optronic sensor in the nose of the missile, negating its guidance method. The second operational mode consists of directing the DEC system at an inbound aircraft using the Type 1007 navigational radar fitted to all British ships. This has the effect of causing the Perspex canopy of the aircraft to glow brightly, depriving the pilot of outside vision and causing severe spatial disorientation. The Perspex itself may be degraded and turned permanently opaque. Finally, if the attacking aircraft is equipped with a head-up display, the optics of the HUD cause the full power of the laser to be concentrated into the pilot's eyes. The frequency and modulation rate of the laser are calculated to do the maximum possible damage to the blood vessels, retina and optic nerve in the pilot's eyes causing permanent and irreversible blindness.[20]

Outfit DEC is very widely installed on British warships and an equivalent system has appeared on Soviet ships. It, and similar systems, are likely to be of growing importance. Although most countries have a few guided air-to-surface missiles in their inventory, numbers are small and serviceability doubtful. In the final analysis, reliance is likely to be placed on unguided high explosive 'iron bombs' which must be visually aimed and delivered from close range and low altitude. Pilots are likely to be seriously deterred from performing iron bomb runs against ships if they believe a DEC-like system will be used against them.

Systems integration

A constant theme repeated in the above sections has been the interrelationships between the various forms of naval EW and the synergistic benefits of using different EW techniques in mutual support. A less obvious, but no less important, relationship exists between electronic warfare equipment (and technique) and other aspects of naval technology. In effect these relationships mean that relevant EW requirements must be included within ships at the earliest stage of the design process. This applies to both the electronic aspects of design (integration

18. *Gulf War Perspective*, distributed by GEC-Marconi Defense Systems. Claims for their equipment validated by Forecast International, Newtown, Connecticut (1993).

19. Dr Norman Friedman, *Desert Victory: The War for Kuwait* (Annapolis 1992).

20. *Outfit DEC*, EW Market Intelligence Report, Forecast International, Newtown, Connecticut (1993)

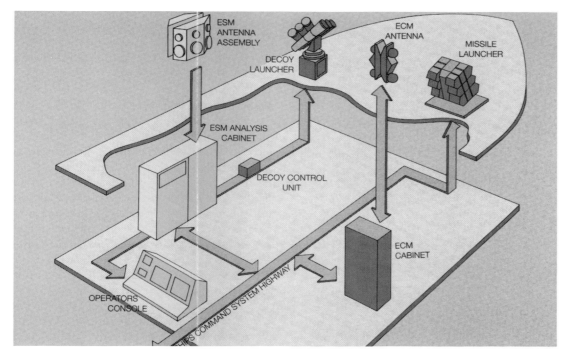

A schematic arrangement of a modern integrated ESM system, in this case the Thorn-EMI Sceptre XL. It is a passive, long range electronic surveillance system for large surface ships, which can detect, analyse and classify hostile surface and airborne radar emitters before they come within range of the ship's radar. It can prioritise threats and designate appropriate countermeasures, and even supply accurate bearing information to launch a first strike missile. (Thorn-EMI)

with other sensors and with the action information/combat system) and to the physical design of the ship (position of sensors and survivability considerations).

The interrelationships between the various forms of naval EW makes integration by including passive detection, active jamming and OTHT tracking within a single package conceptually attractive. This approach was adopted for the US Navy SLQ-32. The problem is that the resulting antenna system is frequently too heavy to be mounted at masthead height and must therefore be carried on top of or even on the sides of the superstructure. On the other hand, using separated ESM, jamming and OTHT arrays eases the difficulties of carrying the equipment high at cost of greater integration problems. This situation again indicates the extent to which superstructure design must be driven by the requirements of the EW suite, and the problem will only be resolved as the advances in electronics technology are reflected in lighter and more compact antenna arrays.

The need for electronic integration has been amply demonstrated during the Second Gulf War. The use of passive ESM by British destroyers has already been briefly mentioned. Perhaps the most dramatic demonstration was the shooting down of an Iraqi Silkworm missile fired at the USS *Missouri* on 25 February 1991. The engagement commenced when an Iraqi coastal battery turned on its target location radar (believed to be a Thomson-CSF set). This was immediately detected by the UAA-2 Abbey Hill ESM equipment fitted to HMS *Gloucester*, which determined the location of the battery to

within 0.5 degree resolution. The ship's highly integrated command system permitted this data to be automatically relayed to the air defence plot and thus to the Type 909(I) Sea Dart fire control radars. These and a Type 992Q search radar were slewed to the correct bearing.

The Iraqi battery fired two missiles which were detected by the British radars as they crossed the Kuwaiti coast some twenty miles from the fleet. The UAA-2 system on HMS *Gloucester* determined that no radar homing signals were being received from the missiles and this, together with certain aspects of their course, indicated that the Silkworms were operating in infra-red homing mode. The British tracking radars lit up when the missiles approached to eleven miles range. Information from the mine avoidance sonars indicated that manoeuvres to place the Silkworms in optimum firing arcs would place the ship in danger of striking mines, so two Sea Dart missiles were fired in what the Royal Navy described as 'an over-the-shoulder, round-the-corner shot'. By the time interception had occurred, one Silkworm had fallen into the sea, probably as a result of gyro failure, but the other was hit at a range of four miles by the Sea Dart aimed at it. The second Sea Dart automatically retargeted itself when its original target vanished and flew through the wreckage of the first Silkworm.[21]

The importance of this action is that it clearly demonstrates the importance of full combat integration on warships and the need fully to integrate all sensors with all weapons. It is also necessary, for example, to integrate data presented by sonar with ESM and radar infor-

mation. This reflects the possibility of a missile submarine, hunted by a frigate, firing a salvo of subsurface-to-surface anti-ship missiles. Fired at point-blank range, the frigate could have less than two seconds to respond. In this case the launch transients detected by sonar would add precious seconds to the warning time, permit chaff clouds to be deployed and allow active jamming to be initiated. ESM equipment could also be readied to ensure that the missile was radar-guided by picking up the homing head. Finally, fire control radars would be pointed at the location of the launch point to commence engaging the missile as soon as it emerged from the sea.[22]

Consideration of the interrelationships between a warship's EW effectiveness and other aspects of her design are frequently very subtle and lead to some unexpected conclusions. In an earlier section it was shown that the seeker in an anti-ship missile generally homes in on the centre of the target's return, seeing the ship as a complex mass of point and corner reflectors. It therefore follows that careful design of the ship's hull and superstructure can distort the radar image perceived by the missile and deflect it from the centre of the ship. The British Type 23 frigate is designed with careful attention to the radar cross-section for precisely this reason. Once the missile is deflected away from the centre of the ship, decoying by chaff is eased and any hits are likely to be in less vulnerable sections of the ship.

This raises the question of ship survivability. At first sight, the provision of armour protection (steel or Kevlar) to a ship seems unrelated to its EW capability. In fact, built-in provisions for ship survivability have numerous direct benefits to her EW performance. The idea that a ship could be sunk by a single hit is a new one and, until 1945, any design team producing a major hull on that basis would be considered incompetent. Essential facilities were duplicated and protected by armour plate. It was assumed that ships would be hit (frequently) and were

21. Antony Preston (ed), *NAVINT* (8 November 1991).
22. *C³I Market Overview*, C³I Market Intelligence Report, Forecast International, Newtown, Connecticut (1993).

The increasing importance of EW is leading to a new emphasis on 'stealth' features in warship design. The US experimental craft Sea Shadow *was designed to test such features (among other advanced technologies), and results from the vessel have been incorporated into the new US* Arleigh Burke *class.* (USN)

siles are reduced, with proportional increases in success rates. In this respect, ship damage control is also a vital component of EW efficiency.

Another direct relationship exists between the efficiency of point-defence systems and EW capability. As point-defence guns and missiles become more effective, the missiles must be designed with higher performance and more complex attack patterns. Supersonic anti-ship missiles cannot, by the laws of physics, skim the sea surface as closely as subsonic missiles, while missiles pursuing an evasive course with repeated sharp turns also cannot follow the sea surface as closely as straight-runners. Thus the effect of efficient point-defence systems is to push inbound missiles up, away from the sea surface, and make them more vulnerable to jamming and decoying. The increased approach height also increases the range at which the inbound missile can be detected by ESM and thus improves the efficiency of the point-defence system. Also, a missile that runs in high will tend to hit high, limiting its ship-killing potential.

The ability of an individual ship to survive hits is of key importance to the EW defence of the battle fleet as a whole. As long as a ship stays afloat, even as a helpless wreck, she will continue to attract missiles and dilute attacks on other, as yet undamaged, warships. This enhances the effectiveness of their EW systems. If damage can be controlled, flooding limited and fires put out (all areas in which the US Navy excels), it will be difficult for an attacker to determine the extent of the damage inflicted. If surviving radars can continue to radiate or their emissions can be simulated by jammers, the problems in determining the ship's status are multiplied. Many naval exercises have demonstrated the fact that officers commanding attacking warships will continue to pump missiles into their targets until their magazines are empty or the victim 'sinks'. This points to a substantial fleet-wide command and control and damage assessment problem. One possible resolution to this situation is the use of ESM and related technologies in determining whether damaged ships are crippled or merely hurt. Attack damage assessment remains, however, a largely insoluble problem in the naval environment until the victim of the attack finally sinks.

Stuart Slade

expected to keep fighting. This approach was dropped after the end of the Second World War but is now being revived. The revival of damage limitation in ship design has numerous advantages from an EW point of view. If ships are made more difficult to sink (with improved compartmentation, armour protection to vital areas, quadruplicated vital facilities and other similar provisions), the missiles must be equipped with significantly larger warheads to defeat these protective measures.

Already existing anti-ship missiles have shown a disturbing inability to sink ships. They can smash the superstructure and leave the ship a floating wreck, but they do not actually sink the target. As a rule of thumb, missiles follow the square law, and doubling the warhead size quadruples the weight of the missile if speed and range are to be maintained. This restricts the ability of the missile to sea-skim and the increased approach altitude of the weapon makes it more vulnerable to jamming and decoying. Also, if the design of the ship is such that the damage inflicted by hits removed from the centre can be contained, the importance of distorting the ship's radar image is enhanced. Finally, if the damage inflicted by near-misses can be contained, the acceptable margins for decoying mis-

13

Propulsion

IN 1945, MAJOR surface warships were all steam-powered, generally by turbines. Diesels, limited to a unit power of about 2000 or 3000 horsepower, were widely used in smaller craft, particularly landing craft, and were the surface powerplants of all submarines. The only other powerplants in service were gasoline (petrol) internal combustion engines in many small fast combatants such as motor torpedo boats (and in some landing craft), and Walter gas turbines in a very few German submarines. Almost half a century later, conventional steam plants are declining to near-extinction. Gas turbines power many surface warships, and powerful diesels are now quite common in surface combatants. The Walter gas turbine, so promising in 1945, has not entered service since. On the other hand, nuclear steam power has changed naval warfare.

Principles

All powerplants obey the same laws of thermodynamics. A working fluid, such as air (in a gas turbine) or water (in a steam engine) is heated; as much as possible of that heat energy is converted into mechanical energy, much (but not all) of which drives the ship. Overall efficiency is how much of the chemical (or nuclear) energy in the fuel is converted into shaft horsepower. That depends on three quite different kinds of efficiency. Combustion efficiency is how much of the chemical or nuclear energy is converted into usable heat. Thermal efficiency (which depends on the difference between maximum temperature and outlet temperature, after work has been done) is how much of the heat goes

into mechanical work. Mechanical efficiency is how much of the mechanical work is turned into shaft horsepower. A naval engineer also seeks the most compact powerplant, and perhaps the quietest.

No one kind of engine is most efficient in all three categories. Higher air pressure promotes more efficient combustion, since more highly compressed air is denser when it burns. Much depends, however, on how the heat of combustion is transferred to the working fluid (in a diesel, for example, the air heated by fuel burning in it *is* the working fluid, but in a boiler much depends on how the water circulates past the source of heat). That is why a diesel, which burns its air at very high pressure, is extremely fuel-efficient. The drive towards greater thermal efficiency explains why navies sought higher-temperature (and consequently higher-pressure) steam plants before and after the Second World

War. Then there is mechanical efficiency: not all of what the working fluid does is useful. For example, in a piston engine (such as a diesel), energy goes into constantly starting and stopping each piston, and some of that effort goes into useless vibration. Turbines are far more efficient mechanically. On the other hand, as the working fluid expands through a turbine, some of it inevitably rushes past the blades and its energy is lost altogether. Much less is lost that way in a piston engine, so a slow-acting one can be quite efficient mechanically.

Two other considerations have also been important in modern naval plants: manpower-efficiency and silencing. In 1945 naval manpower was relatively inexpensive; that steam plants often required hundreds of men to watch their gauges was considered quite unimportant. Through the postwar period, however, all Western navies suffered from cuts in manpower. That was partly

A major driving force in naval machinery development since the war has been the rising cost of manpower. This manifested itself as a desire for fewer skilled operatives and, as navies became volunteer forces, the need to provide better working conditions. The main machinery control room of HMS Devonshire, *shown here when the ship was new in 1962, is a far cry from the conditions endured by earlier generations of engine room personnel.* (CMP)

a matter of budget (British naval plans were often denoted by the number of naval personnel, in thousands), but it was also an indirect effect of the rise of electronics. As shipboard weapon systems became more complex, a greater fraction of the highly-qualified men had to be devoted to running and maintaining them. That affected machinery because boiler operation became more complex at the same time, as steam conditions rose. The US Navy in particular suffered some serious accidents in the 1960s because it was thought, very erroneously, that steam plants were still simple mechanisms which could be left to less sophisticated operators. Gas turbines and diesels require many fewer operators and gas turbines in particular can be maintained largely by replacement rather than by repair at sea.

Silencing became more and more important for anti-submarine warfare. In general, rotating machinery is far quieter than a diesel, with its regular firing rate. That made gas turbines the natural successors to steam turbines in any warship involved in ASW. Turbines do make some noise, particularly the whine of their reduction gearing. In the US and British navies (and, in the 1980s, in the Soviet navy) submarine turbines were silenced by mounting them and their gearing on rigid rafts with sound-insulated fixings to the hulls. Some surface ships, probably beginning with the US *Spruance* class, were similarly silenced. Gas turbines also produce noise in the air (a characteristic jet whine), but that is relatively easily dealt with. From about the early 1980s on, diesels have been silenced by mounting them on rafts, with hoods over them to carry away the noise of firing and exhaust.

Steam machinery

In 1945 it appeared that steam was the only way to achieve high power for high speed in any large surface warship. Prewar dreams of fast diesel-powered capital ships (with attendant very long range) had not borne any fruit, apart from the German 'pocket battleships'. Despite German plans for a diesel-powered destroyer, it seemed that diesel power would collide with an inherent limit well below the power needed by a fast surface combatant ship. Carriers, cruisers, destroyers, even fast frigates needed far more.

To run most efficiently, a steam plant must operate at higher pressure and temperature. The prewar US Navy chose higher steam conditions (600psi, 850°F) in the mid 1930s specifically because they offered the sort of very long endurance needed for Pacific warfare. The resulting plants were both very efficient (and much envied by a British fleet cursed with much lower steam conditions and hence with much less efficient plants) and quite reliable under combat conditions. The British and Dutch navies found themselves adopting the standard US destroyer plant (as used in the *Fletcher*, *Sumner* and *Gearing* classes) for postwar destroyers of the *Daring* and *Friesland* classes (the earlier Dutch *Holland* class used machinery designed for the prewar *Isaac Sweers* class: in two cases ordered for those ships, and in the other two ordered by the Germans). The Italian navy adopted similar plants for its postwar *Impavido* and *Audace* class destroyers and *Andrea Doria* and *Vittorio Veneto* class cruisers, in some cases at somewhat higher power levels. The Japanese probably adopted the standard US destroyer plant for their post-

war steam destroyers (they reached higher steam conditions, 850psi and about 900°F, in their *Shirane* and *Haruna* class helicopter-carrying destroyers and *Tachikaze* class missile destroyers).

Painfully aware of the inadequacy (including low endurance) of its wartime low-pressure plants (typically 300psi at 640°F in the standard three-drum Admiralty boilers of its late-war 'C' class destroyers, 400psi at 600°F in the carrier *Ark Royal* and 'Battle' class destroyers), the postwar Royal Navy wanted a series of new steam plants. It sponsored the formation of YARD (Yarrow Admiralty Research and Development) to develop boilers and PAMETRADA (Parsons and Marine Engineering Turbine Research and Development Association) to develop turbines. The initial driving force was the need to provide enough power for the new ASW frigates (Type 12, then Type 14). These 30,000shp plants operated at 550psi and at 860°F (450°C). The later 30,000shp plant in the 'County' class operated at 700psi and 900°F. As reboilered, the modernised carrier *Victorious* had 440psi/750°F Foster-Wheeler boilers. The new plants were designated in a 'Y' series (for YARD), beginning with Y.100 in the first Type 12 frigates (Y.136 and Y.160

The Dutch destroyer Groningen *was one of the eight-ship* Friesland *class that adopted the US steam turbine plant from the wartime* Gearing *class. Compared with the preceding, and otherwise similar,* Holland *class which used a prewar 45,000shp plant, the* Friesland*s developed 60,000shp. They were rated at 36kts, but one is supposed to have attained 42.8kts on trials. The high-pressure, high temperature American plant was the best steam machinery available in the postwar decade. (C & S Taylor)*

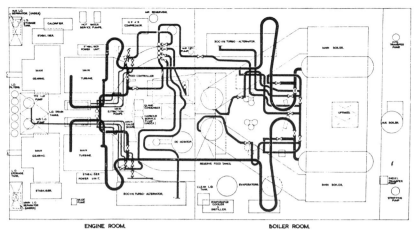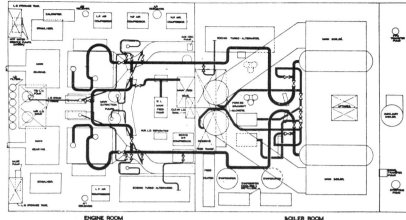

Admiralty steam plant arrangements: Y.100 (above) and Y.136 (right).

were modified versions for the later *Leander*s).

The prewar French navy had been very interested in high steam conditions, and the postwar *Surcouf* class French destroyers and E 50/52 class frigates were powered by locally-designed and -manufactured Rateau turbines fed by Indret boilers (500psi, 725°F). Work continued on higher steam conditions. The carriers, the cruiser *Colbert*, the *Suffren*s and the frigate *Aconit* steamed at higher conditions (640psi, 840°F).

High steam conditions were not always successful, partly because existing materials were inadequate. The prewar and wartime Germans sought much the same qualities as the US Navy (they expected ships to operate in the Atlantic for long periods as raiders), but the resulting plants were both terribly unreliable and quite inefficient. The Soviets had built a high-pressure destroyer prototype, *Opitnyi*, before the war. They captured a complete 1600psi German plant, planned for a large destroyer/scout cruiser, but did not put it into production. This plant may have been installed in a test ship.

Even before the war, the then US Bureau of Engineering sought greater efficiency through higher steam conditions. Postwar, its successor, the Bureau of Ships, decided to adopt a new generation of 1200psi plants. They proved more efficient but also more temperamental, just as other new technology, in weapons and sensors, demanded a larger fraction of a limited pool of highly capable sailors. As might have been expected, by the mid 1960s ageing 1200psi plants were breaking down. Accidents could be quite dangerous: very high pressure steam can cut a man in half. The US Navy found itself abandoning high-pressure plants in new ships in favour of gas turbines, which were far easier to run and to maintain.

One other postwar steam development deserves mention: pressure-firing, an attempt to

achieve greater combustion efficiency. A pressure-fired boiler is fed air compressed by a gas turbine (itself powered by exhaust gas). Because combustion is so much more efficient, the boiler can be far smaller than a conventional unit. Because it is smaller, it can be started up (heated) far more quickly. The Russians were the first to place it in service, in the prototype destroyer *Neustrashimy* (Project 41: Nato designation *Talinn*), in 1952. It was also installed in the *Kotlin* (Project 56), *Kynda* (Project 58), *Moskva* (Project 1123), *Kresta* (Project 1134), *Kiev* (Project 1143), *Kuznetzov* (Project 1143.5) and *Sovremennyy* (Project 956) classes. The version in the Project 41/56 destroyers may have been driven by the ship's turbo-generator, since these ships never seemed to emit the characteristic turbine whine of a pressure-fired plant (a recent Russian design history makes it quite clear, however, that they used some form of pressure-firing). These ships introduced high steam pressure (910psi) into Russian practice. Reportedly the pressure-fired plants were quite noisy: hence the use of gas turbines in ships designed primarily for ASW, such as the *Kara* (Project 1134B) and *Udaloy* (Project 1155) classes; the *Kresta II*s were too far along to change powerplants when their role shifted from ASuW to ASW.

All of the Russian steam plants had their own designators. TV-6, 30,000shp per shaft, powered the *Skoriy* (Project 30 bis) class destroyers (412 psi, 620°F). The last prewar type was TV-7, in the *Sverdlov* (Project 68) class, 25,270shp per shaft. Project 41 (TV-8) produced 33,000 shp per shaft. TV-10 was the low-powered *Riga* class (Project 50) plant. The developed TV-12 pressure-fired plant in a *Kresta* produces 45,500shp per shaft; it is uprated to 50,000shp in a *Sovremennyy*. Steam conditions are 910psi and 932°F (500°C). The *Moskva* plant was probably similar, and *Kiev* and *Kuznetzov* presumably have four TV-12s each. No other steam plant

designations have emerged. Missing numbers may include those for the postwar large-ship (*eg* Project 82R battlecruiser) plant and perhaps for the plant in the *Kola* class (Project 42), which was different from that in the *Riga*. It is not clear whether nuclear submarine plants were included in the same series.

The US version of pressure-firing was invented for proposed (but abortive) radar picket submarines (it could start up very quickly when the submarine surfaced, to provide enough power for the required high surface speed). It was installed in *Brooke* and *Garcia* class frigates (1200psi, 950°F), and it figured prominently in US escort ship planning for the 1960s. It died a political death. Until the two pressure-fired designs, Gibbs & Cox had been responsible for the machinery designs of virtually all US destroyers and escorts. However, Bethlehem Steel designed the powerplants of the two pressure-fired ships. Reportedly the legendary naval architect, William F Gibbs, pressured the navy to revert to a more conventional (hence better-tested) type of plant for the mass-production *Knox* class, to regain primacy in US destroyer and escort machinery design. Ironically, the *Knox*es turned out to be the last US non-nuclear steam-powered escorts.

The great drawback of steam plants was their complexity. For example, they needed numerous highly-trained men to monitor their many gauges. Maintenance was complex and expensive. Furthermore, a steam plant could not be started very quickly. Its boiler had to be heated, often over four or more hours, before the plant could be lit off. Hence the decline of steam plants in recent years.

Nuclear power is the one great exception: virtually unlimited endurance at high power was clearly worth a great deal of complexity. There are also other benefits. A nuclear ship does not suffer uptake gas problems, which corrode or damage antennas. She also has enormous amounts of

electric power always available, which is apparently a very significant point in carrier operation. The principles of nuclear plants are covered in the chapter on submarines.

Such powerplants are quite heavy. It is sometimes argued that not all of that weight is really necessary. Ships rarely operate at full speed (for example, they cannot use sonar effectively beyond a much lower speed), so there may be little point in providing extreme endurance for speeds above, say, 20kts. Instead, a nuclear plant may be combined with a fossil-fuelled boost plant, to achieve relatively short spurts at high speed. The main current example is the Russian *Kirov* class, in which a separate oil-fired steam plant (about 50,000shp) boosts the 90,000shp nuclear plant; the abortive carrier *Ulyanovsk* was apparently to have had a similar (but doubled) plant. The large intelligence-collection ship *Urals* (SSV-33, Nato code-name *Kapusta*) has a four-shaft CONAS (combined nuclear and steam) plant, rated at 98,800shp; presumably two shafts are nuclear, two fossil-fuelled. Russian writers sometimes describe the *Kirov* nuclear plant as the boost element, but that seems most unlikely. They have also suggested that, to alleviate environmental concerns, such a ship could get under way on fossil power, then switch to nuclear at sea (in fact the fossil plant produces far more environmental damage in its immediate neighbourhood). The Soviets designed a nuclear-gas turbine plant for a projected 12,000-ton carrier escort, code-named *Anchar*, but the project was abandoned as the Soviet Union began to collapse in 1990. US proposals for a combined nuclear-gas turbine or nuclear-steam plant were fruitless.

Diesel engines

Overall, the much better combustion efficiency of a diesel more than makes up for the greater mechanical efficiency of a steam plant, so that a diesel offers far greater overall efficiency. That was well known even before the First World War, and schemes for very long range diesel-powered capital ships were mooted as early as

1912. They were furthest advanced in Germany, where diesels powered the three 'pocket battleships' and where auxiliary diesels were installed in cruisers to provide them with very long cruising range. Unfortunately, diesels vibrate: it proved quite difficult to build satisfactory large naval diesels.

For a given level of technology, each cylinder of a diesel can deliver only so much power. Each time the piston thrusts down, it twists the crankshaft. Energy is lost in this torsion. As cylinders are added, it becomes more and more difficult to keep the crankshaft reasonably rigid, so there is a practical limit to the output of a single engine. Because the pistons do not push down together, their strokes twist the crankshaft, which vibrates torsionally (in twist). For each crankshaft, there is a particular rate of vibration at which each additional thrust increases the level of vibration, a situation called resonance. When the diesel runs at resonance speed, it breaks up. Thus a particular diesel generally cannot run at particular speed ranges. That is clearly a far more significant limitation for warships than for merchant ships.

Diesels operate on a two- or four-stroke cycle. In the latter, the piston sucks air into the cylinder on the first (down) stroke, then rises to compress it, then makes a single (downward) power stroke, then rises to expel the burnt air from the cylinder. In a two-stroke engine, fresh air is blown into the cylinder and burnt gas driven out as the piston falls past the exhaust ports. Every down stroke is a power stroke, but the length of the effective stroke is limited, since the hot gas leaves the cylinder through the exhaust ports in its side. In addition, a two-stroke diesel uses some of its power to drive a blower. In 1945 the US Navy used two-stroke diesels in its submarines; the Germans used four-stroke types.

Warship, including submarine, diesels were

generally limited in height, *ie* in stroke. The power output of each cylinder depends on the volume swept out on each stroke, so the shorter the stroke the more strokes the diesel must make to produce a given output. The faster the diesel runs, the worse its vibration and the less reliable it is. This problem was far less important for merchant ships, which could accommodate much taller engines. Also, to achieve the very high power required by a combatant, several engines must be combined, into a plant much larger than an equivalent steam plant.

After 1945 there was considerable interest in making diesels more compact, mainly to power fast combatants. In this case the advantage of the diesel (over the gasoline engines formerly used) was that its fuel did not create an explosive vapour. There was also considerable interest in making submarine diesels more compact.

Many favoured an unusual engine configuration which increased the number of cylinders without requiring a longer crankshaft. The other, quite successful, postwar means of boosting diesel power was supercharging, in which combustion air was compressed before it entered the cylinder. The supercharger could be driven either mechanically, from the crankshaft, or by exhaust gas (turbo-charging). In either case, it spent some engine power to increase combustion efficiency.

The wartime Germans had been unique in using Daimler- (later Mercedes-) Benz diesels rather than gasoline engines in their fast attack craft (*S-Boote*). Most were 2050bhp twenty-cylinder four-cycle vees (MB 501), which were eventually uprated (by about 25 per cent) with superchargers as MB 511 (the smaller vee-sixteen MB 502 was supercharged as MB 512). In 1944 a development of the MB 511, MB 518, developed 3000bhp at 1720rpm for thirty minutes. Such engines were used in the few boats (later the *Silbermöwe*, or Type 149 class) built immediately after the war for the new Naval Border Guard (*See Grenze Schutze*), the forerunner of the Federal German Navy. Thus five were powered by MB 518As, and a sixth by an alternative 3000bhp sixteen-cylinder vee Maybach MD-870. Eleven *Plejad* class boats built for Sweden in 1952–60 were also powered by MB 518s (later redesignated 20V672). The new German navy ordered three series of fast attack boats: Type 140 (*Jaguar* class) powered by MB 518Bs; Type 141 (*Jaguar* class) powered by Maybach MD-871s; and Type 142 (*Zobel* class) powered by MB 518Cs. MB 518 offered very light weight (less than 2kg/bhp) at a fuel rate of 0.17–0.18kg/ bhp; it developed 3000bhp for half an hour at 1720rpm or 2790bhp for three hours at 1680rpm (or it could cruise at 2275bhp at 1580rpm). The Maybach engine was heavier (2.7kg/bhp) and operated at higher pressure; it offered 2650bhp for an hour at 1750rpm or it could cruise at 2400bhp at 1670rpm. Both types were developed further, into MB 518D (2900–3500bhp) and MD-1081/1082 (3000–3600bhp and 3750–4500bhp).

In 1969 Mercedes-Benz merged with Maybach and with MAN-Turbo to form Motoren Turbinen Union (MTU). Its MD-871 and MD-872 (16V538) powered the widely-used French 'Combattante II' missile boat, the German version of which was Type 148. The slightly later Type 143 was powered by MTU 16V956TB91s (4000–4600bhp). Similar engines power 'Combattante III' missile boats in the Nigerian navy (the Greek and Tunisian boats have 20V538s with similar output, using more but smaller cylinders). MTU diesels power the widely-sold Lürssen FPB and PB 38, 45, 57, and 62 types and are widely used in other types. There is also a 331 series (*eg* 12V331TC92, 3500bhp, in Costa Rican 105ft patrol boats). In each case, the first two digits are the number of cylinders (in vee configuration, *eg* 16V is a sixteen-vee).

By about 1974 MTU had developed its 12V956 and 16V956 into the water-cooled turbo-charged 20V956TB92, which produced 4900–6000bhp at a specific weight of 2.73kg/bhp. These engines are also used in combined plants, such as the CODOG (combined diesel or gas) installation in Brazilian Mk 10 (*Niteroi* class) frigates (four 16V956TB91 plus two Olympus TM3B gas turbines; with one Olympus in the Indonesian frigates; a similar combination with one or two LM 2500 in Korean frigates). MTU also makes a large 5750bhp 20V1163 suitable for frigates (as in the Colombian and Malaysian FS 1500 class and the Turkish MEKO 200s). This is the engine in the Chinese-built Thai 'Jianghu III' class frigates and also in their US-built PFMM Mk 16s. Some MEKOs and the Thai *Khamronsin*s use the 4420bhp 12V1163 version.

The British developed the Napier (later Paxman) Deltic from the earlier German Junkers opposed-piston two-stroke aircraft diesel, an example of which had been captured. In the original inline engine, each cylinder drove two crankshafts, at top and bottom (the combustion space was between the two opposed pistons). In the Deltic, each crankshaft was the centre of a vee, so in cross-section the engine as a whole resembled the triangular form of the Greek letter delta. Each arm of the letter contained two opposed pistons. In this way a large number of cylinders could be added together without placing too many pistons on any one crankshaft, but also without multiplying the number of separate engines. The three shafts of each engine were geared together. The eighteen-cylinder fast attack boat version produced 2535bhp for fifteen minutes (at 1900rpm) and could sustain 1900bhp at 1700rpm. It weighed only 1.9kg/bhp. Deltics powered British ('Dark' class, in service from 1954 on; others were built for Finland and Japan) and Norwegian ('Nasty' class) fast attack boats. A projected 5000hp Compound Deltic would have incorporated a turbo-charger carried within the triangular frame, contributing 30 per cent of the power directly and also adding to the power output of each cylinder. Deltics also powered minecraft

A high spot of postwar British diesel development was the ingenious Napier Deltic, but this lightweight engine was complex and, after Paxman took over the design, the company concentrated on more conventional powerplants. Paxman has been a successful exporter of naval diesels, the Valenta 16CIA shown here, for example, powering US Coast Guard cutters and the US Navy's new Cyclone *class patrol boats. (Paxman)*

(the 'Hunt's have 850bhp Deltic 9-59Ks; the earlier 'Ton's have 1500bhp Deltic 18A-7As) and diesel locomotives ashore.

Deltic was quite complex. Many British-built fast craft for export users are powered by Paxman diesels, such as the 4485bhp Valenta 18RP200 (in the Kenyan and Omani 'Province' class), the 3000bhp Valenta 12CM, the 2400bhp Ventura 16RP200, and the 1750bhp to 1830bhp Ventura 16YJCM. The new *Sandown* class minehunters are powered by 1000bhp Valenta 6RPA 200EMs. Type 23 frigates use 1800bhp Valenta 12RPA 200CZs as the diesel generators of their CODLAG (combined diesel-electric and gas) powerplants.

For larger ships, the British decided at the end of the Second World War to develop a modular Admiralty Standard Range (ASR) series. The 1550bhp 16VVS version powered Type 41 and 61 class frigates (eight diesels each); the 1840bhp 16VVS-AS21 powered submarines (two each). Unfortunately, the ASR diesels were not quite powerful enough to provide sufficient speed, 27kts or more, for the new ASW frigates

The wartime supremacy of German S-boats was at least partly attributable to superior diesel technology, and postwar the development continued. The Type 140 boats of the late 1950s were powered by derivatives of the wartime Mercedes-Benz MB 518 engine, while the otherwise similar Type 141 used Maybach MD-871s. A significant export success for the latter was the Turkish order for nine of the Type 141 powered by Maybach diesels – one of these, Melten, *is pictured at speed in November 1983. (L & L van Ginderen)*

Large diesel-powered ships have always been a rarity in the Royal Navy, but perhaps overly impressed by the performance of wartime German diesel warships like the notorious 'pocket battleships', the British decided to develop a series of such engines which eventually emerged in the 1950s as the modular Admiralty Standard Range. One application was in the Type 61 and Type 41 frigates (for aircraft direction and anti-aircraft duties respectively), which gave the ships an unusual funnel-less profile. As clearly shown here by Lynx, *a Type 41, the exhausts were led up inside the masts, without undue interference with the electronic arrays they carried. (C & S Taylor)*

(Types 12 and 14), so new steam plants had to be developed. Similarly, they were rejected for a series of planned ocean minesweepers, for which a new steam plant would also have been required. Modern British diesel-powered warships are powered by a variety of commercial diesels; the ASR series never did turn out to be the expected universal powerplant.

The US Navy tried a 'pancake' in which the cylinders were arranged radially around the vertical crankshaft, as in an aeroplane engine mounted on end. Wartime pancakes powered some US sub-chasers, but the postwar version for submarines was quite unsuccessful. Instead, versions of the standard wartime inline Fairbanks-Morse two-cycle opposed-piston engines were used. These engines had powered wartime frigates; postwar they powered amphibious ships and some export frigates (PF-103 class).

Most US diesel surface craft were powered by General Motors diesels, the standard wartime type being the 250bhp 6-71. It and 8V-71 (400bhp) have been used as cruise diesels in some fast attack boat CODOG powerplants. The larger 12V71 produces 645bhp (1125bhp in turbo-charged version) and 16V71 produces 700bhp; 8V71 powered the 'Swift' boats of the Vietnam War (12V71 powered the Mk II and

Mk IV versions as well as the Israeli-built equivalent, the *Dabur*; but the Israelis switched to MTU 12V396s for the bigger and faster *Dvora*). The much larger 900bhp 16-267 and -567 (sometimes rated at 1400bhp) and 16-268 and 12-278 were used in landing ships and large patrol craft (16-567 was used postwar, for example, in the modernised version of the 173ft PC for Chile and Turkey and the Danish *Hvidjørnen* class). Later equivalents included the 12V92 (900bhp) and the 6V149 (for Coast Guard 95-footers and their export versions) and 16V149 (1235bhp, 1600bhp in developed version) for patrol craft. Presumably the first digit or two indicate the number of cylinders in each case.

A few French lightweight diesels were used on board French-designed fast patrol craft (P48S, 'Super PATRA', PR-72 classes). The most powerful were the 2760bhp SACM vee-sixteen units in the Moroccan PR-72s and the 5500bhp units in the Peruvian PR-72s. The French enjoyed far greater success with large Pielstick diesels for frigates and large amphibious units.

The Soviets adopted fast-running diesels for fast attack craft, beginning with the M50 (1200bhp) vee-twelve derived from the wartime W-2 tank engine (in the T-34 and later tanks); it had also been tried in a Pe-8 four-engined bomber. Four such engines powered the *P-4* class of the early 1950s, at least some *P-6*s (Project 183), a variety of Chinese fast attack craft (*Houku*, *Huachuan*, *P-6*, *P-4* and also *Shanghai* class patrol boats), East German light torpedo boats (*Iltis*, *Hydra* and Type 131 classes) and the Finnish *Nuoli* class. The M50 also survives in minor Soviet-built craft such as *Poluchat* class torpedo retrievers/patrol boats, *Shmel* (Project 1204) class river gunboats and *Zhuk* (Project 199) class patrol boats (some of which have 1500bhp M420 diesels). Although 1000–

1500bhp engines had been developed in wartime, they had not entered service.

Some units of the next type, P-6 (Project 183), were powered by the M503 of forty-two cylinders, consisting, in effect, of seven six-cylinder engines 'pancaked' together horizontally, to achieve 4000bhp (2.9lb/bhp). This engine also powers the *Osa* (Project 205) and related classes. At low speeds banks of cylinders (layers in the pancake) could be cut out to reduce fuel consumption. The M503A was rated at 600 hours between overhauls (750 if de-rated to 3285bhp at 1500rpm, running at 3620bhp/1700rpm for 15 per cent of the time or 4000bhp/2200rpm for 10 per cent of the time). However, in practice the engine tended to run hot and noisy, often breaking down (eg, rubber fuel hoses frequently split).

The next step was the fifty-six cylinders (seven eight-cylinder layers) in the M504 (5000bhp), which powers *Osa II* class boats. Two of these engines can be combined to drive a common shaft, as in the double M504 (M517) powering *Grisha*s and *Nanuchka*s (M507 is a double M503). All of these engines proved quite unreliable; hence the shift to gas turbines in the *Tarantul* (Project 1241) class, conceived as direct successors to the *Osa*s. The M503 and M504 were widely exported or licence-built abroad, eg in China. M520 is a next-generation 5400bhp fifty-six-cylinder diesel, which was intended to power the East German *Sassnitz* (BALCOM 10; Project 151) class missile patrol boats. The M521-TM5 (8665bhp) is a tropicalised paired M504 (end to end with a gearbox between) for the Indian navy. *Natya* (Project 266M) and *Yurka* (Project 266) class minesweepers are powered by a derated version of the M503, the 2500bhp M503B (-3E in export units). That recalls the British choice to power minecraft with fast attack boat engines, because such craft

Soviet Grisha *class corvettes are powered by an elaborate installation with paired 56-cylinder diesel units driving a common shaft, plus gas turbine boost. The diesels proved mechanically unreliable, and in the succeeding* Tarantul *propulsion was all gas turbine.* (MoD, Crown Copyright)

need so much power (for towing) within small dimensions. No M501 or M502 is known; presumably they were earlier experimental radial diesels.

Soviet submarines and sub-chasers were generally powered by slower-running two-stroke Kolomna diesels in a D series, which began with the 2000bhp 1D of the prewar 'S' class. Since the 'S' was designed by the Germans (by IvS, in Holland), 1D was presumably descended directly from the German two-stroke MAN submarine diesels of the First World War, which were copied between the wars in both the United States (for submarines built prior to 1932) and in Japan (the Germans adopted faster-running four-stroke diesels in the 1930s). The 'S' class itself was redesigned to become the postwar *Whiskey*. The 600bhp 11D powered the later 'M' class (Series XV) small submarines. The standard postwar submarine diesel was the 2000bhp 37D, two of which powered a *Whiskey* (Project 613) or *Romeo* (Project 633) class submarine; three powered the larger *Zulu* (Project 611) or *Foxtrot* (Project 641). This engine also powered the *Don* class (Project 310) submarine tenders/command ships, as might have been expected for standardisation. Others in the series were 9D (1100bhp) for a *Kronstadt* class patrol boat or a *T-43* class ocean minesweeper; 30D (twelve cylinders, 1840bhp) for an *SO-1* class (Project 201) sub-chaser; 40D (2500bhp) in a *Polnocny* class landing ship or a Polish *Obluze* class patrol boat; and 61D3 (6000bhp) in a *Petya* (Project 159). *Koni* class (Project 1159) corvettes use eighteen-cylinder two-stroke 8000bhp 68B (perhaps more properly 68D) diesels as their cruise plants, presumably because the faster-running M517s in earlier similar ships proved so unreliable. There is also a series of diesel generators used for diesel-electric propulsion, most prominently 2D42 diesel-generator sets (1825bhp) in *Juliett* (Project 651), *Tango* (Project 641BUKI), later *Foxtrot* (Project 641), and *Kilo* (Project 877) class submarines. This series includes the 1800bhp 13D100 which powers *Ivan Susanin* class patrol icebreakers and the

For conventional submarines the Soviet preference was for relatively slow running two-stroke diesels, in a series given a D suffix. The standard postwar engine was the 2000bhp 37D, three of which powered the Zulu *class shown here.* (MoD, Crown Copyright)

750bhp 5-2D42 which powers *Sorum* class armed tugs.

Gas turbines

In effect gas turbines, which were conceived (but not put into service) well before the Second World War, superseded high-powered steam turbines. A gas generator replaces the boiler of a steam turbine. Usually it is a series of combustion chambers fed by air compressed by blades driven by a turbine run by the hot exhaust. An alternative, tried mainly in France, is a free-piston gas generator, in effect a diesel without an attached crankshaft. In either case, the hot gas is directed into a power turbine. Compared with a steam turbine, a gas turbine offers much lighter unit weight and much quicker starting. Typically the entire unit is so small that it can be taken up the uptake for servicing or replacement.

The first naval gas turbine was the Walter submarine powerplant. In it, hydrogen peroxide runs over a catalyst bed. Dissociation produces a hot mixture of oxygen and steam. Fuel burned in the oxygen adds energy to the steam, which is the working fluid of the gas turbine. The Walter turbine was attractive because it could

run without using air, and thus could provide considerable power underwater. All three victorious allies tried to perfect it postwar, without much success.

Most postwar interest in gas turbines was inspired by the new jet aircraft engines. Gas turbines generally ran faster and hotter than steam turbines, so they produced more power in less space. However, they were not nearly as fuel-efficient, and (at least at first) their very high temperatures made them unreliable. After all, 100 hours of safe operation is a great deal for an aircraft (whose average flight may last little over an hour), but it is nothing for a ship which is expected to remain at sea for, say, 60 days (1440 hours).

Gas turbines have another peculiarity. They are efficient only over a very narrow power range. Moreover, although a gas turbine may well evolve to produce far more power than originally expected, at any one point in time the naval architect is confronted by a unit of quite fixed output. Once a type of turbine has been chosen, then, increases in power come in large, fixed increments. For example, in the case of the US *Spruance* class, four engines were chosen over three, partly because three LM 2500s could not provide quite enough power. Also, it

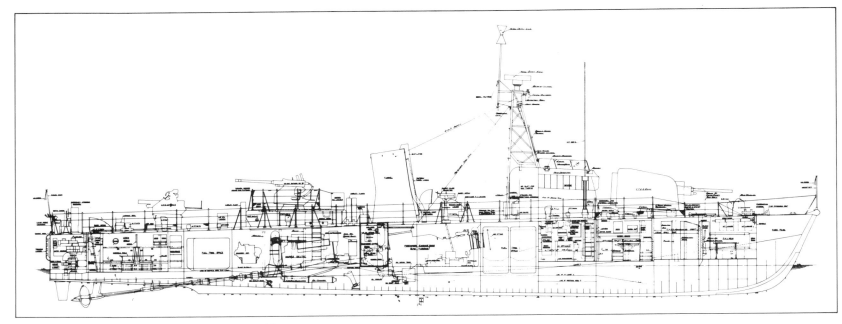

The general arrangement drawing for the British Bold
Pioneer, *powered by an early CODAG installation.
The G.2 gas turbine occupied the forward engine room,
beneath the funnel; the diesels were installed behind.
Interestingly, although the boats went into service with
diesels removed from wartime German S-boats, the
drawings show Napier Deltics in the after engine room.
(NMM)*

was not clear how the power of three engines
could be distributed efficiently among two
shafts (electric coupling was considered but rejected).

Furthermore, like a steam turbine, a gas turbine cannot reverse. Steam turbines are generally provided with separate astern stages, but
that has proved impractical with gas turbines (it
was seriously suggested in at least one case, that
of the Olympus). Two solutions have been used.
One is a controllable reversible-pitch propeller
(CRPP), which is very common in, for example,
the US Navy. The CRPP adds complexity and,
it is sometimes suggested, some reliability problems. It is also likely to be noisier than a fixed-
pitch propeller. The alternative is a reversing
gearbox, which is also complex. The Russians
seem to have adopted such gearboxes from the
first; they came rather later in the West.

At first, the promise of the gas turbine was
mainly that it could provide great power (albeit
at low efficiency) in a very compact package. A
heavy conventional plant could provide efficient
cruising power; for high speed (boost power),
the gas turbine could be cut in. For example, the
Royal Navy installed combined steam and gas
(COSAG) turbine powerplants in several classes
('County' and *Bristol* class missile destroyers and
'Tribal' class frigates). Alternatively, a big diesel
could provide long cruising endurance (and re-

versing power). At high speeds it might be cut
out (CODOG, combined diesel *or* gas turbines),
or its power might be added to that of the gas
turbine (CODAG, combined diesel *and* gas turbine). Eventually it became possible to build
efficient cruise turbines, so ships were built with
cruise and boost gas turbines (COGOG or
COGAG). Surely the most elaborate of all such
combinations is CODLAG (combined diesel-
electric and gas turbine), used in the new British
Type 23 frigates ('Duke' class). The diesel generators are carried high in the ship, so that their
noise does not enter the water. The ship can,
therefore, operate extremely quietly on her
electric motors. Alternatively she can run on her
four gas turbines, which can function as a
COGAG plant; or the two can be combined.

The British, who had invented the jet engine,
quite naturally were the first to apply it to marine propulsion. The first such unit, chosen in
1945, was the 2500hp Gatric, an F.2 aero-engine with a four-stage power stage added; it
suffered from low efficiency (due to its low compression ratio). Two such engines were to have
been installed in a Fairmile 'D' torpedo boat,
but that proved impractical, and ultimately one
replaced the centreline gasoline engine of a 116ft
motor gunboat (MGB), *MGB 2009*. Trials
began in 1947; they revealed some problems:
the Gatric engine suffered when it sucked in salt
spray, and, like an aircraft jet, it was extremely
noisy.

They were successful enough to encourage
the Admiralty to choose CODAG machinery
for a series of new fast attack craft begun in 1948
('Bold' class), using Mercedes-Benz diesels and
a new 4500hp Metropolitan-Vickers G.2 turbine based on the Beryl jet engine. Again trials

revealed problems, such as compressor stall
(which could sometimes be brought on by salt
deposits on blading) and destruction of the entire compressor (which was made of aluminium
alloy) whenever any one blade broke. G.2 had a
higher compressor ratio (4:1 rather than 3.5:1 in
F.2), and the next step, G.4, had an even higher
ratio (6.3:1) to achieve increased power
(5000shp). It was installed in the Italian *Lampo*
class gunboats, ordered in 1958 and in service in
1964. The Admiralty plans proved premature,
and early postwar fast attack craft were driven
by wartime-type gasoline engines (Packards).
However, in 1946 the Admiralty ordered a
lightweight engine, the 5400shp RM 60, ultimately for installation in the converted steam
gunboat *Grey Goose*. In 1953 she became the
first warship in the world to be powered entirely
by gas turbines. Since the boat would have only
two such engines, Rolls-Royce provided RM 60
with a complex cycle for low-speed efficiency,
with a very high compression ratio (18:1).

The Admiralty was also interested in frigate
or destroyer powerplants. In 1946 it had ordered a 6500shp engine, EL 60A, from English
Electric, based on steam turbine (*ie* relatively
heavy weight) philosophy, specifically for installation in a Lend-Lease destroyer escort, HMS
Hotham, replacing her 6000shp steam plant.
The design was very conservative, with a low
compression ratio, and therefore with a requirement for a very large air intake. Even before RM
60 was ready, it was clear that it represented a
superior approach, and the EL 60A programme
was cancelled in 1952.

All of this effort showed that the ideal naval
gas turbine would be a relatively simple lightweight unit based on an existing aircraft engine.

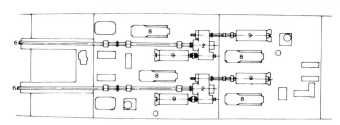

High speed diesel installation (Descubierta class)

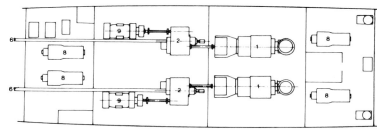

CODOG machinery arrangement (Vosper Mk 5 frigate)

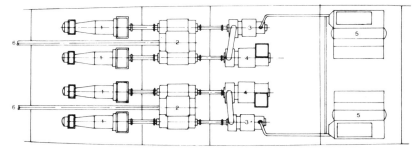

COSAG machinery arrangement ('County' class)

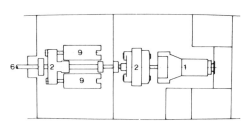

CODAG machinery arrangement (Commandant Riviere class)

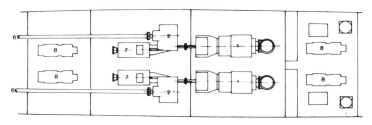

COGOG machinery arrangement (Type 21 frigate)

Key

1. Gas turbine
2. Gearbox
3. High pressure steam turbine
4. Low pressure steam turbine
5. Steam boiler
6. Propeller shaft
7. Gas turbine (cruising)
8. Auxiliary generator
9. Diesel engine

Typical machinery arrangements, combining diesels, gas turbines and steam turbines.

Efforts to gain efficiency at low power (such as regeneration, which means passing exhaust gas over the intake air to heat it) came to be seen as excessively complex. The argument that a large-ship engine had to be heavily built to withstand shock was also rejected.

In 1953 the Admiralty asked YARD and Metropolitan-Vickers to investigate gas turbine boost plants for escorts; that soon meant plants for a new destroyer (the 'super *Daring*' which became the 'County') and for a new frigate (the 'Tribal'). The chosen COSAG frigate plant was

12,500shp base steam plus 7500shp gas boost (for a total two-thirds the power of a Type 12 or *Leander*); the destroyer would have a 15,000shp gas turbine and a 15,000shp steam turbine on each shaft. Metropolitan-Vickers initially planned a 15,000shp destroyer turbine (G.5) and a 7500shp frigate turbine (G.6), but decided in the end to standardise on 7500shp (two per

The British interest in gas turbines for large ships culminated in the 1966–68 conversion of the Type 14 frigate Exmouth *to an all-gas installation of Olympus main engine with two Proteus turbines for cruising, all geared to the same shaft. The ship underwent an extensive series of tests, which confirmed the Royal Navy's preference for total gas turbine propulsion. (CMP)*

shaft in the destroyer). The first ship so powered, the first Western gas turbine warship, was the frigate *Ashanti*. G.6 gas turbines were also installed in the rebuilt Italian cruiser *San Giorgio* and the frigates *Alpino* and *Carabiniere*. All three used CODAG propulsion. *Ashanti* made an enormous impression. Although her boost engine increased her speed by only 3kts to 4kts, it offered quick start-up and manoeuvring.

Although G.6 was ultimately derived from aero-engine practice, it was deliberately made heavy for reliability and shock resistance. It was already obvious that a small fast attack boat (a 'Brave') did not need an extraordinarily reliable engine, since its lightweight aero-derived unit could be replaced without placing the boat in drydock. Furthermore, existing jet engines had proved extremely reliable in what was increasingly seen as a very tough environment. The natural conclusion was to use a modified lightweight aero-engine, which could be removed at sea up its air intake or uptake. By this time, too, some very powerful aero-engines were in service.

Bristol-Siddeley first proposed a marine version of its big Olympus jet in 1959, to meet a German requirement for something more powerful than the 13,000shp Brown-Boveri unit then planned for the *Köln* class. The company hoped to achieve 22,000shp, and in 1962 the Germans contracted for a design study: an Olympus gas generator coupled to a Brown-Boveri power unit. It was planned for a new gas turbine frigate, but the Germans decided to buy the US *Charles F Adams* class instead. Then in 1963 the British Admiralty ordered its own study of a marinised Olympus; a prototype was ordered in 1964. By this time it had already been in air force service for some years, ultimately as the Olympus 201 in the Vulcan medium bomber (giving 17,000lb of thrust, equivalent to 22,000shp). A fixed electricity generating version entered service in 1962. The marine Olympus (TM series) began at 20,000shp, and was ultimately developed to produce 37,500shp. The engine began tests in August 1966, and first went to sea on an operational warship in 1968 on board the Finnish CODAG corvette *Turunmaa*. The Admiralty bought Olympus as the boost engine in a new class of Type 82 COSAG destroyers, beginning with HMS *Bristol*.

Bristol was conceived as a carrier escort; and the new carrier would have had a steam plant.

The German navy was another early exponent of the gas turbine but, rather than using aircraft engines, adapted concepts from land power station machinery. The Köln class frigates of the 1950s, represented here by Karlsruhe, combined MAN diesels with Brown-Boveri gas turbines. (C & S Taylor)

Then in 1966 the carrier was cancelled. Now the Royal Navy could reconsider the use of steam plants, which were very manpower-intensive, since only the carrier had to have a steam plant (not least to power her catapults). An all-gas-turbine ship would use much less manpower. The new destroyer (Type 42) and frigate (Type 21) were cast as all-gas-turbine ships. They needed an efficient low-power cruise turbine: the 4000shp (later 5000shp) Rolls-Royce Tyne, derived from the turboprop which powered the Vanguard airliner, as well as the Bréguet Atlantic. As the RM 1A it became a standard cruise engine in the Argentine, British, Dutch, and Japanese navies. Compression ratio was 12:1 (compared with 7:1 in the Proteus, which had similar output), and specific fuel consumption 0.49lb/hp/hr, very close to the 0.4 offered by a diesel (G.2 offered 0.82, and Proteus, described below, 0.58). As in other gas turbines, efficiency fell off very quickly at lower power, *eg* consumption was over 0.60lb/hp/hr at half-power (2000shp).

The first British COGOG warship was the Type 42 (*Sheffield* class) destroyer, powered by two 28,000shp Olympus and two 4250shp Tynes, a combination repeated in the Type 21 and Type 22 frigates, in the Dutch *Tromp* and *Kortenaer* classes, and in the Argentine Type 42s and MEKO 360s. The *Invincible* class light carriers were powered by four Olympus turbines (COGAG: the ship can cruise on one engine).

The only drawback in the existing COGOG arrangement was that in a frigate the cruise turbine was good for only about 16–18kts. By the late 1960s it appeared that sonar search speed might well rise to 22–25kts, so a more powerful cruise engine was needed. Alternatively, boost engine efficiency could be improved so that a ship could run efficiently at partial power on her boost engines. The Royal Navy chose the cruise engine solution, and in August 1972 it awarded a contract for a design study of a marinised Rolls-Royce Spey turbofan. This engine had been in service since the early 1960s, in aircraft such as the Buccaneer, Nimrod, the British version of the Phantom fighter, and the Trident airliner. As the TF-41, it powered the US A-7. This version, the most powerful, was marinised. It turned out that this SM 1A engine could produce 14,750hp for cruising (maximum power was 17,000shp), and it could easily be developed to give 19,750shp). There was considerable interest in redesigning the Type 22 to be powered by two Tyne and two Spey (instead of Olympus), for economical operation in the important 18–25kt range, but this was only achieved with the later ships. The first British ships to be designed for Speys are Type 23 ('Duke' class) frigates, with two SM 1A (18,770shp each) or two SM 1C (26,150shp each). The new Japanese 4400-ton destroyers are powered by two Kawasaki-built SM 1Cs and two GE-IHI LM 2500s in a COGAG combination, a somewhat peculiar choice since both engines have about the same output.

The British derived a very successful small-ship engine, the 4500shp Bristol Proteus, from a turboprop of the same name. It began trials in HMS *Brave Borderer*, a torpedo boat, in 1958, and is now widely used. Proteus was originally intended for a new series of medium-size fast patrol boats conceived in 1954. Alternatives considered at the time were three Deltics, two

British experimental work with gas turbine fast attack craft came to fruition with the Proteus-powered 'Brave' class. Small numbers of basically similar boats were exported by the designers, Vospers, including six for the Danish navy. Two, including Søridderen seen here, were built at Portsmouth and the other four under licence at Copenhagen Navy Yard. This class differed from the 'Brave's in their low power diesels for slow-speed loiter. (Vosper Thornycroft)

G.4s, two Deltics and one G.4, and two Compound Deltics. The diesel plants were rejected because their power–speed characteristics did not match the expected requirements. The G.4s were not quite satisfactory; but three Proteus were just right. They offered nearly the same endurance at 43kts as the three Deltics offered at 31, with a maximum speed (half fuelled) of 49 rather than 40kts (the G.4s offered less endurance and a maximum of 44kts). A contract for two boats was let in 1956 (but the Royal Navy withdrew from coastal operations the following year, as a result of a major Defence Review). In 1978 an uprated Proteus (6000shp) appeared.

The US Navy became interested in marine gas turbines even before the Royal Navy, but it took much longer to adopt them. As in the Royal Navy, gas turbines were extensively tested in the decade after 1945, and a frigate (destroyer escort) installation was planned (albeit not carried out). BuShips' interest was concentrated on steam plants, both nuclear and high-pressure; reportedly Admiral Rickover himself resisted work on gas turbines for fear that it would dilute the nuclear effort. On the other hand, a CONAG combination plant was seriously proposed in 1956 as a way of fitting a heavy nuclear plant into a relatively small destroyer hull.

The first US gas turbine warships were the fast *Asheville* class gunboats, designed specifi-

cally to deal with Soviet-built missile boats; the first was launched in 1966. The boost portion of their CODOG plant was a 14,000shp GE gas turbine. Proteus and Tyne gas turbines were installed in several experimental hydrofoils built at about the same time. Many ships had gas turbine turbo-generators, mainly built by Solar, beginning with a class of minesweeping boats (MSBs) in which space was critical.

This turned out to be a false start. The first major US gas turbine ships were the *Hamilton* class high-endurance Coast Guard cutters, powered by Pratt & Whitney FT4A gas turbines (14,000shp, based on the J-75 jet) and Fairbanks-Morse diesels. They had been preceded by four medium-endurance cutters (*Reliance* class: WMEC 615–619) with CODAG plants (two 1500bhp Cooper-Bessemer diesels and two 2000shp Solar gas turbines). These cutters were re-engined in 1986–90.

The key decision, however, was to power the big *Spruance* class destroyers (ordered 1970) with four LM 2500 gas turbines in COGAG configuration. This choice was largely a consequence of a fatal accident with a 1200psi plant, which in turn could be traced to lack of skilled boiler room personnel. The accident turned the then Secretary of the Navy against the existing steam plants; gas turbines were the only viable alternative. The LM 2500, a marinised TF-39 turbofan, also powered the *Pegasus* class hydrofoils and the *Perry* class frigates. It has become an extremely successful export engine, serving in most Western navies and also being sold to China.

Power output was originally 20,000shp (18,000 in the missile hydrofoils). However, these engines are rated at 25,000shp in the *Arleigh Burke* class. Then the rating increased to 26,250shp for warships. In May 1993 the standard rating

was increased to 29,500shp for a warship and 32,000shp for a sealift ship. These figures, moreover, applied to the engine running on a hot (100°F) day; it would be even more powerful on a cool day. As in the case of the Olympus, such increases have become common in high-powered naval gas turbines.

The issue of low-speed economy persists. The obvious solution is to recapture some of the heat energy lost in the exhaust. For some time the US Navy considered using it to generate steam, a concept called RACER, but that died because it was far too unwieldy. It seems more likely that engines will be modified so that the exhaust heats combustion air. For example, in mid 1993 GE announced a recuperated version of its engine, LM 2500R; exhaust air heats intake air. The company claimed a better than 30 per cent improvement in efficiency at low power levels, using a recuperator in the exhaust stack. Other changes were relatively minor: a new combustor, redesigned high-pressure turbine blades, and variable-area turbine nozzles in the power turbine. These kinds of changes will probably be applied to other current gas turbines.

Roughly contemporary with the 'Tribal's were the German *Köln* class frigates. Unlike the British and the Russians, the Germans used turbines based on steam turbine or land power-plant concepts (13,000shp Brown-Boveri units, in this case boosting a diesel plant comprising four 3000bhp sixteen-cylinder MAN diesels).

It now appears that Admiral Gorshkov was responsible for the first gas turbines in Soviet warships, in the *Poti* (Project 204), *Petya* (Project 159) and *Kashin* (Project 61) classes. All were built under Khrushchev's 1959–65 Seven Year Plan, which was intended (among other things) to achieve a quantum jump in the level of Soviet military technology. For the *Poti*s, the

The world's first all-gas-turbine warships were the Soviet Kashin *class. This stern view of* Stroynyy *emphasises the substantial trunking required by gas turbine ships, the two pairs of uptakes showing up dark against the light superstructure.* (MoD, Crown Copyright)

requirement was apparently very high speed and quick acceleration, to deal with the new fast submarines. They had a pair of 20,000shp M-1 aircraft turbines (presumably adapted turboprops, which compressed air and drove it through venturi tubes abaft the diesel-driven

propellers) and a pair of 4000bhp M503A diesels. The larger (and slower) *Petya*s also had CODAG powerplants, consisting of two 15,000shp M-2 turbines (lifetime 1000 hours) and a single 6000bhp 61V-3 diesel. The single diesel, driving the centreline propeller, was good for 16kts; the gas turbines added another 10kts. The next-generation *Grisha* (Project 1124) used either M-2 or a more powerful 19,000shp M-8 gas turbine. However, it had two diesels (two 10,000bhp M504s) and only one gas turbine, providing it with a higher cruising speed.

The Soviets switched to all-gas-turbine plants in *Tarantul I/II* (Project 1241, designed in the early 1970s). Its M-15 plant consists of a pair of 12,000shp PR-77 boost turbines and a pair of 4000shp DMR-76 cruise turbines. The export version (as in India) has NK-12MV boost turbines (NK-12 is a standard turboprop engine, which powers the Tu-95/142 'Bear' bomber). In *Tarantul III* (in service from 1987 on), the Soviets shifted back to a diesel (M504) cruise plant. The *Tarantul* gas turbine plant also appears in the recent *Mukha* and *Muravey* class ASW hydrofoils (the latter has only the boost element).

The *Kashin* class missile destroyers (Project 61) were the first all-gas-turbine warships in the world. Design work began in 1957. The M-2 was developed into the 36,000shp M-3 for the *Kashin*, using a pair of 18,000shp non-reversing gas turbines geared to each shaft, with a design lifetime of 500 hours at 24kts. An alternative design using paired 15,000shp turbines (which were more economical and longer-lived) was rejected for insufficient output, and a three-shaft alternative was not considered.

As in the West, the turbines were derived from aircraft (in this case, turboprop) practice. An unusual feature was that they drove through

reverse-reduction gears, so no separate astern unit or controllable-reversible propeller was needed. Specified lifetime was 3000 hours: 100 at full power, 200 at 80 per cent, and 2700 at 50–60 per cent power. Compared with the earlier steam turbine Project 56 destroyer (*Kotlin*), Project 61 developed a similar output at about half the overall weight. The ship could start up in ten minutes, reach 30kts in another two to three minutes, and full speed (about 35kts) in another five or six minutes, almost 24 times faster than a steam destroyer.

The next-generation M-5, in *Kara* (Project 1134B) and *Slava* (Project 1164) class cruisers, develops 60,000shp per shaft, also using paired turbines. These ships have 8000shp cruise turbines on each shaft, in COGOG configuration. *Slava* probably has the same powerplant. The new Indian *Delhi* is to have a pair of 27,000shp AM-50s, which may be slightly derated export versions of M-5, with one (rather than two) turbines per shaft.

Destroyers and frigates have COGAG plants. Total power per shaft is 28,000shp in a *Krivak* (Project 1135); presumably that comprises a slightly uprated 20,000shp M-8 plus the 8000shp boost turbine of the contemporary *Kara*. An *Udaloy* (Project 1155) or a *Neustrashimyy* (Project 1154) has a 24,300shp boost turbine (probably a further uprated M-8) and a 12,100shp cruise turbine on each shaft. In keeping with Soviet concepts of standardisation, the cruise turbine may well be the same as the *Tarantul* boost turbine.

Norman Friedman

Neustrashimyy, *the first of the latest Russian frigate class, has a COGAG plant with cruise and boost turbines on each shaft. The ship has acquired heat baffles on the top of the funnels since the design was first seen.* (German Navy)

Bibliography

Compiled by Norman Friedman

GENERAL

For the period up to about 1980, the main reference is the yearbook *Jane's Fighting Ships*, various publishers (London, annually). However, from about 1980 on, the biennial *Combat Fleets* (English edition prepared by A D Baker III, Naval Institute Press) is far superior, not least with regard to the weapons and electronic systems aboard ships. For combatant ships, *Conway's All the World's Fighting Ships 1947–1982*, 2 vols, Conway Maritime Press (London 1983) is valuable because it corrects numerous misstatements in contemporary reference books. An updated edition, which will take advantage of the vast amount of new information new available on Soviet/Russian warships, is in preparation.

For naval weapons, *Jane's Weapons Systems*, Jane's Yearbooks (London, annually) provides useful data for the period from 1969 to its demise in 1988. Much more comprehensive data is available in Norman Friedman, *The Naval Institute Guide to World Naval Weapons Systems*, Naval Institute Press (Annapolis 1989 and 1991, with supplement to be published late in 1993).

NORMAN FRIEDMAN, *Modern Warship Design and Development*, Conway Maritime Press (London 1980).
A comprehensive, if now somewhat dated, account of trade-offs in postwar surface warship design. No later equivalent account exists.

——, *The Postwar Naval Revolution*, Conway Maritime Press and Naval Institute Press (London and Annapolis 1987).
Concentrates on the first postwar decade. It is largely based on British official documents released in the 1980s, and includes sketches of numerous unrealised projects, such as the big missile cruisers of the early 1950s.

Several books cover specific navies:

AUSTRALIA

ROSS GILLETT, *Australian and New Zealand Warships Since 1946*, Child & Assoc (Brookvale 1988).

CANADA

KEN MACPHERSON and J BURGESS, *The Ships of Canada's Naval Forces 1910–1981*, Collins (Toronto 1981).

GERMANY

SIEGFRIED BREYER and GERHARD KOOP, *Die Schiffe und Fahrzeuge der deutschen Bundesmarine 1956–1976*, Bernard & Graefe (Munich 1978).
Includes ships taken over from other navies and types planned but not built.

H MEHL and K SHAEFER, *Die Andere Deutsche Marine*, Transpress (Berlin 1992).
The full story of the East German Navy, as it could be told after the fall of East Germany; it includes the story of the planned submarine project, quashed after the 1953 revolt.

SPAIN

A AGUILERA and V ELIAS, *Buques de Guerra Espanoles 1885–1971*, Ed San Martin, (Madrid 1980).

J L COELLO LILLO, *Buques de la Armada Espanola: La Ayuda American y el Programa de Modernizacion*, Aldaba (Madrid 1992).
The US-assisted modernisation programme of the 1950s and 1960s; does not include later new construction.

SOUTH AFRICA

A DU TOIT, *South Africa's Fighting Ships, Past & Present*, Ashanti (Rivonia, Australia 1992).

SOVIET UNION

NORMAN POLMAR, *Guide to the Soviet Navy*, Naval Institute Press (Annapolis 1977, 1983, 1986, 1991).
The first edition was co-edited with Siegfried Breyer; it supersedes the earlier book by Breyer. *Combat Fleets* tends to be more comprehensive, but this book has larger-format photographs, and some of the detail views are particularly good. Various editions also contain essays on such topics as Soviet naval industry and Soviet naval tactics. One problem is that Polmar tends to be somewhat alarmist; his over-rating of the Soviets is particularly obvious in the final edition.

UNITED KINGDOM

D K BROWN, *A Century of Naval Construction*, Conway Maritime Press (London 1983).
A history of the Royal Corps of Naval Constructors, providing significant insights into postwar British naval design, including the important frigate programme.

ERIC GROVE, *Vanguard to Trident*, The Bodley Head and Naval Institute Press (London and Annapolis 1987).
Focuses on policy issues, which explain the ships built for the Royal Navy after 1945.

H T LENTON, *Warships of the British and Commonwealth Navies*, Ian Allen (London 1966 and 1969).
Greatly enlarged versions of the earlier pocket publication, *British Warships*, Ian Allan (London 1958 and 1962).

J E MOORE, *Warships of the Royal Navy*, Jane's and Naval Institute Press (London and Annapolis 1979).
Continued a series of Ian Allan books on the British/Commonwealth fleets.

UNITED STATES

Ships and Aircraft of the US Fleet, Naval Institute Press (Annapolis 1950, 1958, 1965, 1972, 1975, 1978, 1981, 1984, 1987, 1992), prepared by JAMES C FAHEY (1950–65), by SAMUEL L MORISON and J ROWE (1972-75) and by NORMAN POLMAR (1978 to date).
Editions vary considerably in content; Polmar's recent ones have contained considerable historical material. *Combat Fleets* tends to be more comprehensive.

NORMAN FRIEDMAN, *The US Maritime Strategy*, Jane's Information Group (London 1989).
Discusses the strategy that shaped the US Navy of the 1980s, including its specific impact on warship design.

——, *US Naval Weapons*, Conway Maritime Press and Naval Institute Press (London and Annapolis 1983).
Covers the period from 1883 on, including the changing tactical rationale for various weapon. This book includes tables of sonars and airborne radars, along with data on the weapons.

For specific US ship types, see the *Illustrated Design Histories* mentioned below. There is a general section on naval missiles, but no specific books are listed for nuclear weapons, anti-air warfare or auxiliary ships. In the first two cases, many of the weapons and radar books will provide valuable insights. There seems to be no good published treatment of auxiliaries, and specifically of underway replenishment.

AIRCRAFT CARRIERS

ROGER CHESNEAU, *Aircraft Carriers of the World*, Arms & Armour and Naval Institute Press (London and Annapolis 1984).

FRANCIS DOUSSET, *Les Porte-Avions Français*, Editions de la Cité (Paris 1978).
This book is apparently based on official documents; it includes several abortive projects, as well as data on French carrier aircraft.

NORMAN FRIEDMAN, *British Carrier Aviation*, Conway Maritime Press and Naval Institute Press (London and Annapolis 1988).
Covers both the ships and their aircraft, drawing on documents declassified through the mid 1980s.

——, *Carrier Air Power*, Conway Maritime Press (London 1981).
Overall analysis of relationships between aircraft and their carriers, in historical context.

——, *US Aircraft Carriers: An Illustrated Design History*, Naval Institute Press (Annapolis 1983).
Very detailed history of the development of its carriers.

ALAN RAVEN, *Essex Class Carriers*, Naval Institute Press (Annapolis 1988).
Shows these ships in their many postwar guises, heavily altered from their wartime appearance. Details of fittings, including most of the standard postwar radar and radio antennas.

STEFAN TERZIBASCHITSCH, *Aircraft Carriers of the US Navy*, Conway Maritime Press and Naval Institute Press (London and Annapolis 1980).
Concentrates on appearance changes. Companion volume on escort carriers has some postwar material.

ROSS WATTON, *The Aircraft Carrier Victorious*, Conway Maritime Press (London 1991).
Shows details of the ship's very elaborate postwar reconstruction.

SURFACE COMBATANTS

NORMAN FRIEDMAN, *US Cruisers: An Illustrated Design History*, Naval Institute Press (Annapolis 1984).
This and the following book are part of a series of detailed studies which place US warship development in its full political and strategic context.

——, *US Destroyers: An Illustrated Design History*, Naval Institute Press (Annapolis, 1982).

JOHN JORDAN, *Soviet Warships: The Soviet Surface Fleet, 1960 to Present*, Arms & Armour and Naval Institute Press (London and Annapolis 1983; new edition, Arms & Armour only 1992, featuring ships from 1945 on).
Concentrates on destroyers and larger units; the new edition pays particular attention to electronic warfare antennas. Although data have been overtaken by recent Russian publications, the photographs and drawings are still well worth while.

JOHN LIPIETT, *Type 21*, Ian Allan (London 1990).
This and the following titles form a series of monographs on modern British warship classes.

LEO MARRIOTT, *Royal Navy Frigates Since 1945*, Ian Allan (London 1983 and 1990).

——, *Type 42*, Ian Allan (London 1985).

——, *Type 22*, Ian Allan (London 1986).

——, *Royal Navy Destroyers Since 1945*, Ian Allan (London 1989).

C J MEYER, *Leander Class*, Ian Allan (London 1984).
Includes foreign variants.

RICHARD OSBORNE, *The Leander Class*, World Ship Society (Kendal 1992).

ROBERT L SCHEINA, *US Coast Guard Cutters & Craft 1946-1990*, Naval Institute Press (Annapolis 1990).
The US coast Guard is larger than many navies, and in wartime it is subordinated to the US Navy.

STEFAN TERZIBASCHITSCH, *Cruisers of the US Navy 1922–1962*, Naval Institute Press and Arms & Armour (Annapolis and London 1988).
Excellent pictorial coverage of the post-1945 US cruiser fleet, including the missile conversions.

Note that in 1992–93 the Russian journal *Morskoi Sbornik* began publishing articles on postwar warships; as of the summer of 1993 (issue 4-93) articles on the *Sverdlov* class cruisers and *Skoriy* (Project 30), *Tallinn* (Project 41), *Kotlin* (Project 56), and *Kashin* (Project 61) class destroyers had appeared. Some of the propulsion information on the latter three classes has been used in the current text. This series also included the Project 183/205 (*Komar/Osa*) type missile boats and the Project 661 (*Papa*) class submarine. Apart from the submarine, each article included an inboard profile of the ship in question. The same magazine had previously published what amounted to a design history of Soviet carriers, from the *Kiev* class on, but without much detail.

SUBMARINES

JOHN D ALDEN, *The Fleet Submarine in the US Navy*, Naval Institute Press (Annapolis 1979).
Includes considerable material on postwar use of these submarines, including their several incarnations for special roles.

NORMAN FRIEDMAN, *Submarine Design and Development*, Conway Maritime Press and Naval Institute Press (London and Annapolis 1984).
Thus far the only comprehensive published discussion of modern submarine design, including weapons and sonars.

——, *US Submarines Since 1945: An Illustrated Design History*, Naval Institute Press (Annapolis, forthcoming 1994).
Much of the US detail in Chapter 3 above is taken from the manuscript for this book.

ULRICH GABLER, *U-Bootbau*, Wehr und Wissen (Bonn 1978).
Gabler designed the postwar German submarines. This is a book about diesel submarine design practice, with few numbers and very little interest in weapon systems, but it contains a series of excellent cross-sectional drawings of submarines. The same publisher produced an English-language version a few years later.

JOHN JORDAN, *Soviet Submarines: 1945 to the Present*, Arms & Armour (London 1989).
A very useful summary of knowledge to date; revelations about Soviet submarine design have not been nearly as extensive as those about surface ships. Excellent photographs, including mast details.

HENRI LE MASSON, *Les Sous-Marins Français*, Editions de la Cité (Paris 1980).
This book includes sketches of the abortive early French nuclear submarine designs.

NORMAN POLMAR and JURIEN NOOT, *Submarines of the Russian and Soviet Navies, 1718–1990*, Naval Institute Press (Annapolis 1991).
Useful but overtaken by recently released information, for example articles in the Russian naval journal *Morskoi Sbornik*.

EBERHARDT RÖSSLER, *The U-boat*, Arms & Armour and Naval Institute Press (London and Annapolis 1981).
Concentrates on U-boats of the two World Wars, but includes considerable postwar material. It is probably the only comprehensive account of German development.

——, *Die Torpedos der Deutschen U-Boote*, Koehler (Herford 1984).

——, *Die Sonaranlagen der deutsche U-Boote*, Koehler (Herford 1991).
Includes a detailed account of postwar German submarine sonars, many of which have been exported.

MINE COUNTERMEASURES VESSELS

H DE BLOIS, *La Guerre des Mines dans la Marine Française*, Editions de la Cité (Paris 1982).

G K HARTMANN, *Weapons That Wait: Mine Warfare in the US Navy*, Naval Institute Press (Annapolis 1979 and 1992).
Includes details of abortive mine countermeasures systems of the 1960s.

T MELIA, *Damn The Torpedoes*, Naval Historical Centre, (Washington 1991).
US mine countermeasures up through the Iran–Iraq War.

FAST ATTACK CRAFT

C BORGENSTAM and B NYMAN, *Motor Torpedo Båt*, CB Marinlitteratur (Karlskrona 1981).
Swedish MTB history.

——, *Attack Till Sjoss*, CB Marinlitteratur, (Karlskrona 1985).
Swedish steam torpedo boats, heavy motor torpedo boats, and missile attack craft.

CHRISTOPHER CHANT, *Small Craft Navies*, Arms & Armour (London 1992).
A current inventory of craft in service, with some considerable discussion of the development of weapons and power-plants.

HARALD FOCK, *Schnellboote*, Koehler (Herford 1974 and 1986).
Encyclopedic coverage of postwar fast attack craft on a country-by-country basis. These volumes continue Fock's coverage of Second World War and prewar fast attack craft, published in German and then in English.

NORMAN FRIEDMAN, *US Small Combatants: An Illustrated Design History*, Naval Institute Press (Annapolis 1987).
Includes extensive coverage of advanced hull forms: hydrofoils and surface effect craft, also of US riverine craft of the Vietnam War.

JOHN MARIOTT (ed), *Brassey's Fast Attack Craft*, Brassey's (London 1978).
Inventories systems as well as craft, at the high water mark in enthusiasm for small missile boats.

AMPHIBIOUS FORCES

M L BARTLETT (ed), *Assault From the Sea*, Naval Institute Press (Annapolis 1983).

M H H EVANS, *Amphibious Operations*, Brassey's, (London 1990).

Anti-Submarine Warfare

W Hackmann, *Seek and Strike*, HMSO (London 1984).
Although the subtitle indicates only that it carries the sonar/ASW story to 1954, this book actually goes beyond into the 1960s.

J R Hill, *Anti-Submarine Warfare*, Ian Allan and Naval Institute Press (London and Annapolis 1985).
Tends to concentrate more on overall strategic and tactical issues than on technical ones; a useful overview. However, it does not recognise some of the strategic issues raised by the US Maritime Strategy of the 1980s.

Naval Missiles

B Estival, *Les Missiles Navals*, Editions Larivièr; Docavia No 32 (Paris nd, but probably 1990).
Includes anti-aircraft, anti-ship, anti-submarine and strategic missiles, and accounts of missile combat; much unusual material on French systems.

—— and J Guillot, *L'Extraordinaire Aventure de l'Exocet*, Editions de la Cité (Paris 1988).

Bill Gunston, *The Illustrated Encyclopedia of the World's Rockets and Missiles*, Salamander (London 1979).
Still the only attempt at an encyclopedia of missiles, though dated in places and somewhat over-impressed by British and some Soviet weapons.

D G Kiely, *Naval Surface Weapons*, Brassey's (London 1988).
Tends to concentrate on British and European systems.

A Rabinovich, *The Boats of Cherbourg*, St Martin's Press (New York 1988).
The story of the first Israeli missile boats and their Gabriel missile.

H M Sapolsky, *The Polaris Missile System Development*, Harvard University Press (Cambridge 1972).

S J Zaloga, *Soviet Air Defence Missiles*, Jane's (London 1989).
Includes naval air defence missiles.

——, *Target America: The Soviet Union and the Strategic Arms Race, 1945–1964*, Presidio Press (Novato 1993).
The single best account of Soviet strategic weapons development, including naval ballistic missiles; it is based in part on recently-published Russian material.

Radar and Combat Direction Systems

Norman Friedman, *Naval Radar*, Conway Maritime Press and Naval Institute Press (London and Annapolis 1981).
Includes a catalogue of postwar Western radars, largely superseded by sections of the same author's *Naval Institute Guide to World Naval Weapons Systems*.

P E Law, Jr, *Shipboard Antennas*, Artech (Dedham 1983, 1986).
US systems only. In many cases this book provides more on the system than simple antenna details. It includes communications and navigational devices.

W T T Packenham, *Naval Command and Control*, Brassey's (London 1989).
Rather general, but it provides important insights into command links between ships and between ships and overall headquarters.

Electronic Warfare

J A Boyd *et al*, *Electronic Countermeasures*, Peninsula Publishing (Los Altos, 1978).
Reprint of a formerly Secret handbook published in 1961; it includes both radar and acoustic countermeasures as then understood.

D G Kiely, *Naval Electronic Warfare*, Brassey's (London 1988).
Examples are all British; tends to downplay alternatives such as US systems.

A Price, *The History of US Electronic Warfare, Vol II: The Renaissance Years, 1946–64*, Association of Old Crows (Arlington 1989).
Mainly airborne, but includes early naval countermeasures to Styx. A third volume, to cover Vietnam, is planned; it should include details of the numerous emergency anti-Styx and anti-ASM fits for US warships.

Propulsion

C E Preston, *Power for the Fleet: The History of British Marine Gas Turbines*, Eton Publishing (Eton 1982).

M Saarlas, *Steam and Gas Turbines For Marine Propulsion*, Naval Institute Press (Annapolis 1978).

Glossary of Terms and Abbreviations

Compiled by Eric Grove. This list assumes some knowledge of ships and does not include the most basic terminology. Because of the widespread use in this book of recently released Soviet official Project numbers, a list of the classes to which they relate is appended.

AAW. Anti-Air Warfare.

acoustic mine. A mine activated by sound. The mine listens for the characteristic signature of the desired target. When introduced in the Second World War the mines listened for an increase in general noise, but now it is possible to tune a mine to specific frequencies. Acoustic activation is often combined with magnetic (*qv*) and/or pressure (*qv*) sensors.

Action Data Automation Weapon System. A British computerised tactical data system primarily for air defence ships. There are a number of variants: ADAWS-1, first fitted in 1965 to Batch 2 'County' class destroyers (*qv*); ADAWS-2 fitted to HMS *Bristol*; ADAWS-3, intended for the abortive CVA-01; ADAWS-4 used in Batch 2 Type 42 destroyers; ADAWS-5 used in Ikara (*qv*) conversions of *Leander* class frigates; ADAWS-6 used in the first two *Invincible* class carriers; ADAWS-7 used in Batch 2 Type 42 destroyers; ADAWS-8 fitted in Type 42 destroyers fitted with 2016 sonar; ADAWS-9 intended for the abortive Type 43 destroyers; ADAWS-10 used in *Ark Royal*, the final *Invincible* class carrier.

active sonar. A sonar that detects its target by receiving sound it has transmitted. Active sonar is not dependent on the sound emitted by the target. Its major disadvantage is that it gives away the user's position.

AD. Destroyer tender. US Navy/Nato classification. The 'A' in this and other similar designations stands for 'auxiliary'.

ADA. Action Data Automation. An early British computerised tactical data system. The project was begun in 1954 and the first equipment went to sea in HMS *Eagle* ten years later. The system co-ordinated inputs from the ship's own radars, other ships and aircraft. The computer stored information, evaluated threats, calculated interceptions and passed out information to fighters and other AAW systems. It substituted for sixty men previously employed in the action information organisation (*qv*) of a carrier.

ADAWS. Action Data Automation Weapon System (*qv*).

ADLIPS. Automatic Data Link Plotting system. A Canadian tactical data system, development of which began in 1970 to replace manual plotting in the least expensive way possible. First fitted in prototype form to HMCS

Athabaskan in 1976, the production equipment was fitted to all the smaller RCN destroyers between 1981 and 1985.

AE. Ammunition ship. US Navy/Nato classification.

AEFS. Fleet replenishment ship. US Navy classification.

Aegis. American Mk 7 anti-air warfare weapons system. This is the most advanced AAW (*qv*) system in the world, integrating SPY-1 phased array radars with SM-2 SAMs (*qv*). It equips the USN *Ticonderoga* class cruisers and *Arleigh Burke* class destroyers and the Japanese *Kongo* class destroyers. It consists of a Command and Decision System, Display System and Weapons Control System, which together in the Mod-3 variant, employ 17 computers and 11 minicomputers. Aegis can handle 128 tracks simultaneously. It entered service in USS *Ticonderoga* in 1983.

AEW. Airborne Early Warning. Surveillance radars carried in fixed-wing aircraft or helicopters to provide a more comprehensive picture of the air threat, especially at low altitudes.

AF. Store ship. US Navy classification.

AFS. Combat store ship. US Navy classification.

AGI. Intelligence collector. US Navy classification. Commonly applied during the Cold War to Soviet trawler-type intelligence gatherers.

AIO. Action Information Organisation. The systematic organisation of information from electronic and other sensors to compile a three-dimensional tactical picture and allow the efficient prosecution of threats above, on and below the sea. First developed manually in the Second World War, primarily to cope with AAW (*qv*), it has now been mechanised with the advent of computerised combat data systems.

AIP. Air Independent Propulsion. A propulsion system for non-nuclear submarines that reduces reliance on diesels for charging the batteries or substitutes for diesel propulsion. An early form of AIP was the steam turbine using hydrogen peroxide fuel, but more reliable modern forms of AIP include closed cycle diesels and Stirling engines using liquid oxygen and fuel cells of various types.

AK. Cargo ship. Nato classification.

AKA. Attack cargo ship. US Navy classification.

AKS. Stores issue ship. US Navy classification.

antenna mine. A mine actuated by a wire antenna rather than horns. First developed by the USA in the First World War, these mines are activated by a target touching or nearing the antenna forming an element in a simple battery which actuated the firing circuit. This greatly increased a mine's lethal radius, being especially useful in the ASW (*qv*) role.

AO. Oiler (*qv*). US Navy/Nato classification.

AOG. Gasoline tanker. US Navy classification.

APA. Attack transport. US Navy classification.

APL. Applied Physics Laboratory of Johns Hopkins University (USA).

AR. Repair ship. US Navy/Nato classification.

ARM. Anti-Radar Missile. A missile fired usually by an aircraft that homes on radar emissions by a seeker in the missile head locking on to the defender's radar. Such a missile forces the enemy to shut off his radars, thus diminishing his ability to deal with subsequent or simultaneous attacks.

AS. Submarine tender. US Navy/Nato classification.

ASROC. Literally 'Anti-Submarine Rocket'; American ASW (*qv*) missile widely used by US and allied navies. The conventional warhead is a homing torpedo (Mk 44, later Mk 46); there was also a nuclear variant with a Mk 17 nuclear depth charge armed with a 1 kiloton W-44 warhead. Maximum range 10,000yds. ASROC is fired either from an octuple box launcher or a multi-purpose SAM (*qv*) launcher to a range programmed from sonar data. When a specified amount of time has elapsed the rocket motor is shut off to allow the missile to fall in the target area in which the payload is dropped.

ASTER. An advanced family of French AAW missiles with active terminal guidance, for use against both aircraft and missile targets. There are two variants, ASTER 15 (15km range) and ASTER 30, the latter with a booster for use against longer range threats (out to 70km). The two may be used in combination. ASTER will be fitted to the French carrier *Charles De Gaulle* and will form the basis of the international AAW system fitted to the forthcoming Anglo-French–Italian 'Common New Generation Frigate'.

ASuW. Anti-Surface Unit Warfare.

ASW. Anti-Submarine Warfare.

aviso escorteur. Escort sloop. The French term 'aviso', used for a small sailing warship, is best translated in English by 'sloop', the term used for similar vessels in the days of sail, and also used for British escort vessels/colonial gunboats built in the first half of the twentieth century. The designation 'aviso' was used for similar French ships built for colonial policing duties. The term 'aviso escorteur' was coined in 1959 for the *Commandant Rivière* class ships, previously 'Escorteurs d'Union Française' (French Union Escorts', *ie* escort vessels capable of being used for policing the erstwhile French Union).

AVTAG. Low octane ('wide cut') aviation gasoline/petrol used in jet aircraft in their earlier days. It differed from the petrol used in piston engined aircraft, which had to be of a much higher octane rating.

'baby flat-top'. Nickname for a small aircraft carrier.

ballistic missile. A missile that throws an unpowered warhead into a ballistic trajectory that will carry it to the target. Both power and guidance is provided in a short boost phase. Ballistic missiles are usually used for long range bombardment of shore targets.

battlecruiser. A large traditional gun-armed capital ship of high speed, usually achieved by sacrificing armour protection. The term was latterly loosely applied to large surface combatants with lighter gun armaments than contemporary battleships such as the American 'large cruisers' (*qv*). It is also used, equally loosely, for the unusually large former Soviet *Kirov* class RKRs (*qv*).

battleship. A large, heavily armoured gun-armed capital ship.

Bear trap. A system for operating helicopters from small ships, pioneered by the Canadians, in which the helicopter is hauled onto the deck by a cable shot into the deck from the helicopter.

Bofors. A Swedish armaments manufacturer, particularly associated with its 40mm automatic gun.

bow transducers. Sonar transmitter/receivers mounted in the bow.

BPK. Large anti-submarine ship (Russian).

Breda. Italian armaments manufacturer.

C³I. Command × Control × Communications × Intelligence. The synergy of the techniques of managing operations by which authoritative commanders can effectively use intelligence to communicate their orders to subordinates.

C⁴I. Command × Control × Communications × Computers × Intelligence. The addition of computers to the C³I (*qv*) system to transform its effectiveness. All modern systems rely on mechanised data handling. There is now a tendency to refer to C⁴I² (C⁴I × Information), with the addition of 'information' that is not strictly 'intelligence'.

CA. Heavy cruiser. US Navy/Nato designation.

CAAIS. Computer Aided Action Information System; a British tactical data system simpler than ADAWS (*qv*) designed primarily for frigates. The staff requirement was issued in 1966 and production began in 1969. There were a number of versions: DBA-1 in Batch 1 *Leander* class frigates; DBA-2 for Type 21 frigates;

DBA-3 for the carrier *Hermes*; DBA-4 in 'Hunt' class minehunters; DBA-5 in Seawolf equipped Batch 3 *Leanders* and Batch 1 Type 22s. The CAAIS has also been exported.

CAH. Helicopter carrying heavy cruiser. A version of the US/Nato designation system used for the Royal Navy *Invincible* class 'through deck cruisers'/aircraft carriers.

CC. Command ship. US Navy classification. Used for the former CLC (*qv*) USS *Northampton* from 1962 until 1977 and for the USS *Wright*, a former CVL (*qv*) rebuilt for the role.

CDS. Comprehensive Display System. A British pioneering analogue computerised AAW (*qv*) plot-compiling system used in conjunction with the 984 three-dimensional radar. First fitted in the aircraft carrier *Victorious* when recommissioned after rebuilding in 1957.

CG. Guided missile cruiser. US/Nato designation. Most DLGs (*qv*) were redesignated CG on 30 June 1975.

CGN. Nuclear powered guided missile cruiser. US designation. Nuclear powered variant of the CG above. USS *Long Beach* has been a CGN all her life and the *Virginia* class were commissioned as such. The other CGNs were commissioned as DLGNs (*qv*) and redesignated on 30 June 1975.

chaff. Reflective foil deployed in clouds of small pieces to confuse radar. It is usually deployed by rockets and forms a reflective plume that confuses the radar homing heads on anti-ship missiles. Chaff provides an incoming missile with multiple targets, seductive echoes and misleading information as to the centre of the radar reflections of the target at which the missile is aimed.

CIC. Combat Information Center. US term; known in the Royal Navy as the Operations Room ('Ops Room'). The space below decks where information is handled, and the battle fought. This is the nerve centre of the modern warship and has replaced the bridge as the place from where a commanding officer fights his ship. It contains the consoles of the combat data system (*qv*).

CIWS. Close-In Weapons System. A last-ditch weapon system designed to deal with missiles that have leaked through the outer layers of defence. Typical CIWS are Vulcan-Phalanx (*qv*) and Goalkeeper (*qv*).

CL. Light cruiser (*qv*). US Navy/Nato designation.

CLC. US Navy classification. Tactical Command Ship, originally Task Fleet Command Ship. Used by the USS *Northampton*, built on a cruiser hull, from completion in 1953 to 1962.

CLK. Hunter-killer ship. US designation used briefly for USS *Norfolk*, laid down in 1949. Before completion in 1951 she was designated DL (*qv*).

CMB. Coastal Motor Boat. Early British designation for motor torpedo boat.

CNO. Chief of Naval Operations (US).

CODAG. Combined diesel and gas turbine propulsion.

CODLAG. Combined diesel-electric and gas turbine propulsion.

CODOG. Combined diesel or gas turbine propulsion.

COGAG. Combined gas turbine propulsion (with turbines connected together).

COGOG. Combined gas turbine propulsion (with alternative cruise and full power turbines).

Combattante. The names of a class of French fast attack craft.

contact mine. A mine exploded by contact with the target. The usual type of contact mine is set off by an electric current produced when a ship breaks open the batteries in the horns of the mine that is floating close to the surface, tethered to a base sunk on to the seabed. An alternative is the antenna mine (*qv*).

corvette. The term was recoined in modern times by the Royal Navy for its 1000-ton escorts built from 1940, and has usually been used for surface combatants in the 500–1000-ton category of limited endurance and capability best employed in coastal and patrol work. Corvettes have, however, always had the potential for higher endurance operations in the absence of more capable assets. France used the term very differently from the mid 1960s until 1988 for large destroyer type ships smaller than the 5–6000-ton DLG (*qv*) type 'frigates'. This was a rather more accurate use of the term historically; nineteenth-century corvettes were smaller frigates, both types of 'cruiser'.

cruise missile. A long range missile that flies to its target, either a ship or a land objective, using aerodynamic surfaces for lift and usually a jet engine for propulsion. The term is particularly associated with weapons such as the American Tomahawk (*qv*).

cruiser. Traditionally a larger surface combatant usually capable of operating independently and used both for fleet reconnaissance and trade defence. By 1945 modern cruisers were ships of at least 8000 tons, and the larger examples were over 16,000 tons. The term began to die out for new Western construction but became more common again in 1975 when the USA redesignated its DL/DLG (*qv*) type ships, which were comparable in size to the cruisers of the first half of the century. A modern definition of cruiser might be 'a large combatant with a comprehensive range of capabilities including area air defence, usually of at least 7000 tons in standard displacement to give sufficient room for all systems'.

CSGN. Nuclear powered guided missile strike cruiser. US Navy classification. The addition of the term 'strike' implied a substantial anti-ship capability with Tomahawk (*qv*) and Harpoon (*qv*) missiles. A 16–17,000-ton CSGN was projected by the US Navy in the 1970s, but the project was abandoned because of cost.

CV. Aircraft carrier. US Navy/Nato classification. Usually used only for large 'fleet' aircraft carriers with general purpose capabilities, including ASW as well as strike and AAW.

CVA. Attack aircraft carrier. US Navy/Nato classification. Originally used for the abortive USS *United States* of 1949 but adopted for all CVs (*qv*) and CVBs (*qv*) on 1 October 1952 to reflect the new emphasis on nuclear attack in their role. When the role of these ships became more general purpose with the decommissioning of the specialised ASW (*qv*) CVS (*qv*) ships, the classification reverted to CV on 30 June 1975.

CVAN. Nuclear powered attack aircraft carrier. Nuclear powered versions of the above; in effect only USS *Enterprise*, redesignated CVN on 30 June 1975.

CVB. Aircraft Carrier, Large. US Navy classification. Used for the armoured 'battle' aircraft carriers of the *Midway* class from construction to 1952.

CVE. Aircraft Carrier, Escort. US Navy classification. Small ships usually built on mercantile or mercantile type hulls.

CVL. Small Aircraft Carrier. US Navy/Nato designation. Medium carriers built on cruiser hulls to supplement CVs in fleet operations during the Second World War. Can be used more generally, for smaller general purpose 'light' carriers, notably the British 'light fleet carriers' of the *Colossus*, *Majestic* and *Hermes* classes.

CVR. Crystal video receiver. A device commonly used in ESM systems which receives all signals over a fairly wide frequency band.

CVS. Anti-submarine warfare support carrier. US Navy classification originally adopted in1953 for the *Essex* class CVs converted to the role, the term is now applied to the British *Invincible* class ships. These are now officially designated CVSG, reflecting the Sea Dart SAM (*qv*) armament.

CVV. Abortive American medium sized carrier concept.

DASH. Drone Anti-Submarine Helicopter. An unsuccessful American attempt to use a remotely controlled unmanned helicopter to deliver homing torpedoes within 200yd of submarine targets 10,000yd away. The system proved very difficult to control reliably and was withdrawn from service prematurely despite many ships being fitted to carry it, both in the US Navy and Japanese MSDF. Of the 746 DASH drones built over half were lost at sea.

DATS. Deep Armed Team Sweep minesweeping system. A method of sweeping rising ASW (*qv*) mines by explosively cutting the cables that hold them to the ocean floor in deeper Continental Shelf waters, down to 200m. A wire with explosive cutters is deployed between two vessels with 'kites' to depress the sweep to the required depth.

DCA. British submarine tactical data system.

DCB. Improved British submarine tactical data system.

DD. Destroyer. US Navy/Nato classification.

DDE. Escort destroyer/anti-submarine destroyer. US Navy/Nato classification, which implies retention of the high speed characteristic of a traditional destroyer.

DDG. Guided missile destroyer. US Navy/Nato classification.

DDH. Helicopter-carrying destroyer. US Navy classification.

DDK. Hunter-killer destroyer. US Navy classification. Used 1948–50 for conversions of USS *Carpenter* and USS *Robert E Owens* intended for offensive operations along the lines of the CLK (*qv*) *Norfolk*.

DDR. Radar picket destroyer. US Navy/Nato classification.

DE. *See* destroyer escort. In Nato terminology 'Ocean Escort'; replaced 1975 by FF (*qv*).

DEC. British laser dazzle sight (*qv*). First deployed experimentally in the Falklands war. Its name reflects its origin in fire and control direction technology.

DEG. Guided missile destroyer escort (*qv*). US Navy classification. Replaced by FFG (*qv*) on 30 June 1975.

degaussing. Altering or reducing a ship's magnetic field using electrical coils to neutralise the effect of magnetic mines. This changes the ship's magnetic signature such that the actuating mechanism of the mine will not be activated.

DER. Escort vessel radar picket. US Navy classification.

destroyer. Formerly a destroyer of torpedo boats, latterly a medium general purpose surface combatant of between about 2500 and 7000 tons with the speed and capabilities to undertake the most demanding combat operations, including participation in fast carrier battle groups. Large 'destroyers' differ from 'cruisers' (*qv*) of equivalent size in that they lack comprehensive capability, *eg*, no area defence system. Large 'frigates' usually differ from small 'destroyers' primarily in terms of lower speed and more austere engineering arrangements. The British designated their DLGs (*qv*) 'destroyers' and kept the term for the Type 42 air defence ships.

destroyer escort. An American term for a smaller, slower destroyer type ship designed primarily for convoy escort.

Destroyer Leader. A larger destroyer originally used as a flagship for destroyer flotillas. Classification used from 1951 for former CLK (*qv*) *Norfolk* and the first two *Mitscher* class ships. Changed to 'frigate' (*qv*) in 1954 but DL (*qv*) classification letters retained.

destructores caza submarinas. A Spanish term for ASW (*qv*) destroyer.

DIFAR. Directional Frequency Analysis and Recording. A directional variant of LOFAR (*qv*). A sonobuoy fitted for DIFAR has two beam patterns at right angles to each other. It measures two components of the sound signals it receives, sending information that can be processed to give the direction of the target to within 10–15 degrees.

distillate. A type of petroleum fuel similar to kerosene/paraffin.

DL. Frigate (American classification name used 1954–75); formerly Destroyer Leader, used from 1951 for large destroyer/small cruiser type ships.

DLG. Guided missile 'frigate', American designation *see above*, reclassified CG (*qv*) 30 June 1975. Term used by Royal Navy for its large 'County' class 'destroyers', sometimes misunderstood as 'Destroyer Light Guided Missile'. Generic term for large destroyer/small cruiser equipped with area defence surface-to-air missiles.

DLGN. As above but nuclear powered.

DX. Experimental US destroyer programme of late 1960s.

DXG. Guided missile destroyer, variant of DX (*qv*).

ELINT. Electronic Intelligence. The gaining of intelligence from the receipt of emissions in the electro-magnetic spectrum. This can range from direction-finding or threat warning using the existence of a radar or radio signal to detailed code breaking analysis of hostile communications.

EMCON. Emission Control: reducing or preventing radio/radar emissions to evade detection.

EMP. Electro-Magnetic Pulse. The pulse of high electro-magnetic energy caused by the interaction of the radiation of a nuclear weapon with the Earth's atmosphere. EMP effects are greatest with ground bursts and high air bursts; in the latter case the effects can be very widespread. EMP can cause serious damage to electrical circuits unless they are hardened against it.

EO. Electro-optical. Systems that use electromagnetic emissions in the visible and near visible spectrum to provide imaging information for sensors.

escort destroyer. A British Second World War term for smaller and/or older destroyers (*qv*) built or converted for convoy escort operations; reclassified as 'frigates' (*qv*) in 1947.

escorteurs d'escadre. Squadron escorts; *ie* large destroyers (*qv*) (French).

ESM. Electronic Support Measures; intercept receivers to identify and classify electronic emissions in order to give early warning of attack and to provide passive detection of air and surface forces beyond the horizon.

EW. Electronic Warfare. The exploitation of the electro-magnetic spectrum for military purposes. It includes the gathering of ELINT (*qv*) of all kinds and the application of active countermeasures such as jamming and the generation of false targets.

Exocet. A widely used French anti-shipping missile deployed in air, surface and sub-surface launched variants. Range varies from 42 to 70km according to version.

FAC. Fast Attack Craft.

FAC-M. Fast Attack Craft – Missile.

FCC. Flag Command Center: the shore station of the commander of the US Atlantic or Pacific fleet.

FF. Frigate. US Navy classification, adopted to replace DE (*qv*) on 30 June 1975 (*not*, despite common usage in USA, 'fast frigate').

FFG. Guided missile frigate. US Navy classification, adopted to replace DEG on 30 June 1975.

fleet train. The auxiliaries required to fuel and supply a fleet.

Fleet Rehabilitation and Modernisation Program. A programme to modernise older US warships begun as a result of a 1958 study of the material readiness of the fleet. The study concluded that 'the US fleet is not in an acceptable state of readiness' and that total rehabilitation of middle-aged ships, especially destroyers, should be carried out. In November 1958 a high level conference recommended three stages of conversion: FRAM I, a complete rehabilitation of all shipboard components to give eight more years of life; FRAM II, sufficient rehabilitation for five years' more service; and FRAM III, overhaul for three more years. FRAM III was dropped early in 1959 but FRAM I and FRAM II conversions were given the highest priority 'comparable to that of Polaris'. FRAM I was applied to 79 *Gearing* and *Carpenter* class destroyers; FRAM II to 16 DDE and DDR *Gearing* derivatives, 31 *Allen M Sumners* and 3 *Fletcher* DDEs. Plans to give four DERs (*qv*) FRAM II conversions were dropped, but FRAM II conversions were given to eight CVS (*qv*) and nine 'Guppy' (*qv*) submarines, four DE based fast transports (APDs) and seven *Cabildo* and *Ashland* class LSDs (*qv*).

Flexible Response. A strategy involving a number of responses to attack, conventional

escalating to nuclear, adopted by the USA in the early 1960s and by Nato in 1967.

FLIR. Forward Looking Infra-Red. Equipment to allow night vision by the use of infrared sensors which project television-like images on to a cathode ray tube.

FMCW. Frequency-Modulated Continuous Wave. In a continuous wave radar the set transmits continuously without pulsing; the frequency can be changed or 'modulated' over time.

FML. Frequency Memory Loops. A device by which electronic countermeasures equipment recalls the signal coming in to reproduce or distort it.

FOSM. Flag Officer Submarines (GB).

FRAM. Fleet Rehabilitation and Modernisation Program (*qv*).

frégate légère. Light frigate (French). A new designation used for the 3500-ton *La Fayette* class ships of the 1990s. These are austere vessels with limited equipment, notably no shipboard sonar.

frégates. French term for DL/DLG (*qv*). Always used for the *Suffren* class. The designation was extended to the *Tourville*s in 1971 before launch and was extended to the *Georges Leygues*, *Cassard* and *Aconit* classes in 1988.

frégates de surveillance. Lightly equipped French OPV (*qv*) type ships. Six ships of the *Floreal* class began delivery in 1991.

Fresnel lenses. A way of making a flat lens by using interference phenomena.

frigate. A medium sized surface combatant of 1750 to 3000 tons designed primarily to protect merchant and similar shipping from submarines and aircraft; term also used 1954–1975 by the USA and still by France for DL/DLG type ships. The modern use of the designation originated in the need to find a new name for the larger ocean going twin-screw 'corvettes' of the Second World War. 'Frigate', in the past a larger corvette, seemed one solution, although eighteenth- and nineteenth-century frigates had been the ancestors of modern cruisers. The Royal Navy now classifies as 'frigates' all its major surface combatants orientated primarily to ASW (*qv*).

FSU. Forward Support Unit for mine countermeasures vessels (GB).

gas turbine. A rotary internal combustion engine where fuel is burned with air to provide gas to drive turbine blades connected to a shaft. The shaft is then connected through a gearbox to a propeller. At first only used for small craft, gas turbines are now standard propulsion machinery for warships up to and including smaller aircraft carriers.

Gatling. A rotary, multi-barrelled machine gun.

Goalkeeper. A Dutch CIWS (*qv*) based around a heavy 30mm Gatling (*qv*) gun.

goniometer. An instrument for determining the direction of an arriving electromagnetic signal used in EW (*qv*).

Grog. The Mk 23 British torpedo.

Guppy. Greater Underwater Propulsive Power: a modernisation programme for American Second World War fleet submarines. The reconstruction involved increased battery capacity, streamlining and, usually, a snorkel.

Harpoon. American anti-ship missile. A widely exported long range, jet propelled surface submarine and air launched missile. Range 75 miles surface launched; 120 miles air launched.

heavy cruiser. A larger cruiser (*qv*) usually with 8in gun main armament.

Hedgehog. British designed multiple spigot mortar ahead throwing ASW (*qv*) weapons.

HF/DF. High Frequency Direction-Finding. A technique first exploited at sea during the Second World War to detect the position of enemy units by identifying and fixing their high frequency radio emissions.

HUK. Hunter-killer group.

Hunter Killer Light Cruiser. An American concept of the early postwar period of a cruiser (*qv*) type ship for offensive ASW (*qv*) operations.

hurricane bow. An aircraft carrier bow with continuous plating from the flightdeck to the waterline.

hydrobatics. Extreme underwater manoeuvres similar to aerobatics in the air.

hydrofoil. A surface skimmer using the lift effects of submerged foils.

IFF. Identification Friend or Foe. A radar transponder, mounted typically in aircraft, which responds to a radar signal by sending out a coded message that indicates to a friendly platform that the target detected is friendly.

IFM. Instantaneous Frequency Measurement. Used with CVR (*qv*) for frequency measurement.

Ikara. An Australian designed ASW (*qv*) missile.

ISAR. Inverse Synthetic Aperture Radar. A radar technique that allows an image of the shape of a target to be put on to a cathode ray tube to allow identification. It uses the motion of the target to produce the same effect as the motion of the platform in normal synthetic aperture radar (*qv*).

'jeep carrier'. A nickname for escort carriers (*qv*).

kamikazes. Japanese suicide pilots and aircraft used for anti-ship duties in 1944–45.

kerosene. American term for British paraffin.

Kevlar armour protection. Proprietary lightweight fabric based ceramic armour fitted to thin steel plating.

LAMPS. Light Airborne Multi-Purpose System. American shipborne helicopters used for ASW (*qv*) detection and attack and ASuW (*qv*) over-the-horizon targeting. LAMPS I was the Kaman SH-2F Seasprite; LAMPS III is the Sikorsky SH-60B Seahawk.

LAMS. Local Area Missile System. A British project for an advanced 15km range anti-missile system that evolved into the longer ranged system projected for the new Anglo–French–Italian common new generation frigate.

LAN. Local Area Networks (computers). The networking of a number of computers into a single distributed system. This is a feature of modern combat data systems that makes them less prone to catastrophic failure.

large cruiser. The *Alaska* class of 12in gun armed 27,500-ton American heavy cruisers often called 'battlecruisers' (*qv*).

Laser Dazzle Sight. A weapon designed to use laser light to dazzle enemy pilots. Deployed by the Royal Navy as DEC (*qv*) in the 1980s.

LCAC. Landing Craft Air Cushion (hovercraft).

LCC. Amphibious Command Ship.

LCI. Landing Craft, Infantry.

LCM. Landing Craft, Mechanised.

LCT. Landing Craft, Tank.

LCU. Landing Craft, Utility.

LCVP. Landing Craft, Vehicle and Personnel.

Lend-Lease. The system whereby material was transferred free of charge from the US to allies, 1941–45, in return for leases on bases in the American sphere of influence.

LHA. Amphibious assault ship (general purpose); US Navy classification, *Tarawa* class.

LHD. Amphibious assault ship (multi-purpose). US Navy classification, *Wasp* class.

light carrier. *See* light fleet carrier.

light cruiser. Cruiser (*qv*) of any size with 6in gun main armament or smaller.

light fleet carrier. Smaller aircraft carrier built to supplement larger aircraft carriers in main fleet operations; name officially used by Royal Navy for *Colossus*, *Majestic* and *Hermes* classes laid down 1942–45.

lobe patterns. Rounded segmented divisions in radar coverage caused by reflection of energy from the surface of the sea.

LOFAR. Low-Frequency Analysis and Recording. The processing and integration of narrow band passive sonar data to provide detection of quiet underwater targets. LOFAR techniques first developed in the 1950s allowed the development of effective long range passive sonars of all types.

LPD. US originated classification, amphibious transport dock (misunderstood in UK as 'Landing Platform Helicopter').

LSD. Dock landing ship.

LST. Tank landing ship.

LVT. Landing Vehicle, Tracked.

LVTP. Landing Vehicle, Tracked, Personnel Carrier.

LX. US Navy designation; new multi-purpose landing ship planned in 1990s.

MAD. Magnetic Anomaly Detector, fitted to aircraft to detect distortions in the Earth's magnetic field caused by a submerged submarine. A short range aid to classification rather than a detector in its own right.

magnetic mine. Mine activated by the magnetic field of a passing target. Every ship has a distinctive magnetic signature and magnetic mines can be tuned accordingly. Magnetic actuation is often combined with some other form of influence action, *eg* acoustic (*qv*).

MATCH. Manned Anti-Submarine Torpedo Carrying Helicopter. A British concept for using small helicopters to deliver ASW (*qv*) weapons to ranges possible with 1960s' sonars. The first MATCH helicopter was the Westland Wasp which entered service in 1963.

MCM. Mine Countermeasures. Mines can be countered by *sweeping*, the use of a wire sweep to cut the cables of moored mines or sweeps simulating target signatures to detonate influence mines; or *hunting*, using sonar to find mines for disposal by divers or unmanned underwater vehicles. In addition, the signature of a ship can be reduced/changed by such measures as degaussing (*qv*).

MDAP. Mutual Defense Aid Program. The US programme begun in the early 1950s to supply defence equipment to Cold War allies.

'meatball'. Light image seen by pilot in mirror landing aid.

MEKO. German family of frigates (*qv*) built for export.

MFP. Marine-Fahr-Prahme; German Second World War naval store ferry.

MGB. Motor Gun Boat.

minehunter. A vessel designed to hunt mines using sonar.

minesweeping. Drawing cables through the water to cut mine cables or explode influence mines.

missile cruiser. A cruiser (*qv*) equipped with guided missiles as main armament; especially Soviet SSM (*qv*) ships.

MMS. Motor Minesweeper (*qv*).

Moose Jaw sonar. Western codename for large Soviet low frequency 'Orion' sonar mounted on *Moskva* and *Kiev* class large aircraft carrying cruisers. Its range was reportedly 40km.

Motor Mine Sweeper. Small British minesweepers built during the Second World War. There were two main variants: *MMS 1-118/123-312*, 105ft, 255 tons; *MMS 1001-1090*, 126ft, 360 tons. Ships of both types were built for the RCN. Ships of both types remained in service until the late 1950s.

MPA. Maritime Patrol Aircraft. Land based types such as Neptune, Shackleton, Nimrod, P-3 Orion, Atlantique.

MSC. Minesweeper, Coastal. US Navy/Nato designation. Also Military Sealift Command (*see below*).

MSTS. Military Sea Transportation Service. The US Navy's postwar sealift organisation created out of the Naval Ocean Transport Service on 1 October 1949. It took over the Army Transportation Corps' oceangoing ships and transports in 1950. On 1 August 1970 MSTS became Military Sealift Command (MSC). MSC is commanded by an active duty vice-admiral but most of its staff are civilian.

MTB. Motor Torpedo Boat.

MTI. Moving Target Indicator. A general term for the filtering out of 'clutter' on radar screens (*ie* the rejection of unwanted echoes) so that moving targets can be followed on the screen. It implies some form of memory within the radar system so that successive echoes or the results of successive radar scans can be compared.

nanosecond. A thousand millionth (American billionth) of a second (10^{-19}).

Nato. North Atlantic Treaty Organisation.

natural-circulation reactor. A nuclear reactor in which water circulates by natural convection rather than by being pumped.

Naval Tactical Data System. The standard American combat data system. The world's first shipboard tactical data system based on programmable solid-state computers and using multiple computers in a distributed tactical data processing system. It was also the first in the world to use automatic computer-to-computer data exchange via data links between ships.

NCR. Natural-Circulation Reactor (*qv*).

NCTR. Non-Co-operative Target Recognition. Means by which radar can recognise targets without co-operative action by the target such as IFF (*qv*).

NTDS. Naval Tactical Data System (*qv*).

Oerlikon. Swiss gun manufacturer especially associated with 20mm guns.

oiler. Tanker for refuelling ships.

OPV. Offshore Patrol Vessel. A lightly armed and equipped vessel but with sufficient endurance for presence on constabulary and surveillance patrols.

Oropesa float. Torpedo shaped float as used to support standard contact wire minesweeping gear. The float substitutes for the second minesweeper required by earlier equipment. *Oropesa* was the name of the British ship in which the gear was developed during the First World War.

OTH radars. Over the Horizon radars. Radars that bounce beams off the ionosphere to detect targets beyond line of sight. These use very large arrays and therefore are only deployable ashore.

OTHT. Over the Horizon Targeting. Planning long range missile engagements to exploit weapons such as Tomahawk (*qv*). During the 1980s the US Navy developed a system for such engagements with intelligence information being stored on a data base exploited by a Force Over-the-Horizon Track Co-ordinator (FOTC). The data base is compiled by combining various ELINT (*qv*) and other sources linked by satellite communications. The USSR developed much cruder systems in the 1960s using reconnaissance aircraft and direct data linkage to allow OTH engagements by cruise missile carrying submarines.

Otomat. Franco-Italian anti-ship missile. A turbojet engine gives relatively long range, up to 60km in the Mk 1 version and 180km for Mk 2. It is used by the Italian navy and has been widely exported. It is carried in surface combatants and is used by Egypt and Saudi Arabia for coast defence.

Oyster. Nickname for German Second World War pressure mines.

PAP. Poisson-Auto-Propulseur; French designed remotely controlled mine destruction and inspection system.

passive sonar. Sonar that listens for sounds emitted by targets. Modern systems of signal processing, notably LOFAR (*qv*), allow long range passive detection against relatively quiet targets. Passive sonar is preferred by users, especially submarines, because it does not reveal the position of the user.

patrol frigate. Name adopted for a time in 1970s for more austere frigate projects, notably the American *Oliver Hazard Perry* class, eventually rated FFG (*qv*). It was a derivative of the 'PF' letter classification (*qv*).

PC. US Navy classification for 'submarine chaser', *ie* small coastal ASW ship. The designation was abolished in 1968. Nato adopted PC in its system for 'Coast Escort'.

peak energy. Sharp burst of maximum energy at a given frequency used by ESM (*qv*) systems for detecting radars.

PG. *See* PGM.

PGM. US Navy classification for 'Motor Gunboat', later redesignated 'Patrol Gunboat'. Applied to *Asheville* class ships (225 tons) built in the late 1960s; redesignated PG, 1 April 1967. Also 'Precision Guided Munition'. Usually used for weapons that achieve very precise guidance through the use of reflected laser energy or electro-optical sensors, *eg* the Paveway series of laser guided bombs and the Maverick family of air-to-ground missiles.

picket ship. Ships deployed at a distance from the targets being defended to provide radar early warning.

Polaris. The first American type of underwater, submarine launched ballistic missile. There are three types: A-1 with a range of 1200nm; A-2 with a range of 1500nm; and A-3 (also used by the British) with a range of 2500nm. A-3 carried three multiple re-entry vehicles (MRVs) instead of a single warhead, and was further modified in Britain with an advanced MRV system, 'Chevaline'.

pressure hull. The basic hull of a submarine designed to withstand high underwater pressure.

pressure mine. A mine triggered by the changes in water pressure caused by a passing target.

PRF. Pulse Repetition Frequency; the rate at which a radar's pulses repeat. Increasing PRF produces clearer returns, but limits range. Radar designers have to balance PRF with peak power and signal length.

PSW. Pro-Submarine Warfare. Operations by other forces against hostile ASW (*qv*) forces designed to help submarines reach or remain in their operational areas. The USSR felt forced to engage in extensive PSW to support its SSBNs (*qv*).

PT boat. Traditional US Navy designation for motor torpedo boat, literally 'patrol torpedo' boat. Used until the early 1960s.

PTF. US Navy classification for 'Fast Patrol Boat', from 14 August 1968, 'Fast Patrol Craft'. Adopted in 1962 for a new generation of boats and also applied to older PT boats reactivated.

PUFFS. Passive Underwater Fire-Control Feasibility Study; name given to an American passive sonar ranging system for submarines.

pulse-doppler technology. A radar technique for moving target detection using the doppler shift of returning echoes.

radar frequency bands. The different ranges of frequency in which radars share common characteristics: *eg* S band 2000–4000 m/hz, C band 4000–8000 m/hz.

radar picket. *See* picket ship.

RAN. Royal Australian Navy.

RAT. Rocket Assisted Torpedo, an early American ASW (*qv*) missile. It was evaluated aboard the destroyer *Sarsfield* in 1957. Its accuracy was too poor to deliver existing torpedoes effectively and it was abandoned in favour of ASROC (*qv*), which was originally designated RAT 'C'.

Regulus. A family of jet propelled American naval land attack cruise missiles (*qv*). The Subsonic Regulus I had a range of 575 miles and was operationally deployed in submarines, cruisers and aircraft carriers; 514 were built. It was operational 1954–64. An entirely new 1200-mile range Regulus II was cancelled in favour of Polaris (*qv*).

RKR. Russian 'Rocket Cruiser'; large or medium sized ship equipped with anti-ship missiles as primary armament.

RWR. Rapid Response Warning Radar. Radar designed to give the fastest possible warning of an incoming threat.

S-boat. 'Schnellboote' (*qv*).

Sa'ar. Type of Israeli FAC (*qv*).

SAG. Surface Attack Group. A group of surface ships not containing an aircraft carrier; especially one intended for ASuW. The advent

of Tomahawk (*qv*) and Harpoon (*qv*) led the US Navy to coin the term in the late 1970s.

SAM. Surface-to-Air Missile.

SAR. Synthetic Aperture Radar. Radar which uses the motion of the platform and computer processing to build up a detailed near visual type impression of the target.

SATIR. *System zur Auswertung Taktischer Informationen auf Raketenzerstören*; command system for the German guided missile destroyers and later frigates.

SCANFAR. Radar system originally fitted to USS *Enterprise*.

SCB. Ship Characteristics Board (US Navy). SCB numbers are given to ship designs, *eg* SCB-127 was the design of the aircraft carrier *Kitty Hawk* and SCB-101.66 the design for the rebuild of the USS *Midway*.

Schnellboote. 'Fast boat'; German Second World War designation for MTB (*qv*).

SCS. Sea Control Ship. Abortive 1970s' US project for a small 10,000-ton carrier operating helicopters and STOV/L (*qv*) aircraft.

sea sled. An advanced hull concept with a 'W' shape.

Sea Dart. British second generation long range shipborne SAM (*qv*). Rocket boosted with a ramjet sustainer motor, the missile has a range of 40 miles. Guidance is semi-active radar homing.

Seacat. First generation short range British shipborne SAM (*qv*). Radio command guided, the missile has a range of 5000yd and a maximum altitude of 3300ft. It cannot engage supersonic targets.

SEAL. 'Sea–Air–Land' teams; US Navy Special Forces.

Seaslug. First generation long range British shipborne SAM (*qv*). Rocket powered with strap-on boosters, its range in the Mk 2 version was 24.3nm. Beam-riding guidance limited it capability against manoeuvring targets. Mk 2 missiles had improved capability against low flying and surface targets. It armed the 'County' class DLGs and was exported with them to Chile.

secondary battery. The lighter guns carried by a major warship.

SENIT. *Système d'Exploitation Naval des Informations Tactiques* (*qv*); French tactical data system.

SEWACO. Signal Sensor Weapon Control System; Dutch tactical data system.

SHINPADS. Shipboard Integrated Processing and Display System; Canadian UYC-501 (V) tactical data system used in the *Halifax* class frigates and rebuilt 'Tribal' class destroyers. This is a fully distributed system, all its minicomputers being usable in any role.

SHR. Superheterodyne Receiver. A receiver which is finely tuned to a certain frequency band.

side array. A sonar array mounted along the side of a vessel.

SIGINT. Signals Intelligence. Intelligence gleaned from the enemy's radio traffic. It can include both analysis of the existence of certain kinds of signal in certain places and certain quantities, and the decoding of signals using cryptanalysis to reveal their content.

Signature. The characteristic emission of a particular target.

SIOP. Single Integrated Operational Plan. The central nuclear war plan for American strategic nuclear forces. The first SIOP was drawn up in December 1960 and it has been updated at intervals to reflect changes in strategic doctrine.

SKR. Designation for Russian 'Guard Ship'; used for smaller, less capable frigate-type ships.

SLEP. Service Life Extension Program: originally a refit programme for the larger US aircraft carriers to extend their lives by fifty per cent (fifteen years). USS *Saratoga* entered Philadelphia Naval Shipyard for the first SLEP in 1980. Subsequently used for any similar programme, *eg* that to extend the lives of the British Landing Ships Logistic.

sloop. Frigate (*qv*) type ship.

snorkel. Mechanism to allow diesel submarines to use air while submerged; sometimes called 'snort' in Britain.

sonobuoy. A buoy dropped into the water to search for submarines with sonar.

SOSUS. Sound Surveillance System. The American system of large bottom passive sonar (*qv*) arrays, the first elements of which began to be deployed in the 1950s. This allows detection of submarines over ranges of hundreds of miles. This was the first application of LOFAR (*qv*) techniques.

Squid. British ahead throwing depth charge mortar.

SSBN. Nuclear Powered Ballistic Missile Submarine.

SSCS. Surface Ship Control System; British tactical data system. A distributed combat data system being fitted to the British Type 23 frigates after the failure of the original Computer Aided Command System (CACS).

SSGN. Nuclear powered cruise missile submarine. US Navy/Nato classification.

SSK. Conventionally powered hunter-killer submarine. Originally applied only to specialised ASW boats, the term has become general to distinguish conventionally powered boats from SSNs (*qv*).

SSM. Surface-to-Surface Missile.

SSN. Nuclear powered hunter-killer submarine. US Navy classification that has become general.

steam turbine. Steam powered rotary engine.

STOVL. Short Take Off Vertical Landing. Aircraft capable of vertical take off, such as the Sea Harrier, can carry much larger payloads if they make short take-off runs. Hence this is the normal mode of operation, the vertical flight capability being confined to landing.

submarine escort. Submarines escorting battle groups.

Subroc. Submarine Rocket; US underwater-to-underwater ASW missile, first deployed in 1965. The missile was fired from a submerged submarine, broke surface and flew to a point over the enemy submarine as it appeared on the firing submarine's sonar. It then dropped a 1.5 kiloton W-55 nuclear depth charge. Maximum range was 28.5 miles. Subroc was withdrawn from service in 1988.

supply ship. Ship carrying supplies for a fleet.

surface effect craft. Rigid sided hovercraft used only at sea.

Système d'Exploitation Naval des Informations Tactiques. French tactical data system

derived from NTDS (*qv*). SENIT 1 was used in the *Suffren* class DLGs; SENIT 2 in the *Surcouf* class destroyers and aircraft carriers *Foch* and *Clemenceau*. SENIT 3 in *Aconit* and the *Tourvilles*; SENIT 4 in the *Georges Leygues* class; SENIT 5 was projected for the A 69 corvette; and SENIT 6 was fitted to the *Acmit* class.

T-CBL. Tentative Conceptual Base Line; an abortive 1970s' American design for a medium sized aircraft carrier.

tail-sitter. Early V/STOL (*qv*) aircraft of the 1950s that sat vertically on their tails.

Talos. American naval SAM (*qv*) designed to deal with threats at long range (50nm). A large ramjet powered missile with rocket boost, it could only be carried in cruisers. Beam riding guidance was used with semi-active and later anti-radar terminal homing. There was a nuclear version and the missile also had a surface-to-surface capability. Talos was in service from 1957 to 1979 and was used operationally in Vietnam.

target motion analysis. The analysis of passive sonar bearing in a submarine to determine the movement of a target.

Tartar. First generation semi-active homing American short range SAM (*qv*) designed to engage low and medium sized targets between 2000 and 15,000yd. Chosen to arm the *Charles F Adams* class destroyers, it completed technical evaluation in 1961. It was also mounted as secondary armament in guided missile cruisers. Tartar, like all early systems, was unreliable and it was replaced from 1968 by a similar but improved Standard Missile-1 (Medium Range).

tattle-tale ships. Ships which mark and follow potential enemy vessels to monitor their position for possible attack.

TCSS. British 'Torpedo Control System Submarine', tactical data handling system installed in SSNs (*qv*). TCSS-9 was the first fully computerised British submarine AIO (*qv*), introduced in 1973.

TDC. Torpedo Data Computer.

TDCC. Through Deck Command Cruiser, one of the designations of the British *Invincible* class CVS.

Terrier. First generation medium range American SAM (*qv*), first deployed in 1955. A compact, two-stage beam rider, its guidance was later altered to semi-active homing. There was a nuclear version. Maximum range increased from 20 miles to 40 miles in later variants. Used to arm both cruisers and DLGs (plus one experimental DDG), 8000 were built, production ending in 1966. Terrier was replaced by the similar but more reliable Standard Missile-1 (Extended Range).

TFCC. Tactical Flag Command Centre; aboard the flagship of a deployed US battle group.

Through Deck Cruiser. A large cruiser (*qv*) with a deck along its entire length; effectively a small aircraft carrier. The term was coined for the British *Invincible* class ships when they were first planned. 'Aircraft carriers' were politically unacceptable.

TI radars. Target Indication Radars.

TMA. Target Motion Analysis (*qv*).

Tomahawk. American long range cruise missile (*qv*). There are several variants: Tomahawk Land Attack Missile – Nuclear (TLAM-N);

Tomahawk Land Attack Missile – Conventional (TLAM-C); Tomahawk Anti-Ship Missile (TASM) and a bomblet version of TLAM-C often called TLAM-D. Ranges for each type are respectively 1350, 675, 250 and 470 miles. The land attack types use terrain contour matching guidance; TASM uses radar homing. Tomahawk is launched from surface ships or submarines.

torpedo data computer. Computer fitted to provide fire control solution for torpedoes.

towed array. Long array of sonar transducers towed behind surface ships or submarines for long range passive detection of submarines.

TWS. Track-While-Scan; a radar with a form of memory which can correlate the differing positions of particular targets on subsequent sweeps. A modern TWS radar can maintain track data on several targets.

Typhon. An abortive and ambitious US Navy SAM (*qv*) programme cancelled in the 1960s.

unrep. Underway replenishment. During the Second World War the US Navy pioneered techniques of refuelling and re-storing underway by ships coming alongside and passing material by hose and jackstay. Helicopters can also be used for vertical replenishment (vert-rep). Unrep is essential for any navy to acquire operational reach.

VDS. Variable Depth Sonar. A sonar with a transducer that can be lowered to optimum depth to be effective. The effectiveness of hull mounted sonars can be greatly reduced by different layers of temperature and salinity that act as barriers to longer range propagation. VDS is also very useful for minehunting, as the sonar can be placed close to the sea bottom being examined for mines.

V/STOL. Vertical/Short Take Off and Landing aircraft. Although the USSR developed a crude V/STOL fighter, the Yak-38 Forger, the most effective such aircraft is the Harrier/ Sea Harrier family used at sea by the United Kingdom, United States, Spain, Italy and India. This uses a vectored thrust jet for maximum flexibility. More countries are adopting this aircraft, which allows limited organic air power to be provided cheaply by relatively small ships.

V/STOL carrier. A carrier for the above. Typical such vessels are the 20,000-ton British *Invincibles*, the 16,700-ton Spanish *Principe de Asturias* and the 13,370-ton Italian *Guiseppe Garibaldi*.

VSTOL. See V/STOL.

Vulcan/Phalanx. An American type of Gatling (*qv*) CIWS (*qv*) system using a 20mm rotary gun.

Walter boat. A submarine powered by hydrogen peroxide, an early form of AIP (*qv*).

WARMS. War-Only Operating Modes.

'Whale'. Soviet Walter submarine prototype.

wing-in-ground-effect (WIG). A skimming technology that uses the air trapped between a wing and the surface of the Earth. The Soviet Union developed two types of WIG craft, the 'Utka' and the 'Orlan'. The 'Utka is 190ft long and displaces 125 tons; the 'Orlan' is 246ft and displaces 400 tons. Their operational radius is in the order of 1000nm at 250kts flying at a height of 5m.

wire-guided torpedo. A torpedo guided via information transmitted along a wire connecting it to the launching platform.

Provisional listing of known project class numbers of major combatants used by the Soviet navy, with their normally used Western assigned class name.

1. *Leningrad* class flotilla leader.

7. *Gnevnyi* class destroyer.

7U. *Storozhevoi* class destroyer.

23. *Sovetskiy Soyuz* class battleships.

24. Successor battleship design.

26. *Kirov* class cruiser.

29. *Yastreb* class frigate.

30. *Ognevoi* class destroyer.

30bis. *Skoryy* class destroyer.

35. *Mirka* class small anti-submarine ship.

35M. *Mirka II* class small anti-submarine ship.

38. Modified *Leningrad* class leader.

39. *Uragan* class torpedo boat.

41. *Tallinn* class destroyer.

42. *Kola* class frigate.

45. *Opitnyi* class destroyer.

48. *Leningrad* follow on leaders.

50. *Riga* class frigate.

53. *Tral* class coastal minesweeper.

56. *Kotlin* class destroyers.

56A. *Kotlin* SAM class destroyer.

56M. *Kildin* class missile ships.

57. *Krupnyy* class destroyer.

57M. *Kanin* class destroyer.

58. *Kynda* class missile cruisers.

61. *Kashin* class destroyers.

67EP. *Sverdlov* class missile conversion *Admiral Nakhimov*.

68. *Chapaev* class cruiser.

68bis. *Sverdlov* class cruiser.

68U. *Sverdlov* command cruiser conversions.

68A. Modified *Sverdlov* class cruiser.

69. Abortive *Kronshtadt* class battlecruiser.

71. Abortive prewar aircraft carrier.

72. Abortive postwar aircraft carrier.

73. *Vladimir Polukhin* class fleet minesweeper.

75. *Sverdlov* class missile conversion *Dzerzhinskii*.

82. Abortive postwar battlecruiser.

128. *Pchela P-8/10* class fast attack craft.

133. *Parchim* class small anti-submarine ship.

159. *Petya I* class patrol ship.

159A. *Petya II* class patrol ship.

159AE. *Petya III* class patrol ship.

183. *Komar/P-6* class fast attack craft.

188. *MP-8* class landing ship.

199. *Zhuk* class coastal patrol craft.

201. *SO-1* class large patrol craft.

204. *Poti* class small ASW ship.

205. *Osa* class fast attack craft.

205M. *Osa 2* class fast attack craft.

205P. *Stenka* class border patrol ship.

206. *Turya* class hydrofoil.

206MP. *Matka* class hydrofoil.

254. *T-43* class minesweeper.

255. *T-301* class minesweeper.

257. *Vanya* class minesweeper.

264. *T-58* class minesweeper.

264M. *T-58* class radar picket.

266. *Yurka* class minesweeper.

266M. *Natya* class minesweeper.

310. *Don* class command tender.

317. *Alesha* class minelayers.

361. *K-8* class minesweepers.

368. *Poluchat* class coastal patrol craft.

376. *Ilyusha* class minesweeper.

450. *MP-4* class landing ship.

532. *T-58* class minesweeper.

611. *Zulu* class submarine.

613. *Whiskey* class submarine.

615. *Quebec* class submarine.

617. *Whale* class submarine.

627. *November* class submarine.

628. *Golf* class submarine.

633. *Romeo* class submarine.

641. *Foxtrot* class submarine.

641B. *Tango* class submarine.

651. *Juliett* class submarine.

652. Abortive *Juliett* strategic missile submarine derivative.

653. Abortive strategic cruise missile submarine.

658. *Hotel* class submarine.

659. *Echo 1* class submarine.

661. *Papa* class submarine.

665. *Whiskey Long Bin* class submarine.

667. *Yankee* class submarine.

667B. *Delta I* class submarine.

667BD. *Delta II* class submarine.

667BDR. *Delta III* class submarine.

667BDRM. *Delta IV* class submarine.

670. *Charlie I* class submarine.

671M. *Charlie II* class submarine.

671/671M. *Victor* class submarine.

675. *Echo II* class submarine.

675M. Modified *Echo II* class submarine.

685. *Mike* class submarine.

690. *Bravo* class submarine.

705. *Alfa* class submarine.

771. *Polnocny 15B* class landing ship.

773. *Polnocny 9C* class landing ship.

775. *Ropucha* class landing ship.

877. *Kilo* class submarine.

940. *India* class submarine.

941. *Typhoon* class submarine.

945A. *Sierra I* class submarine.

945B. *Sierra II* class submarine.

949. *Oscar* class submarine.

949A. *Oscar II* class submarine.

956. *Sovremennyy* class destroyer.

971. *Akula* class submarine.

1123. *Moskva* class helicopter cruiser.

1124. *Grisha I* class small ASW ship.

1124P. *Grisha II* class small ASW ship.

1124M. *Grisha III* class small ASW ship.

1124 EhM. *Grisha V* class small ASW ship.

1134. *Kresta I* class missile cruiser.

1134A. *Kresta II* class large ASW ship.

1134B. *Kara* class large ASW ship.

1135 *Krivak I* class frigate.

1135M. *Krivak II* class frigate.

1135P. *Krivak III* class frigate.

1141. *Babochka* class ASW hydrofoil.

1141. 1M. *Tarantul II* class missile boat.

1141. 1MP. *Tarantul III* class missile boat.

1143. Large aircraft carrying cruisers *Kiev* and *Minsk*.

1143M. Large aircraft carrying cruiser *Novorossiysk*.

1143. 4. Large aircraft carrying cruiser *Baku/Gorshkov*.

1143. 5. Aircraft carrier *Admiral Kuznetsov*.

1144. *Kirov* class large missile cruiser.

1154. *Neustrashimyy* class frigate.

1155. *Udaloy* class large ASW ship.

1159. *Koni* class frigate.

1164. *Slava* class cruiser.

1172. *Alligator* class landing ship.

1174. *Ivan Rogov* class landing ship.

1206. *Pelikan* class air cushion minesweepers.

1234. *Nanuchka I* class small missile ship.

1234. 1. *Nanuchka III* class small missile ship.

1239. *Dergach* class surface effect ship.

1240. *Sarancha* class missile hydrofoil.

1241. 1. *Tarantul I* class missile boat.

1241. 1M. *Tarantul II* class missile boat.

1241. 2. *Pauk* class small anti-submarine ship.

1244. *Svetlyak* class ASW patrol boat.

1256. *Andrusha* class minesweeper.

Index